M000105719

Applied Bioremediation of Petroleum Hydrocarbons

BIOREMEDIATION

The *Bioremediation* series contains collections of articles derived from many of the presentations made at the First, Second, and Third International In Situ and On-Site Bioreclamation Symposia, which were held in 1991, 1993, and 1995 in San Diego, California.

First International In Situ and On-Site Bioreclamation Symposium
1(1)   *On-Site Bioreclamation: Processes for Xenobiotic and Hydrocarbon Treatment*
1(2)   *In Situ Bioreclamation: Applications and Investigations for Hydrocarbon and Contaminated Site Remediation*

Second International In Situ and On-Site Bioreclamation Symposium
2(1)   *Bioremediation of Chlorinated and Polycyclic Aromatic Hydrocarbon Compounds*
2(2)   *Hydrocarbon Bioremediation*
2(3)   *Applied Biotechnology for Site Remediation*
2(4)   *Emerging Technology for Bioremediation of Metals*
2(5)   *Air Sparging for Site Bioremediation*

Third International In Situ and On-Site Bioreclamation Symposium
3(1)   *Intrinsic Bioremediation*
3(2)   *In Situ Aeration: Air Sparging, Bioventing, and Related Remediation Processes*
3(3)   *Bioaugmentation for Site Remediation*
3(4)   *Bioremediation of Chlorinated Solvents*
3(5)   *Monitoring and Verification of Bioremediation*
3(6)   *Applied Bioremediation of Petroleum Hydrocarbons*
3(7)   *Bioremediation of Recalcitrant Organics*
3(8)   *Microbial Processes for Bioremediation*
3(9)   *Biological Unit Processes for Hazardous Waste Treatment*
3(10) *Bioremediation of Inorganics*

Bioremediation Series Cumulative Indices: 1991-1995

For information about ordering books in the Bioremediation series, contact Battelle Press. Telephone: 800-451-3543 or 614-424-6393. Fax: 614-424-3819. Internet: sheldric@battelle.org.

Applied Bioremediation of Petroleum Hydrocarbons

Edited by

Robert E. Hinchee and Jeffrey A. Kittel
Battelle Memorial Institute

H. James Reisinger
Integrated Science & Technology, Inc.

BATTELLE PRESS
Columbus • Richland

Library of Congress Cataloging-in-Publication Data

Hinchee, Robert E.
    Applied bioremediation of petroleum hydrocarbons / edited by Robert
    E. Hinchee, Jeffrey A. Kittel, H. James Reisinger.
        p.   cm.
    Includes bibliographical references and index.
    ISBN 1-57477-007-1 (hc : acid-free paper)
    1. Petroleum chemicals—Environmental aspects. 2. Bioremediation.
    I. Hinchee, Robert E. II. Kittel, Jeffrey A. III. Reisinger, H. James.
    TD196.P4A67 1995
    628.5'2—dc20   95-32257
                                                                        CIP

Printed in the United States of America

Additional copies may be ordered through:
Battelle Press
505 King Avenue
Columbus, Ohio 43201, USA
1-614-424-6393 or 1-800-451-3543
Fax: 1-614-424-3819
Internet: sheldric@battelle.org

CONTENTS

FOREWORD

This book and its companion volumes (see overleaf) comprise a collection of papers derived from the Third International In Situ and On-Site Bioreclamation Symposium, held in San Diego, California, in April 1995. The 375 papers that appear in these volumes are those that were accepted after peer review. The editors believe that this collection is the most comprehensive and up-to-date work available in the field of bioremediation.

Significant advances have been made in bioremediation since the First and Second Symposia were held in 1991 and 1993. Bioremediation as a whole remains a rapidly advancing field, and new technologies continue to emerge. As the industry matures, the emphasis for some technologies shifts to application and refinement of proven methods, whereas the emphasis for emerging technologies moves from the laboratory to the field. For example, many technologies that can be applied to sites contaminated with petroleum hydrocarbons are now commercially available and have been applied to thousands of sites. In contrast, there are as yet no commercial technologies commonly used to remediate most recalcitrant compounds. The articles in these volumes report on field and laboratory research conducted both to develop promising new technologies and to improve existing technologies for remediation of a wide spectrum of compounds.

The articles in this volume focus on petroleum hydrocarbon bioremediation, with an emphasis on pilot-scale and field-scale applications. The application of bioremediation to petroleum hydrocarbons is undoubtedly the niche in which the technology is most completely developed. Petroleum hydrocarbons in the form of fuels, oils, solvents, and crude oil are the most common contaminants at sites that require remediation. As a result, we have seen the development and application of a variety of technologies. Unfortunately, there still is a lack of well-documented field experience on important considerations such as mass balance calculation, scientific controls, and detailed engineering and cost analysis. It is hoped that the articles in this volume will improve that situation. Further, the editors believe that the lessons learned during the development of technologies for the bioremediation of petroleum hydrocarbon contamination will assist in a similar development of technologies for the remediation of more recalcitrant compounds.

The editors would like to recognize the substantial contribution of the peer reviewers who read and provided written comments to the authors of the draft articles that were considered for this volume. Thoughtful, insightful review is crucial for the production of a high-quality technical publication. The peer reviewers for this volume were:

Lawrence Acomb, *Geosphere, Inc.*
Bruce Alleman, *Battelle Columbus*
Settimio Arazzini, *Castalia* (Italy)
Basil C. Baltzis, *New Jersey Institute of Technology*

Yared Bereded-Samuel, *Washington State University*
Robert Blanchette, *University of Minnesota*
David Boone, *Oregon Graduate Center*
Dan R. Bostrom, *Barr Engineering Co.*
Murielle Bouchez, *CEA, Centre de Cadarache DCC, DESD* (France)
G. Boyer, *Metcalf & Eddy, Inc.*
Paul M. Bradley, *U.S. Geological Survey*
Gijs D. Breedveld, *Norwegian Geotechnical Institute*
James Brierley, *Newmont Metallurgical Services*
Robin L. Brigmon, *Oak Ridge Inst. for Science and Education*
Tormod Briseid, *SINTEF Oslo*
Richard A. Brown, *Groundwater Technology, Inc.*
Gaylen Brubaker, *Remediation Technologies, Inc.*
David L. Burton, *University of Manitoba*
Paolo Carrera, *Eniricerche S.p.A* (Italy)
Abraham S.C. Chen, *Battelle Columbus*
Soon Haing Cho, *Ajou University, College of Engineering* (Korea)
John D. Ciampa, *General Electric Environmental and Facility Programs*
Luis A. Cifuentes, *Texas A&M University*
Michael A. Cole, *University of Illinois*
Ed Coleman, *MK Environmental*
Yves Comeau, *Ecole Polytechnique* (Canada)
John M. Corgan, *Amoco Production Co.*
James E. Cornish, *MSE, Inc.*
M. Amine Dahmani, *University of Connecticut*
Andrew Darnall, *Integrated Science & Technology, Inc.*
Lee A. Deobald, *Innovative BioSystems, Inc.*
David Depaoli, *Oak Ridge National Laboratory*
Kate Devine, *Biotreatment News*
Charles E. Downs, *Conoco, Inc.*
Chandra S. Dulam, *University of Connecticut*
Geraint Edmunds, *Alberta Environment*
Tad Fox, *Battelle Columbus*
Marilyn M. Franck, *Westinghouse Savannah River Co.*
Volker Franzius, *Federal Environmental Agency* (Germany)
Phillip A. Gauglitz, *Battelle Pacific Northwest*
Peter Grathwohl, *University of Teubingen (Germany)*
Duane Graves, *IT Corporation*
Julian Gray, *Integrated Science & Technology, Inc.*
Ipin Guo, *Alberta Environmental Centre*
Gary R. Hater, *Waste Management, Inc.*
Terry C. Hazen, *Westinghouse Savannah River Technology Center*
Gorm Heron, *Technical University of Denmark*
Franz K. Hiebert, *RMT/Jones & Neuse, Inc.*
Kevin R. Hosler, *Wastewater Technology Centre* (Canada)
Michael H. Huesemann, *Battelle Pacific Northwest*

Ben Keet, *Geo & Hydro Milieu* (The Netherlands)
Jeffrey Kittel, *Battelle Columbus*
Eric Klingel, *IEG Technologies Corporation*
Dan Kraft, *Booz Allen & Hamilton, Inc.*
William F. Lane (USA)
Margaret Lang, *Stanford University*
William Langley, *IEG Technologies Corporation*
Ronald F. Lewis, *U.S. Environmental Protection Agency*
Douglas S. Lipton, *Levine-Fricke, Inc.*
Thomas Lockhart, *Eniricerche S.p.A* (Italy)
Chih-Jen Lu, *National Chung Hsing University* (Taiwan)
Ja-Kael Luey, *Battelle Pacific Northwest*
Stuart Luttrell, *Battelle Pacific Northwest*
Michael M. Martinson, *Delta Environmental Consultants, Inc.*
Victor F. Medina, *RMT Inc.*
Rodolfo Mendoza, *Centro de Ecofisiologia Vegetal CONICET*
(Argentina)
Giorgio Migliorini, *Castalia* (Italy)
Korneliusz Miksch, *Silesian Technical University*
Robert Miller, *Oklahoma State University*
Klaus Müller, *Battelle Europe*
H. S. Muralidhara, *Cargill, Inc.*
Karl Nehring, *Battelle Columbus*
Robert Norris, *Eckenfelder, Inc.*
Robert Olfenbuttel, *Battelle Columbus*
Brian O'Neill, *Grace Dearborn, Inc.* (Canada)
Charles Peng, *Barr Engineering Company*
Anders Persson, *ANOX AB* (Sweden)
Brent M. Peyton, *Battelle Pacific Northwest*
George Philippidis, *National Renewable Energy Lab*
Andrea Preuss, *Degussa AG/VT-PB* (Germany)
P.H. (Hap) Pritchard, *U.S. Environmental Protection Agency*
Don E. Richard, *Barr Engineering Company*
Bruce E. Rittmann, *Northwestern University*
Alan Seech, *Grace Dearborn, Inc.* (Canada)
Eric Senior, *University of Natal* (Rep. of South Africa)
Ronald C. Sims, *Utah State University*
Marina Skumanich, *Battelle Seattle Research Center*
Larry Smith, *Battelle Columbus*
Jan Stepek, *EA Engineering Science & Technology, Inc.*
Joanna Surmacz-Górska, *Silesian Technical University*
Michael Travis, *AGRA Earth & Environmental, Inc.*
Jean-Paul Vandecasteele, *Institut Français du Pétrole*
Mike E. Vermace, *University of Iowa*
F. Michael von Fahnestock, *Battelle Columbus*

Terry Walden, *BP Research*
Lenly J. Weathers, *University of Iowa*
Marty Werner, *State of Washington Dept. of Ecology*
Peter Werner, *Technical University of Dresden*
Mark Westray, *Remediation Technologies, Inc.*
Patricia White, *Battelle Pacific Northwest*
Tom Zwick, *Battelle Columbus*

The figure that appears on the cover of this volume was adapted from the article by Myers et al. (see page 447).

Finally, I want to recognize the key members of the production staff, who put forth significant effort in assembling this book and its companion volumes. Carol Young, the Symposium Administrator, was responsible for the administrative effort necessary to produce the ten volumes. She was assisted by Gina Melaragno, who tracked draft manuscripts through the review process and generated much of the correspondence with the authors, co-editors, and peer reviewers. Lynn Copley-Graves oversaw text editing and directed the layout of the book, compilation of the keyword indices, and production of the camera-ready copy. She was assisted by technical editors Bea Weaver and Ann Elliot. Loretta Bahn was responsible for text processing and worked many long hours incorporating editors' revisions, laying out the camera-ready pages and figures, and maintaining the keyword list. She was assisted by Sherry Galford and Cleta Richey; additional support was provided by Susan Vianna and her staff at Fishergate, Inc. Darlene Whyte and Mike Steve proofread the final copy. Judy Ward, Gina Melaragno, Bonnie Snodgrass, and Carol Young carried out final production tasks. Karl Nehring, who served as Symposium Administrator in 1991 and 1993, provided valuable insight and advice.

The symposium was sponsored by Battelle Memorial Institute with support from many organizations. The following organizations cosponsored or otherwise supported the Third Symposium.

Ajou University–College of Engineering (Korea)
American Petroleum Institute
Asian Institute of Technology (Thailand)
Biotreatment News
Castalia
ENEA (Italy)
Environment Canada
Environmental Protection
Gas Research Institute
Groundwater Technology, Inc.
Institut Français du Pétrole
Mitsubishi Corporation
OHM Remediation Services Corporation
Parsons Engineering Science, Inc.

RIVM–National Institute of Public Health and the Environment
(The Netherlands)
The Japan Research Institute, Limited
Umweltbundesamt (Germany)
U.S. Air Force Armstrong Laboratory–Environics Directorate
U.S. Air Force Center for Environmental Excellence
U.S. Department of Energy Office of Technology Development
(OTD)
U.S. Environmental Protection Agency
U.S. Naval Facilities Engineering Services Center
Western Region Hazardous Substance Research Center–
Stanford and Oregon State Universities

Neither Battelle nor the cosponsoring or supporting organizations reviewed this book, and their support for the Symposium should not be construed as an endorsement of the book's content. I conducted the final review and selection of all papers published in this volume, making use of the essential input provided by the peer reviewers and other editors. I take responsibility for any errors or omissions in the final publication.

Rob Hinchee
June 1995

Hydrocarbon Bioremediation — An Overview

H. James Reisinger

ABSTRACT

Bioremediation is the process that transforms xenobiotics introduced into the environment to a less toxic or innocuous form, or mineralizes them to inorganic species (e.g., carbon dioxide and water). The processes can be carried out through either aerobic or anaerobic pathways by indigenous heterotrophs or by specially engineered organisms. For some xenobiotics, the process can also be carried out by cometabolic processes, which use another compound as the carbon and energy source. This technique can be applied either in situ or ex situ. The papers in this volume report real-world applications of a variety of hydrocarbon bioremediation approaches, including biopiling, bioventing, bioslurping, landfarming, electrobioreclamation, and biovertical circulation wells. Other papers in this volume deal with problems in translating laboratory and field-scale pilot test data to full-scale operating systems. Such issues include biodegradation enhancement, nutrient and electron acceptor delivery, alternative electron acceptors, and integration of biological, chemical, and physical approaches to hydrocarbon remediation.

INTRODUCTION

Hydrocarbons, as a class, are used as fuels, solvents, and feedstocks in the textile, pharmaceutical, and plastics industries; they represent one of the most often used fractions of petrochemicals in the industrialized world. The American Petroleum Institute (API) reports that in 1994 the average crude oil input to refineries in the United States was 14,045,000 barrels (bbl) per day (API 1995). From this stock, delivered product averaged 7,605,000 bbl of gasoline; 1,485,000 bbl of kerosene and jet fuel; 3,181,000 bbl of distillate fuel oil; 984,000 bbl of residual fuel oil; and 4,484,000 bbl of miscellaneous oils, solvents, and lubricants (API 1995).

Following production in the refinery, hydrocarbon products are transported by ship, rail, and truck to points of use or to distribution facilities, where they are stored in either underground or aboveground tanks in preparation for final use. They are then conveyed through underground or aboveground pipelines. During each of these processes, numerous opportunities exist for the introduction of these products into the environment. In addition to releases during the transport and storage of hydrocarbons, opportunities for mishandling and spillage exist during the various manufacturing processes that use these products. Such processes often produce hydrocarbon wastes that require disposal; methods of disposal also serve as potential mechanisms through which hydrocarbons can be introduced to the environment. The large volumes of hydrocarbons produced, used, and disposed of on a global basis make it no surprise that this large and useful class of petrochemicals constitutes a large portion of the subsurface contamination throughout the world.

As a class, hydrocarbons have a wide range of physicochemical characteristics. Their molecular weights range from very low to very high, as do their boiling points. They can be very fluid or very viscous. They can be very volatile or relatively nonvolatile, and they can be highly soluble or rather insoluble. Many of the hydrocarbons and mixtures thereof are also less dense than water. This variability in physicochemical character causes the behavior of individual hydrocarbons and mixtures of different hydrocarbons in the subsurface environment to vary greatly.

Once introduced into the subsurface, hydrocarbons immediately begin to interact with the matrix through which they are migrating. The interactions and the degree to which they occur are a function of the physicochemical characteristics of the hydrocarbons themselves and the surrounding matrix. In the vadose zone, highly volatile hydrocarbons (i.e., those with high vapor pressures) tend to volatilize and become part of the vadose zone atmosphere. Those that have a high affinity for the solid matrix through which they are migrating (i.e., they have high organic carbon partitioning coefficients or octanol:water partitioning coefficients) tend to adsorb to the solid matrix or to partition into autochthonous organic carbon. Hydrocarbons that are highly soluble in water tend to dissolve in vadose zone water. As the liquid-phase hydrocarbon makes its way through the vadose zone, it coats the soil particles and migrates into pores, creating a residual phase. Figure 1 is a conceptual model of hydrocarbon distribution in the vadose zone.

If the volume of hydrocarbon introduced to the subsurface exceeds the residual capacity of the vadose zone soils, it will continue to migrate vertically until it reaches the water table or a low-permeability unit, where it will accumulate and spread laterally. This lens of phase-separated hydrocarbon (PSH), along with the soil residual hydrocarbon in the vadose zone, then serves as a source of contamination for the underlying groundwater. As the PSH rests on the water table, or more correctly on the surface of the capillary fringe, it rides vertically with the water table's seasonal fluctuation. This fluctuation creates a zone of high hydrocarbon concentration often referred to as the smear zone. PSH in the soil pores in this zone is submerged and surrounded by groundwater for at least part of the year. It typically is rather immobile and, owing to its intimate association with the aquifer, acts as a very significant source of dissolved contamination.

Hydrocarbon enters groundwater thereby creating a dissolved phase as a result of solubilization. The degree of solubilization is a function of the solubility of the hydrocarbon compound. Compounds with high solubilities — hydrophilic

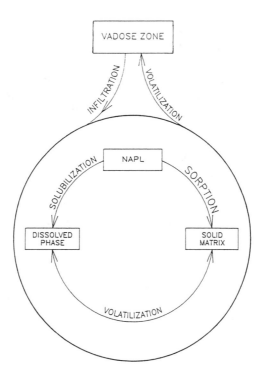

FIGURE 1. Conceptual groundwater-partitioning model. NAPL = nonaqueous-
phase liquid.

compounds — dissolve to create high dissolved-phase concentrations. In contrast,
those with low solubilities — hydrophobic compounds — dissolve sparingly in
groundwater. Although the degree to which an individual compound will dissolve in groundwater is a function of that compound's aqueous solubility, the
same is not the case for hydrocarbon mixtures. A compound's solubility in a
mixture is a function of the mole fraction of that compound in the overall mixture.

Once dissolved, hydrocarbons migrate with the flowing groundwater via
advective dispersive transport. The dissolved hydrocarbons, however, are transported at a rate slower than the groundwater velocity. The degree to which the
velocity of a hydrocarbon compound is retarded is a function of its interaction
with the solid matrix through which it migrates; more specifically, it is a function
of the degree of interaction with naturally occurring organics. Those compounds
with a lower affinity for the solid matrix migrate at rates that are higher than
those with a higher affinity. This variable retardation causes the compounds in
the dissolved-phase plume to separate; this separation — differential transport —
is analogous to laboratory chromatography (Hinchee & Reisinger 1987). Hydrophilic and oleophobic compounds tend to be found on the leading edge of the
dissolved phase plume, while hydrophobic and oleophilic compounds tend to be

found nearer to the hydrocarbon source. Figure 2 shows a conceptual model of hydrocarbon interactions in the dissolved phase.

Some hydrocarbon compounds potentially elicit adverse human health and environmental effects when introduced into the environment; therefore, a need for remediation frequently exists. Over the past decade, approaches to hydro-carbon remediation have evolved extensively. When the need for hydrocarbon remediation was initially recognized, cleanup goals generally focused solely on PSH recovery. As our knowledge of the dynamics of hydrocarbon behavior in the subsurface and of the associated potential impacts grew, the focus evolved, shifting to dissolved-phase remediation.

In the early stages of this phase of the evolution, most dissolved-phase remediation was carried out using groundwater extraction and treatment. Treated groundwater was either reinfiltrated or discharged to surface water or to a waste-water treatment facility. However, these systems enjoyed very little success. In some instances, extraction and treatment systems operated for many years with little reduction in dissolved-phase hydrocarbon concentrations and with very little overall mass removal. In other instances, system operations did result in dissolved-phase hydrocarbon concentration reductions and the systems were deactivated. Yet, during follow-up sampling, dissolved-phase concentrations

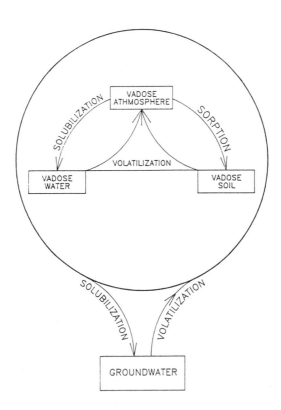

FIGURE 2. Conceptual three-compartment vadose-partitioning model.

frequently returned to their preremediation concentrations. This observation led to the conclusion that the vadose zone was serving as a secondary source of groundwater contamination and that vadose zone remediation was necessary to truly remediate the sites.

A number of approaches to vadose zone remediation have been developed. Excavation followed by disposal in a landfill was, perhaps, the first and most obvious solution. However, it created a great deal of site disruption and did not truly remediate the soil; instead, it transferred the contamination from one location to another. Vacuum-enhanced hydrocarbon extraction (i.e., soil venting) was developed as a vadose zone remediation tool in the late 1970s and early 1980s, and it grew to be one of the most frequently used approaches owing to its ease of implementation and cost effectiveness. Other approaches that were developed over the years include soil washing, landfarming, aboveground vacuum extraction, and stabilization.

From the earliest days of concern over hydrocarbon in the environment, many considered bioremediation a viable means of remediation. Perhaps the first application of bioremediation at a hydrocarbon-contaminated site was the work done by Richard L. Raymond (Brown et al. 1994). At the site of a 1972 gasoline release from a pipeline in Pennsylvania, Raymond attempted to bio-remediate dissolved-phase hydrocarbon via in-well aeration to introduce oxygen to the saturated zone (Raymond 1976). One of the key findings of Raymond's seminal work was a realization of the importance of oxygen delivery to the over-all subsurface biodegradation process. From Raymond's first project through the early 1980s, oxygen, the terminal electron acceptor of choice, was delivered to the dissolved phase at concentrations controlled by its solubility in water (i.e., about 10 mg/L at 15°C). In response to this realization, workers at the Texas Research Institute (TRI) initiated evaluations of hydrogen peroxide as a source of oxygen to support hydrocarbon bioremediation (TRI 1982). At this same time Brown, Norris, and Raymond conducted parallel hydrogen peroxide column studies (Brown et al. 1986). These investigations focused on stimulating dissolved-phase bioremediation by delivering oxygen to the saturated zone in concentrations higher than saturation.

In the late 1980s, increased emphasis was once again placed on vadose zone remediation. An increased focus on air quality and the realization that vacuum-enhanced vapor extraction was incapable of efficiently addressing higher-molecular-weight, lower-vapor-pressure hydrocarbons caused, at least in part, this change. The need for a technique that truly remediated hydrocarbons as opposed to transferring them from the vadose zone to the atmosphere, as does vacuum extraction without off-gas treatment, became apparent. An answer to this perceived need was bioventing, which actually had its foundation in research conducted by TRI in 1980 and 1984 (TRI 1980; 1984). Chevron Research and Technology Company patented a bioventing process in 1988 (Ely & Heffner 1988). Others, in the course of applying conventional vacuum-enhanced vapor extraction, observed decreases in hydrocarbon concentrations beyond those that could be attributed to volatilization alone (Ostendorf & Kampbell 1989). They attributed this decrease to biodegradation. The most extensive work in the bioventing arena to date has been carried out by the U.S. Air Force Center for Environmental Excellence through their Bioventing Initiative.

Another area of bioremediation in which a great deal of effort is currently being expended, in which there is a great deal of interest, and about which there is a great deal of controversy is air sparging. This in situ approach to subsurface remediation consists of injecting air under pressure into the saturated zone. Air sparging originally was thought to integrate both dissolved-phase and vadose zone remediation, and it was believed that volatilization was the primary mechanism affecting remediation. However, research conducted by Johnson (1994) suggested that biodegradation plays a major role in hydrocarbon removal in the saturated zone during air sparging.

Other approaches to hydrocarbon bioremediation currently are being used or evaluated. These include soil washing with surfactant and nutrient solutions, vertical circulation wells, application of alternative electron acceptors, and intrinsic bioremediation.

MICROBIOLOGICAL CONSIDERATIONS

The driving force behind hydrocarbon bioremediation is the microorganisms that can utilize hydrocarbons as sources of energy and food to develop and maintain cell mass. These organisms produce enzymes, used in their metabolic pathways, to extract energy from the degradation of hydrocarbon molecules. As such, they are heterotrophic; that is, they depend on external sources of carbon to satisfy their energy and cellular growth needs in much the same manner as many other organisms, including humans.

The organisms residing in the soil that are responsible for bioremediation include bacteria, fungi, and protozoans. Of these, bacteria appear to play the dominant role in hydrocarbon degradation. Just as a great variety of organisms exist in the soil (Alexander 1961), many organisms can, to a greater or lesser extent, utilize hydrocarbons to satisfy their cell growth and energy needs. Of the total suite, or consortium, of organisms in the soil, a dominant organism or group of organisms exists that, through natural selection, has developed because they can thrive in the unique physical and chemical setting in which they reside. Although the dominant organism or organisms generally predominates in terms of numbers and biomass, other organisms exist within the consortium. As long as the physical and chemical regime does not change, the population dynamics do not change. However, when the environment changes — for example through the introduction of hydrocarbon contamination — the population changes in response. Those organisms that are best adapted to the new environment assume the position of dominance. Their dominance is a function of their capacity to utilize hydrocarbons as a primary source of carbon and energy in their metabolism and of their ability to better compete in the new environmental setting.

The metabolic pathways that hydrocarbon-degrading heterotrophs use can be either aerobic (i.e., they utilize oxygen as the primary electron acceptor) or anaerobic (i.e., they utilize an alternative electron acceptor such as nitrate or sulfate). Although hydrocarbons can be degraded via both pathways, the aerobic pathway is generally considered to proceed most rapidly and most efficiently because aerobic reactions require less free energy for initiation and yield more energy per reaction (Cookson 1995). Eq. 1 is the stoichiometric relationship for aerobic mineralization of a representative hydrocarbon (toluene):

$$C_6H_5 - CH_3 + 9O_2 \rightarrow 7CO_2 + 4H_2O \qquad (1)$$

By contrast, the following is the stoichiometric relationship of anaerobic mineralization of hydrocarbon (toluene) using nitrate as the electron acceptor:

$$C_6H_5 - CH_3 + 6NO_3 \rightarrow 7CO_2 + 4H_2O + 3N_2 \qquad (2)$$

Borden et al. (1995) have suggested that the aerobic process dominates in the presence of oxygen. However, when the oxygen in the system is depleted, denitrification processes dominate.

Indigenous organisms with the ability to biodegrade hydrocarbons are present in most subsurface systems; thus, many workers believe that it is unnecessary to introduce nonindigenous organisms to address hydrocarbon in the environment biologically. Although specially adapted bacteria are sometimes introduced, they are difficult to distribute and they often cannot compete with the indigenous population. As a result, they soon become a minor element of the consortium.

For a microbiological consortium to successfully degrade a given xenobiotic, a number of conditions must be met. The compound(s) must be biodegradable; that is, they must be compatible with the enzymes produced in the metabolic pathways of the organisms present. They must also be of a form that produces adequate energy and carbon for the organisms to use. The environmental setting also must be hospitable for the organisms. The most significant environmental factors include pH, temperature, moisture content, terminal electron acceptor content, and macronutrient content and form (i.e., nitrogen and phosphorus). If these factors are not satisfactory, biodegradation will occur at a rate that is less than optimal, or it will not occur at all. Therefore, one of the primary tasks facing the bioremediation practitioner is optimization of the environmental setting.

IN SITU BIOREMEDIATION

Hydrocarbon bioremediation can be carried out either in situ or ex situ. In situ approaches include bioventing, intrinsic bioremediation, soil washing with biological enhancement, biosparging, and bioenhancement through vertical circulation wells. The primary advantage of in situ bioremediation is that it is carried out without removing the hydrocarbon-impacted soil and groundwater. Although eliminating the need to remove the impacted medium from the site is a significant advantage, a number of challenges still must be addressed for in situ bioremediation to take place. The most significant of these is delivering the terminal electron acceptor and, less importantly, nutrients to the point of use. As discussed above, a number of approaches to solving this problem have been proposed. These have included injecting stabilized hydrogen peroxide and nutrients to address dissolved-phase hydrocarbon. These approaches have, however, enjoyed only limited success because the formation's hydraulic conductivity controls the distribution of the hydrogen peroxide. The electron acceptor and/or nutrient may be consumed or may adsorb to the soil before reaching the impacted zone. To a large extent, bioventing has overcome the distribution problem in the vadose zone. In this process, oxygen, the electron acceptor, is delivered in a gaseous form through air injection. The advantage to this approach to delivery lies in the higher diffusivity of gases in a porous medium.

EX SITU BIOREMEDIATION

The ex situ approach to hydrocarbon bioremediation is carried out aboveground by physically extracting the impacted medium. It is commonly applied to dissolved-phase contamination via pumping and treatment with aboveground bioreactors. These may be in the form of sequencing batch reactors or other forms of fixed-film or disk reactors. Soils are treated aboveground via landfarming, biopiling, and composting. The primary advantage to these ex situ approaches is the degree of control that can be exerted over the processes being used to manipulate the system. The primary disadvantage is the expense and disruption associated with removal, treatment, and disposal or replacement of the impacted medium.

CONCLUSIONS

The papers in this volume represent a broad cross section of the approaches that are currently being applied to hydrocarbon bioremediation. They are the state of the art, as we know it today, and they present practical applications of the techniques. As such, they contain not only theoretical considerations and reports of successful applications, but they also describe the difficulties encountered in real-world application. Perhaps their greatest contribution is communicating these difficulties and, consequently, facilitating future applications of this growing and highly effective approach to hydrocarbon remediation.

REFERENCES

Alexander, M. 1961. *Introduction to Soil Microbiology*. John Wiley & Sons, Inc., New York, NY.
American Petroleum Institute. 1995. *Monthly Statistical Report*. Volume 18, No. 12. American Petroleum Institute, Washington, DC.
Borden, R. C., C. A. Goney, and M. J. Becker. 1995. "Geochemical Indications of Intrinsic Bioremediation." *Ground-Water* 33(2): 180-189.

Brown, R. A., R. D. Norris, and R. L. Raymond. 1986. *Stimulation of Bio-Oxidation Process in Subterranean Formations*, May 13, 1986, U.S. Patent 4,588,506.

Brown, R. A., R. J. Hicks, and P. M. Hicks. 1994. "Use of Air Sparging for In Situ Bio-remediation." In R. E. Hinchee (Ed.), *Air Sparging for Site Remediation*, pp. 38-55. Lewis Publishing, Inc., Boca Raton, FL.

Cookson, J. T., Jr. 1995. *Bioremediation Engineering Design & Application*. McGraw-Hill, Inc., New York, NY.

Ely, D. L., and D. A. Heffner. 1988. *Process for In Situ Biodegradation of Hydrocarbon Contaminated Soil*. U.S. Patent No. 4,765,902.

Hinchee, R. E., and H. J. Reisinger. 1987. "A Practical Application of Multiphase Transport Theory to Ground Water Contamination Problem." *Ground Water Monitoring Review*, (Winter): 84-92.

Johnson, R. L. 1994. "Enhancing Biodegradation With In Situ Air Sparging: A Conceptual Model." In R. E. Hinchee (Ed.), *Air Sparging for Site Remediation*, pp. 14-22. Lewis Publishers, Boca Raton, FL.

Ostendorf, D. W., and D. H. Kampbell. 1989. "Vertical Profile and Near Surface Trays for Field Measurement of Volatile Pollution in the Subsurface Environment." *Proceedings of NWWA Conference on New Techniques for Quantifying the Physical and Chemical Properties of Heterogeneous Aquifers*. National Water Well Association, Dublin, OH.

Raymond, R. L. 1976. "Beneficial Stimulation of Bacterial Activity in Ground Water Containing Hydrocarbons." *AICHE Symposium, Series 73*: 390-404.

Texas Research Institute. 1980. *Laboratory Scale Gasoline Spill Venting Experiment*. American Petroleum Institute Report No. 7743-5: JST.

Texas Research Institute. 1982. *Enhancing the Microbial Degradation of Underground Gasoline by Increasing Available Oxygen*. Final Report, American Petroleum Institute, Washington, DC.

Texas Research Institute. 1984. *Forced Venting to Remove Gasoline Vapor From a Large Scale Model Aquifer. American Petroleum Institute*. Final Report No. 82101-F:TAV.

International Activities in Bioremediation: Growing Markets and Opportunities

David J. Glass, Thomas Raphael,
Risto Valo, and J. Van Eyk

ABSTRACT

Bioremediation continues to play an increasingly important role in remediation of the world's hazardous wastes, and is becoming a widely
accepted tool of mainstream remediation firms. International markets
should grow faster than the United States market because most other
countries are only beginning to duplicate the extensive regulatory framework that drives the United States remediation market, and many are
only now beginning to inventory and prioritize their waste sites. Bioremediation should grow dramatically along with the overall world
remediation market, and may be positioned more favorably than in the
United States, because of the existing track record of success and an
increased willingness to try innovative technologies in light of the limitations of existing methods.

WORLD MARKETS FOR BIOREMEDIATION PRODUCTS AND SERVICES

Environmental remediation markets around the world are driven by government regulation. The United States has the world's most advanced, complex
network of environmental regulations that creates by far the single largest market
in the world. However, sizable markets also exist, or are expected to arise, in
Europe, Canada, and the Pacific Rim. Generally, bioremediation markets exist
in most countries with an established environmental industry and an infrastructure for hazardous waste remediation or management.

We estimate that the 1994 world bioremediation market was $290 to
440 million, of which the United States accounted for the lion's share of $160 to
210 million (see Table 1). Europe is the second largest bioremediation market,
with an estimated $105 to 175 million in 1994. Other markets exist in Canada
and Australia. Our estimates include the costs of products and services used
in the bioremediation of contaminated media.

Applied Bioremediation of Petroleum Hydrocarbons

TABLE 1. World bioremediation markets 1994-2000 (in millions of U.S. dollars)[a].

Market	1994	1997	2000
World	290-440	450-700	800-1,350
United States	160-210	225-325	350-600
Europe	105-175	180-300	375-600
Germany	70-100	100-150	250-350
Netherlands	10-20	15-35	30-60
Scandinavia	10-20	15-35	30-60
United Kingdom	5-10	7.5-20	15-30
Other Europe	10-25	42.5-60	50-100
Canada	15-35	30-50	50-100

(a) Source: Authors' estimates.

Total 1993 environmental spending in the United States (solid and hazardous waste management, site remediation, air- and water-pollution control, and various other consulting, engineering, and analytical services) has been estimated at between $100 and $134 billion (*Environmental Business Journal* [*EBJ*] 1994; Berkowitz 1994). Hazardous waste remediation makes up only a portion of this total, with estimates of this market in the early 1990s ranging from $4 to $12 billion (*EBJ* 1994; Berkowitz 1994; Walker and Shooter 1992; Glass 1993). Bioremediation makes up only a small percentage of this market.

Recent estimates put total European environmental spending at U.S. $84 to $94 billion (Berkowitz 1994; *The Economist* 1993). As shown in Table 2, the European market can be divided into several tiers, based on the severity of national environmental regulations and policies (*EBJ* 1991; Metzger 1990). Even within the top tier countries, site remediation markets are well behind the United States. Many of these countries have only recently conducted inventories to identify and prioritize their hazardous waste sites. Although there are estimated to be more than 150,000 hazardous waste sites in the nations of the European Union (EU) (*EBJ* 1991), only a small fraction of these have begun to be remediated (see Table 3). Several of the Nordic countries, as well as the Netherlands, have completed site inventories, but very little actual remediation work has been undertaken outside of top tier countries such as Denmark, the Netherlands, or Germany (Rosén 1992). The total European market for site remediation is likely to be no higher than $3 to 6 billion per year (Glass 1993).

Bioremediation's share of this market, although small, is expected to grow. There is a long history of public and private sector activities in biological techniques in Europe, particularly in the established practices of landfarming and soil washing (often combined with some form of biodegradation). Both of these technologies are aided by the pronounced trend in much of Europe toward

TABLE 2. Tiered structure of European environmental markets[a].

Tier 1	Tier 2	Tier 3	Tier 4
Denmark	Austria	Greece	Former Eastern Bloc
Germany	Belgium	Portugal	
The Netherlands	Finland	Spain	
Norway	France		
Sweden	Ireland		
Switzerland	Italy		
	Luxembourg		
	United Kingdom		

(a) Sources: Metzger 1990; *Environmental Business Journal* 1991.

centralized soil treatment facilities that can treat tens of thousands of tons of soil per year. Germany and the Netherlands are the clear European leaders, but bioremediation takes place in other European countries, notably the United Kingdom and the Nordic countries.

After Europe, the next largest single market for environmental remediation is Canada, with about $10 billion in total annual environmental spending in 1990 (Lorenz 1992). There is considerable interest in bioremediation in Canada, and we estimate the 1994 market to be $15 to 35 million. Environmental markets also

TABLE 3. Hazardous waste sites known or estimated in selected European countries[a].

Country	Estimated Number of Sites	Year of Estimate	Estimated Cost of Remediation (U.S. $)
European Union	150,000	1990	$200 billion
Germany	150,000–200,000	1993	$100 billion
Netherlands	ca. 100,000	1993	$30–120 billion
Finland	10,000–25,000	1995	n.a.[b]
Denmark	6,000–12,000	1991	$4 billion
Sweden	>6,000	1995	$7 billion
Norway	>2,000	1995	n.a.

(a) Sources: *Environmental Business Journal* 1991; Porta et al. 1994; Metzger 1990; Rosén 1992; Franzius 1993; Mischgofsky et al. 1993; Rosén, Mischgofsky, personal communications.
(b) n.a. = not available

exist in Australia, Japan, and elsewhere in the Pacific Rim, particularly Taiwan and Singapore. These markets are small, but have great potential for growth, and some bioremediation activity is beginning in the Pacific Rim as well.

We expect toughening environmental regulations to expand world markets for remediation in general and for bioremediation specifically. For example, recently adopted EU environmental regulations not only create a greater demand for cleanup, but also have begun to proscribe existing practices, which may hasten the interest in alternative treatment technologies. In addition, tougher regulations will eventually force the second and third tier European countries to step up their environmental activities, which will also create new opportunities for innovative technologies.

BIOREMEDIATION
IN THE UNITED STATES

Overview. The hazardous waste remediation industry in the United States is a large, diverse industry that exhibited rapid growth throughout the 1980s, but which is showing signs of maturity in the 1990s (Berkowitz 1994). The market is dominated by large national and regional consulting and engineering firms that are capable of conducting site remediations using a number of traditional and innovative technologies. Many of the larger U.S. remediation companies combine the consulting and contracting functions generally found in separate companies in Europe, and thus also perform investigations and feasibility studies.

Although the traditional techniques of incineration and landfilling are extremely well entrenched, innovative technologies such as bioremediation have begun to make inroads in recent years. Many of the leading consulting/engineering firms have developed expertise in many innovative methods including bioremediation, although there continues to be a role for smaller companies specializing in specific techniques. Bioremediation is now practiced to some degree by the majority of remediation firms in the United States, but still commands only a small share of the overall remediation business.

Market and Site Characteristics. With some exceptions, remediation of polluted soils and other contaminated sites in the United States is driven by federal, state, or local government regulation. The laws and regulations governing hazardous waste remediation are described in more detail elsewhere (Bakst 1991; U.S. EPA 1993). In recent years, a major new market for site remediation has been created by the activities of two other federal government agencies, the U.S. Department of Defense (DoD) and the U.S. Department of Energy (DOE), each of which has established programs to manage the remediation of sites under its control (U.S. EPA 1993). The estimated number of sites covered by these programs is shown in Table 4.

Hazardous waste sites in the United States are characterized by a wide range of contaminants, resulting from a variety of industrial uses. The most common

TABLE 4. Estimated contaminated sites in the United States[a].

Type of Site	Estimated Number of Sites	Likely to Be Remediated	Year of Estimate
Superfund	36,814	1,235	1992
RCRA[b]	80,000	1,500–3,000	1993
LUST[c]	1,500,000	200,000–600,000	1992
DoD	24,446	7,313	1991
DOE	n.a.	4,000	1992

(a) Source: U.S. Environmental Protection Agency (1993).
(b) RCRA = Resource Conservation and Recovery Act of 1976.
(c) LUST = leaking underground storage tanks.

arose from various types of chemical manufacturing, metal plating, wood preserving, and petroleum refining (U.S. EPA 1993). The most common contaminants found at Superfund sites are volatile organics such as trichloroethylene (TCE) and tetrachloroethene, the BTEX compounds (benzene, toluene, ethylbenzene, and the xylenes), and heavy metals (U.S. EPA 1993). DoD sites are characterized by a range of contaminants including petroleum hydrocarbons, solvents, heavy metals, polychlorinated biphenyls (PCBs), pesticides, and explosives. Many DOE sites are contaminated with radioactive wastes resulting from decades of nuclear weapons manufacture, in addition to the usual range of hazardous contaminants (U.S. EPA 1993).

Technologies Practiced. A wide range of bioremediation technologies is practiced in the United States today, including in situ treatment of groundwater; in situ and ex situ treatment of contaminated soil; reactor-based treatment of groundwater, industrial wastewater, sludges, soil slurries, and vapor-phase contamination; and the treatment of marine oil spills using microbial inoculants or fertilizers. In situ biorestoration of aquifers was first practiced in the 1970s (Raymond et al. 1975), and today is practiced in a number of ways. These include using hydrogen peroxide as an oxygen source, or bioventing, biosparging, and related methods, where gaseous oxygen is used to stimulate biodegradation (Hinchee et al. 1990). Soils are also remediated in situ. One new method under investigation is the "lasagna" method for treatment of clay-like soils by applying an electric field to separate contaminants into layers where biodegradation occurs.

Ex situ soil bioremediation often includes the use of special nutrients or additives or the addition of selected microbial cultures ("bioaugmentation"). Several firms use specialized bioreactors for a variety of purposes, including treatment of groundwater (e.g., in conjunction with pump-and-treat methods) or vapor-phase contamination (e.g., resulting from air stripping operations). In fact, biological methods are often combined with other physical or mechanical methods, such as air stripping, ultraviolet (UV) oxidation, or soil washing. Biological techniques have also been used against marine oil spills. Both biostimulation and bioaugmentation approaches have been tested against open-sea spills and polluted beaches, although the technique may not be applicable to all spills (U.S. Congress Office of Technology Assessment 1991). Finally, there is some interest in using microbial or plant biomass to bioaccumulate or solubilize heavy metals. (See U.S. EPA [1992] for an overview of many of these technologies.)

Bioremediation's growth has been aided by U.S. EPA's efforts to promote innovative technologies. Among these have been the Bioremediation Field Initiative, which tracks approximately 150 sites in 40 states where bioremediation is being implemented or is under consideration (U.S. EPA 1994), and the Bioremediation Action Committee, whose several working groups are charged with evaluating research and policy needs for the promotion of bioremediation, and have prepared protocols for field and laboratory bioremediation projects, recommended research and educational priorities, and established the Bioremediation Product Evaluation Center.

Industry Structure. Table 5 lists the major firms in the United States active in bioremediation. Profiles of many of the leading companies can be found in Glass (1994).

In keeping with the majority of the hazardous waste market, the bioremediation market is serviced by a combination of diversified engineering firms and specialty companies, the latter often functioning as subcontractors or vendors. With very few exceptions, the consulting/engineering firms that practice bioremediation are service oriented and do not offer proprietary products or technologies. Almost all the major national or regional environmental engineering firms are capable of conducting in situ bioremediation of soil or groundwater, or ex situ soil bioremediation, and many use specialized bioreactors or other hardware.

The second major sector includes service-oriented companies whose primary or only remediation capability is biological. Many are startup companies, founded to commercialize specific microbial strains or reactor technologies, sometimes licensed from universities. Some of these companies have conducted innovative research on new bioremediation techniques, and are often the only commercial entities introducing innovative technologies.

Comprising another sector are the manufacturers and distributors of microbial cultures. Many of these are small companies whose products can be used for a number of purposes (for example, municipal or industrial wastewater treatment). Few of these strains are unique or proprietary and there is little differentiation among these products, although one new trend is toward the use of fungal inocula, such as the white-rot fungus. Very few of these companies conduct remediations themselves, but rather are suppliers or sometimes subcontractors to the larger firms carrying out site cleanups.

In addition, a number of firms sell nutrients, peroxides, surfactants, and similar products that can accelerate or facilitate bioremediation. Other firms market specialized or proprietary hardware. Finally, a significant number of large firms conduct bioremediation research or are active in site remediation, primarily to address their own hazardous waste sites. These companies include chemical companies, pharmaceutical firms, and oil companies.

Market Trends. Although growth in the overall site remediation market in the United States has slowed in recent years, bioremediation continues to make

TABLE 5. United States bioremediation companies.

Diversified Consulting and Engineering Companies	Dedicated Bioremediation Service Providers	Manufacturers and Distributors of Microbial Cultures
AGI	ABB Environmental Services, Inc. (Bioremediation Division)	A&V, Inc.
Am-Re Services	Advanced Bioremediation Services, Inc.	Alpha Environmental Biosystems
AWD Technologies	Advanced Manufacturing and Development	American Biosystems
Battelle	Arctech, Inc.	B&S Research, Inc.
Billings and Associates	Bio-Recovery Systems, Inc.	Biogee International
CET Environmental Services	Bioremediation Consulting	Biogenesis International
CH2M Hill	Bioremediation Service, Inc.	Bioscience Management, Inc.
Chester Environmental	Bioremediation Technology Services	BioVersal USA, Inc.
Delta Environmental Consultants	BioSolutions	Coastal Biotechnology, Inc.
Du Pont Environmental	BioSystems Technology, Inc.	CytoCulture Environmental Biotechnology
Earthfax Engineering	Bogart Environmental Services	Ecology Technology International
Eckenfelder, Inc.	Cognis, Inc.	Enviroflow
EMCON Associates	Detox Industries	Environmental Biotechnologies
ENSR Consulting and Engineering	Ecova Corporation	ERI/InterBio
ERM	Encore Environmental	EODT Services
Fluor Daniel	ENSITE	Fifco International
Geraghty & Miller	Envirex	Geo-Microbial Technologies, Inc.
Groundwater Technology, Inc.	Envirogen	GreenSource, Inc.
Halliburton Environmental	Environmental Technical Applications	Intech One-Eighty
Harding-Lawson Associates	Enviros	K-Zyme
Hayward Baker Environmental	ESE Biosciences	L. F. Lambert Spawn
ICF-Kaiser	Lambda Bioremediation Systems	Marine Systems
In-Situ Fixation	Matrix Remedial Technologies	Medina Bioremediation Products
International Environmental Technology	Microbial Biotechnology, Inc.	Mycobac, Inc.
International Technology Corporation	Microterra, Inc.	Mycotech Corporation
Kemron Environmental Services	Petro Environmental Technologies	Oil-Spill Eaters, Inc.
Laidlaw Environmental Services	Phytotech, Inc.	Oppenheimer Environmental
OHM Remediation Services Corporation	SBP Technologies	Osprey Biotechnics
Radian Corporation	TreaTek-CRA	Petrol Rem
Remediation Technologies, Inc. (RETEC)	Waste Stream Technology	Polybac Corporation
Resna Industries	Yellowstone Environmental Science	Quantum Environmental Technologies
Roy F. Weston		Solmar Corporation
Terra Systems		Sybron Chemicals
The Traverse Group		Tesoro Environmental Products
Woodward-Clyde Consultants		Tienzyme
		Worne Biotechnology

TABLE 5. (continued).

Manufacturers of Bioreactors	Marketers of Nutrients and Surfactants	Other Industrial Companies
BioTrol, Inc.	Absorption Corporation	Allied Signal
BioVac Environmental Services	FMC Corporation	Alcoa
Bohn Biofilter	Formula Group	Chevron
EG&G	Grasso Environmental	Ciba-Geigy
Lancy Environmental Systems	Interox America	CYTEC Industries
Tekno Associates	Microenvironment	Dow Chemical
TRI-BIO, Inc.	Oil Spill Eater International	Exxon
Zimpro/Passavant	Praxair	General Electric
	REGENESIS Bioremediation Products	J.R. Simplot
		Lockheed Missiles and Space
		Monsanto
		Zeneca

inroads. There continue to be some concerns in the mainstream environmental community about the efficacy of biological techniques and the ability to rigorously prove their effectiveness. However, due to an increased emphasis on protocol development and other means of technical demonstration, and to the educational and promotional efforts of the U.S. EPA, biotreatment has become accepted and practiced by a large segment of the remediation industry, and is becoming better accepted by federal and local regulators.

Most observers expect bioremediation to continue to gain market share, particularly for markets like underground storage tanks, for which the technology is well suited. However, overall growth should slow later in the decade or early in the next century, if only because bioremediation is amenable at most to a fixed percentage of sites. We expect that the market by the year 2000 could reach $350 to $600 million (see Table 1).

Another significant trend in the past few years is the less prominent role being played by dedicated bioremediation companies. These companies often find it hard to compete with the diversified companies for larger jobs, but more importantly, companies relying solely on bioremediation techniques are precluded from bidding on jobs where biotreatment cannot be used. Some companies have solved this problem by acquiring smaller firms to obtain expertise in other remediation technologies. Other dedicated bioremediation companies have been acquired by larger, diversified companies. In any event, the "balance of power" has shifted away from the dedicated companies and their proprietary technologies toward diversified companies with a service-based, nonproprietary approach. Small companies and universities may continue to develop and test innovative technologies and new (possibly even genetically engineered) microbial strains, and some of these may successfully address niche markets. But for the foreseeable future, the service-oriented firms should dominate the U.S. bioremediation market.

BIOREMEDIATION IN EUROPE

Bioremediation in Germany

Overview. The last two decades have seen considerable growth in the German environmental cleanup market, due to increasing government regulation. Research on in situ biorestoration took place in Germany as early as 1982, with the first technical paper on a completed bioremediation project published by Battermann and Werner (1984). Research and development at universities and other research centers began in about 1985. The first companies to bring bioremediation to the market in the mid-1980s were Umweltschutz Nord, biodetox, and Hochtief.

The German government has promoted bioremediation in several ways, including a bilateral agreement on waste site cleanups between the U.S. EPA and the Bundesministerium für Forschung und Technologie (BMFT, the Federal Ministry for Research and Technology), which features the use of bioremediation at two German sites: the Haynauer Strasse 58 site in Berlin and the Burbacher Hütte site in Saarbrücken (Sanning and Stietzel 1993). The BMFT has also sponsored 16 bioremediation projects, at a total cost of DM 20 million (U.S. $12 million) (Porta et al. 1994).

Market and Site Characteristics. The largest target markets for the bioremediation industry in Germany are mineral oil-contaminated soil and groundwater, followed by biological off-gas treatment and specialized biological wastewater treatment. Soil cleanup efforts have also focused on abandoned gaswork sites, coal gasification facilities, and abandoned refineries.

The German Federal States (Länder) are responsible for registration and risk assessment of suspected contaminated sites. In November 1993, the total number of suspected contaminated sites was estimated at 137,000, including about 84,000 abandoned waste disposal sites and 53,000 abandoned industrial sites (Franzius 1993). In addition, more than 4,000 warfare-related sites and approximately 10,000 military sites may be contaminated. By the time the registration is complete, the total may rise as high as 250,000 suspected contaminated sites (Franzius 1993).

Contaminated soils are regulated under the Soil Protection Program, enacted in 1985 (Visser 1994) and the 1989 Special Report on Contaminated Soils. Different treatment options, including bioremediation, are sometimes possible depending on the quality and quantity of the contaminants. In general, large, centralized soil treatment stations require permits under the waste laws, whereas mobile, on-site treatment plants can be operated without permits. In practice most hydrocarbon-contaminated soils are treated by ex situ, on-site or off-site bioremediation methods (Raphael and Glass 1995). Large quantities of contaminated soil are commonly cleaned off site. The country's central soil cleaning stations have a total capacity of approximately 1.5 million metric tons per year (Kielburger and Schmitz 1993).

Technologies Practiced. Bioremediation of soils in Germany has largely been restricted to mineral-oil-hydrocarbon, and BTEX contamination. Few projects have attempted to remediate polycyclic aromatic hydrocarbons (PAHs) or halogenated compounds. Technologies for soil bioremediation include static treatment (carried out in situ, and generally employing aeration and treatment of off-gases) and dynamic treatment (conducted ex situ and involving mechanical mixing of the contaminated soil). In either case, soil bioremediation is often carried out with addition of special fertilizers and surfactants, and sometimes with addition of organic or inorganic materials for better percolation (disintegration of the soil structure). As in the United States, biological activity is stimulated by the use of either pure oxygen or hydrogen peroxide as a source of oxygen, or the use of nitrate as an alternative electron acceptor in certain situations.

In addition, bioreactors are used to treat fine particles arising from soil washing or to treat small quantities of contaminated soil directly. Among other technologies that have been practiced are fixed-bed bioreactors for cleaning contaminated groundwater, wastewater, and landfill leachate; biological elimination of nitrate from groundwater, with fixed-bed or rotating-drum bioreactors; biological off-gas treatment; and biological elimination of heavy metals from wastewater.

Industry Structure. Today, over 150 companies are active in bioremediation in Germany (Porta 1991; Porta et al. 1994; Raphael and Glass 1994, 1995). Those companies with significant expertise are shown in Table 6.

The German remediation industry resembles that in the United States, with a number of national and regional consulting or engineering firms conducting or designing waste remediations using a variety of treatment technologies. Among the firms that have developed expertise in bioremediation are Hochtief, Bilfinger und Berger, and Züblin as general building contractors, and TAUW and Trischler und Partner as pure consultants in site investigation and remediation. Other participants include manufacturers of industrial gases, like Linde or Messer Griesheim, or of hydrogen peroxide, like Degussa (Raphael and Glass 1994, 1995).

In addition, as in the United States, several well-known firms specialize in biological treatment methods. Many of these are smaller companies, some of which are subsidiaries of larger industrial companies. Germany's largest bioremediation firm is Umweltschutz Nord, with more than 400 employees working in bioremediation. The firm conducts ex situ treatment of large quantities of contaminated soils using bioremediation and soil washing, and has established operations throughout Germany and elsewhere in western and eastern Europe.

Argus Umweltbiotechnologie performs microbial treatments of contaminated soil and groundwater, using in situ techniques as well as landfarming, bioreactors, and biofilters. Biodetox, an early German participant active in many fields of bioremediation, specializes in bioreactors for industrial wastewater treatment, and owns one of the first bioremediation centers in the country. ContraCon uses soil washing in combination with biological treatment, and Cognis uses small contained systems for small quantities of soil. Several of these companies, including Umweltschutz Nord, biodetox, Lobbe, Hochtief, and Gebr. Huber, are operating central soil bioremediation stations (Kielburger and Schmitz 1993).

TABLE 6a. European bioremediation companies (Germany and The Netherlands).

Germany	The Netherlands
Argus Umweltbiotechnologie	Bioclear Environmental Biotechnology
Barsel, C.	BKH Consulting Engineers
Bauer und Mourik Umwelttechnik & Co.	ClairTech
BGT Boden - und Grundwasser-technologie	De Ruiter Milieutechniek
Bilfinger + Berger	Delft Geotechnics
biodetox Gesellschaft zur biologischen	DHV Consulting Engineers
Schadstoffentsorgung	DSM Research
Braunschweiger Umwelt-biotechnologie	Ecotechniek
BSR-Bodensanierung und Recycling	Grontmij
Buck Umwelttechnik	Heidemij Realisatie
Caro Biotechnik	Heijmans Milieutechniek
Cognis	HWZ-Bodemsanering
ContraCon Gesellschaft für Sanierung von Böden und	IWACO
Gewässern	NBM Bodemsanering
Degussa	Mourik Groot-Ammers
DMT Deutsche Montan Technologie (Cubis)	Oosterhof Holman
Ebiox	Paques
Envicon	TAUW Milieu
GfS Gesellschaft für Boden und Grundwasser Sanierung	VAM
Hansatec	Witteveen & Bos-Consulting Engineers
Hochtief	

Germany (cont.): Holzmann, HP-Biotechnologie, Gebr. Huber Umwelttechnik, HUT Hannover Umwelttechnik, IMA, IST Institut für Sicherheitsforschung und Umwelttechnik, Keller Tiefbau, Linde, Lobbe, MAG Maschinen- und Anlagenbau Grimma, Messer Griesheim, Preussag Noell Wassertechnik, Rheinhold & Mahla, Ruhrkohle Umwelttechnik, Sotec Saarberg Ökotechnik, TAUW Milieu, TGU Technologieberatung Grundwasser und Umwelt, Trischler und Partner, Umweltschutz Nord, Wayss & Freitag, Züblin Umwelttechnik

TABLE 6b. Other European bioremediation companies.

Scandinavia	United Kingdom	France	Italy	Russia
Norway Algea Produkter Aquateam ENCO SINTEF Terrateam **Denmark** A/S Marius Pedersen Bioteknisk Jordrens Carl Bro Dansk Jordrens Hedeselskabet KK Miljøteknik **Sweden** ABITEC AGA Alron Chemical ANOX Banverkert Marksanering i Sverige Skanska VBB-VIAK **Finland** Alko Bioteam Company Ekokem Neste Nordic Envicon Soil and Water Ltd.	Archaeus Technology Development BioTal Limited British Nuclear Fuels Brown and Root Dames and Moore Groundwater Technology International International Bioremediation Services Land Restoration Systems MB Geosphere Shell Research Viridian Bioprocess **Belgium** EMR HAECON Environmental Consultants Solvay VITO	ANTEA (BRGM Group) Burgeap CGE Compagnie Générale des Eaux Elf Aquitaine ESYS Geoclean IBS Biopol Institut Français du Pétrole Merile Rhône-Poulenc SERPOL Valtech Industry **Switzerland** Bioferment Ebiox NeoVac	Castalia Eniricerche Genova Montecatini **Austria** ALTEC-Alpine Umwelttechnik BIUTEC Biotechnologie btf Biotechnologische Forschungsgesellschaft BVT Biologische Verfahrenstechnik Intergeo Porr Umwelttechnik Proterra Umwelttechnik	Bios Groop, Ltd. Innovatsoniye Bioteknologiya **Czech Republic** Dekonta Ekosystem **Hungary** Biokör **Lithuania** Biocentras

Market Trends. After a period of dramatic growth, the German bioremediation market has slowed somewhat, due to the effects of the recession and the lower prices caused by increased competition. Nevertheless, bioremediation's share of the market should continue to grow as additional central soil-cleaning stations are brought on line. We believe that the German market should reach $250 to $350 million (U.S.) by the end of the century (Table 1).

Large, full-service remediation centers will continue to dominate the market in the future, but there is also a trend toward small transportable treatment systems that can be operated without a permit. Biotreatment should also make inroads in groundwater treatment, where activated carbon for treating air-stripped off-gases and groundwater will begin to be replaced by biological techniques.

Growth of the overall European bioremediation market should see the expansion of existing bioremediation companies and their technologies, which should place existing German firms in a good position to address these markets. Although not all the leading companies in Germany will be able to follow this trend, those companies already having subsidiaries outside Germany, such as Umweltschutz Nord, Lobbe, Cognis, ContraCon, and TAUW, should have good opportunities to expand.

Bioremediation in the Netherlands

Overview. The Netherlands is one of the more progressive countries in Europe with regard to environmental protection. Several laws enacted within the past 25 years have led to increased emphasis on environmental remediation and pollution prevention (Staps 1989; Soczo and Visscher 1991). Work on innovative biotreatment techniques has been carried out since at least the mid-1980s by the Rijksinstituut voor Volksgezondheid en Milieuhygiene (RIVM, the National Institute of Public Health and Environmental Protection), the TNO (Netherlands Organization for Applied Scientific Research) and the consulting and research institute Delft Geotechnics (Staps 1989; Soczo and Visscher 1991). The Netherlands' first large-scale bioventing experiment began in 1982 and cost an estimated 1 million guilders (U.S. $600,000) over 3 years.

The Dutch government over the years has instituted several programs to promote the adoption of bioremediation (Soczo and Visscher 1991). Currently in the works is a 5-year, 40-million guilder (U.S. $24-million) program to promote research and demonstration projects on in situ soil bioremediation, that will be administered by the Netherlands Research Program on In Situ Soil Bioremediation (NOBIS) (J. Kooijman, personal communication).

Market and Site Characteristics. There are estimated to be approximately 5,000 contaminated gasoline stations, 230 to 250 coal gasification plants, and perhaps as many as 100,000 operational industrial sites requiring some form of remediation (Mischgofsky et al. 1993; J. Kooijman, personal communication). Cleaning these sites might cost 50 to 200 billion guilder (U.S. $30 to $120 billion), with current annual spending estimated at 400 million guilder (U.S. $240 million) (E. Mischgofsky, personal communication). The major contaminants at these sites are believed to be petroleum hydrocarbons, chlorinated hydrocarbons, PAHs, PCBs, and heavy metals (J. Kooijman, personal communication).

The Dutch program for soil remediation has been based on the Soil Cleanup Guideline of 1983 and, until recently, featured three levels (the A-B-C levels). The A level was the reference value for clean soil or groundwater; the B level, 5 to 10 times higher, was the "trigger" level where further investigation would be needed; at the C level (another 5 to 10 times higher), remediation investigation and risk assessment would be required, often leading to obligatory cleanup (Mischgofsky et al. 1993). Although intended to take into account specific site information, most cleanups were based primarily on the A-B-C levels (Visser 1994), with the B-levels often used as the goal (Mischgofsky et al. 1993).

Recent changes to this system have created difficulties for bioremediation. The A and C levels have been reformulated based on ecotoxicological assessment of potential human exposure, potential environmental spread of contaminants, and the background levels in soil, and the B levels have been eliminated (Visser 1994). Although this is generally a favorable development, the standards for mineral-oil hydrocarbons have not been reformulated and the endpoints remain extremely low (J. Kooijman, personal communication). Although the goals for many cleanups can still be negotiated with local authorities on a case-by-case basis, these low endpoints are hard to achieve by bioremediation. Because of the prevalence of hydrocarbon-contaminated soils and groundwater, this has severely constrained the use of bioremediation in the Netherlands in the past 1 to 2 years.

Technologies Practiced. Contaminated soils are being treated using several biological methods, including landfarming, in situ biorestoration, and bioreactors. Most soils are treated off site (in central stations), with landfarming and soil washing being popular options. Several corporations are actively pursuing landfarming, including NBM Bodemsanering, De Ruiter Milieutechnologie, Mourik Groot-Ammers, VAM, Heijmans, Oosterhof Holman, and Heidemij Realisatie, many of which conducted successful remediations beginning in the late 1980s.

Several institutions are actively developing bioreactors for treating soil slurries, sludges, groundwater, and other contaminated media, including purification of waste gases. The TNO has demonstrated two different bioreactor systems that can remediate soils and sludges, for which Heidemij has commercial rights. Other companies developing bioreactors are Witteveen & Bos, which is commercializing a rotating bioreactor for oil-contaminated soils developed by the Agricultural University of Wageningen (LUW), and TAUW Milieu, which has used a variety of bioreactor approaches since 1986. In addition, DHV Consulting Engineers is commercializing a dry-bed filtration reactor developed at LUW, and BKH Consulting Engineers is collaborating with the Technical University of Delft on an activated sludge reactor for groundwater.

Industry Structure. As in many European countries, the remediation industry is split into two sectors. On the one hand are the consultants, who conduct site assessments and recommend remedial options. Remediations are carried out by the contractors, generally larger companies capable of conducting a variety of technologies. Several of the larger companies combine both functions. As in Germany, a number of companies, such as Heidemij, Heijmans, and NBM Bodemsanering, are operating central soil cleaning stations.

Among the consultants with bioremediation expertise are Delft Geotechnics, Grontmij, IWACO, TAUW, and DHV. Delft Geotechnics, established in 1934, has conducted a number of pilot and demonstration projects in soil and aquifer bioremediation, including a large-scale demonstration project involving remediation of gasoline and diesel oil from soil by a combination of bioventing and stimulated biodegradation, and an ongoing large-scale biosparging demonstration project. TAUW Milieu was established in 1928, and began bioremediation activities in the 1980s. TAUW has developed a fixed-film reactor called Biopur® for BTEX and other contaminants, for treating groundwater and vapor-phase contaminants resulting from air stripping. Grontmij, a large consulting firm, has performed a number of research investigations of bioremediation and is supervising one field remediation. Bioclear Environmental Biotechnology, founded in 1988, carries out laboratory and pilot-scale feasibility studies, and supplies cultured microorganisms through selective enrichment for remediation.

Among the contracting/consulting firms, Heidemij is the leader, having extensive activities in soil washing, land-farming, in situ biorestoration, and bioreactors. Heidemij practices a proprietary ex situ soil treatment technology called CumBac. Through its recent merger with Geraghty & Miller and its other subsidiaries, Heidemij has operations in numerous European countries and the United States. Other contracting firms with bioremediation experience include Oosterhof Holman, which is carrying out four ongoing projects, mostly involving petroleum contamination; De Ruiter, which has carried out at least two bioremediation projects on hydrocarbon-contaminated sites; and NBM Bodemsanering, which plans to open a biological soil cleaning station in the summer of 1995.

Market Trends. There continues to be a great deal of interest in biological technologies in the Netherlands. However, the current regulatory system has clearly put a chill on the short-term growth of bioremediation for cleanup of hydrocarbon-contaminated soils and groundwater. The growing pressure to take the future use of the site into account in risk assessment may cause this to change over time. Until there is some regulatory relief, it is hard to see significant growth in bioremediation's market share. We estimate that the Netherlands accounted for $10 to $20 million of the 1994 European market, and this share will probably hold steady for the next few years, but may possibly grow later in the decade.

Bioremediation in the Nordic Countries

Overview. The northern countries of Scandinavia are beginning to address the need to remediate environmental pollution. Denmark is often considered one of the more progressive countries on environmental matters, where concerns over the cleanliness of soils and groundwater have arisen because so much of the nation's drinking water comes from groundwater. Sweden, Norway, and Finland also have a growing awareness of environmental problems, although few sites have been successfully remediated.

Market and Site Characteristics. The regulatory regime for site classification and remediation in the Nordic countries is described in Rosén (1992) and Visser (1994). On the basis of ongoing inventories, there may be as many as 25,000 to 40,000 contaminated sites in Denmark, Finland, Norway, and Sweden (Rosén 1992). The Finnish Ministry of the Environment completed its inventory in 1994, and estimated that there are 10,000 to 25,000 contaminated sites in that country, of which 1,200 will need restoration within the next 20 years.

There is a fair amount of similarity among the types of contaminated sites found in the Nordic countries. Most common are sawmills (contaminated with chlorophenol-based fungicides), wood-preserving sites (contaminated with PAHs and heavy metals), former city gas or coke plants, military installations, and sites contaminated with hydrocarbons and PCBs (Rosén 1992). Much of the bioremediation activity in Scandinavia has focused on the wood-preserving sites.

Industry Structure and Technologies Practiced. The Scandinavian remediation industry is generally split between contractors and consultants. There is also a significant role for central soil cleaning stations, particularly in Denmark. Over 100,000 tons of contaminated soil have been treated at the three permanent Danish sites for biological treatment, operated by Bioteknisk Jordrens, KK Miljøteknik, and Dansk Jordrens. Other activities in Denmark have included landfarming of TCE-contaminated soil at a refinery in Kalundborg, and an oil-spill remediation at Alborg (Rosén 1992).

Among companies active in Norway is Aquateam, the Norwegian Water Technology Center, a consultancy organization that has been involved in several bioremediation field projects or laboratory evaluations, including one project using bioremediation at a 60,000-metric ton coke works site. The Norwegian Geotechnical Institute (NGI) and SINTEF have undertaken pilot-scale remediation of hydrocarbon-contaminated soil, and the NGI has also begun a research program to study the potential applicability of bioremediation for creosote-contaminated sites (Rosén 1992). ENCO is involved with remediation projects for the Norwegian Defense Ministry (C.-G. Rosén, personal communication).

In Sweden, creosote and PAH contamination at a former city gas plant and tar factory in Stockholm are being remediated both in situ and ex situ by the Swedish company Skanska along with the British firm BioTal Ltd. (see below). Also in Sweden, the gas manufacturer AGA is investigating bioventing applications, including a project to deodorize a portion of the 1995 World's Fair grounds in Vienna (Rosén 1992). The consulting firm VBB VIAK has conducted several projects, including a creosote-contaminated site in Vansbro. Small-scale bioremediation of oil spills has been carried out by Alron Chemical and Marksanering i Sverige AB.

In Finland, the consulting firm Soil and Water Ltd. can remediate chlorophenols using pure bacterial cultures, and can also can clean oils and creosote from soil, and oils and solvents from groundwater. Nordic Envicon Ltd. has recently begun full-scale bioremediation of chlorophenol-contaminated groundwater using a 5-m^3 fluidized-bed bioreactor. Since 1984, about 40 full-scale bioremediations of chlorophenol-contaminated sites have taken place or are in progress in Finland. Permanent facilities for biotreatment do not yet exist, but several sites are contemplated for the near future.

Market Trends. In 1992, ABITEC AB, in a study for the Nordic Industrial Fund, estimated the market potential for the Nordic countries to be U.S. $68 to 170 million by the end of the 1990s (Rosén 1992). However, early hopes for rapid growth proved unfounded as the overall remediation market has been slow to develop (C.-G. Rosén, personal communication). Today, the market could be as high as $10 to 20 million (U.S.), with additional growth likely as more attention is turned to site remediation, although future growth may be slowed by strict target cleanup levels, as is the case in the Netherlands. Many observers feel that bioremediation can play a major role in the growing remediation industry in this region, because a large proportion of the contaminated sites are believed to be amenable to biodegradation.

Bioremediation in the United Kingdom

To date, environmental legislation has not been strict enough to provide sufficient incentive for the growth of the remediation industry in the United Kingdom. There is no explicit soil-protection legislation, and remediations are generally conducted as specific sites are proposed for redevelopment (Visser 1994). Britain's need to comply with toughening EU regulations may force this status quo to change.

Nevertheless, several bioremediation companies are found in the United Kingdom. BioTal Limited, perhaps the UK's leader, was founded in the early 1980s, and specializes in in situ and ex situ soil bioremediation, the use of fungal cultures in soil remediation, and other techniques such as soil vapor extraction. In addition to the Swedish project mentioned above, BioTal has conducted about 20 bioremediation projects in the United Kingdom and elsewhere in Europe, including in situ and ex situ treatment of coal tar-contaminated soils at the Greenbank Gasworks site in Blackburn, one of the largest bioremediation projects ever conducted in Europe.

Land Restoration Systems is a 9-year-old company that has developed expertise in several remediation technologies, including in situ and ex situ bioremediation and the use of bioreactors. The company has conducted more than 300 projects in the United Kingdom and western Europe, many of which have involved bioremediation. Viridian Bioprocessing, a biotreatment joint venture between Rhône-Poulenc (France) and the engineering company AMEC, develops specialized bioreactors using a library of hundreds of bacterial species and microbial consortia. The company has claimed success in treating pentachlorophenol using site-specific microbial isolates in an 8-m^3 pilot reactor. Viridian has entered into a consortium arrangement with MB Geosphere, a subsidiary of a Scottish engineering company and a German construction company that is beginning to apply bioremediation to soil contamination.

International Bioremediation Services Limited (IBS) is affiliated with the U.S. company Enviroflow, and specializes in the production and application of bacterial products. IBS identifies, isolates, and grows naturally occurring cultures, and sells Enviroflow's dried bacterial cultures in the United Kingdom. The company claims success in more than 100 completed remediation projects, including several involving oil spills, and also has sister companies in France, Denmark, and Australia.

Among other companies in the United Kingdom are Archaeus Technology Group Ltd., which in 1991 successfully remediated hydrocarbon-contaminated soil from a leaking storage tank, using air and nutrient addition in situ, and Shell Research, which has developed an Upflow Anaerobic Sludge Blanket reactor, which it has used with a consortium of methanogens and sulfate reducing bacteria to biotreat a zinc smelter site in the Netherlands. In addition, several U.S. companies have subsidiaries or branches in the United Kingdom, including Groundwater Technology and Dames and Moore.

The current bioremediation market in the United Kingdom is probably less than U.S. $10 million. In spite of the high level of interest and existence of several established companies, this market (along with the overall remediation market) is unlikely to grow too rapidly until the country's environmental regulations are toughened.

Bioremediation in Other European Countries

There is beginning to be a significant interest in bioremediation in other European countries, even where the overall remediation markets are not as well advanced. Representative companies are included in Table 6.

Several companies practice bioremediation in France, including Burgeap, which has been involved in four bioremediation projects with the French petroleum institute (IFP), and BRGM, which has collaborated with Elf Aquitaine and ESYS on the use of in situ bioremediation with addition of nutrients and microbes, to treat hydrocarbon-contaminated soils.

In Switzerland, Ebiox, a subsidiary of Ebnöther, is the leading bioremediation company. It has been in the business since the mid-1980s, and has established a joint venture with Sybron (United States) to build bioremediation-based soil-recycling facilities throughout Europe, and has developed a vacuum heap system for biotreatment of mineral-oil hydrocarbons. The Belgian firm Haecon Environmental Consultants has applied its BIO-C process for the treatment of contaminated sludges at about a dozen sites in Belgium and the Netherlands. The process uses Sybron's ABR bacterial cultures and a special nutrient formulation to stimulate aerobic biodegradation in situ.

Several bioremediation companies have developed in the former Eastern bloc. Biocentras, a Lithuanian company with an office in the Czech Republic, has developed a bacterial/fertilizer product for oil degradation and a process for treating contaminated soil and groundwater. Biokôr of Hungary conducts in situ soil bioremediation using bioventing, ex situ soil biotreatment and landfarming, and in situ groundwater remediation using biostimulation. Among Russian companies are Bios Groop, Ltd., which has developed a product for marine oil-spill biodegradation, and Innovatsoniye Bioteknologiya, which is marketing vapor-phase bioreactors for VOC treatment.

In addition, a number of universities and research institutes in the Eastern countries maintain active research programs in bioremediation. Several of the German companies shown in Table 6, such as Biopract and BioPlanta, are head-quartered in the eastern Länder; in addition, numerous other German companies such as Umweltschutz Nord and Xenex have established branch offices or sub-sidiaries in the former socialist nations.

BIOREMEDIATION IN CANADA

Canada is considered to have a progressive environmental regulatory struc-ture. The federal Department of the Environment was created in 1971; and its actions are often supplemented by environmental agencies in each of the pro-vinces. The country's programs for classification and remediation of contami-nated sites are described in Visser (1994). The Canadian Environmental Protection Act was adopted in 1988 and the Green Plan in 1990. The Green Plan features $100 million (Canadian) to move environmental technologies to the marketplace and $20 million (Canadian) for environmental innovation. Several federal and provincial programs foster the development of innovative technologies and include several bioremediation projects.

There are a number of bioremediation companies in Canada, as shown in Table 7. Although many of these companies focus on other aspects of environ-mental microbiology, such as mineral leaching ("biomining"), there is considerable

TABLE 7. Canadian bioremediation companies.

ADS Associés Ltée.	Grace Dearborn, Inc.
B. V. Sorbex, Inc.	Griffin Remediation Services
Beak Consultants, Ltd.	Groupe Serrener
Bercan Environmental Resources, Inc.	Jacques Whitford Environmental
Biogenie, Inc.	KRH Environmental
Biopaq Lavalin	Novacor Research and Technology
Bio-Rem	OHM Remediation Services of Canada
Boojum Research Limited	Ortech International
C.A.R.E. International	Prairie Biological Research
Conestoga-Rovers & Associates, Ltd.	Recbiomine
DOC Environmental Control, Ltd.	Sanivan Group
Enviromega	SNC Group, Inc.
Enviromine, Inc.	Westec Microbes, Ltd.
GDC Environment	

public and private sector interest in the use of biological methods for hazardous waste treatment.

Beak Consultants, a multidisciplinary consulting firm that has long been active in bioremediation, has used in situ bioremediation to treat a 4.5 acre (1.8 ha) chemical transfer facility in North Toronto where soil and groundwater were contaminated with tetrachloroethene and vinyl chloride. The firm has conducted other projects using biological methods to remediate aquifers.

Grace Dearborn, Inc., a subsidiary of W. R. Grace and Company, has used a strain of *Flavobacterium* to remediate PCP-contaminated soils at wood-treatment facilities, and has developed a soil additive called Daramend that facilitates natural biodegradation of creosotes, PAHs, and hydrocarbons in ex situ soil treatment. Daramend has been successfully demonstrated at a number of sites in Canada and the United States.

Biogenie, Inc., founded in 1987, has conducted in situ bioremediation of a diesel-contaminated former electrical generating plant in Quebec, which resulted in 70% reduction of mineral-oil and grease concentrations in the first 4 months. The company has also developed a proprietary biopile process for vapor-phase biofiltration, and has experience with microbial and fungal cultures for PAH degradation.

Griffin Remediation Services uses a bioaugmentation approach for soil remediation, coupled with the use of diatomaceous earth as an additive to improve soil porosity. GDC Environment has tested an experimental strain of bacteria for its ability to remediate river sediments in the St. Lawrence near the town of Saint-Zotique. Bercan Environmental Resources discovers, develops, and manufactures packaged microbial cultures for wastewater treatment and other uses. Bio-Rem Technologies has developed and tested at pilot scale a microbial treatment for phthalate esters.

BIOREMEDIATION IN THE PACIFIC RIM

Bioremediation in Australia

In Australia, several universities are actively pursuing bioremediation research, and U.S. companies like Groundwater Technology and Woodward-Clyde have expanded into this market. Among Australian companies is CRA Advanced Technical Development, which has completed several commercial cleanups of PAH and hydrocarbon contamination. It is conducting landfarming-based remediations for its parent company, CRA Ltd., an Australian mining company, and is researching other in situ and bioreactor-based cleanup methods. The Broken Hill Proprietary Company, a steel and resources firm that is Australia's largest company, has been funding bioremediation research jointly with the Australian government's major research organization, the Commonwealth Scientific and Industrial Research Organization (CSIRO). Among the active university groups are the Microbiology Research Unit at the University of Canberra, which has developed an oil-spill bioremediation process, and LaTrobe University, which is collaborating with Scott and Furphy, an engineering firm, to commercialize a process using fungi to degrade organochlorines such as DDT and PCBs. In fact, Saftec, a division of Scott and Furphy, has used the white-rot fungus for PCB degradation in U.S. field trials.

Bioremediation in Japan

Until recently, there has been very little reported interest in bioremediation in Japan. A $15-million basic research program was established between a Japanese research consortium and Michigan State University to identify biodegradative organisms and study the genetics and evolution of these traits. The Japan Research Institute, a group of twelve companies and several government agencies, has established the Bioremediation Consortium, which sponsored a 1993 conference in Tokyo and has begun a biotreatability study at a Japanese site. Obayashi Corporation, a general contractor, recently announced plans to conduct a 3-year test of bioremediation on Kuwaiti soils contaminated in the 1991 Gulf War.

A 1993 U.S. Department of State fact-finding mission identified a fair amount of bioremediation research at Japanese companies, government agencies, and universities (Davatelis and Kneller 1993). Among the companies visited were EBARA Research Company, which is working with a vapor-phase reactor for TCE biodegradation using methane-oxidizing microbes and other reactors; Mitsubishi Petrochemical Company, which had several active research programs; NKK Corporation, which has a microbial desulfurization process for hydrometallurgical plants; and Kurita Water Industries, Ltd., which is developing genetically engineered microbes for TCE degradation.

It often appears to Western observers that Japan has not officially recognized that it has any environmental problems to be remediated. This fact-finding visit may have uncovered evidence that the Japanese power structure is awakening to the need for environmental remediation in the wake of decades of industrialization.

CONCLUSIONS

Significant bioremediation activities are taking place around the world. As remediation markets fully develop outside the United States, biological treatment techniques should enjoy greater acceptance than has been the case in the United States because these technologies are better established and have a proven track record of successful use in the United States and Europe. We are optimistic that world bioremediation markets will continue to show dramatic growth in the coming decade, into the next century.

REFERENCES

Bakst, J. 1991. "Impact of Present and Future Regulations on Bioremediation." *J. Ind. Microbiol.* 3: 13-22.

Battermann, G., and P. Werner. 1984. "Removal of a Mineral Oil Subsurface Contamination Through Microbial Degradation," *Gwf-Wasser/Abswasser 125*.

Berkowitz, J. 1994. Presentation at Environmental Business Council of New England, March 15.

Davatelis, G., and R. Kneller. 1993. "Bioremediation in Japan: An Overview 1993," U.S. State Department.

Environmental Business Journal. 1991. "EC Market Looks Good to U.S. Firms." 4(3): 1.

Environmental Business Journal. 1994. "The U.S. Environmental Industry 1990-2010." 7(4): 1.

Franzius, V. (German Environmental Protection Agency). 1993. Speech at the Euro-Forum symposium in December 1993.

Glass, D. J. 1993. *The Promising Worldwide Bioremediation Market*. Decision Resources, Waltham, MA, December.

Glass, D. J. 1994. "Exploring the U.S. Market for Hazardous Waste Bioremediation," *The National Environmental Journal*, 4(1): 56-62.

Hinchee, R. E., D. C. Downey, and R. N. Miller. 1990. "Enhancing Biodegradation of Vadose Zone JP-4 Through Soil Venting." In *Proceedings of Hazardous Wastes and Hazardous Materials*, p. 387. Hazardous Materials Control Research Institute, Silver Spring, MD.

Kielburger, G., and H. J. Schmitz. 1993. "Bodenbehandlungszentrun: Die Jagd nach dem Boden hat Begonnen," *TerraTech*, September, p. 52.

Lorenz, W. T. 1992. "Markets with Strong Potential for Export of American Expertise." In *Proceedings of the Tenth Annual Hazardous Materials and Management Conference*, pp. 259-279. Tower Conference Management Company, Glen Elyn, IL.

Metzger, B. H. 1990. *European Environmental Trends in the 1990s: Implications for Management*, Arthur D. Little, Inc., Cambridge, MA.

Mischgofsky, F. H., F. A. Weststrate, and W. Visser. 1993. "An Integral Cluster Approach for Containment, Remediation and Monitoring of Groundwater Pollution in Large, Industrial Areas." In H.J.P. Eijsackers and T. Hamers (Eds.) *Integrated Soil and Sediment Research: A Basis for Proper Protection*, Kluwer Academic Publishers, Dordrecht, The Netherlands.

Porta, A. 1991. "A Review of European Bioreclamation Practice." In R. E. Hinchee, R. F. Olfenbuttel (Eds.), *In Situ Bioreclamation: Applications and Investigations for Hydrocarbon and Contaminated Site Remediation*, pp. 1-13. Butterworth-Heinemann, Stoneham, MA.

Porta, A., J. K. Young, and P. M. Molton. 1994. "In Situ Bioremediation in Europe." In R. E. Hinchee, D. B. Anderson, F. B. Metting Jr., G. D. Sayles (Eds.), *Applied Biotechnology for Site Remediation*, pp. 1-20. Lewis Publishers, Ann Arbor, MI.

Raphael, T., and D. J. Glass. 1994. *Bioremediation in Germany: Technologies, Markets and Leading Practitioners*, DEVO Enterprises, Inc., Washington, DC.

Raphael, T., and D. J. Glass. 1995. "Bioremediation in Germany: Markets, Technologies, and Leading Companies." In R. E. Hinchee, J. A. Kittel, and H. J. Reisinger (Eds.), *Applied Bioremediation of Petroleum Hydrocarbons*, pp. 35-45. Battelle Press, Columbus, OH.

Raymond, R. L., V. H. Jamison, and J. O. Hudson. 1975. "Beneficial Stimulation of Bacterial Activity in Ground Waters Containing Petroleum Products," API Publication Number 4427, American Petroleum Institute, Washington, DC.

Rosén, C.-G. 1992. *Bioremediation: State of the Art in the Nordic Countries in an International Perspective*, Nordic Industrial Fund, Oslo.

Sanning, D. and H. Stietzel. 1993. "United States/German Bilateral Agreement on Hazardous Waste Site Clean-up Projects." In F. Arendt, G. J. Anokkee, R. Bosman, and W. J. van den Brink (Eds.), *Contaminated Soil '93*, Kluwer Academic Publishers, Dordrecht.

Soczo, E. and K. Visscher. 1991. "Research and Development Programs for Biological Hazardous Waste Treatment in the Netherlands." In G. S. Sayler, R. Fox and J. W. Blackburn (Eds.), *Environmental Biotechnology for Waste Treatment*, pp. 261-269. Plenum Press, New York, NY.

Staps, J.J.M. 1989. "International Evaluation of In-Situ Biorestoration of Contaminated Soil and Groundwater." In *Third International Meeting of the NATO/CCMS pilot study on "Demonstration of Remedial Action Technologies for Contaminated Land and Groundwater"*.

The Economist. 1993. "The Money in Europe's Muck." November 20, pp. 71-72.

U.S. Congress Office of Technology Assessment. 1991. "Bioremediation for Marine Oil Spills — Background Paper." U.S. Government Printing Office, Washington, May.

U.S. Environmental Protection Agency. 1992. *The Superfund Innovative Technology Evaluation Program: Technology Profiles Fifth Edition.* EPA/540/R-92/077, Washington, DC, November.

U.S. Environmental Protection Agency. 1993. *Cleaning Up the Nation's Waste Sites: Markets and Technology Trends.* EPA 542-R-92-012, Washington, DC, April.

U.S. Environmental Protection Agency. 1994. *Bioremediation in the Field*, Issue Number 11, Washington, DC, July.

Visser, W.J.F. 1994. *Contaminated Land Policies in Some Industrialized Countries, Technical Soil Protection Committee.* The Hague, the Netherlands.

Walker, C. S., and D. Shooter. 1992. *Market Development for Remediation Services in the United States.* Spectrum Environmental Management Industry Series, Decision Resources, Burlington, MA, May 6.

Bioremediation in Germany: Markets, Technologies, and Leading Companies

Thomas Raphael and David J. Glass

ABSTRACT

Bioremediation has become an internationally accepted remediation tool. Commercial bioremediation activities take place in many European countries, but Germany and the Netherlands are the clear European leaders, with both having a long history of public and private sector activity in biological technologies. The German bioremediation market has been driven by government regulation, in particular the waste laws that apply to contaminated soils. The 1994 German market for bioremediation is estimated at $70 to 100 million (U.S.$). There are at least 150 companies active in bioremediation in Germany, most of which practice bioremediation of hydrocarbon-contaminated soils, either in situ or ex situ. Because of their predominance in the current European market, German firms are well positioned to expand into those nations in the European Union (EU) currently lacking an environmental business infrastructure.

INTRODUCTION

Although the United States, with an estimated $150 to 180 million 1993 market (Glass 1993; Jennings Group 1993), accounts for more than half of the world bioremediation market, significant activities and technological advances are taking place elsewhere in the world, particularly in Europe. In fact Europe, the world's second largest bioremediation market, had an estimated $90 to 120 million (U.S. $) market in 1993, which could grow to as much as $600 million by century's end (Raphael and Glass 1994; see Table 1). Germany and the Netherlands are the clear European leaders in commercial bioremediation. Both countries have a long history of significant public and private sector activity in bioremediation and related technologies. With a $60 to 80 million 1993 market, up from $30 million in 1992, Germany makes up more than half the current European market, with growth to $350 million possible by the year 2000 (Raphael and Glass 1994).

Site remediation markets generally lag behind the markets in the United States even in those European countries considered to be the most progressive

TABLE 1. World bioremediation markets 1993-2000 (in millions of U.S. dollars)[a].

	1993	1994	1995	1997	2000
Germany	60-80	70-100	90-120	100-150	250-350
Europe	90-120	105-175	130-180	180-300	375-600
United States	150-180	160-210	175-300	225-325	350-600
World	250-350	290-440	320-520	450-700	800-1,350

(a) Source: Authors' estimates.

in environmental matters (e.g., Denmark, Germany, the Netherlands, Norway, Sweden, and Switzerland). Many European nations have only recently conducted inventories to identify and prioritize their hazardous-waste sites. In 1990, it was estimated that more than 150,000 hazardous-waste sites existed in the EU member states, but only a small fraction of these have begun to be remediated (*Environmental Business Journal* 1991; Rosén 1992).

In Germany, the Federal States (Länder) are responsible for registration and risk assessment of suspected contaminated sites. Some of the Länder are still in the process of creating their contaminated sites registers; others, such as North-Rhine Westphalia, have finished doing so. In November 1993, the total number of suspected contaminated sites was estimated at 137,000, including about 84,000 abandoned waste disposal sites and 53,000 abandoned industrial sites (Franzius 1993). By the time the registration is complete, the total may rise to as high as 250,000 suspected contaminated sites.

THE GERMAN REMEDIATION MARKET

The last two decades have seen considerable growth in the German environmental cleanup market, as public interest in cleaning contaminated sites has led to increasing government regulation, particularly relating to curbing water and soil pollution. The largest target markets for the bioremediation industry in Germany in the 1990s are mineral oil-contaminated soil and groundwater, followed by biological off-gas treatment and specialized biological wastewater treatment. This paper discusses primarily the situation for bioremediation of contaminated soils in Germany.

In spite of economic problems resulting from reunification, the need for clean, available land for construction of new factories in the eastern Länder should create a continuing demand for environmental remediation. A special federal fund of 13 billion DM (U.S. $7.8 billion) was established for the cleanup of the largest contaminated industrial sites in the new Länder of the former East Germany (Schmitz 1993).

The system of regulation of contaminated soils in Germany is very different from that in the United States. In Germany, wastes are not generally categorized as either "hazardous" or "nonhazardous." Used substances or soils are considered to be "waste" if it is not possible to recycle them, or if remediation is judged to be necessary for the public interest, in which case disposal must follow the strict procedures and laws concerning waste management. Different treatment options, including bioremediation, sometimes are possible depending on the quality and quantity of the contaminants. The demands on "soil protection" at operational industrial sites may not as strong as for abandoned sites (Visser 1994).

Generally, large centralized soil-treatment stations require permits under the waste legislation, whereas mobile on-site treatment plants can be operated without permits. For example, an ex situ mobile soil bioremediation plant (heap or pile) can be operated without any permit for 6 months on site, if the soil is subsequently reused or recycled on site.

In practice most hydrocarbon-contaminated soils are treated by ex situ, on-site, or off-site bioremediation methods. Because traditional disposal options often are limited, other commonly used methods for treating contaminated soil are soil washing in large, centralized soil washing stations or in transportable plants; fixation, encapsulation (e.g., in concrete), or — for contaminated sites — hydraulic prevention (i.e., creating hydraulic barriers in groundwater); and soil vapor extraction and off-gas treatment, mostly with activated carbon.

THE GERMAN BIOREMEDIATION MARKET: EUROPE'S LEADER

Historical Perspective

There is a long history of public and private sector activities in biological treatment methods in Germany, particularly in the relatively established practices of landfarming (i.e., ex situ soil bioremediation) and soil washing. Pioneering work on more innovative biotreatment techniques has been carried out by German companies, universities, and research institutes since the early 1980s (for example, Battermann and Werner 1984). Today, several academic institutions are active in bioremediation research; most of these are active members of Deutsche Gesellschaft für Chemisches Apparatewesen, Chemische Technik und Biotechnologie (DECHEMA), or Vereinigung für Allgemeine und Angewandte Mikrobiologie (VAAM). The first companies to bring bioremediation to the market in the mid-1980s were Umweltschutz Nord, biodetox, and Hochtief.

The German government has supported technological developments in bioremediation since 1986. More recent programs include a bilateral agreement on waste-site cleanups between the Federal Ministry for Research and Technology (BMFT) and the U.S. Environmental Protection Agency, which features the use of bioremediation at two German sites, the Haynauer Strasse 58 site in Berlin and the Burbacher Hutte site in Saarbrücken (Sanning and Stietzel 1993). BMFT reportedly has sponsored 16 bioremediation projects at a total cost of 20 million DM (U.S. $12 million) (Porta et al. 1994).

We estimate the 1994 German bioremediation market at approximately U.S. $70 to 100 million. This represents a modest increase from 1993, after a period of rapid growth earlier in the decade. The current market corresponds to approximately 200,000 metric tons of bioremediated soil, groundwater, off-gas, and specialized wastewater treatment, at an average price of $80 to 120 per metric ton of soil. Looking ahead to the year 2000, the total market, including central bioremediation stations, on-site projects, off-gas treatment, microorganisms, plants, analytical capacity, fertilizers, mixing machines, and so on, could reach perhaps $250 to 350 million (see Table 1).

Technologies Practiced: Focus on Hydrocarbon-Contaminated Soils and Groundwater

Bioremediation of soils in Germany is largely restricted to sites contaminated with mineral-oil hydrocarbons and with benzene, toluene, ethylbenzene, and xylenes (BTEX). Few projects have attempted to remediate polycyclic aromatic hydrocarbons, and these have met with minimal success. There is very little activity on halogenated substances.

Technologies for soil bioremediation include static or dynamic heap (ex situ) treatment. Static treatment is carried out on site or off site, generally with aeration and treatment of off-gases. A common time scale at German temperatures is 6 to 12 months. Soil treatment also can be dynamic, with the contaminated soil mixed by large, specially developed machines. The time scale for such activities is 6 to 9 months on site or 3 to 6 months in central stations, depending on the temperature. In both static and dynamic systems, treatment can be carried out outdoors, in tents or special buildings, or covered with plastic sheaths. In either system, soil bioremediation often is carried out with addition of special fertilizers, surfactants, and sometimes with addition of organic or inorganic materials for a better percolation (disintegration of the soil structure). As in the United States, biological activity is stimulated by the use of either pure oxygen or hydrogen peroxide as a source of oxygen, or the use of nitrate as an alternative electron acceptor. Microbial cultures sometimes are used for bioaugmentation.

A few companies, such as Umweltschutz Nord, Cognis, and Hydrogeologie Nordhausen (HGN) have developed proprietary bioreactor systems to provide improved, faster processes. Other technologies and the companies developing them are: fixed-bed bioreactors for cleaning of contaminated groundwater (e.g., TAUW), wastewater (e.g., biodetox, Envicon), and landfill leachate (e.g., Wehrle); biological elimination of nitrate from groundwater with fixed-bed bioreactors (e.g., Preussag); and biological off-gas treatment (e.g., Braunschweiger Umwelt-biotechnologie).

Major Bioremediation Firms

Today, there are more than 150 companies active in bioremediation in Germany (Porta 1991, Porta et al. 1994, Raphael and Glass 1994). Those companies with significant expertise and published references are listed in Table 2.

TABLE 2. Leading German bioremediation companies[a].

Alois Lauer Stahl- und Rohrleitungsbau GmbH
Argus Umweltbiotechnologie GmbH
Baresel, C. AG
Bauer und Mourik Umwelttechnik GmbH & Co.
BGT Boden - und Grundwassertechnologie GmbH
Bilfinger + Berger AG
biodetox Gesellschaft zur biologischen Schadstoffentsorgung mbH
Braunschweiger Umweltbiotechnologie GmbH
BSR-Bodensanierung und Recycling GmbH
Buck Umwelttechnik GmbH
Caro Biotechnik GmbH
Cognis GmbH
ContraCon Gesellschaft für Sanierung von Böden und Gewässern mbH
Degussa AG
DMT Deutsche Montan Technologie (Cubis AG)
Ebiox AG
Envicon GmbH
Gebr. Huber Bodenrecycling GmbH
GfS Gesellschaft für Boden und Grundwassersanierung GmbH
Hansatec GmbH
Hochtief AG
Holzmann AG
HP-Biotechnologie GmbH
HUT Hannover Umwelttechnik GmbH
Hydrogeologie Nordhausen (HGN)
IMA GmbH
IST Institut für Sicherheitsforschung und Umwelttechnik e.V.
Keller Tiefbau Gmbh
Linde AG
Lobbe GmbH
MAG Maschinen- und Anlagenbau Grimma GmbH
Messer Griesheim GmbH
Preussag Noell Wassertechnik GmbH
Rheinhold & Mahla GmbH
Ruhrkohle Umwelttechnik GmbH
SOTEC Saarberg Ökotechnik GmbH
TAUW Infra Consult B.V.
TGU Technologieberatung Grundwasser und Umwelt GmbH
Trischler und Partner GmbH
Umweltschutz Nord GmbH & Co.
Wayss & Freitag AG
Wehrle Werk AG
Züblin Umwelttechnik GmbH

(a) Companies listed are those with significant bioremediation capacities or experience, and published references for soil, air, or water remediation.

The German remediation industry resembles that in the United States, with a number of national and regional consulting or engineering firms conducting or designing waste remediations using a variety of treatment technologies. Among those firms that have developed expertise in bioremediation are Hochtief, Bilfinger und Berger, and Züblin as general building contractors, and TAUW and Trischler und Partner as pure consultants in site investigation and remediation. Other participants include manufacturers of industrial gases, such as Linde or Messer Griesheim; or hydrogen peroxide, such as Degussa.

Trischler und Partner used bioremediation to clean benzene, toluene, and xylene (BTX)-contaminated groundwater at the Rhein-Main Air Base and an abandoned refinery in Hanau. Messer Griesheim used in situ bioremediation to clean contaminated groundwater at a refinery site at Speyer, near Heidelberg; TAUW is using in situ methods to remediate BTX-polluted groundwater at an abandoned gasworks site.

In addition, as in the United States, several well-known firms specialize in biological treatment methods. Many of these are smaller companies, some of which are subsidiaries of larger industrial companies. Germany's largest bioremediation firm, Umweltschutz Nord, has more than 400 employees working in bioremediation. The firm conducts ex situ treatment of large quantities of contaminated soils using bioremediation, and has established operations throughout Germany and elsewhere in western and eastern Europe.

Other examples include Argus Umweltbiotechnologie, which performs microbial treatments of contaminated soil and groundwater using in situ techniques and landfarming, bioreactors, and biofilters; biodetox, an early German participant active in many fields of bioremediation that specializes in bioreactors for industrial wastewater treatment and owns one of the first bioremediation centers in the country; and ContraCon, which uses soil washing in combination with biological treatment. Other notable companies include TAUW, specializing in bioreactor systems primarily for groundwater remediation, and Cognis, which uses small container systems for small quantities of soil and which sells a do-it-yourself bioremediation product, Biocrack (Kopp-Holtwiesche 1994). Several other companies use containers for on-site soil bioremediation, including HGN, Alois Lauer, biodetox, and HP-Biotechnologie.

Several of these companies, including Umweltschutz Nord, biodetox, Lobbe, Hochtief, and Gebr. Huber, are operating central soil bioremediation stations (Kielburger and Schmitz 1993). The total capacity of these stations is approximately 1.5 million metric tons per year (see Table 3 and Figure 1).

In addition to companies offering bioremediation services, there are companies that support the bioremediation industry. These include manufacturers of fertilizers and nutrients (e.g., Cognis's Biocrack product), special plastic sheaths for heap treatment (Plouquet), special soil disintegration machines (Backhus), and substrates for optimizing the structure of the soil (Deutsche Perlite).

TABLE 3. Bioremediation capacity in central remediation stations. (Excerpted with permission from Kielburger and Schmitz 1993.)

Operating Company	Town	Bioremediation Capacity: Metric Tons per Year	Status
Bilfinger und Berger	Mannheim	10,000	starting 94
Umweltschutz Nord	Altbach	30,000	starting 94
Arge Wayss & Freitag	Tettnang	3,000	since 92
BORAG	Marktoberdorf	6,500	since 93
Gebr. Huber	Munich	30,000[a]	since 91
Rheinhold & Mahla	Munich	50,000	in planning
Rheinhold & Mahla	Würzburg	50,000	in planning
Umweltschutz Ost	Berlin	40,000	since 90
Haemeister Umwelttechnik	Grosskreuz	20,000[a]	since 92
Oecotec-afu	Velten	60,000[a]	in planning
Umweltschutz Nord	Bremen	40,000	since 89
SAN	not fixed	not fixed[a]	in planning
Umweltschutz Nord	Hamburg	40,000	since 92
Hansatec	Wilhelmsburg	8-10,000	since 92
hutec Holzmann./ Umweltschutz Nord	Neu-Isenburg	30,000	since 93
Conrader Umwelt.	Warnemünde	?	?
Lobbe	Karpin	?	?
svt	Jörnstorf	?	?
Hochtief	Poppendorf	10,000	in planning
Umweltschutz Nord	Langhagen	42,000	since 92
Lobbe	Bergfeld	2,000	since 93
IMA	Tribsees	50,000	starting 94
Ratjens	Dranske	?	starting 94
Hochtief	Essen	3,000	since 92
Landers	Wesel	8,000	starting 93
Stadtwerke	Düsseldorf	10,000	starting 93
Arge BSM-hutec	Münster	15,000	since 91
Greitens	Münster	?	pilot plant
BSR	Bochum	25,000	in planning
Umweltschutz Ruhr	Gladbeck	72,000	since 93
Thyssen	Hattingen	11,400	in planning
AGR	Gelsenkirchen	600	starting 94
Trienekens	Haus Forst	1,000	since 92
?	Cologne	10,000	in planning
Bonnenberg & Drescher	Aldenhoven	40,000	planning
Lobbe	Iserlohn	5,000 m^3	operation
IBU	Werl	2-4,000	?
GRT/Umweltschutz Nord	Bardowick	6,000	since 88
GRT/Umweltschutz Nord	Balje/Hörne	2,400	since 91
Biermann	Klein Eilstorf	?	in operation

TABLE 3. (continued).

Operating Company	Town	Bioremediation Capacity: Metric Tons per Year	Status
Umweltschutz Nord	Ganderkesee	10,000	since 92
biodetox	Ahnsen	5,400-8,000	since 88
Umweltschutz Mitte	Northeim	6,600	since 87
Umweltschutz Südwest	Morbach	30,000	starting 93
IMA	Saarburg	18,000	starting 93
IMA	Germersheim	15,000	since 93
Reutemann & Zeller	Mutterstadt	2,500	since 91
Rheinhold & Mahla	Ludwigshafen	1,500 m^3	starting 93
RUT	Schwarze Pumpe	?	starting 95
Umweltschutz Grumbach	Grumbach	16,500	since 91
BSB	Bischofswerder	20,000	in planning
Gröberner Dep.	Gröbern	168,000[a]	starting 94
Dierichs & Hagedorn	Altbernsdorf	24,500	starting 93
Dierichs & Hagedorn	Schildau	16,500	since 93
MUEG	Espenhain	15,000	starting 94
Umweltschutz Grumbach	Oelzschau	1,650	since 93
S.D.R.	Pohritzsch	5,400-8,000	starting 94
S.D.R.	Dautzschen	6,000	in planning
Anlagenbau & Umweltprojekt	Kyhna	22,000	in planning
SAN	? (Saxonie)	?	?
BSB	Bitterfeld	50,000[b]	starting 94
Umweltschutz Mitte	Bad Lauchstädt	?	starting 93
MUEG	Halle	15,000	since 93
GRT/Umweltschutz Nord	Magdeburg	7,000	since 93
Rheinhold & Mahla	Magdeburg	80,000	starting 94
Hochtief	Lützen	?	?
SAN	?	?	?
SAN	?	?[a]	?
SOTEC	Hamburg	10,000	starting 94
KS	?	?	?
GSU	Flensburg	20,000	since 90
Grohe & Co.	Itzehoe	?	in planning
SGDA	Merkers	20,000	since 91
SGDA	Föritz	5,000	since 91
SGDA	Grossbreitenbach	8,000/ 30,000	since 91/ starting 94
Dr. Schilling	Wormstedt	30,000[a]	since 92
Hochtief	Nora/Weimar	13,000	starting 94
Rheinhold & Mahla	Menteroda	80,000	starting 94
Rheinhold & Mahla	Jena	?	in planning

(a) Combination of washing and bioremediation.
(b) Combination of bioremediation with other remediation methods.

Bioremediation Market Trends

Today, large quantities of contaminated soil are mostly cleaned off site. We expect that the large remediation centers that can carry out a full variety of remediation technologies will continue to garner a greater market share in the future. A trend can already be seen toward small transportable treatment systems that can be operated without a permit.

● = in operation   ◐ = in construction   O = in planning

FIGURE 1. Central bioremediation stations in Germany. (Reprinted with permission from Kielburger and Schmitz 1993.)

Biotreatment should also make inroads in groundwater treatment, where activated carbon for treatment of air-stripped off-gases and groundwater will begin to be replaced by biological techniques. At present, there is no market for specialized microorganisms in Germany: the existing bioremediation companies are mostly service-based. There is, however, a small existing market for feasibility and biotreatability studies.

Growth of the European bioremediation market should see the expansion of existing bioremediation companies and their technologies, with a corresponding growth of biotreatment experience in handling an increasing number of contaminated situations. Because Germany and the Netherlands have the greatest commercial activity in bioremediation in Europe, their bioremediation know-how will spread over Europe as unification continues to those countries that have large environmental problems but which lack an existing infrastructure for environmental remediation. Although not all the leading companies in Germany will be able to follow this trend, those companies that already have subsidiaries outside Germany (e.g., Umweltschutz Nord, Lobbe, Cognis, ContraCon, and TAUW) should have good opportunities to expand.

The former socialist nations of Eastern Europe have a great many problems with contaminated soil and wastewater. Today it is not clear where the money necessary for environmental remediation will come from. However, there are about 10 German companies that already have subsidiaries in eastern Europe, and almost all German bioremediation firms have branches or affiliates in the eastern Länder, with some actually headquartered in the east. These companies will be best positioned to remediate the environmental problems of the east. Eventually, there should be a large environmental market in these countries, especially if manufacturing companies want to use the very cheap labor force in Eastern Europe, and because of the need to build factories on clean ground and to build up modern, cost-effective wastewater-treatment systems.

CONCLUSIONS

Bioremediation is a large, thriving industry in Germany, with a planned increase in capacity of bioremediation in central stations to 1.5 million metric tons per year. An increasing number of companies are active in bioremediation, and the market size in 1994 was estimated at $70 to 100 million. German firms are well positioned to expand outside Germany into the growing markets of the new Europe.

REFERENCES

Battermann, G., and P. Werner. 1984. "Removal of a Mineral Oil Subsurface Contamination Through Microbial Degradation," *Gwf-wasser/Abswasser* 125.
Environmental Business Journal 1991. "EC Market Looks Good to U.S. Firms." 4(3): 1.

Franzius, V. (German Environmental Protection Agency). 1993. Speech at the Euro-Forum Symposium in December 1993.

Glass, D. J. 1993. *The Promising Worldwide Bioremediation Market.* Decision Resources, Waltham, MA.

Jennings Group. 1993. *U.S. Bioremediation Market, 1994-2000.*

Kielburger, G., and H. J. Schmitz. 1993. "Bodenbehandlungszentrum: Die Jagd nach dem Boden hat begonnen," *TerraTech, September*: 52.

Kopp-Holtwiesche, B. 1994. "Mobile Biological Soil Cleaning," *Umwelt* 24(10): 499.

Porta, A. 1991. "A Review of European Bioreclamation Practice," In R. E. Hinchee and R. F. Olfenbuttel (Eds.), *In Situ Bioreclamation: Applications and Investigations for Hydrocarbon and Contaminated Site Remediation*, pp. 1-13. Butterworth-Heinemann, Stoneham, MA.

Porta, A., J. K. Young, and P. M. Molton. 1994. "In Situ Bioremediation in Europe." In R. E. Hinchee, D. B. Anderson, F. B. Metting Jr., and G. D. Sayles (Eds.), *Applied Biotechnology for Site Remediation*, pp. 1-20. Lewis Publishers, Chelsea, MI.

Raphael, T. and D. J. Glass. 1994. *Bioremediation in Germany: Technologies, Markets and Leading Practitioners*, DEVO Enterprises, Inc., Washington, DC.

Rosén, C.-G. 1992. *Bioremediation: State of the Art in the Nordic Countries in an International Perspective*, Nordic Industrial Fund, Oslo.

Sanning, D., and H. Stietzel. 1993. "United States/German Bilateral Agreement on Hazardous Waste Site Clean-up Projects." In F. Arendt, G. J. Anokkee, R. Bosman, and W. J. van den Brink (Eds.), *Contaminated Soil '93*, Kluwer Academic Publishers, Dordrecht.

Schmitz, H.-J. 1993. "Ten Large Projects Agreed Upon by Federal Government and New Länder," *TerraTech*, September: 15.

Visser, W.J.F. 1994. *Contaminated Land Policies in Some Industrialized Countries, Technical Soil Protection Committee*, The Hague, The Netherlands.

Contamination of Sites Formerly Occupied by Russian Troops in Poland

Andrzej Spychała, Korneliusz Miksch,
and Joanna Surmacz-Górska

ABSTRACT ━━━━━━━━━━━━━━━━━━━━━━━━━━━━━

This paper summarizes an investigation carried out on Polish terrain occupied by Russian Federation military troops. The investigation identified natural environmental devastation, pollution, and contamination. Quantitative estimation of the devastation and its economic evaluation are provided. The results of the investigation are as follows: 406 ha have been contaminated by petrochemical products; 22.7 ha are chemically polluted; and 6,500 ha of underground water, as well as 17.5 ha of surface water, cannot be classified. On 15,300 ha the soil has been degraded, of which landfills comprise an area of 98 ha. No toxic warfare agents have been detected, nor any radioactivity levels exceeding those characteristic of the given region.

INTRODUCTION

In response to an order of the Polish State Inspectorate of Environmental Protection, the ecological damage caused by troops of the Russian Federation was identified and evaluated. The investigation was conducted from September 1992 to November 1993. Troops of the Russian Federation were located mostly in the western and northwestern part of Poland in 59 regions, which differ enormously in size from one to another and which cover a total area of about 700 km². Based on a preliminary evaluation of these areas and on final inventory reports, 21 regions with an overall area of about 600 km² (i.e., 86% of the total) were selected for further investigation. Figure 1 shows their location.

All the regions shown in the map had been taken over by the troops of the Russian Federation after World War II. Previously they had been military premises of the German army. Each had a complex of barracks, as well as a fueling base (petrol station) with capacities up to 102,000 m³, their total volumetric

FIGURE 1. Location of the investigated regions.

capacity amounting to about 460,000 m^3. In later years, these regions were extended and adapted to the requirements of modern warfare. The regions included airfields; fueling bases; ammunition stores; a naval harbor; and military complexes comprised of shooting ranges, barracks and blocks of flats, and depots of nuclear weapons. The principal aims of the investigation were as follows:

- To identify and determine the extent of pollution, damage, and environmental contamination
- To determine the threat of environmental pollution (e.g., in the case of water intakes)
- To evaluate financially the ecological damage
- To specify imminent hazards and remediation activities that should be undertaken first.

CONTAMINATION OF THE SOIL AND GROUNDWATER

Contamination Caused by Crude Oil

Contamination brought about by products deriving from crude oil has been encountered in all the investigated regions. It was caused not only by transfer stations, pipelines many kilometers long, and fuel-distribution stations and fuel tanks, but also by repair shops and garages. An area of about 406 ha and a volume of about 18,400,000 m^3 has been contaminated. Permeable contaminated sand, gravel, and sand-gravel mix constitute 82% of the total contaminated environment (15,100,000 m^3); the remaining part is cohesive soil (clay, silt). Contamination extends to a maximum of 30 m below the surface:

- 0 to 10 m: 15,200,000 m^3 (83%)
- 10 to 20 m: 2,800,000 m^3 (15%)
- 20 to 30 m: 400,000 m^3 (2%)

The level of pollution varies considerably within the range from a few mg/kg dry mass to several tens of thousands mg/kg dry mass. In 15 regions, layers of fuel floating on the surface of underground water have been observed, with thicknesses of up to 5 m. The overall area of these layers amounts to about 90 ha. The volume of this floating fuel has been estimated to be about 93,000 m^3. The total amount of crude-oil derivatives deposited in the subsurface environment, including floating fuels, has been estimated at about 155,000 m^3. Investigations have proved, however, that some of this contamination has been caused by the previous tenants of these sites, i.e., by the German army.

Other Types of Pollution

In regions contaminated by crude-oil derivatives, pollution caused by other chemical substances has also been encountered. These include heavy metals (cadmium, zinc, copper, lead, chromium, nickel, mercury, and arsenic), free cyanides, phenols, detergents, and polycyclic aromatic hydrocarbons (PAHs), as well as deicing salts applied on airfields. Their content in the soil exceeds background levels by a few up to several tens of times.

The background levels (e.g., of heavy metals) depend on the situation and characteristics of the investigated region. The area surrounding Borne Sulinowo, for instance, may be considered a very clean region, whereas the area surrounding Legnica is strongly contaminated with heavy metals from a copper mill.

As a consequence of the soil contamination, the underground water of the first water-bearing layer is polluted. It has been estimated that, in an area of about 65 km^2, this underground water was essentially contaminated by the aforesaid substances. Its volume amounts to about 145,000,000 m^3.

In some regions, other chemical substances were detected. In two regions they occur over considerable surface areas:

1. At Borne Sulinowo, contaminants include rocket propellant SAMINA, nitric acid, sulfur-organic substances, disinfectants, phenols, solvents, derivatives of benzenedicarboxylic acid, cresols, calcium hypochlorite, and di-, tri-, and tetrachlorobiphenyls. The contamination covers an area of 14 ha. The volume of contaminated soil amounts to about 780,000 m^3.
2. At Świętoszów, contaminants include halogenic derivatives; di-, tri-, and tetrachlorobenzenes; di-, tri-, tetra-, and pentachlorobiphenyls; hexachloro-melamine; and calcium hypochlorite. These contaminants cover an area of 5.7 ha. The volume of contaminated soil amounts to about 100,000 m^3.

SURFACE WATER POLLUTION

Of the investigated regions 14 regions include surface water with a total area of 465 ha. An area of 17.5 ha of surface water (3.8% of the whole water) was found to be beyond classification. Some water reservoirs contain waste material, including unexploded shells and landmines.

DAMAGE AND CONTAMINATION OF THE SURFACE

The investigated areas include a number of landfills, totalling about 98 ha. They are estimated to have a volume of more than 2,100,000 m^3. The largest are Borne Sulinowo (30.0 ha), Świętoszów (15.0 ha), Kluczewo (9.5 ha), Strachów (7.0 ha), and Legnica (6.5 ha). The surface degradation of the vegetative soil layer covers an area of about 153 km^2, including shooting ranges, tank-testing grounds, etc.

RADIOACTIVE CONTAMINATION

The troops of the Russian Federation probably had three depots of nuclear weapons. Two of them have been located and investigated. Nuclear shell heads were not loosened, so that no contamination by radioactive substances occurred. Moreover, the level of gamma radiation in all the investigated regions is typical of the background. Also, the level of beta radiation approaches the values suggested by Central Laboratory of Radiological Protection as natural. No alpha radiation has been detected.

CONCLUSIONS

Every investigated area has been fully documented, including a final report specifying the most important imminent dangers and the most urgent activities to be undertaken. The ecological damage is presented in Table 1.

Within the areas once occupied by troops of the Russian Federation, both the underground water and the water reservoirs on the surface must be carefully monitored (local monitoring). For this purpose, the boreholes that have been drilled for observation could be used. Because of military operations, these regions should be treated as areas of heightened risk; it is very probable that not all sources of contamination (particularly the smaller ones) have yet been detected.

One area of about 210 ha is to be considered an ecological disaster area because of floating fuel, chemical contamination, and waste dumping sites. This constitutes about 0.35% of all the investigated areas. The area of contaminated land, excluding the regions used for military training (which caused considerable degradation of the vegetative soil layer) amounts to about 70 km², which makes up 12% of the total investigated area.

TABLE 1. Results of investigations of the sites once occupied by troops of the Russian Federation.

Kind of Contamination and Damage	Contaminated Area (ha)	Volume of Contamination (million m³)	Percentage of Total Area	Percentage of Global Costs
Caused by crude-oil derivatives	406	18.4	0.70	69.21
Chemical (toxic) contamination	21.7	0.97	0.04	0.18
Groundwater pollution	6,500	145.0	10.40	29.40
Surface water pollution	17.5	0.4	0.03	0.04
Degraded vegetative soil layer	15,300	—	25.30	0.44
Landfill	98	2.1	0.16	0.73

U.S. Bioremediation Market:
Yesterday, Today, and Tomorrow

Kate Devine

ABSTRACT

The use of bioremediation for full-scale cleanup has increased dramatically throughout the past 10 years. This growth in activity is expected to continue through the year 2000. It is estimated that fewer than 10 companies offered field-level bioremedial services prior to 1985. Although the market today still is dominated by a small number of companies, the total number of firms claiming to offer services and/or products for bioremediation purposes has grown to over 1,000. It is estimated that aggregate bioremediation revenues for 1994 through 2000 will equal $2 to $3 billion (1994 dollars). This revenue will be generated in the initial part of this 7-year period primarily from underground storage cleanup, with revenues from hazardous waste sites becoming an increasingly important factor by accounting for the majority of revenues in the latter years. Market opportunities exist in technology development and implementation including biosparging, centralized treatment facilities for petroleum-contaminated soils, biofilters, and improvements in the cost-effectiveness of the technology.

INTRODUCTION

Technical advances and regulatory events of the 1970s and 1980s have influenced the development and use of bioremediation (Table 1) with significant growth in full-scale cleanup of petroleum, industrial and hazardous waste sites occurring in the past few years. For example, in 1992, case study data supplied to the U.S. Environmental Protection Agency (EPA) by some of the more prominent companies offering bioremedial services indicated that over 80% of 132 cases submitted were either at full field level or field pilot level (Devine 1992). Although such data can be an indication of the increasing use of the technology, the U.S. EPA terms bioremediation an "innovative technology," which it defines as a "treatment method for which performance and cost data are inadequate to support routine use" (U.S. EPA 1993).

TABLE 1. Selected events influencing the development and use of bioremediation.

Decade	Events
1970s	• The fate and effects of petroleum hydrocarbons became areas of intense research for both microbiologists and ecologists. • Pioneering biotreatment research work was performed in land applications on petroleum wastes, hydrocarbons, pesticides, and other organics. • Oleophilic fertilizers were developed to enhance the degradation of petroleum in marine environments. • The U.S. Environmental Protection Agency (EPA) was formed. • Congress passed the Resource Conservation and Recovery Act (RCRA), which included a program to manage hazardous wastes from cradle to grave. • The first Earth Day focused public attention on preservation of natural resources.
1980s	• A petroleum-degrading bacterium was the first patented microorganism created by genetic engineering technology. • Environmental regulations created the need for cost-effective technologies for treating organic compounds in soil and water. • Anaerobic transformation and cometabolic degradation of chlorinated solvents in the presence of various oxygenases were described. • The capabilities of white-rot fungi (*Phanerochaete chrysosporium*) in degrading complex chlorinated organic compounds were demonstrated. • Successful, full-scale bioremediation of hydrocarbons in soil became commonplace. • The oil tanker, *Valdez*, was wrecked on the Alaskan coast focusing significant attention on bioremediation of marine and shoreline oil spills. • Congress passed the Comprehensive Environmental Response, Compensation, and Liability Act (CERCLA or Superfund), which addressed orphaned waste, liability, compensation cleanup, and emergency response for hazardous substances released to the environment. • Superfund Amendments and Reauthorization Act (SARA) was passed. • Underground storage tank regulations were passed. • States followed suit in enacting their own legislation for state-level programs governing hazardous site cleanup, management practice, cleanup standards, and enforcement tools.

Source: Compeau (1993).

Therefore, to gain more definition on the current status and future potential of bioremediation from a market perspective, a study was conducted focusing on the number and types of companies claiming bioremedial expertise, the number and types of sites likely to be treated via bioremediation, the revenues generated from such sites, market opportunities for bioremediation use, and factors for successful enterprise in the future.

PROCEDURE

For this study, bioremediation was defined as the management of soil, sludge, water, or an airstream to encourage optimal microbial activity for degradation or detoxification of target industrial, petroleum, and hazardous wastes. Information was compiled from personal interviews with representatives of selected companies offering bioremedial services and/or products; 128 written survey responses from 102 companies described as remediation and consulting/engineering firms, 53 companies who claimed to be equipment suppliers, and 16 microbial product suppliers (the total is greater than 128 because many respondents identified with more than one market segment); readily available government data on underground storage tank sites and other sites; and other government publications. The survey included questions on number of employees, number and types of projects undertaken, types of contaminants treated, and services offered. Company representatives were interviewed to gain insight as to the status of the technology and cost of cleanup of various sizes and types of sites. Published government data were used to estimate the number of sites where bioremediation would be utilized.

RESULTS

Applications

The majority of field experience in the earlier years was land treatment of petroleum-contaminated soils; more sophisticated techniques employed on a wider range of contaminants have been seen in recent years. The company survey results showed 70% or more of 87 remediation and consulting/engineering firms responding to the applicable questions claimed experience in in situ soil and groundwater. Almost one-half of the respondents had started more than five land-treatment projects; one-third or less claimed five or more projects in in situ work. Based on 90 remediation and consulting/engineering firms providing information on contaminant expertise, three-quarters or more claimed experience with gasoline or jet fuel/diesel or heavy oil/sludge or solvents. One-half listed experience with creosote/pentachlorophenol (PCP) or other polyaromatic hydrocarbons (PAHs), and one-third listed bioremedial services offered for pesticides or nitrate/munitions. About one-quarter also claimed expertise in polychlorinated biphenyls (PCBs). The market is expected to become increasingly concentrated in in situ applications. Stimulation of indigenous microorganisms has historically comprised the vast majority of treatments and continues to account for a large percentage of sites treated.

For 1994 to 2000, the number of underground storage tank (UST) cleanups utilizing bioremediation is estimated at over 28,000. Comprehensive Environmental Response, Compensation, and Liability Act (CERCLA or Superfund), state Superfund, Resource Conservation and Recovery Act (RCRA), Department of Defense, and other federal agency and private sites using bioremediation will constitute about 5,700 cleanups (The Jennings Group and DEVO Enterprises, Inc. 1993). These estimates are based on government site statistics and an estimated percentage of these sites where bioremediation would be used.

Number of Companies

The number of remediation and consulting/engineering firms offering bioremediation services and products has steadily increased over the last 5 years (Figure 1). Based on the survey results and information on firms offering services and products, it is estimated that the number of companies with significant field experience (defined as more than 20 bioremediation projects completed) 10 years ago was no more than 10. By 1993, the number of companies with that level of field experience had increased three to four times. A few remediation firms and consulting/engineering companies (about 10) dominate the market, accounting for 60% to 70% of the revenues accrued. There are fewer than five prominent microbe producers, which generate 55% to 65% of the revenues from the sale of microorganisms for bioremediation purposes. The equipment sector is very fragmented, with many companies claiming to be suppliers (The Jennings Group and DEVO Enterprises, Inc. 1993).

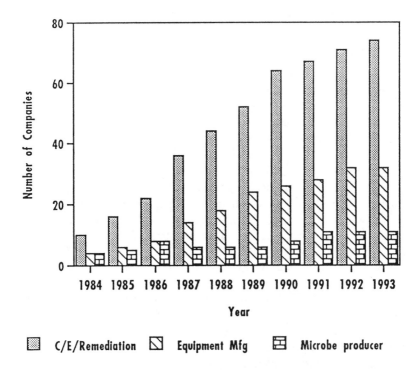

FIGURE 1. Growth in the number of surveyed companies in the bioremediation market, 1984-1993 (based on 128 companies surveyed). C/E = consulting/engineering.

Size of Companies

Companies offering bioremediation goods and services are generally small. About 40% of the over 100 remediation and consulting/engineering firms who responded to the survey have fewer than 50 employees; 90% and 60% of the microbe and equipment suppliers, respectively, have fewer than 50 employees (The Jennings Group and DEVO Enterprises, Inc. 1993).

Revenues and Profit Margins

In 1993, estimated revenues generated equaled $150 to $175 million for remediation and consulting/engineering, with about $6 to $7 million for microbe production and about $2 to $4 million for bioreactors used for bioremediation, comprising a total of $158 to $186 million for 1993. It is estimated that the market has doubled over the last 5 years (The Jennings Group and DEVO Enterprises, Inc. 1993). These estimates are based primarily on interviews with representatives of companies offering bioremediation services and products.

The majority of UST cleanups are expected to take place in this century, provided that sufficient government cleanup funds are available. A cumulative total of $1.5 billion for UST cleanups is anticipated through the year 2000. Estimated costs for bioremediation cleanups were calculated based on government data on the number of sites and percentage employing in situ bioremediation and land treatment, and company representative cost input. The non-UST market is expected to comprise an increasing percentage of the total revenues as the decade progresses. The non-UST market, also based on government data and company representative information concerning the distribution in size and estimated average cost of various sized projects, is $725 million to $1.32 billion. Therefore, the 1994 to 2000 bioremediation market is estimated to be $2.2 to $2.8 billion in total revenues (1993 dollars) (The Jennings Group and DEVO Enterprises, Inc. 1993) (Figure 2).

According to company representatives, gross profit margins have been lowered over the past 5 years due to changing customer requirements, an increasing number of service companies, and the economic recession of the late 1980s and early 1990s. The gross profit margin of UST work is 10% to 15% but more sophisticated projects have a gross profit margin of 40%. Microbial producers reported 40% to 50% margins with equipment manufacturers in the 25% to 35% range (The Jennings Group and DEVO Enterprises, Inc. 1993).

DISCUSSION

The future for bioremediation holds significant potential with respect to a broader range of applications and techniques. There is a move toward greater in situ treatment of contaminants. Bioventing, biosparging, natural attenuation, and broader application of bioremediation to organic chemicals, including chlorinated solvents, are expected to increase. Bioremediation of inorganics is a longer-term prospect.

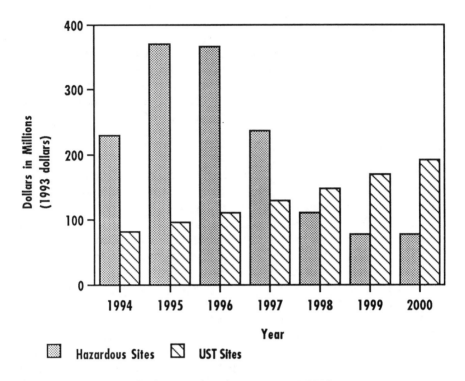

FIGURE 2. Bioremediation market forecast, 1994-2000.

Numerous improvements in the basic application of bioremediation and field implementation are expected. These developments are expected to include improved reactors; use of biofilters in vapor-phase reactors and the application of biofilters as a treatment add-on for pump-and-treat and vapor extraction projects; improved site characterization techniques and technologies, including subsurface characterization and location of contaminants; better definition of the biochemical pathways, mechanics, and kinetics for biological separation and destruction; development of better tools for the simulation, design, application, monitoring, and control of the bioremedial process; better control over in situ applications through improved control over the environment for the microorganisms; improved nutrient delivery systems; encapsulation of microbes and nutrients to provide better transport characteristics; use of foam or microbubbles to improve the transport of oxygen for in situ applications; more efficient use of surfactants to enhance the separation of contaminants from soil; greater recognition of using both aerobic and anaerobic processing to degrade recalcitrant contaminants; pneumatic or hydrofracturing of consolidated soils to improve subsurface treatment or vapor extraction; use of electrical fields to move contaminants and microbes; and horizontal drilling to improve delivery and collection systems.

In order for bioremediation to be used at an increasing rate in the rest of this century, several factors must be realized. These factors include an increase in the

number of successfully completed projects; continued awareness of bioremediation's potential on the part of regulators, as well as customers and environmental
consultants; continued improvement in bioremediation technology and its application to an increased range of contaminants; cost reduction efforts by service suppliers; and a regulatory environment that will not present a major hindrance to
the use of the technology (The Jennings Group and DEVO Enterprises, Inc. 1993).

If these factors are realized, selected market opportunities are expected to
become more significant in the future. These market opportunities include
increased use of bioventing and biosparging, centralized bioremediation facilities
for petroleum-contaminated soil, biofilters, and continued improvement in the cost
effectiveness of bioremediation (The Jennings Group and DEVO Enterprises, Inc.
1993).

REFERENCES

Compeau, G. 1993. "History of Selected Events Affecting Bioremediation." Unpublished paper.
    Enviros Incorporated, Kirkland, WA.
Devine, K. 1992. *Bioremediation Case Studies: An Analysis of Vendor Supplied Data.* EPA/600/
    R-92/043, U.S. Environmental Protection Agency. Office of Research and Development.
    Washington, DC.
The Jennings Group and DEVO Enterprises, Inc. 1993. *Bioremediation Market, 1994-2000.*
    Columbia, NJ and Washington, DC.
U.S. EPA. 1993. *Cleaning Up the Nation's Waste Sites: Markets and Technology Trends.* EPA 542-
    R-92-012. U.S. Environmental Protection Agency, Office of Solid Waste and Emergency
    Response, Washington, DC.

States' Attitudes on the Use of Bioremediation

Kate Devine and Lori L. Graham

ABSTRACT

Results from a telephone survey of state government program coordinators and representatives from companies performing full-scale bioremediation shows differences among states in the use and degree of acceptance of bioremediation for environmental cleanup. The survey also found that states vary in the potential future direction of regulatory activity concerning bioremediation. The survey focused primarily on underground storage tank (UST) cleanups. Diminishing state UST cleanup funds have provided the impetus for many states to consider alternative cost-effective measures in order to continue with cleanups. In recent years, more than 30 states have either implemented programs that consider the cost-effectiveness of various cleanup measures, or are considering adoption of programs that are founded on risk-based corrective action. Less than a dozen states were considered as having made significant strides in innovative technology utilization. Forums whereby state groups can exchange ideas and experiences associated with the practical application of bioremediation will facilitate this nationwide movement towards cost-effective cleanup.

INTRODUCTION

Bioremediation is a proven, full-scale cost-effective technology, particularly for petroleum-related contaminants. However, based on U.S. Environmental Protection Agency data (U.S. EPA 1992), it is estimated that bioremediation is currently being used at less than 10% of UST sites in the United States. Factors that include regulatory parameters, have contributed to this less than maximum implementation of the technology. For example, because few scientific aspects of subsurface contamination are known with absolute certainty, agencies may rely on policy to support decisions about soil- and groundwater-cleanup levels (Walsh 1990). A few years ago many states based their cleanup goals specifically for benzene, toluene, ethylbenzene and xylenes (BTEX) constituents and total petroleum hydrocarbon (TPH) compounds on the Leaching Potential Analysis Method which led to typical parameters of 1 ppm BTEX or 100 ppm TPH for soils at petroleum-contaminated sites. States set these standards without a scientific approach or guidelines and these numbers were adopted across the country in an effort to quickly establish cleanup goals for their state (Liptak and Lombardo 1994).

More recently, many states have been faced with a growing financial crisis as the cost of cleanup increases faster than the growth in petroleum restoration funds (states enter a cooperative agreement with the U.S. EPA that gives them access to use, in part, the Leaking Underground Storage Tank Trust Fund, financed by a tax on fuels (U.S. EPA 1990)). For example, it was estimated in 1992 that if states paid off expected obligations for work that was underway, up to 21 states would report a deficit on their state fund for UST cleanup (Environmental Information 1992). Thus, the need for cost-effective and more complete cleanup solutions is growing ever more imperative in order that these funds be used in the most effective manner. This study assessed state actions being considered or underway to address this issue and potential future direction of bioremediation activities at the state level.

PROCEDURE

This project focused on UST programs because the majority of sites where bioremediation is utilized contain petroleum-related contaminants (Devine 1992); the UST program expects to see a continual rise in the number of contaminated sites for some time to come (Environmental Information, Ltd. 1992) and the UST program is a state-oriented program. State-by-state telephone interviews were conducted with appropriate UST program coordinators in the 48 contiguous states during the winter of 1994/1995. In some instances, more than one state representative within a state was contacted. In addition, representatives of select remediation and consulting and engineering companies performing full-scale bioremediation were contacted to more fully develop certain state scenarios.

RESULTS

General

All state representatives exhibited significant knowledge of the technology, various application techniques and their potential in the UST cleanup market. Almost all representatives contacted were willing to disseminate any available information that might facilitate an understanding of what is transpiring at the state level, both from a technical and regulatory perspective. Several state representatives said that they have seen a pronounced increase in the number of proposals for cleanup that involve bioremediation, utilized alone or with other technologies. Many states indicated that whatever technology could meet their standards would be implemented in cleanup. However, some states (e.g., North Dakota and Louisiana) claimed that utilization of bioremediation is relatively low, in part, because of geological and climatic factors (State of North Dakota 1995; State of Louisiana 1995).

Many states require some type of permit when conducting bioremediation. However, there was great degree of variation in permit-related factors, including the actual methodology employed that would warrant a permit (recirculation of groundwater and/or the injection or nutrients or oxygen), the actual state agency or department involved in handling the permitting, the length of time to issue the permit (which varied from 2 to 6 months) and, whether or not cleanup activity could commence before the permit was actually issued. Some states indicated that the addition of microorganisms was not viewed favorably and would lead to higher scrutiny of a project or additional permitting requirements.

In recent years, a more progressive attitude toward site cleanup has developed due to the rising financial crisis of diminishing state cleanup funds. While many states recognize the need for cleanup standard or program modification, there were differences among states in the degree of current or immediate future direction of regulatory activity concerning bioremediation. Standards based on chemical-specific risk-based approaches as well as issuance of guidance that may call for the explicit consideration of certain technologies in site remedy selection have been initiated in some states. However, no formal policy on bioremediation or any other cleanup technology was seen in most states.

Many states indicated that a risk-based approach was now being considered and some specifically mentioned the possibility of following the State of Texas' lead in its risk-based approach that was adopted into regulation in late 1993. According to a recent survey of state cleanup standards, 33 states may use a risk/health parameter and/or a site specific approach in determining cleanup standards for soil and/or groundwater for certain contaminants in certain instances (Table 1). Additionally, 31 states have requested training on the American Society for Testing and Materials (ASTM) emergency standard guide for risk-based corrective action applied at petroleum release sites (ASTM ES 38-94), more commonly referred to as "RBCA" (pronounced "rebecca") (Table 1). This guidance, compiled by an ASTM subcommittee, standardizes existing Superfund risk assessment methods and promotes the concentration of resources for sites that pose the greatest threat to human health and the environment. The RBCA approach recognizes the diversity of parameters affecting risk, such as contaminant complexity, physical, and chemical characteristics, and uses a tiered approach that tailors assessment and remediation activities to site-specific conditions and risks (ASTM 1994).

Selected States

The highlighted state (alphabetical order) programs that follow exhibit the currently changing regulatory atmosphere and illustrates those with more progressive actions or programs implemented or under way. Although results are focused primarily on UST, a few instances of hazardous waste programs are also given to more fully exhibit a particular state's regulatory approach.

TABLE 1. States requesting ASTM RBCA[a] guidance training and/or employing site-specific or risk-based cleanup standards.

State	Site-Specific or Risk Standards[b]	RBCA Training	State	Site-Specific or Risk Standards[b]	RBCA Training
Alabama	✓	✓	Montana	✓	✓
Alaska	✓	✓	Nebraska	✓	✓
Arizona	✓	✓	Nevada		
Arkansas			New Hampshire	✓	✓
California		✓	New Jersey		✓
Colorado		✓	New Mexico		
Connecticut		✓	New York	✓	✓
Delaware	✓		North Carolina	✓	✓
Florida	✓		North Dakota	✓	
Georgia	✓	✓	Ohio	✓	✓
Hawaii			Oklahoma		
Idaho	✓	✓	Oregon	✓	✓
Illinois	✓	✓	Pennsylvania	✓	✓
Indiana	✓	✓	South Carolina	✓	✓
Iowa	✓	✓	South Dakota		✓
Kansas			Rhode Island		✓
Kentucky			Tennessee		
Louisiana	✓	✓	Texas	✓	✓
Maine			Utah	✓	✓
Maryland	✓		Vermont	✓	
Massachusetts	✓		Virginia	✓	✓
Michigan		✓	Washington	✓	✓
Minnesota	✓		West Virginia	✓	✓
Mississippi		✓	Wisconsin	✓	
Missouri	✓		Wyoming	✓	

(a) ASTM RBCA — American Society for Testing and Materials Risk-Based Corrective Action.
(b) Although established cleanup levels exist, risk assessment or site-specific options may be used for soil and/or groundwater for certain contaminants in certain instances.
Sources: *Soils* (1994) and McNeely (1995).

California. California has been known historically for the numerous government organizations involved in site oversight (e.g., tank inspection, closure, and cleanup activities can include involvement of the city, the local fire department, the county, the Air Quality Management District, the regional board, the state board, and the Department of Health Services [State of California 1989]). This is very different from other states, in which typically only one or two more centralized agencies are involved. Yet, even with this amount of government oversight, California was the site for one of the largest bioremediation endeavors to date, one that entailed land treatment of 300,000 yd^3 of petroleum hydrocarbon-contaminated soil. Closure was announced in the summer of 1991 (*Biotreatment News* 1991). More recently, the state has exhibited a significant interest in RBCA, having studied the effect of RBCA on its UST program (McNeely 1995). Also, a "plume-a-thon" is being conducted that began in the fall of 1994 and is expected to continue until the summer of 1995. Data are being collected on 1,500 UST sites to ascertain the extent of contamination and migration. The state also has drafted a policy on the concept of nonattainment zones whereby a site with groundwater that cannot be feasibly treated is monitored or closed. This policy, oriented to odor and taste criteria, would raise the state cleanup standards. For example, a current benzene standard of "nondetect" or 1 ppb would increase 10 to 100 times, to 10 to 100 ppb (Dooher 1995). Such policy would allow for use of certain containment techniques, such as a "microbial fence" (Swett 1995).

Delaware. Delaware reports that streamlining activity in permitting has been underway for some time (State of Delaware 1995).

Florida. Florida has issued state guidelines for intrinsic bioremediation. Also, there is a new petroleum rule to be issued in 1995 that will list intrinsic bioremediation as a potential treatment technology for Florida sites (State of Florida 1995).

Iowa. In Iowa, a bill addressing UST legislation was introduced in the state legislature in late 1994. The state has guidance in the form of a corrective action plan, to be completed by consultants, which mentions bioremediation (State of Iowa 1994). Additionally, a field demonstration in Iowa of the Institute of Gas Technology's (IGT) biological and chemical treatment process for polycyclic aromatic hydrocarbon (PAH)-contaminated soils was funded in part by the Iowa Department of Natural Resources (IGT n.d.).

Massachusetts. In October 1994, a soil bioremediation pilot program was enacted that is designed to provide information from a maximum of 20 sites to identify how best to regulate such projects in order "to protect the environment, encourage innovative solutions to remediate contaminated sites, and respond to issues raised by the regulated community" (State of Massachusetts 1994). Currently, there are 10 sites in a pilot program that is monitoring nitrogen levels which are of concern to the state water pollution control authorities. The ultimate goal of the monitoring project is a potential reduction in the permitting require-ments to those conducting bioremediation in the state (State of Massachusetts 1995). Additionally, in 1993, Massachusetts became the first state to establish the Licensed Site Professional program, whereby routine supervision of hazardous waste sites is shifted from state regulators to licensed private sector individuals (*Biotreatment News* 1994a).

Michigan. In 1989, a partnership of the oil and gas industry, the state regulators, and the academic community — the Cooperative Bioremediation Research for Michigan, or CoBioRem — was formed to perform laboratory and fieldwork to ascertain the effectiveness and cost of in situ oxygen-enhanced aerobic bioremediation for soil and groundwater contaminated through petroleum leaks and spills (*Biotreatment News* 1993a). CoBioRem claims that the groundwater remediation system entailing amendment and reinjection was the first approved in the United States (1991) that did not require conventional, aboveground water treatment prior to reinjection. Also, Michigan uses a three-tiered ranking of cleanup criteria for hydrocarbon-contaminated groundwater: (1) background levels, (2) generic residential levels, and (3) generic industrial/commercial or site-specific criteria (Jerger 1995). This method, adopted in 1990, allows the Responsible Party (RP) to determine which type of criteria to apply, which then must be approved by the state (State of Michigan 1995).

Minnesota. Minnesota encourages the cleanup of petroleum-contaminated soil by recommending three options: landfarming (one-half of the sites in the state use this method), biopile/composting, and thermal treatment. State guidance is soon to be issued for biopile and composting methods, and a general permit for composting is also expected in 1995. It is claimed that the Brainerd Superfund site, within the state of Minnesota, is the first Superfund site in the USA at which bioremediation was employed; the decision to implement the technology was based on 2 years of field studies and a cost differential of $20 million for use of bioremediation versus incineration (*Biotreatment News* 1993b).

Nevada. Nevada developed a risk-based policy many years ago (1988) that became a regulation in October 1990. A total of 11 factors, including contaminant concentration, type of contaminant, sources of migration, and contaminant depth, are outlined in this regulation as the parameters to consider when the soil is above the action level (State of Nevada 1995).

New Hampshire. New Hampshire began amending its soil policy in 1989 and has gone through six revisions to date (State of New Hampshire 1995). The state has developed chemical-specific risk-based soil cleanup standards by using fate and transport models and risk assessment methods. The state claims that use of such guidelines results in timely and cost-effective remediation and allows for concentration of remediation efforts on more significant sources of human health or environmental risk (Liptak and Lombardo 1994). New Hampshire has estimated that use of risk-based soil cleanup guidelines would have saved the state $500,000 at a particular site where the soil was ultimately disposed (Liptak and Lombardo 1994).

New Jersey. In April 1994, the State Department of Environmental Protection's Site Remediation Program issued "Evaluation of Bioremediation Treatability Work Plans." This five-page document discusses the potential of contaminated media to support microbial activity; the degradability of contaminants and maximum concentration that can be degraded; field optimization; and some common problems of bioremediation treatability studies (Marinucci 1994). Additionally, in an effort to eliminate regulatory barriers to the use of innovative technologies, the state passed two rules prior to 1994. One rule establishes that the RP can outline its own workplan and enter into a memorandum of agreement with the state. The other rule promotes innovative technologies by identifying technologies, including bioremediation, as permanent remedies that, if chosen, do not require the RP to do a remedial alternative analysis, which is similar to a feasibility study (*Biotreatment News* 1993c).

New York. The state of New York has drafted "Small Scale Bioremediation," a do-it-yourself guide for bioremediating 100 yd^3 or less of petroleum hydrocarbon-contaminated soil. The final version is expected to be published in the spring of 1995 (State of New York 1995). Additionally, some legislative action regarding RBCA has been initiated (McNeely 1995). In the area of hazardous waste, New York recently completed a concurrent demonstration of three different bioremediation techniques by three different vendors at an upstate Superfund site. The intent of the Multi-Vendor Treatability Demonstration was to promote and utilize alternative treatment technologies wherever those methods are more efficient and cost-effective than conventional approaches at permanently remediating inactive hazardous waste sites (*Biotreatment News* 1994b).

North Carolina. North Carolina is in the process of developing guidance on passive bioremediation (State of North Carolina 1995).

Ohio. The Ohio UST program has a site ranking system whereby site cleanup criteria are established based on factors such as the future use of the site, contaminants, and concentration (Jerger 1995).

South Carolina. South Carolina claims that bioremediation has been encouraged for some time. A state-formed committee recommended that a group of petroleum marketers, state people, and consultants be assembled to assess the current UST program. South Carolina is now in the midst of changing its criteria to a RBCA-like program (State of South Carolina 1995).

Texas. In the early 1990s, Texas was forced to move towards a more cost-effective approach in its cleanup program when its state cleanup fund of $150 million, more than the national program, was expended (McNeely 1995). Texas was the first state to incorporate a risk-based approach in its UST regulations in late 1993 (Swett 1995). Additionally, the Oil Spill Prevention Response Act has funded $1.25 million for the Coastal Oil Spill Simulation project for testing and bioremediation and other chemical countermeasures (*Bioremediation News* 1993b).

Utah. Utah has several actions underway. It is in the process of revamping its cleanup standards to the ASTM standard, it is streamlining its UST program, it is instituting a consultant certification process, and currently keeps consultants abreast of what is transpiring in the program (State of Utah 1995).

Vermont. In order for consultants to be aware of innovative technologies, the State of Vermont dedicates certain days in which outreach to consultants is conducted (State of Vermont 1995).

Wisconsin. Wisconsin issued an emergency rule in February 1993 that stipulates that three cleanup options be submitted to the state prior to site remediation if the RP will seek reimbursement from the state's petroleum cleanup fund. One of these options must be natural biodegradation. Additionally, there is a formal task group in the Wisconsin Department of Natural Resources to assess how state internal procedures may be limiting the use of innovative technologies (*Biotreatment News* 1993d).

DISCUSSION

There is a logical correlation between states or areas of the country with a significant amount of industry and, consequently, a significant number of contaminated sites, and the inception of cost-effective programs either being considered or already in place.

Based on the information collected, only the state of Wisconsin has actually specified bioremediation in a regulation that mandates that intrinsic bioremediation be considered as a cleanup alternative. However, a few other states are considering or implementing programs that are favorable for utilization of innovative technologies, including bioremediation. Based on the information collected, the states viewed as the most conducive for full scale bioremediation, particularly on petroleum hydrocarbon-contaminated soil sites regulated under a state UST program, include: California, New York, New Jersey, Michigan, New Hampshire, Nevada, Texas, Minnesota, and Wisconsin. On a U.S. Environmental Protection Agency regional basis, therefore, Regions 2, 5, and 9 (Figure 1) would be considered as having the most favorable regulatory climate for innovative technologies, including bioremediation.

A risk-based approach bodes well for innovative technologies, such as bioremediation, which otherwise might not be able to meet strict standards that are based on the traditional TPH and BTEX levels cited earlier. Such measurements obscure the real risks to human health and the environment. Use of a risk-based approach can lead to cleanup levels that can be achieved through the use of bioremediation. With the Republican-led Congress that resulted from the November 1994 elections, the focus on delegation of government to the states, may lead to more decision-making authority in state environmental programs. The federal government may play an increasing role in education through continuance and possible expansion of select programs, committees, seminars, data collection, and written information dissemination.

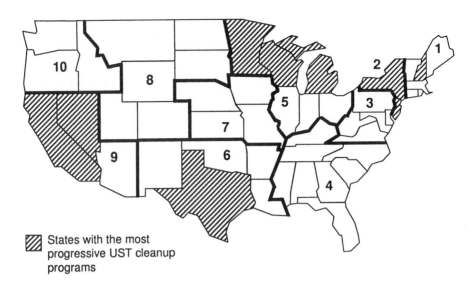

FIGURE 1. States with progressive UST cleanup programs (heavy outline indicates U.S. EPA regions).

RECOMMENDATIONS

Given that state representatives have significant and growing practical knowledge of the technology, continued support should be given at the state and federal level for state representatives to attend conferences or seminars to facilitate the exchange of ideas and experiences associated with the practical application of bioremediation. Significant opportunities for communication may also be afforded by the continued development of Internet discussion groups or other electronic forums for the exchange of information specifically regarding the use and implementation of innovative technologies, including bioremediation, as solutions for environmental cleanup. Moreover, with the gradual increase in states' acceptance of risk-based assessment approaches to determine specific on-site cleanup standards for UST sites and/or priority ranking for site cleanups, governmental focus could be directed to public education as to the benefits and/or risks of such approaches.

LIMITATIONS OF THE STUDY

Results of the study were based on discussions with selected state and company representatives and, therefore, in certain instances, may not be entirely representative of a state's regulatory status as pertains to the use of bioremediation. Additionally, in some instances, information collected on a state seemed positive in some respects and negative in other respects and had to be considered for a final conclusion to be drawn concerning an overall regulatory atmosphere. While every effort was made to speak with a representative of each state, some representatives who may have had influential information could not be interviewed. The conclusions drawn pertaining to the most progressive state programs were based on readily available information.

ACKNOWLEDGMENTS

The number of representatives with whom conversations took place totaled over 45. The authors wish to thank all of the state government and industry representatives who took the time to be interviewed by telephone and, in some instances, supplied additional information in text form.

REFERENCES

ASTM. 1994. *Emergency Standard Guide for Risk-Based Corrective Action Applied at Petroleum Release Sites, ES 38-94.* American Society for Testing and Materials. Philadelphia, PA.

Biotreatment News. 1991. "Microbes Clean Up Former Petroleum Tank Farm." 1(9).

Biotreatment News. 1993a. "Michigan Public and Private Sectors Advance Bio Use." 3(10):5.

Biotreatment News. 1993b. "Industry Calls for Risk-Based Regulatory Approach." 3(10):6.

Biotreatment News. 1993c. "States Encourage Use of Bioremediation." 3(10):8.

Biotreatment News. 1993d. "Wisconsin Issues New Rule Requiring Consideration of Passive Bioremediation." 3(6):1 and 7.

Biotreatment News. 1994a. "Dutch Cleanup Relies on Engineered Biotreatment Cells — GTI Employees Among First Licensed Site Professionals." 4(2):12 and 16.

Biotreatment News. 1994b. "First of Its Kind Bio Demonstration Held at New York Site." 4(12):3 and 1417.

Devine, K. 1992. *Bioremediation Case Studies: An Analysis of Vendor Supplied Data.* EPA/600/R-92/043. U.S. Environmental Protection Agency, Office of Research and Development. Washington, DC.

Dooher, B. 1995. Personal communication with K. Devine. University of California at Los Angeles, School of Engineering. Los Angeles, CA.

Environmental Information, Ltd. 1992. *The Underground Storage Market: Its Current Status and Future Challenges.* Minneapolis, MN.

IGT. n.d. "Technology Spotlight: Manufactured Gas Plant Site Remediation (Solid Phase/Land Farming)." Institute of Gas Technology fact sheet. Des Plaines, IL.

Jerger, D. E. 1995. Personal communication with K. Devine. OHM Corporation, Findlay, OH.

Liptak, J. F., and G. Lombardo. 1994. "The Development of Chemical-Specific Risk-Based Soil Cleanup Guidelines Results in Timely and Cost Effective Remediation." New Hampshire Department of Environmental Services, Groundwater Protection Bureau, Concord, NH.

Marinucci, A. 1994. "Evaluation of Bioremediation Treatability Work Plans." New Jersey Department of Environmental Protection and Energy, Bureau of Evaluation and Risk Assessment, Site Remediation Program, Trenton, NJ.

McNeely, S. 1995. U.S. Environmental Protection Agency, Office of Solid Waste and Emergency Response, Office of Underground Storage Tanks. Personal communication with K. Devine. Washington, DC.

Soils. 1994. "State Cleanup Standards for Hydrocarbon Contaminated Soil and Groundwater." Dec.: 14-60.

State of California. 1989. "Leaking Underground Fuel Tank Manual: Guidelines for Site Assessment, Cleanup, and Underground Storage Tank Closure." State of California, Leaking Underground Fuel Tank Task Force.

State of Delaware. 1995. Personal communication with K. Devine. Department of Natural Resources and Environmental Control. New Castle, DE.

State of Florida. 1995. Personal communication of state representative with K. Devine. Department of Environmental Regulations. Tallahassee, FL.

State of Iowa. 1994. Personal communication of state representative with L. Graham. Department of Natural Resources, Des Moines, IL.

State of Louisiana. 1995. Personal communication with L. Graham. UST Trust Fund, Baton Rouge, LA.

State of Massachusetts. 1994. "Innovative Technology Pilot: Soil Bioremediation." Department of Environmental Protection, Boston, MA.

State of Massachusetts. 1995. Personal communication of state representative with K. Devine. Department of Environmental Protection, Bureau of Waste Site Cleanup, Boston, MA.

State of Michigan. 1995. Personal communication of state representative with K. Devine. Michigan Department of Natural Resources, Environmental Response Division, Lansing, MI.

State of Minnesota. 1995. Personal communication of state representative with L. Graham. Minnesota Pollution Control Agency, St. Paul, MN.

State of Nevada. 1995. Personal communication of state representative with K. Devine. Department of Conservation and Environmental Protection, Carson City, NV.

State of New Hampshire. 1995. Personal communication of state representative with K. Devine. Department of Environmental Services, Groundwater Protection Bureau, Concord, NH.

State of New York. 1995. Personal communication of state representative with K. Devine. New York State Department of Environmental Conservation, Albany, NY.

State of North Carolina. 1995. Personal communication of state representative with L. Graham. Division of Pollution Control, Raleigh, NC.

State of North Dakota. 1995. Personal communication of state representative with K. Devine. Department of Health, Bismarck, ND.

State of South Carolina. 1995. Personal communication of state representative with K. Devine. Department of Health and Environmental Control, Columbia, SC.

State of Utah. 1995. Personal communication of state representative with K. Devine. Salt Lake City, UT.

State of Vermont. 1995. Personal communication of state representative with K. Devine. Waterbury, VT.

Swett, G. 1995. Personal communications with K. Devine. Retec, Tucson, AZ.

U.S. EPA. 1990. *RCRA Orientation Manual.* EPA/530-SW-90-036. U.S. Environmental Protection Agency, Office of Solid Waste, Washington, DC.

U.S. EPA. 1992. *Technologies and Options for UST Corrective Actions: Overview of Current Practice.* EPA/542/R-92/010. U.S. Environmental Protection Agency, Office of Solid Waste and Emergency Response Technology Innovation Office and Office of Underground Storage Tanks, Washington, DC.

U.S. EPA. 1995. "OSWER Directive 9610.17: Use of Risk-Based Decision-Making in UST Corrective Action Programs." Memorandum from U.S. Environmental Protection Agency, Office of Solid Waste and Emergency Response Assistant Administrator to Regional Administrators. Washington, DC.

Walsh, W. J. 1990. "Making Science, Policy, and Public Perception Compatible: A Legal/Policy Summary." *In Groundwater and Soil Contamination Remediation: Toward Compatible Science, Policy, and Public Perception,* pp. 206-249. National Academy Press, Washington, DC.

A Comparative Cost Analysis of Petroleum Remediation Technologies

Kimberly L. Davis, Gregory D. Reed, and Lee Walter

ABSTRACT

Underground storage tank (UST) site cleanup data were studied to determine cost trends based on site characteristics and the percentage of cleanup completed. Costs and stage of cleanup were taken from a database documenting all costs reimbursed to UST owners from the Tennessee Petroleum UST Trust Fund. Site characteristics for the study sites were obtained from environmental assessment reports and corrective action plans submitted to the State of Tennessee. Using this information, the cost-effectiveness of biological treatments was compared to conventional means of remediation. The results of the study showed that sites using biotreatment exhibited lower overall costs than sites that used conventional treatment exclusively.

INTRODUCTION

As bioremediation continues to gain credibility as a viable technology for treating petroleum-contaminated soils, regulatory review of this cleanup process is increasingly favoring the selection of this cost-effective technology over traditional means of cleanup. Uncertainties previously associated with bioremediation are being reduced as comprehensive and reliable data are compiled, demonstrating the degree of performance to be expected for varying site conditions. This research project is a continuation of University of Tennessee Waste Management Research and Education Institute work starting in 1992 (Davis et al. 1994, Smith 1994), which had the overall objective of examining the use of soil bioremediation in Tennessee UST corrective action. The focus of this previous work was to compare the cost of projects using different types of biological soil treatment with the costs associated with projects using more conventional types of corrective action (e.g., landfilling and incineration). Also, different factors associated with site characteristics were studied to determine their influence on the overall cost of cleanup. These parameters included volume of soil treated, contaminant type, contaminant concentration, geographic location, and petroleum-release date. Cost trend analysis indicated that ex situ soil bioremediation exhibited a slight cost advantage over in situ bioremediation and other conventional treatment technologies. This effect was attributed to the simplicity of ex situ bioremediation, which may involve only excavating, spreading, applying nutrients, and periodic tilling.

Since 1992, the ease of data retrieval for the purposes of this project has greatly improved over our initial efforts, due to improved data collection and filing at the state level. The addition of a great number of sites to the UST program has resulted in a much larger, more representative data set for the continuation of this study. The newly assembled data were studied to determine cost trends based on many of the same site characteristics as in 1992, in addition to estimating the approximate duration of site activities. Using this information, the cost-effectiveness of biological treatments was again compared to conventional means of remediation.

METHODOLOGY

The methodology of this project was refined over previous efforts to obtain a representative sampling of UST cleanups per each Tennessee geographical region and treatment technologies used. Costs associated with the UST cleanups were taken from the database documenting all costs reimbursed to UST owners from the Tennessee Petroleum UST Trust Fund. This fund is financed by annual UST fees and a tax levied on petroleum products imported into the state. UST owners are eligible to tap into the trust fund for investigation and cleanup activities if the leaking tanks are properly registered.

Out of a total of 651 sites in the Trust Fund database, 162 sites exhibiting cleanup costs were targeted for this study. Costs are subdivided into four major groups: (1) initial response, (2) release investigation and confirmation, (3) Phase I corrective action (initial installation), and (4) Phase II corrective action (monitoring). Each group is then further broken down into 13 categories, or program tasks to identify the site activity. Sites used in this study all had at least one Phase I corrective action reimbursement application in 1994, indicating that the corrective action system(s) have been installed. The Tennessee Department of Environment and Conservation (TDEC) identification numbers for these sites were cross-referenced to reports submitted to the state (e.g., corrective action plans and environmental assessment reports) to obtain the parameters of interest, shown in Table 1.

RESULTS

A total of 76 sites were included in the database. The remaining 86 sites in the target pool of 162 sites were eliminated due to (1) ongoing litigation which had temporarily halted all activity at the site, (2) lack of a corrective action plan to document site characteristics needed for this study, (3) inadequate data presented in the corrective action plan, or (4) incorrect classification of the site in

TABLE 1. Parameters collected for this study.

Site Tracking Data	Site Characteristics and Cleanup Data	Cost Information
Facility ID Number	Groundwater Treatment Technologies	Environmental Assessment Cost Estimate
Site Name and Address	Soil Treatment Technologies	
	Average Groundwater TPH[a] Concentration[b]	Corrective Action Cost Estimate
Consultant	Average Soil TPH Concentration[b]	Application Dates
Initial Site Characterization Report Date	Volume of TPH-Contaminated Soil Above Cleanup Standards	Actual Reimbursed Costs: · Free Product Removal
Environmental Assessment Report Date	Aerial Extent of Contaminated Groundwater Above Cleanup Standards	· Soil Removal · Soil Treatment · Water Treatment
Corrective Action Plan (CAP) Date	Maximum Depth of TPH Contamination	· Monitoring · Site Assessment
	Soil Type	· Environmental Report
	Groundwater Gradient, Hydraulic Conductivity and Transmissivity	· Implementation of CAP · Operation and Maintenance
	Depth of Bedrock and Groundwater Table	· Application Preparation · Other
	Contaminant Type	
	Groundwater Recovery Rate	

(a) TPH - total petroleum hydrocarbons.
(b) Concentration in milligrams per liter.
(c) Concentration in milligrams per kilogram.

the TDEC database. These sites were distributed throughout Tennessee as shown in Figure 1.

Although the data set was of insufficient size to conduct meaningful statistical analysis on the effect of various site types on treatment costs, it should be noted that the sites represent a wide variety of subsurface conditions. This is due to the varied landscapes of Tennessee between the mountains in the eastern portion of the state and the Mississippi River alluvial floodplain along the western border. The migration of pollution to groundwater supplies has been studied extensively in each of the six major physiographic provinces, which are characterized by unique topography, surface drainage, and geology characteristics. For example, in east Tennessee, groundwater flow is related to rock type and structural control

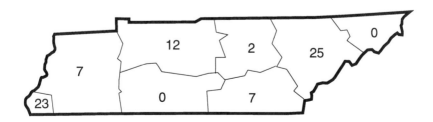

FIGURE 1. Distribution of study sites.

by bedding planes and fractures, whereas in west Tennessee, the permeability of the overlying porous silts and sands regulates fluid transmittal.

Table 2 presents the types of technologies observed in this study, and how they were classified as either "biotreatment" or "conventional treatment." The frequency of usage of treatment technologies observed in this study also is shown. Soil vapor extraction and groundwater extraction/treatment/discharge to a sanitary sewer were the most commonly used soil and groundwater treatment technologies, respectively, representing 21% of the operational units (OUs) observed at the study sites, or 57% of the sites. Biotreatment was used in 20% of the OUs (33% of the sites), with groundwater extraction and reinjection into the contaminated soil plume being the most commonly employed biotreatment. A comparison between 1994 corrective action activities (included in this study) and a separate group of sites which underwent corrective action in 1992 (documented in the previous study) indicates a significant rise in the use of biotreatment, particularly in situ bioremediation of both groundwater and soil.

Average unit costs were calculated (Table 2) and were found to be largely within the ranges of costs reported in literature (U.S. EPA 1992, Bueckman et al. 1991). This data set demonstrated a significant lack of economy of scale, typified by the relationship between cubic meters of contaminated soil and total soil treatment cost (Figure 2). Similar relationships were observed for treatment cost plotted against both aerial extent of the contaminated groundwater plume and total kilograms of total petroleum hydrocarbons in the soil. However, in every case, bioremediation costs were less than conventional treatment costs. Figure 3 summarizes average unit costs observed for the 25 bioremediation sites and the 51 conventional treatment sites.

The relationship of time to the accumulated costs at the 76 sites was also studied, due to the numerous reimbursement applications filed during a typical site's remediation period. Time parameters examined included (1) elapsed time from site discovery to September 1994, (2) elapsed time from site discovery to the last application submittal, (3) elapsed time between the first and last submittal of applications requesting reimbursement for corrective action costs, and (4) elapsed time between the first and last submittal of all applications (including site assessment). The last time parameter exhibited the best overall relationship with treatment costs, and is plotted in 6-month increments against $/square meter of the groundwater plume in Figure 4. Although this figure should be interpreted strictly in a qualitative sense due to the small data set, the relationship of these two parameters demonstrates a trend that was duplicated in other time vs. cost plots. This trend exhibited lower initial costs for bioremediation, which rose upward toward (and sometimes slightly beyond) the cost levels displayed by conventional treatment technologies as treatment progressed. Therefore, although biotreatment may have the initial advantage in lower startup costs, costs related to monitoring, operation, and maintenance may serve to reduce this advantage somewhat over long-term operation. The lower overall unit costs for bioremediation shown in Figure 3 may be attributed to the large number of biotreatment sites with application time spans less than 18 months (80% of the biotreatment sites).

TABLE 2. Treatment technologies observed, associated unit costs, and classification.

Technology Type	Number of Operational Units[a]	Average Unit Cost[b]	Biotreatment	Conventional Treatment
Soil Treatment Technologies				
Excavate and Incinerate	3	309		X
Excavate and Soil Wash	2	70		X
Excavate and Aerate	5	41		X
Soil Vapor Extraction	21	3		X
Bioventing	1	—[c]	X	
No Action (Groundwater Treatment Only)	15	—		
Water Treatment Technologies				
Extract, Treat, and Discharge to Sanitary Sewer	34	18		X
Extract, Treat, and Reinject	9	20		X
Extract, Treat, and Reinject with Nutrients	6	11	X	
Extract, Treat, and Discharge to Local Body of Water	6	12		X
Groundwater In Situ Bioaugmentation	5	8	X	
In Situ Biosparging	3	—	X	
No Action (Soil Treatment Only)	3	—		
Combination Water/Soil Treatment Technologies				
Extract and Reinject with Nutrients for In Situ Soil Bioremediation	7	33	X	
In Situ Biosparging with Soil Vapor Extraction	3	—	X	

(a) Sites may have more than one operational unit if both groundwater and soil are being treated.
(b) Unit costs are reported in dollars per cubic meter of contaminated soil for soil treatment technologies. Unit costs are reported in dollars per square meter of the aerial extent of the contaminated groundwater plume for water treatment technologies and combination water/soil treatment technologies.
(c) A "—" indicates insufficient data available for unit cost calculation or no cost associated with this parameter.

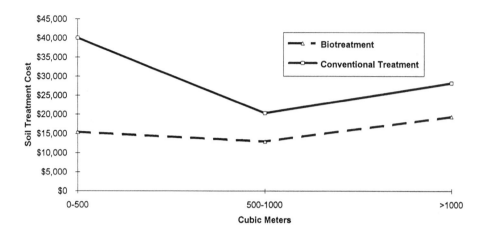

FIGURE 2. Average soil treatment cost as a function of soil volume.

CONCLUSION

Analysis of the 1994 data shows increasing use of more sophisticated bio-remedial technologies over previous years and continued lower overall cleanup costs for sites using soil and/or groundwater biotreatment over other remediation technologies. However, bioremediation has been shown to be successful when used in conjunction with components of conventional treatment methodologies, for example, in the reinjection of nutrient-enhanced groundwater through a con-taminated soil plume. In situ biorestoration techniques also are conducive to the remediation of sites where groundwater extraction or soil excavation is not practical. Overall, the use of biotechnology appears to be gaining strength in

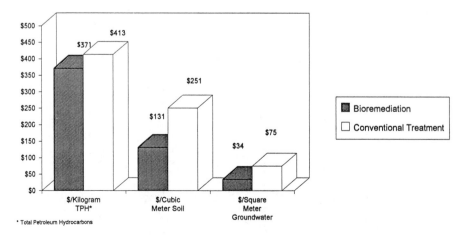

FIGURE 3. Average unit treatment costs.

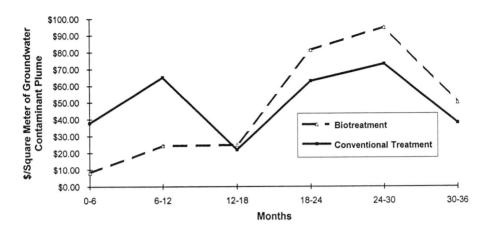

FIGURE 4. Accumulated treatment costs as a function of time.

the remediation arena as a cost-effective cleanup tool, resulting in the establishment of proven techniques and more predictable costs for various site conditions.

ACKNOWLEDGMENTS

The authors would like to express their appreciation to Mr. Chuck Head, director of the Tennessee Department of Environment and Conservation, Petroleum Underground Storage Tank Division, for his support on this project.

REFERENCES

Bueckman, D. S., S. Kumar, and M. R. Russell. 1991. *Underground Storage Tanks: Resource Requirements for Corrective Actions.* University of Tennessee Waste Management Research and Education Institute, Knoxville, TN.

Davis, K. L., H. R. Smith, and S. M. Day. 1994. "A Comparative Cost Analysis: Conventional Treatment Technologies and Bioremediation." In Brian S. Schepart (Ed.), *Bioremediation of Pollutants in Soil and Water*, ASTM STP 1235. American Society for Testing and Materials, Philadelphia, PA.

Smith, H. R. 1994. "A Comparative Cost Analysis of Soil Remediation Technologies." M.S. Thesis, University of Tennessee, Knoxville, TN.

U.S. Environmental Protection Agency. 1992. *Technologies and Options for UST Corrective Actions: Overview of Current Practice.* Office of Solid Waste and Emergency Response, EPA/542/R-92/010, Washington, DC.

Case Study: In Situ and Intrinsic Bioremediation Strategies at a Petroleum Hydrocarbon Site

Andrew F. Gemperline, Robert A. Glascott, and David A. Fulton

ABSTRACT

Hill Air Force Base (AFB) tested several conventional and innovative approaches to develop a cleanup strategy for a jet-fuel release to soil and groundwater at its petroleum, oil, and lubricant (POL) tank farm site. The technologies applied at the site include bioventing (forced-air injection), skimming and sorbent removal of light, nonaqueous-phase liquid (LNAPL), and vacuum-assisted free-product recovery (bioslurping). Detailed field investigation and numerical contaminant transport modeling using BIOPLUME II® documented intrinsic remediation as a viable cleanup alternative for the dissolved-phase contamination. Based on field treatability studies, bioslurping was not as attractive an option as a combination of LNAPL recovery and bioventing to reduce the mass of contaminants in the source at this site. Evaluation of site geochemical data indicated biodegradation occurs through intrinsic processes including aerobic respiration, denitrification, iron reduction, sulfanogenesis, and methanogenesis. The modeling effort concluded that the contamination could be naturally attenuated within 13 years provided there was minimal source removal. Based on these findings and the implementation of a detailed monitoring plan, intrinsic remediation appears to be an acceptable alternative for the cleanup of hydrocarbon-contaminated groundwater versus more conventional remediation technologies.

SITE DESCRIPTION

The site was investigated as a result of petroleum hydrocarbon spills/leaks at the POL facility. Investigations have identified contaminated soil, LNAPL, and dissolved-phase groundwater contamination that extends under the Patriot Hills residential housing area southwest of the POL site (Figure 1). The site is located on deltaic sand, silt, and clay deposits (Feth et al. 1966). The shallow aquifer ranges in depth from 5 to 32 ft (1.5 to 9.8 m) below ground surface (bgs) over the site. The approximate areal extent of LNAPL is 750 by 300 ft (229 to 92 m)

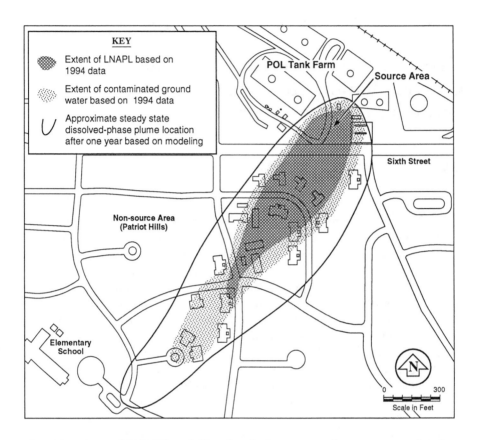

FIGURE 1. Area of LNAPL and dissolved-phase groundwater contamination.

and lies within an area of dissolved-phase contamination that measures 1,650 by 420 ft (503 by 128 m). Apparent LNAPL thicknesses in the source area have been as high as 9.9 ft (3 m). Initial soil gas concentrations ranged from 0.0 to 5.0% oxygen and 0.7 to 12.0% carbon dioxide, which indicated the soil was oxygen-limited.

Cleanup efforts for the source area and nonsource area (Patriot Hills) have focused on three objectives. First, federal and state regulations require removal of LNAPL to reduce and minimize migration of contaminants. Second, contaminants in soil and groundwater must be reduced to levels acceptable to the State of Utah. Third, potential risks of exposure and interruption to residents within the nonsource area must be minimized. Contamination levels at Patriot Hills must be reduced.

Source Removal Approach and Evaluation

Three approaches were employed to remove vadose zone soil contamination, a potential residual source of groundwater contamination, and LNAPL within the source area. These methods included bioventing, skimmer pumps/sorbents, and bioslurping.

To ascertain the effectiveness of bioventing for reducing vadose zone soil contamination, a forced-air injection bioventing study was conducted at two locations within the source area. This study determined in situ respiration rates and air permeability characteristics at the site following established guidelines (Hinchee et al. 1992). The bioventing systems injected air at 24 and 45 in·s of water attaining air injection flowrates of 30 to 17.5 scfm (0.8 to 0.5 m³), respectively. Air permeabilities ranged from 5.1 to 5.6 darcies. The radius of influence observed during the bioventing test for oxygen was approximately 30 ft (9 m). The estimated biodegradation rates ranged from 900 to 2,900 mg/kg/yr, indicating that biodegradation could be stimulated through forced aeration. The initial respiration rates and 6-month shutdown respiration test data are summarized in Table 1.

The skimmer pump/sorbent LNAPL source area recovery system consisted of a specific gravity skimmer pump installed in the monitoring well containing the greatest apparent thickness of LNAPL. In addition, oiliphilic absorbent socks placed in stainless steel perforated bailers were installed in five adjacent wells. Recovery of LNAPL from this combined system was approximately 3 gal (11.4 L) per day over the initial 5 months of product recovery. The recovery rate subsequently decreased to 2 gal (7.6 L) of LNAPL per week over the remaining year, potentially signifying that recoverable LNAPL not bound in the soil matrix was depleting or that the recovery system was ineffective.

As an alternative strategy for LNAPL removal, bioslurping was tested using the same monitoring wells utilized by the skimmer/sorbent recovery systems. Bioslurping was tested because the cone of reduced pressure that it would produce around a well was believed to increase the hydraulic gradient and aquifer transmissivity, thus optimizing LNAPL extraction from the well (Kittel et al. 1994). Cumulative recovery of LNAPL from five 24- to 48-hour bioslurping

TABLE 1. Summary of bioventing respiration rates.

Well/Soil Vapor Probe (SVP) ID	Distance from Air Injection Wells (ft[m])	Initial Respiration Rate (mg/kg/y)	6-Month Respiration Test (mg/kg/y)
SVP-1	50 (15.2)	2,600	NM[a]
SVP-2	35 (10.7)	2,900	1,300
SVP-3	12 (3.7)	2,900	1,500
SVP-3 (duplicate reading)	12 (3.7)	900	400
Background Air Injection Well (BKG-1)		70	70

(a) NM = Not measured because of LNAPL in the soil vapor probe.

tests was approximately 3 gal (11.4 L); however, approximately 4,000 gal (15,200 L) of contaminated groundwater also were recovered. Soil gas pressure data were collected during each bioslurping test and used to calculate the soil gas radius of influence for each test well, as outlined in Hinchee et al. (1992). The bioslurper system extracted an average vacuum of 10 in·s (25.4 cm·s) of mercury (136 in·s [345 cm·s] of water) resulting in a vapor extraction airflow rate ranging from 12 to 16 scfm (0.36 to 0.48 m^3 per min). The radius of influence, where the pressure was greater than 0.1 in·s (0.25 cm·s) of water, ranged from 35 to 59 ft (10.7 to 18.0 m) across the site; however, pressure changes in the subsurface were detected more than 100 m away from some wells. These pressure data, coupled with a measured increase in soil gas oxygen levels from less than 3% to greater than 13%, suggest that the slurping action created by this process aerated the vadose zone soil providing oxygen to stimulate in situ biodegradation.

After the initial LNAPL recovery stabilized, the performance of the bioslurp technology was not appreciably better than the more passive combined skimmer pump/sorbent recovery system. The bioslurp technology also produced additional wastewater and vapor requiring treatment prior to discharge. Wastewater treatment would include handling, transportation, and treatment prior to discharge. Vapor treatment could be achieved by carbon absorption, internal combustion units, or other costly treatment technologies. Consequently, the skimmer pump/sorbent recovery system is more cost-effective for this site and was selected for inclusion in the final Site Corrective Action Plan.

For remediating soil, the bioslurper had the added benefit of aerating the soil and stimulating biodegradation, impacting a comparable radius of influence as bioventing. However, the same effect could be achieved using a bioventing system, which did not require the rigorous operational and maintenance attention as did the bioslurper system. A combined skimmer pump/sorbent and bioventing system was selected because it was as effective and more economical than the more aggressive bioslurper system.

Nonsource Area Approach and Evaluation

The nonsource area is downgradient of the POL and south of Sixth Street (Figure 1) and consists of residual LNAPL, dissolved-phase hydrocarbon contamination in groundwater, and soil contamination associated with the water table. Various treatment technologies, including air sparging with soil vapor extraction, pump and treat, and documenting the risk-management approach of intrinsic remediation were considered for site restoration. Pump and treat and/or air sparging with soil vapor extraction appeared to be viable cleanup options; however, each was considered to be more intrusive to residential activities and thought to be more capital-intensive than alternative approaches. Intrinsic remediation, supported by a modeling effort using the numerical contaminant transport model (BIOPLUME II®), was projected to degrade hydrocarbon contamination in the groundwater prior to reaching a point of exposure and subsequently was evaluated as a cleanup alternative for the site.

To document intrinsic remediation, Hill AFB, the Air Force Center for Environmental Excellence (AFCEE), and the EPA Robert S. Kerr Environmental Research Laboratory (RSKERL) conducted comprehensive field investigations in the nonsource area. The investigations focused on distinguishing between attenuation due to biodegradation versus dilution or sorption processes. This also included demonstrating that the type and quantity of electron acceptors at the site were capable of biotransforming the given contaminant concentration of benzene, toluene, ethylbenzene, and xylenes (BTEX) in the groundwater (Wilson et al. 1994).

Based on site geochemical data, biodegradation occurs through aerobic respiration, denitrification, iron reduction, sulfanogenesis, and methanogenesis. Background concentrations of the electron acceptors available at the site were used to approximate the assimilative capacity of the groundwater (Table 2). Site groundwater has an estimated dissolved-phase assimilative capacity of 30,890 µg/L, whereas the highest observed total BTEX concentration was 21,475 µg/L (Wiedemeier et al. 1994). Consequently, the groundwater has the capacity and ability to degrade dissolved-phase BTEX that partitions from the LNAPL plume.

Modeling using BIOPLUME II® predicts that the dissolved BTEX plume will reach steady state after approximately 1 year and will meet required cleanup levels for groundwater in approximately 13 years, provided the existing LNAPL source area removal system continues during the same period of time (Wiedemeier et al. 1994) (see Figure 1). Conservative logic was applied in the modeling effort because aerobic respiration and denitrification were the only processes considered in the model simulations. However, iron reduction, sulfanogenesis, and methanogenesis are still occurring and, if their estimated assimilative capacities were considered, sulfanogensis would be the dominant degradation process, ensuring complete depletion of the BTEX plume. Other factors influencing the predicted cleanup time frame include reaeration of the groundwater and water table fluctuations. The ability of the unconfined aquifer to recharge the

TABLE 2. Expressed BTEX assimilative capacity of groundwater.

Electron Acceptor or Process	Background Levels (mg/L)	Expressed BTEX (µg/L) Assimilative Capacity
Dissolved oxygen	6	1,920
Nitrate	17	3,570
Ferric hydroxide	50.5	2,300
Sulfate	100	20,500
Methanogenesis	2.04	2,600
Expressed assimilative capacity		30,890
Highest observed total BTEX concentration		21,475

area of contaminated groundwater with the electron acceptors and donors needed for aerobic and anaerobic degradation processes appears to be adequate because of the groundwater velocities observed at the site (1.59×10^{-2} ft/s or 4.85×10^{-3} m/s).

Since intrinsic remediation is a risk management approach, Hill AFB assessed the risk posed by the groundwater contamination. The only potential point of exposure to the shallow contaminated aquifer is the outfall of a stormwater sewer line trench, which may intercept the water table downgradient of the plume. To ensure that the contamination does not reach the storm sewer outfall, a proposed long-term monitoring plan was prepared that includes installation of point-of-compliance monitoring wells downgradient of the plume and adjacent to the storm sewer. The risk due to the inhalation of vapors from LNAPL and groundwater with dissolved-phase hydrocarbons was also studied in the nonsource area. Detectable concentrations of BTEX were measured in near-surface soil gas; however, no completed inhalation exposure pathway for soil gas into homes was discovered. Because site conditions could change during long-term monitoring, a contingency plan to reevaluate these risks was included as part of the Site Corrective Action Plan.

To document the effects of intrinsic remediation over the long term, the proposed site monitoring in the source and nonsource areas will include semiannual sampling of 13 monitoring wells for BTEX, dissolved oxygen, nitrate, ferrous iron, sulfate, and methane. These wells are located upgradient, within, and downgradient of the contaminant plume and they will be used to monitor the effectiveness of intrinsic remediation in reducing the total mass of contaminant within the plume. The monitoring information also will provide data for confirming the modeling results and provide early indications of any potential migration of contamination to downgradient exposure points.

CONCLUSIONS

The selected remedial alternative for controlling the LNAPL in the source area consists of a combination skimmer pump/sorbent recovery system. For contaminated soil in the source area, pilot-scale testing of an air injection bioventing system has proven effective and has been proposed as part of the final remedy. While it is effective as the selected source area remedial approach, bioslurping was not selected because of the additional costs associated with treatment of wastewater and vapor discharges produced by the system. The dissolved-phase groundwater contamination below both the POL site and the nonsource area will be addressed using the risk-management approach of documenting and monitoring intrinsic remediation, with the expectation that contaminants will attenuate naturally. This remedial strategy is appropriate because air monitoring shows that there are no current health risks to the residents, and aquifer conditions will promote biodegradation. BIOPLUME II® modeling concluded that the contamination could be naturally attenuated within

13 years provided current LNAPL recovery efforts continue during that time period. A semiannual groundwater monitoring program, supported by a contingency plan to address any uncertainty in the approach, appears to aid in the regulatory agency's acceptance of the Site Corrective Action Plan.

REFERENCES

Feth, J. H., D. A. Barker, L. J. Moore, R. J. Brown, and C. E. Veirs. 1966. *Lake Bonneville: Geology and Hydrology of the Weber Delta District, Including Ogden, Utah*, U.S. Geologic Survey Professional Paper 518.

Hinchee, R. E., R. N. Miller, and D. C. Downey. 1992. *Test Plan and Technical Protocol for a Field Treatability Test for Bioventing*, Prepared for the Air Force Center for Environmental Excellence, Brooks Air Force Base, Texas, May 1992.

Kittel, J. A., R. E. Hinchee, R. Hoeppel, and R. Miller. 1994. "Bioslurping-Vacuum-Enhanced Free-Product Recovery Coupled with Bioventing: A Case Study." *The Proceedings of the 1994 Petroleum Hydrocarbons and Organic Chemicals in Ground Water: Prevention, Detection, and Remediation Conference*, pp. 255-270.

Wiedemeier, T. H., J. T. Wilson, R. N. Miller, and D. H. Kampbell. 1994. "United States Air Force Guidelines for Successfully Supporting Intrinsic Remediation with an Example from Hill Air Force Base." *The Proceedings of the 1994 Petroleum Hydrocarbons and Organic Chemicals in Ground Water: Prevention, Detection, and Remediation Conference*, pp. 317-334.

Wilson, J. T., F. M. Pfeffer, J. W. Weaver, D. H. Kampbell, T. H. Wiedemeir, J. E. Hansen, and R. Miller. 1994. "Intrinsic Bioremediation of JP-4 Jet Fuel." *Symposium on Intrinsic Bioremediation of Ground Water*, pp. 60-72. EPA/540/R-94/515.

Use of Bioremediation to Resolve a Petroleum Hydrocarbon Contamination Lawsuit

Robert J. Gaglione and Robert S. Johnston

ABSTRACT

Bioremediation was selected to remediate a public works site in the South Bay of San Diego County, California. The soil and groundwater at this site was contaminated with petroleum hydrocarbons and was the subject of extensive litigation. The parties agreed to resolve the dispute by using a combination of bioremediation and excavation/disposal. This paper includes an overview of the legal and technical issues involved in addressing the problems that were encountered and how those problems were solved. A model is presented for economically resolving environmental disputes in which the parties jointly agree to remediation of a site using bioremediation or similar techniques. This case study addresses the problems encountered because of the differing needs and goals of the legal and scientific communities. Notwithstanding the conflicts, it is demonstrated that the parties can, in most cases, work together toward remediation and resolution.

INTRODUCTION

The soil and groundwater at a public works site in the South Bay area of San Diego County were contaminated with petroleum hydrocarbons. The property was the subject of extensive litigation. The parties agreed to resolve the dispute by remediating the site using bioremediation and excavation/disposal.

This paper is an overview of the legal and technical issues involved in addressing the problems that were encountered and the way the parties came together to solve those problems. A model is presented for an economical resolution of environmental disputes in which the parties jointly agree to bioremediation or other state-of-the-art technologies to remediate a site. This case study addresses the problems encountered because of diverging needs and goals of the legal and scientific communities. Notwithstanding the conflicts, the parties can, in most cases, work together toward developing a remediation plan and case resolution.

SITE HISTORY[1]

A parcel of land owned by the city was subdivided into two lots (property #1 and property #2). The land historically was used by the city as its public works yard. Owner A purchased property #1 from the city in 1964. The city continued its public works operation on property #2, a parcel adjacent to property #1. Prior to owner A's purchase of property #1, the city had placed fill material on the lot. It is believed that one layer of this material consisted of undocumented fill from a variety of origins. This undocumented fill included sludge from a nearby creek, street sweepings, and residual material from asphalt operations conducted by the city.

Owner A developed property #1 from 1966 to 1967 by placing imported, compacted fill over the entire lot, installing an underground storage tank (UST), and constructing an office building. The UST was used to store gasoline for owner A's trucks. In 1970, the gasoline dealer removed the UST and supplied a new UST to owner A. The UST remained in place until it was removed in 1988.

Owner A sold property #1 to owner B in 1982. Due to problems obtaining permits from the city, owner B never was able to use the property in the manner originally intended. After 2 years, owner B sold the property to owner C, an excavation and trucking company. Owner B contended that the UST was never used for gasoline or any other purpose. Owner C's business operations included the storage and transportation of hazardous materials, among other things.

Owner C contended that the UST was used only to store waste oil. In September 1988, owner C and the city entered into a contract to sell property #1 back to the city, which still owned property #2. As one of the terms of the sale, owner C was asked to remove the UST, which was still in place on property #1 at the time. When the tank was removed in October 1988, a black, viscous, oil-type material was observed in the excavation and the county ordered owner C to clean up the site. Subsurface investigations revealed that the soil and ground-water were contaminated with gasoline and other heavier hydrocarbons.

SITE CONDITIONS

A review of the information presented in technical site investigation reports indicates that the site conditions consisted of fill soils underlain by bay/lagoonal muds. The bay/lagoonal muds were encountered to the maximum depth explored and consisted of gray to black, fine-to-medium silty clays and clayey silts.

---

[1] The location of the site and identification of the parties have been withheld from this paper. However, it should be noted this paper is based on an actual site in San Diego, California.

As discussed previously, portions of the fill soils contained street sweepings, various organics, and sludge. It is important to note that the presence of organics in the fill soils may cause interference with test results when using U.S. Environmental Protection Agency (EPA) Test Method 418.1 (infrared spectrometer method) due to the presence of asphalt and other organics. EPA Test Method 418.1 was the test method required by the regulators to identify the presence of waste oils and longer-chain hydrocarbons. This is important because the presence of longer-chain hydrocarbons may indicate more resistance to biodegradation methods and may falsely represent abnormally high concentrations of longer-chain hydrocarbons.

The investigations indicated the groundwater was present at a depth of approximately 5 to 8 ft (1.5 to 2.4 m) below ground surface (bgs). Seasonal and tidal fluctuations were observed in the monitoring wells with the groundwater flow to the north. A total of 13 groundwater monitoring wells were installed with 25 borings and trenching excavations to obtain samples to measure for the presence of total petroleum hydrocarbons (TPH) utilizing EPA Test Method 8015 (modified) and total recoverable petroleum hydrocarbons (TRPH) utilizing EPA Test Method 418.1.

The site is situated within the beneficial groundwater use area. The tentative action level for benzene is 1 µg/L (or part per billion) for groundwater in this area.

The problems associated with site mitigation included the presence of several structures. There is a large maintenance and office building on property #1 and a city public works administration building on property #2. The results of the investigation indicated that the product plume had migrated underneath both of the buildings. Table 1 presents the maximum and average contamination in the soil and groundwater found during the investigation. The vertical depths of the TPH/TRPH soil impacts were measured to depths of approximately 10 ft (3 m) bgs.

LITIGATION HISTORY

The first lawsuit involving this site was filed shortly after the discovery of contamination of the soil and groundwater. This case addressed the issue of whether owner C should be allowed to rescind the contract for the sale of the property on the grounds the cleanup was too costly for owner C to be bound to the terms of the contract. The case went to trial. The jury found that there was a mistake of fact and that, therefore, the sales contract was void. Owner C currently owns property #1 and the city is reportedly still interested in purchasing the property from owner C.

After further investigation, the city found out that its own property also was contaminated and looked to the UST on property #1 as the source of this contamination. Property #2, like property #1, was found to have gasoline and heavier hydrocarbon contamination. A second lawsuit was filed by the city

TABLE 1. Soil and groundwater contamination.

	Soil, mg/L		Groundwater, µg/L	
	Maximum	**Average**	**Maximum**	**Average**
TRPH	25,000	3,013	9,200	1,403
TPH	30,800	2,666	93,000	11,200
Benzene	60	13.4	19,400	2,208
Toluene	480	30.4	15,000	1,586
Ethylbenzene	170	28.9	3,370	394
Total xylenes	810	87.2	13,100	1,475
Organic lead	4.1	1.43	<750[a]	
PCBs	0.24	0.0977	<0.5[a]	

(a) Only one sample tested. Result was below the limit of detection indicated.

against owner C. Later, prior owners A and B also were sued. The allegations in the complaint filed in the second lawsuit indicate that the litigation was brought under the following statutes:

- Comprehensive Environmental Response Compensation and Liability Act (42 U.S.C. §§ 9601, et seq.)
- Clean Water Act (33 U.S.C. §§ 1251, et seq.)
- Resource Conservation and Recovery Act (42 U.S.C. §§ 6901, et seq.)
- Federal Underground Storage Tank statutes (42 U.S.C. §§ 6991, et seq.)
- Hazardous Waste Control law (California Health and Safety Code §§ 25100, et seq.)
- Carpenter-Presley-Tanner Hazardous Substance Account Act (California Health and Safety Code §§ 25300, et seq.)
- Porter-Cologne Water Quality Act (California Water Code §§ 13000, et seq.)
- California Underground Storage Tank statute (California Health and Safety Code §§ 25280, et seq.).

Causes of action raised in the litigation included negligence, nuisance, trespass, indemnity, and declaratory relief.

After extensive discovery and investigation, the parties determined that it would be feasible to settle the lawsuit when a bioremediation consultant advised counsel for owners A, B, and C that the site could be mitigated in situ for the "guaranteed" sum of $150,000. Prior to that time, the environmental consultants for the city had suggested that it would cost approximately ten times that amount to clean up the site. The experts for the city recommended a combination of excavation/disposal of contaminated soil and enhanced dual-phase groundwater and soil vapor extraction. Experts for owners A, B, and C were also evaluating several other remedial alternatives that were less expensive than the technology favored by the city's environmental consultants.

TECHNICAL EVALUATION OF IN SITU BIOREMEDIATION

As stated above, the bioremediation consultant supported the use of in situ bioremediation due to the high cost of removing or supporting the on-site buildings, even though the impacts extended vertically only to a depth of 10 ft (3 m). A review of the literature indicates that longer-chain hydrocarbons have been removed from groundwater using bioremediation by a variety of techniques, including injecting nitrates as a primary electron acceptor for the microbial respiration of hydrocarbons. Nitrogen typically is more soluble than traditional electron acceptors, such as hydrogen peroxide, and less toxic (Hutchins et al. 1991).

However, the problem initially encountered was the parties' unfamiliarity with the in situ bioremediation method proposed for this project. The bioremediation consultant's proposal contained a sparging approach combined with groundwater extraction. The consultant's proposal indicated the approach would involve an enzyme-catalyzed bioremediation that "greatly enhances the natural process of metabolic degradation." This process would be aided by the presence of "desorbing agents which dramatically improve the permeability, ultimately freeing desorb contaminants." The bioremediation consultant also predicted mitigation in 3 to 4 months.

SETTLEMENT EFFORTS

When the parties attempted to put the cost "guarantee" in writing, the bioremediation consultant backed out of the deal. The consulting firm would not agree to "guarantee" its work, even though a pilot test on soil taken from the site was successful. Nonetheless, the parties had determined to clean up the site and continued their effort to find a technology that was both economical and effective.

Although the case was ready to go to trial, the parties requested more information from other consultants and contractors. Ultimately, it was determined that the site could be cleaned up using bioremediation and excavation/disposal for approximately $250,000. Because this cost was far less expensive than other estimates that would have come into evidence at a trial, the parties once again entered into settlement negotiations. Eventually the parties reached a deal to clean up the site with everyone agreeing to cooperate.

EVALUATION OF FINAL MITIGATION METHOD

Due to the bioremediation consultant's false promises and the parties' lack of familiarity with the in situ bioremediation program, the ultimate settlement focused on a higher degree of certainty than the previous mitigation program. It should be recognized that in any legal settlement negotiations, the lack of credibility of a consultant or familiarity with a proposed mitigation program can be a critical obstacle in reaching a settlement. As discussed above, the parties reached a settlement because of a changed remediation approach; the approach included excavation of the impacted soils supporting the structures by grouting and using ex situ treatment on site with enhanced bioremediation. However, guarantees could not be provided concerning the certainty (time and costs) for ex situ bioremediation. A review of a U.S. EPA (1994) annual status report for innovative treatment technology indicates that five projects have been selected for bioremediation (ex situ) with a similar project at the Marine Corps Mountain Warfare Center in Bridgeport, California. However, the certainty factors are such that it is difficult to predict, with a level of accuracy, the overall costs and the time involved with the ex situ bioremediation approach.

Ex situ bioremediation also needs to address the growing competition from off-site thermal desorption; competitive costs in the San Diego area for off-site thermal desorption are approaching $40 to $45 a ton (including transportation). The high degree of certainty in terms of fixed costs and a specific timetable for thermal desorption provides stiff competition for use of ex situ bioremediation to resolve legal cases.

RESOLUTION OF PROBLEMS

In this case, many problems were encountered between the legal and scientific community (i.e., the lawyers and the environmental consultants). Typically, environmental consultants are extremely cautious when lawyers are involved and litigation is pending because of the extraordinary scrutiny that will be undertaken by other consultants, lawyers, and regulators. Furthermore, environmental consultants and contractors need to budget with precision — knowing that there will be little or no tolerance for cost overruns. On the other hand, the lawyers and their clients are looking for the most cost-effective solution. Lawyers also want guaranteed results for their clients. In this case, these difficulties were resolved after months of negotiations and continued patience by the trial court judge. This case is an example of the success that can be achieved when all the parties act reasonably and responsibly. When the parties in this case began settlement negotiations, counsel for the city indicated that cleanup costs would exceed 10 times what the defendants were willing to pay to settle the case. Nonetheless, the parties managed to negotiate a settlement, notwithstanding the large disparity in their original positions.

Following sufficient discovery and investigation to allow informed decisions, interested parties can sit down and work together toward a global resolution. Sometimes it is necessary to involve a mediator or settlement judge who is well versed in environmental issues and is able to communicate with environmental consultants. Because there is usually a significant amount of money at stake, all parties, consultants, and counsel should keep an open mind and constantly search for the "middle ground" that everyone can agree to.

MODEL FOR RESOLUTION OF ENVIRONMENTAL CLAIMS

The model for resolution of environmental claims based upon this case study is as follows:

- Identify all potentially responsible parties
- Identify all resources available to the parties (including insurance and public funds)
- Retain a consultant or team of consultants acceptable to the parties (joint consultants should be retained whenever possible)
- Conduct an investigation to define the scope and extent of contamination
- Litigate only if necessary, using alternative dispute resolution (such as arbitration or mediation) whenever possible
- Work with regulators to define an acceptable work plan
- Define and implement a plan to remediate the site and resolve the dispute.

CONCLUSION

This case study is an example of how lawyers and environmental consultants can work together in solving a significant environmental problem to cleanup a site. As counsel once indicated in court, "The earth will be a better place when this case is resolved." Hopefully, these words can be spoken when other environmental disputes are resolved as well.

REFERENCES

Hutchins, S. R., W. C. Downs, G. B. Smith, J. T. Wilson, D. J. Hendrix, D. D. Fine, D. A. Kovacs, R. H. Douglass, and F. A. Blaha. 1991. *EPA Project Summary: Nitrate for Biorestoration of an Aquifer Contaminated with Jet Fuel.* U.S. Environmental Protection Agency, April.

U.S. Environmental Protection Agency. 1994. *Innovative Treatment Technologies: Annual Status Report*, 6th ed. September.

Bench-Scale/Field-Scale Interpretations: An Overview

Alfred B. Cunningham and Brent M. Peyton

ABSTRACT

In situ bioremediation involves complex interactions between biological, chemical, and physical processes and requires integration of phenomena operating at scales ranging from that of a microbial cell (10^{-6} m) to that of a remediation site (10 to 1,000 m). Laboratory investigations of biodegradation are usually performed at a relatively small scale, which is governed by convenience, cost, and expedience. However, extending the results from a laboratory-scale experimental system to the design and operation of a field-scale system introduces (1) additional mass transport mechanisms and limitations; (2) the presence of multiple phases, contaminants, and competing microorganisms; (3) spatial geologic heterogeneities; and (4) subsurface environmental factors that may inhibit bacterial growth, such as temperature, pH, nutrient, or redox conditions. Field bioremediation rates may be limited by the availability of one of the necessary constituents for biotransformation: substrate, contaminant, electron acceptor, nutrients, or microorganisms capable of degrading the target compound. The factor that limits the rate of bioremediation may not be the same in the laboratory as it is in the field, thereby leading to development of unsuccessful remediation strategies (Goldstein et al. 1985; Lee et al. 1988).

INTRODUCTION

Current bioremediation literature is dominated by the investigation of individual phenomena, usually at the bench scale. Relatively few studies address interactions among bioremediation phenomena or consider how phenomenological effects can be integrated to make predictions of field-scale process behavior. The relative absence of practitioner-oriented tools for decision making suggests that a "process engineering" approach is needed to improve the state-of-the-art of bioremediation practice. Process engineering, in the context of bioremediation, involves the integration of site historical information; site geologic, hydrologic, chemical, and microbiological characteristics; lab and field data; and possible remedial actions to make predictions and design decisions. This integration may be in the form of computational tools, such as flow and transport models, that can aid in site-specific system design, operation strategy, and data analysis. Ultimately, a priori predictions need to be compared with field observations of remediation system performance. Publication of evaluation studies will better define the overall uncertainty that surrounds decision-making in bioremediation.

PROCESS SCALEUP

The papers presented in this book are based on a scales-of-observation approach, along with other process engineering concepts, to provide a framework for understanding factors affecting the rate and extent of biotransformation; the intent is to improve the design of subsurface bioremediation systems. Use of three scales of observation (micro-, meso-, and macroscale) facilitates the engineering of bioremediation systems. The scale definitions are arbitrary, but provide a useful conceptual structure for approaching the scaleup problem.

At the microscale, chemical and microbiological species and reactions can be characterized independently of any transport phenomena. Examples of microscale features are the composition of the microbial population and kinetics and stoichiometry of biotransformation reactions. The physical scale of these phenomena is at, or less than, the dimension of the microbial cell (10^{-6} to 10^{-5} m). At the mesoscale, transport phenomena and system geometry are first apparent, with the exclusion of advective or mixing processes. Mesoscale phenomena include diffusion, nonequilibrium sorption, and interphase mass transfer. Mesoscale phenomena reflect, for example, the size of pore channels or soil particles, the characteristic diffusion length, or the dimension of microbial aggregates. The length scale for such features ranges from approximately 10^{-5} to 10^{-2} m. The ability to discern advective or mixing phenomena defines the macroscale. Advection, dispersion, and geologic spatial heterogeneity are examples of macroscale phenomena; the corresponding physical scale is approximately 10^{-2} to 10^2 m or even larger. Table 1 summarizes the scale for many of the phenomena that influence bioremediation. Phenomena are classified according to the smallest scale at which they can be observed. Many of the potentially rate-controlling variables in Table 1 are important at the microscale, but are controlled by transport processes at the macroscale. It is this breadth of scales that must be accounted for during the design of in situ biotransformations.

The phenomena in Table 1 must be considered to determine if bioremediation is applicable to a specific site. The phenomena that limit the actual rate of biotransformation must be determined on a case-by-case basis. For example, if the concentration of active biomass is too low, the (microscale) kinetic reaction rate may limit the overall rate of contaminant bioremediation. If the soil organic carbon content is high, the rate of (mesoscale) desorption of contaminant from within the soil matrix may limit bioremediation. Alternatively, if low pore velocities prevail, (macroscale) advection and dispersion may be the rate-limiting processes. The need to identify and estimate the appropriate rate-controlling

TABLE 1. Phenomena influencing bioremediation.

Scale	Representative Characterization Methods
Microscale	
Microorganisms	Plate counts, gene probe
Degradation pathways	Batch reaction studies
Reaction stoichiometry	Batch reaction studies
Reaction kinetics	Batch reaction studies
Electron acceptors	Chemical analysis for N, P
Nutrients	Chemical analysis
Inhibitors, toxicity	Batch reaction studies
Water activity, pH	Electrochemical probes
Reactions with soil or aquifer matrix	
chemical equilibria	Abiotic reaction studies
Sorption (equilibrium)	Abiotic batch sorption studies
Mesoscale	
Sorption (nonequilibrium)	Abiotic sorption studies
Attachment/detachment (microorganisms)	Biofilm studies
Diffusion	Diffusion chamber tests
Plugging/filtration	Column studies, pressure drop
Interphase transport	Multiphase column studies
Macroscale	
Advection	Well elevations, pump, and tracer tests
Dispersion	Conservative tracer studies
Spatial heterogeneity	Well logs, core permeabilities
Hydrologic properties	Core permeabilities

phenomena dominates the feasibility of an in situ bioremediation project. It is also clear that heterogeneities in the field can substantially complicate the issue in that different phenomena may limit the biotransformation at different locations at a given site.

The approach to scaleup should therefore include the following steps: (1) relevant phenomena must be analyzed to determine which will limit the contaminant biotransformation rate at prevailing subsurface environmental conditions (because the subsurface environment may vary considerably across the site, analysis may conclude that several different phenomena are limiting, depending on the exact location); (2) once a particular remediation strategy is proposed (e.g., pump and treat or nutrient injection/recovery), the situation must be reassessed to determine a new set of probable biotransformation rates and their limiting phenomena; and (3) the outcome of steps 1 and 2 can be used to assess the feasibility of a system design.

ACKNOWLEDGMENTS

The authors acknowledge the support of the National Science Foundation through Cooperative Agreement EEC-8907039 between the National Science Foundation and Montana State University and the U.S. Department of Energy Office of Technology Development VOC Arid Integrated Demonstration. Pacific Northwest Laboratory is operated for the U.S. Department of Energy by Battelle Memorial Institute under contract DE-AC06-76RLO 1830. Special thanks to the Engineering Research Center Industrial Associates and to Conoco, Inc.

REFERENCES

Goldstein, R. M., L. M. Mallory, and M. Alexander. 1985. "Reasons for Possible Failure of Inoculation to Enhance Biodegradation." *Appl. Environ. Micro.*, 50:997-983.
Lee, M. D., J. M. Thomas, R. C. Borden, P. B. Bedient, J. T. Wilson, and C. H. Ward. 1988. "Biorestoration of Aquifers Contaminated with Organic Compounds." *CRC Critical Reviews in Environmental Control*, 18:29-89.

Bioremediation of Crude Oil Spills in Marine and Terrestrial Environments

Roger C. Prince

ABSTRACT

Bioremediation can be a safe and effective tool for dealing with crude oil spills, as demonstrated during the cleanup following the *Exxon Valdez* spill in Alaska (Pritchard et al. 1992; Prince et al. 1994a; Bragg et al. 1994). Crude oil has also been spilled on land, and bioremediation is a promising option for land spills too. Nevertheless, there are still areas where our understanding of the phenomenon is rather incomplete. Research groups around the world are addressing these problems, and this symposium provides an excellent overview of some of this work.

INTRODUCTION

Major spills are rare, so there are not many opportunities for testing marine bioremediation protocols on accidental spills. Researchers are thus constrained to laboratory mesocosms and small field studies; examples of both approaches are provided in this symposium. One thing that should be borne in mind when comparing terrestrial and marine situations is that marine microbiota are principally bacterial, and although oil-degrading fungi have been isolated from such environments (Kirk & Gordon 1988), they are usually considered to be uncommon. In contrast, fungal biomass often exceeds bacterial biomass in soils (Domsch et al. 1980), and fungal degradation of hydrocarbons is likely to be important (Cerniglia 1992). Thus, although oil degrades readily in both soils and beaches, it is quite possible that the details of oil biodegradation are different in the two situations. McMillen et al. (1995) describe their experiments aimed at predicting the biodegradability of different oils spilled on various soils, and find that degradation is very dependent on the oil composition (see also Huesemann 1995), and is slower in sandy soils or those with high salinities. The latter is important, because reservoir waters produced with crude oils often are highly saline, and can be very inhibitory to bacterial and plant growth. Spilled crude oil at production sites may be sufficiently localized that composting is an option, and McMillen et al. (1995) describe their success with this technique (see also McMillen et al. 1993).

Composting is a promising technology for small marine spills too (see Sendstad & Sveum 1983).

Most of this session deals with marine spills, and several papers describe the design and construction of microcosms and mesocosms to mimic beaches subjected to tidal flow (Croft et al. 1995; Ishihara et al. 1995; Ramstad et al. 1995; Sveum et al. 1995). The papers by Ramstad et al. and Sveum et al. are particularly complete descriptions of their elegant systems that mimic the very large water movements that can occur in marine beaches (McLachlan 1982; McLachlan et al. 1985). As an alternative to laboratory studies, two papers report the results of small field experiments (Lee et al. 1995; Venosa et al. 1995). Most of the papers in this symposium focus on the use of indigenous bacteria, with the exception of the work of Ishihara et al. (1995), which presents initial experiments using lyophilized bacteria including *Alcaligenes* strains to stimulate biodegradation. On the largest mesocosm scale, however, they compare the effects of nutrients plus inocula to the addition of neither, so do not address any potential benefit of adding the inocula. Such an advantage has yet to be clearly documented in the field (see Pritchard 1992); in line with this, Venosa et al. (1995) added indigenous bacteria grown on site in a simple reactor in their field test, and saw no benefit over fertilizer alone, although it must be noted that the background levels of nutrients were so high that there was not much scope for enhancement of degradation. Marty and Martin (1993) also saw no increase in biodegradation by adding bacteria with Inipol EAP22 (see below).

Several papers address comparisons of organic and inorganic nutrients to stimulate biodegradation. Ramstad et al. (1995) and Sveum and Ramstad (1995) used their columns and beach mesocosms to test the efficacy of fish meal, "stick water" (a fish meal by-product), and a slow-release inorganic fertilizer (MaxBac) to stimulate microbial degradation of oil on beach sediment. They found that the organic products were much more effective than the slow-release fertilizer they tested, although it must be noted that the slow-release fertilizer did not seem to liberate its nutrients very effectively in their tests. Similarly, Croft et al. (1995) found that the oleophilic Inipol EAP22, which is principally oleic acid and tri-laureth phosphate with a nitrogen content of 7.4% (Ladousse & Tramier 1991), was much more effective at stimulating oil degradation on sand than were equivalent amounts of a slow-release product (MaxBac) that contains 27% nitrogen and no available carbon. This work highlights the importance, emphasized by Bragg et al. (1994), of monitoring nitrogen released into interstitial water, because in all these experiments the MaxBac did not deliver its nutrients on the experimental time scale. Inorganic nutrients can be efficacious (Bragg et al. 1994), and Ramstad and Sveum (1995) show that dissolved nitrate is the most effective form of nitrogen to stimulate oil degradation in their mesocosms. Wrenn et al. (1994) have studied the effects of different forms of nitrogen in respirometric experiments, although the relevance of their concentrations (0.45 to 7.14 mM) to those appropriate for bioremediation (typically < 0.3 mM) is unclear. At such high concentrations they found that ammonium salts led to an acidification which inhibited microbial activity; when this was prevented by adequate buffering, the rate and extent of oil biodegradation was similar in flasks amended with NH_4Cl and KNO_3.

Both groups using organic meals as fertilizers note the occasional occurrence of anoxic zones beneath the applied fertilizer under calm conditions (Lee et al. 1995b; Ramstad et al. 1995; Sveum et al., 1995). This is undesirable; anaerobic conditions are not conducive to rapid oil degradation (see Prince 1993), and such conditions stimulate sulfate-reducing bacteria to generate potentially toxic levels of sulfide that may inhibit aerobic bacteria. Anaerobic zones have not been reported with inorganic fertilizers (Ishihara et al. 1995; Lee et al. 1995; Ramstad et al. 1995; Sveum et al. 1995).

Ishihara et al. (1995) discuss an elegant experiment that dissects the stimulatory effect of nitrate and phosphate fertilizers, alone and in combination, to provide a quantitative explanation of why biodegradation in the field is always so much slower than it is in well-nutriated laboratory flasks; maximal degradation requires several mM nitrate and mM phosphate, which cannot be achieved in the field without potentially causing adverse environmental effects. Fortunately, significant stimulation of oil degradation is seen at much lower levels of nutrients that are unlikely to cause any environmental harm. Their data also show, as one might have expected, that nutrient addition has the most stimulatory effect where natural levels of nutrients are very low.

Lee et al. (1995b) report the latest in an extended series of field trials of bioremediation as a treatment for spills of a light condensate oil from the Nova Scotia production areas (Lee & Levy 1987, 1989, 1991; Lee et al. 1993, 1995a). They have focused on fertilizer application as the remediation strategy, and here they compare organic fish-bone meal with inorganic nutrients. While the former has the greatest stimulatory effect on bacterial productivity, simple inorganic nutrients were most effective at stimulating oil degradation. Indeed their results are very much in accord with their earlier findings with Inipol EAP22 (Lee & Levy 1989); repeated application of inorganic fertilizer stimulated degradation more than a single application, while the reverse was true for the organic fertilizer, presumably because the indigenous microbes "preferred" the partially oxidized carbon in the Inipol or fish bone meal to the fully reduced carbon in the oil (Rivet et al. 1993). It should be noted, however, that the fertilizers were added 12 days after oil was added to the beach enclosures in these experiments. When Inipol was added to beach sediments where oil had been present for 6 months, it stimulated the simultaneous mineralization of hexadecane, phenanthrene, and oleic acid (Prince et al. 1993). It may thus be important to add organic fertilizers such as Inipol or fish bone meal only after the indigenous bacteria have had time to respond to the spilled oil so that there is a substantial population of hydrocarbon degrading bacteria available to compete with other heterotrophs for the nutrients (see also Basseres et al. 1993).

An important result presented by Lee et al. (1995b) is that the natural decline in toxicity of a spilled oil with time, which was monitored with the Microtox® solid-phase test, which seems by far the most sensitive test of ecotoxicity (Hund & Traunspurger 1994), is relatively unaffected by the application of inorganic fertilizer. This is important because some critics have expressed concern that enhanced microbial degradation of oil might liberate partially oxidized, and perhaps potentially toxic, metabolites; Lee et al. (1956b) find no evidence for this with inorganic fertilizer. They did, however, see a slowing of the decrease in toxicity attributable to the oil when organic fertilizers were applied repeatedly, perhaps because of ammonia production from the meal. Their results in the marine environment may be compared to those of Shen and Bartha (1994) on a soil that had been contaminated with fuel oil some 20 years earlier. They found a transient increase in Microtox® toxicity when they initiated bioremediation by adding fertilizer, but even here the toxicity declined to background levels by the second season, when there would still have been significant toxicity in the absence of remediative action. These results in marine and terrestrial systems confirm the expectation that effective bioremediation reduces the overall environmental impact of an oil spill by reducing exposure to bioavailable hydrocarbons.

In the other field trial, Venosa et al. (1995) report the results of a test spill on a sandy beach in the Delaware Bay. Here the background levels of nutrients were sufficiently high (60 µM nitrate) that biodegradation was very rapid even without additional nutrients; the biodegradative half-life of the alkanes was 4 weeks in the absence of added fertilizer, and added nutrients reduced this to 2 weeks.

In summary, it is clear that progress is being made in developing tools for improving bioremediation strategies for crude oil spills. The various mesocosm systems being developed around the world, in conjunction with recently introduced techniques such as the "Sheen Screen" for estimating most probable numbers (MPNs) of oil-degrading bacteria (Brown & Braddock 1990) and the use of conserved internal markers within the oil for estimating biodegradation (Prince et al. 1994b; Bragg et al. 1994), should allow significant progress in the next few years.

REFERENCES

Basseres, A., P. Eyraud, A. Ladousse, and B. Tramier. 1993. "Enhancements of spilled oil biodegradation by nutrients of natural origin." *Proceedings of the 1993 International Oil Spill Conference*, American Petroleum Institute, Washington DC, pp. 495-502.

Bragg, J. R., R. C. Prince, E. J. Harner, and R. M. Atlas. 1994. "Effectiveness of bioremediation for the *Exxon Valdez* oil spill." *Nature 368*: 413-418.

Brown, E. J., and J. F. Braddock. 1990. "Sheen screen, a miniaturized most-probable-number method for enumeration of oil-degrading microorganisms." *Appl. Environ. Microbiol. 56*: 3895-3896.

Cerniglia, C. E. 1992. "Biodegradation of polycyclic aromatic hydrocarbons." *Biodegradation 3*: 351-368.

Croft, B., R.P.J. Swannell, and K. Lee. 1995. "Effect of bioremediation agents on oil biodegradation in medium-fine sand." In R. E. Hinchee, J. A. Kittel, and H. J. Reisinger (Eds.), *Applied Bioremediation of Petroleum Hydrocarbons*, pp. 423-434. Battelle Press, Columbus, OH.

Domsch, K. H., W. Gams, and T. H. Anderson. 1980. *Compendium of Soil Fungi.* Academic Press, New York, NY.

Huesemann, M. H. 1995. "Predictive model for estimating the extent of petroleum hydrocarbon biodegradation in contaminated soils." *Environ. Sci. Technol. 29*: 7-18.

Hund, K., and W. Traunspurger. 1994. "ECOTOX — evaluation strategy for soil bioremediation exemplified for a PAH-contaminated site." *Chemosphere 29*: 371-390.

Ishihara, M., K. Sugiura, M. Asaumi, M. Goto, E. Sasaki, and S. Harayama. 1995. "Oil degradation in microcosms and mesocosms." In R. E. Hinchee, C. M. Vogel, and F. J. Brockman (Eds.), *Microbial Processes for Bioremediation*, pp. 101-116. Battelle Press, Columbus, OH.

Kirk, P. W., and A. S. Gordon. 1988. "Hydrocarbon degradation by filamentous marine higher fungi." *Mycologia 80*: 776-782.

Ladousse, A., and B. Tramier. 1991. "Results of 12 years of research in spilled oil bioremediation: Inipol EAP22." *Proceedings of the 1991 International Oil Spill Conference*, American Petroleum Institute, Washington DC, pp. 577-582.

Lee, K., and E. M. Levy. 1987. "Enhanced biodegradation of a light crude oil in sandy beaches." *Proceedings of the 1987 International Oil Spill Conference*, American Petroleum Institute, Washington DC, pp. 411-416.

Lee, K., and E. M. Levy. 1989. "Enhancement of the natural biodegradation of condensate and crude oil on beaches of Atlantic Canada." *Proceedings of the 1989 International Oil Spill Conference*, American Petroleum Institute, Washington DC, pp. 479-486.

Lee, K., and E. M. Levy. 1991. "Bioremediation: Waxy crude oils stranded on low-energy shorelines." *Proceedings of the 1991 International Oil Spill Conference*, American Petroleum Institute, Washington DC, pp. 541-548.

Lee, K., G. H. Tremblay, and E. M. Levy. 1993. "Bioremediation: Application of slow-release fertilizers on low-energy shorelines." *Proceedings of the 1993 International Oil Spill Conference*, American Petroleum Institute, Washington DC, pp. 449-454.

Lee, K., G. H. Tremblay, and S. E. Cobanli. 1995a. "Bioremediation of oiled beach sediments: Assessment of inorganic and organic fertilizers." *Proceedings of the 1995 International Oil Spill Conference*, American Petroleum Institute, Washington DC, pp. 107-113.

Lee, K., R. Siron, and G. H. Tremblay. 1995b. "Effectiveness of bioremediation in reducing toxicity in oiled intertidal sediments." In R. E. Hinchee, C. M. Vogel, and F. J. Brockman (Eds.), *Microbial Processes for Bioremediation*, pp. 117-127. Battelle Press, Columbus, OH.

Marty, P., and Y. Martin. 1993. "Use of oleophilic fertilizer and selected bacterial communities to enhance biodegradation of crude oil in seawater." *J. Mar. Biotechnol. 1*: 27-32.

McLachlan, A. 1982. "A model for the estimation of water filtration and nutrient regeneration by exposed sandy beaches." *Mar. Environ. Res. 6*: 37-48.

McLachlan, A., I. G. Eliot, and D. J. Clarke. 1985. "Water filtration through reflective microtidal beaches and shallow sublittoral sands and its implications for an inshore ecosystem in Western Australia." *Estuarine Coastal Shelf Sci. 21*: 91-104.

McMillen, S. J., J. M. Kerr, and N. R. Gray. 1993. "Microcosm studies of factors that influence bioremediation of crude oils in soil." *Proceedings of the SPE/EPA Exploration & Production Environmental Conference*, San Antonio, TX, pp. 389-401.

McMillen, S. J., G. N. Young, P. S. Davis, P. D. Cook, J. M. Kerr, A. G. Requejo, and N. R. Gray. 1995. "Bioremediation potential of crude oil spilled on soil." In R. E. Hinchee, C. M. Vogel, and F. J. Brockman (Eds.), *Microbial Processes for Bioremediation*, pp. 91-99. Battelle Press, Columbus, OH.

Prince, R. C., S. M. Hinton, J. R. Bragg, D. L. Elmendorf, J. R. Lute, M. J. Grossman, W. K. Robbins, C. S. Hsu, G. S. Douglas, R. E. Bare, C. E. Haith, J. D. Senius, V. Minak-Bernero, S. J. McMillen, J. C. Roffall, and R. R. Chianelli. 1993. "Laboratory studies of oil spill bioremediation: Toward understanding field behavior." *Preprints of the Division of Petroleum Chemistry, American Chemical Society, 38*, 240-244.

Prince, R. C., J. R. Clark, J. E. Lindstrom, E. L. Butler, E. J. Brown, G. Winter, M. J. Grossman, R. R. Parrish, R. E. Bare, J. F. Braddock, W. G. Steinhauer, G. S. Douglas, J. M. Kennedy, P. J. Barter, J. R. Bragg, E. J. Harner, and R. M. Atlas. 1994a. "Bioremediation of the *Exxon Valdez* oil spill: Monitoring safety and efficacy." In R. E. Hinchee, B. C. Alleman, R. E.

Hoeppel, and R. N. Miller (Eds.), *Hydrocarbon Remediation*, Lewis Publishers, Boca Raton, FL., pp. 107-124.

Prince, R. C., D. L. Elmendorf, J. R. Lute, C. S. Hsu, C. E. Haith, J. D. Senius, G. Dechert, G. S. Douglas, and E. L. Butler. 1994b. "17α(H),21β(H)-hopane as a conserved internal marker for estimating the biodegradation of crude oil." *Environ. Sci. Technol. 28*: 142-145.

Pritchard, P. H. 1992. "Use of inoculation in bioremediation." *Curr. Opinion Biotechnol. 3*: 232-243.

Pritchard, P. H., J. G. Mueller, J. C. Rogers, F. V. Kremer, and J. A. Glaser. 1992. "Oil spill bioremediation: Experiences, lessons and results from the *Exxon Valdez* oil spill in Alaska." *Biodegradation 3*: 315-335.

Ramstad, S., and P. Sveum. 1995. "Bioremediation of oil on shorelines: Effects of different nitrogen sources." In R. E. Hinchee, J. A. Kittel, and H. J. Reisinger (Eds.), *Applied Bioremediation of Petroleum Hydrocarbons*, pp. 415-422. Battelle Press, Columbus, OH.

Ramstad, S., P. Sveum, C. Bech, and L. G. Faksness. 1995. "Modeling shoreline bioremediation: Continous flow and seawater exchange columns." In R. E. Hinchee, G. S. Douglas, and S. K. Ong (Eds.), *Monitoring and Verification of Bioremediation*, pp. 77-86. Battelle Press, Columbus, OH.

Rivet, L., G. Mille, A. Basseres, A. Ladousse, C. Gerin, M. Acquaviva, and J. C. Bertrand. 1993. "N-alkane biodegradation by a marine bacterium in the presence of an oleophilic nutriment." *Biotechnol. Letts. 15*: 637-640.

Sendstad, E., and P. Sveum. 1983. "Oil spill on northern shorelines an evaluation of some options dealing with this problem." *Proceedings of the 1983 International Oil Spill Conference*, American Petroleum Institute, Washington DC, pp. 255-260.

Shen, J., and R. Bartha. 1994. "On-site bioremediation of soil contaminated by No. 2 fuel oil." *Int. Biodeter. Biodeg. 33*: 61-72.

Sveum, P., and S. Ramstad. 1995. "Bioremediation of oil on shorelines with organic and inorganic nutrients." In R. E. Hinchee, J. A. Kittel, and H. J. Reisinger (Eds.), *Applied Bioremediation of Petroleum Hydrocarbons*, pp. 201-217. Battelle Press, Columbus, OH.

Sveum, P., S. Ramstad, L.-G. Faksness, C. Bech, and B. Johansen. 1995. "Physical modeling of shoreline bioremediation: Continuous flow mesoscale basins." In R. E. Hinchee, G. S. Douglas, and S. K. Ong (Eds.), *Monitoring and Verification of Bioremediation*, pp. 87-96. Battelle Press, Columbus, OH.

Venosa, A. D., M. T. Suidan, J. R. Haines, B. A. Wrenn, K. L. Strohmeier, B. L. Eberhart, M. Kadkhodayan, E. Holder, D. King, and B. Anderson. 1995. "Field bioremediation study: Spilled crude oil on Fowler Beach, Delaware." In R. E. Hinchee, J. Fredrickson, and B. C. Alleman (Eds.), *Bioaugmentation for Site Remediation*, pp. 49-56. Battelle Press, Columbus, OH.

Wrenn, B. A., J. R. Haines, A. D. Venosa, M. Kadkhodayan, and M. T. Suidan. 1994. "Effects of nitrogen source on crude oil biodegradation." *J. Ind. Microbiol. 13*: 279-286.

Bioremediation of Soil Contaminated with Hydrocarbons and Heavy Metals

Chris A. du Plessis, Clinton B. Phaal, and Eric Senior

ABSTRACT ━━━━━━━━━━━━━━━━━━━━━━━━━━━━━━━━━━━

This investigation showed that a soil contaminated with petroleum hydrocarbons and heavy metals had sufficient indigenous microbial activity for hydrocarbon biodegradation under nonlimiting conditions. Nutrient supplementation with nitrogen and phosphate, together with aeration, seemed to be the most important factors for enhancing biodegradation. Hydrocarbon biodegradation occurred to a much greater extent under aerobic than under anaerobic conditions. Biodegradation did, however, induce low pH conditions and thus caused high heavy-metal concentrations in the leachate. Anaerobic conditions inhibited hydrocarbon biodegradation with no subsequent drop in pH and low heavy-metal concentrations in the leachate. Thus, anaerobic conditions were shown to facilitate less metal mobility than low pH conditions. Air sparging did not cause a significant increase in biodegradation. Adsorption of heavy-fraction hydrocarbons ($>C_{20}$) to microorganisms and colloidal material in the leachate was suspected of facilitating mobility of these fractions and thus their subsequent detection in the leachate.
━━━━━━━━━━━━━━━━━━━━━━━━━━━━━━━━━━━

INTRODUCTION

The aim of this preliminary study was to examine the effects of microbial catabolism of hydrocarbons in heavy-metal-contaminated soil. The protocol adopted was first to determine whether the microbial population present in the soil had the capacity to effect catabolism of the hydrocarbons because this would be a key determinant of the bioremediation strategy. Because the study was aimed at practical on-site manipulations/supplementations to complement in situ bioremediation practices such as air sparging (Bonazountas & Kallidromitou 1993), the addition of alternative electron acceptors, soil bulking to increase porosity and aeration (Englert et al. 1993), and pH adjustments were tested. The presence of heavy metals with hydrocarbon was particularly problematic, because the conditions favoring hydrocarbon biodegradation could potentially induce heavy-metal mobility in the soil (Labauve et al. 1988). The soil (13% w/w clay) under investigation was contaminated with hydrocarbons (4.4%, w/w, U.S. EPA Method No. 418.1), 311.4 mg/kg (NH_4-extractable) manganese, and 136.7 mg/kg (NH_4-extractable) zinc. The hydrocarbons and metals originated from oil refinery processes. This particular soil had been used as a hydrocarbon disposal and landfarming site for 8 years.

EXPERIMENTAL PROCEDURES AND MATERIALS

Determination of a viable indigenous microbial population capable of hydrocarbon catabolism was made by examining a soil slurry and comparing incubated with nonincubated soil. Contaminated soil (10 g) and 100 mL nutrient medium containing 0.5 g KH_2PO_4, 1.5 g K_2HPO_4, 1 g NH_4NO_3, 0.2 g $MgSO_4 \cdot 7H_2O$, along with 1 mL trace element solution per liter (du Plessis et al. 1995a), was incubated for 30 days in 250-mL Erlenmeyer flasks (without shaking). The nutrient medium depth above the soil was 3 cm to allow sufficient oxygen diffusion (3 mg/L). The soil and supernatant fluid were viewed by scanning electron microscopy (SEM) (Hitachi S-570 SEM) to determine the presence of microorganisms. Nonincubated, contaminated soil was flushed with distilled water (10 mL water to 5 g soil) to separate the planktonic from the attached microbial population. The soil and supernatant fluid were viewed separately.

Two soil columns were set up for each treatment, one of which was supplemented with a 10% (v/v) inoculum with each addition of nutrients. The inoculum was derived from incubation (20 days, 30°C) of cultures of naphthalene, phenol, and petroleum catabolizers as well as Cu- and Cd-resistant bacteria batched with the contaminated soil. The soil columns were polyvinyl chloride pipes (diameter 4.5 cm, length 25 cm) with silicone rubber seals. Glass wool was used to prevent soil displacement from the columns. Soil and soil/ash mixtures (1:1 w/w ratio) were packed dry by shaking with a shaker, and the total pore volume for each column was calculated. The bulk density of the soil in the columns was calculated after accurate weighing and averaged 1.05 g/cm³. The ash-supplemented soil also had a bulk density close to this average. The industrial coarse ash was mainly (80%) in the 1- to 4-mm-diameter range. The particle density of the soil and coarse ash was determined by measuring water displacement after expelling all air. The pore volume was calculated from the bulk and particle density. All treatments were incubated at 30°C.

Treatments

Treatment 1, FC. Sufficient nutrients and inoculum were added weekly to the column weekly to allow free drainage. The nutrients and/or inoculum mixture were supplied at a very slow rate until free drainage occurred.

Treatment 2, FC/2. This treatment was similar to Treatment 1, but the nutrients and inoculum were added every 2 weeks.

Treatment 3, Sat(SO4). The columns were saturated with nutrients (and inoculum). The medium in this case was similar to that of Treatments 1 and 2, but all the nitrogen in the nutrient medium was in the form of $(NH_4)_2SO_4$. The columns were supplemented by vertical displacement from the base. The soil columns were allowed to drain freely once a week prior to resaturation.

Treatment 4, Sat(NO3). Treatment 4 was similar to Treatment 3, but in this case all the nitrogen was in the form of KNO_3.

Treatment 5, Ash. Soil was mixed with coarse ash (Table 1) in a 1:1 (w/w) ratio and treated the same as in Treatment 1.

Treatment 6, Ash Sp. Treatment 6 was similar to Treatment 5, but here the column was sparged from the bottom after free drainage had ceased. The sparging rate was approximately 50 pore volumes per day and the column air outlet was equipped with an "Orbo 32" activated carbon vapor trap.

TABLE 1. Size distribution and chemical analysis of the contaminated soil and coarse ash.

Size Distribution % (w/w)		
Size Fractions	**Ash**	**Soil**
>9.5 mm	33.3	–
4.0 – 9.5 mm	29.8	–
2.0 – 4.0 mm	15.0	–
0.02 – 2.0 mm	17.5	75.0
0.002 – 0.02 mm	4.2	12.0
< 0.002 mm	0.2	13.0
Chemical Analyses		
Parameter	**Ash**	**Soil**
P (Bray 1)	15.4 mg/kg	5 mg/kg
Zn	2.55 mg/kg	136.7 mg/kg
Mn	4.00 mg/kg	311.4 mg/kg
C	0.99% (w/w)	2.91% (w/w)
Total N	0.04% (w/w)	0.11% (w/w)
pH (H_2O)	9.21	7.15
CEC[a]	3.07 cmol(+)/kg	29.0 cmol(+)/kg
Total hydrocarbons	–	4.4% (w/w)

(a) CEC is cation exchange capacity.

Leachates

The leachates from all columns were collected and the volumes recorded. Gram stains and light microscope observations were made regularly to determine whether microorganisms were present in the leachates. A composite sample of the first 50 days of each treatment was used to determine the pH of the leachate. Samples were frozen on collection to minimize chemical change during storage until enough sample had been collected for the required analyses. A subsample of all treatments was analyzed for Mn and Zn by atomic absorption spectroscopy (Varian AA-275). A second heavy-metal analysis of the leachate at the end of the experimental period was made. At the termination of the 70-day experimental period the columns were destructively sampled. The soils were then homogenized, and the hydrocarbons were extracted and analyzed by gas chromatography (du Plessis et al. 1995b). Biodegradation assessment was made with the use of the Biodegradation Index, which considers the relative concentrations of hydrocarbons larger and smaller than a C_{20} alkane in chromatograms of the contaminated soil before and after treatments (du Plessis et al. 1995b). Heavy-metal concentrations in the leachate were determined by atomic absorption spectroscopy.

RESULTS AND DISCUSSION

SEM of the contaminated soil after 30 days incubation with nutrients clearly showed the presence of microorganisms. The nonincubated soil had considerably fewer detectable microorganisms, although the supernatant fluid did contain some bacteria. This indicated that, although the microbial population was not readily detected in the nonincubated soil, probably due to the relatively low numbers, the soil did contain a potential population of hydrocarbon degraders that rapidly increased in numbers (approximately 10 times) in an oxygen- and nutrient-rich environment. Light microscope examination of the leachate from the columns showed that bacteria were indeed present in all the samples. The presence of bacteria in the leachate indicated microbial presence in the soil columns and the possible migration of these organisms through the soil.

From Figure 1 it can be seen that following FC treatment, the leachate had a relatively low pH in comparison with most of the other treatments; this could be attributed partly to organic acid production during hydrocarbon catabolism (Labauve et al. 1988). Unfortunately, because of the low volume of leachate generated in the *FC/2* and *Ash Sp* treatments, the pH values could not be determined. The *Ash* treatment caused considerably higher pH values, but it is believed that these were due to the presence of ash (pH_{water} 9.21) rather than a lack of catabolic activity. The relatively low pH generated in the FC treatment was thought to have been a major contributing factor affecting high metal concentrations (particularly Mn) in the leachate (Figure 1). Figure 1 illustrates the relatively high Mn concentrations caused by the FC treatment. The highly

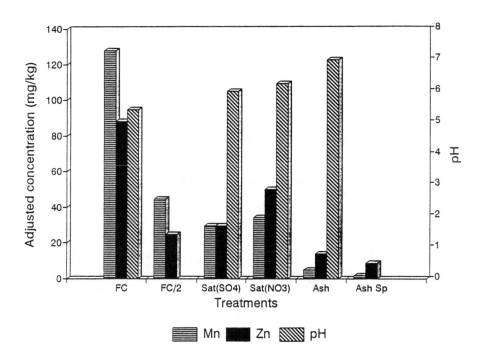

FIGURE 1. Composite (50 days) pH values and manganese and zinc concentrations of column leachates (adjusted for pore volume flushes). Only average values for the duplicate treatments are given because of the similarity in results. The Mn concentrations were adjusted for the pore volumes flushed through the columns.

aerobic conditions in the *Ash* and *Ash Sp* treatments were probably responsible for low Mn concentrations, because the metal would be mostly in the oxidized nonmobile state. The low Mn concentrations for the anaerobic treatments, *Sat (SO4)* and *Sat(NO3)*, were ascribed to the high pH and anaerobic complexation of Mn with sulfide. This was substantiated by the observation of gold-colored iron pyrite, particularly in the *Sat(SO4)* treatment column. Figure 1 also shows the Zn concentrations with the *FC* treatment, which were also pH-related. The anomalously high Zn concentration in the *Sat(NO3)* treatment could not be satisfactorily explained. The trend of relatively high Mn and Zn concentrations in leachates for, particularly, the *FC* and *FC/2* treatments continued throughout the 70-day experimental period.

Hydrocarbon degradation as assessed by the biodegradation index is shown in Figure 2, where it is clear that the addition of inoculum did not have a beneficial effect on biodegradation (a low index number, <1, is indicative of biodegradation). This indicates that the indigenous microbial population is capable of hydrocarbon catabolism once growth limitations have been alleviated, and

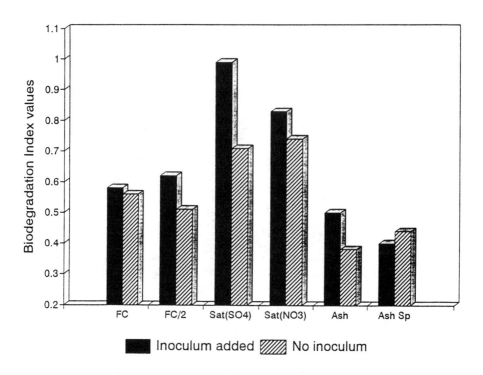

FIGURE 2. Biodegradation index values for the various treatments.

confirms previous observations of the indigenous population. The slightly lower
biodegradation recorded with inoculum-supplemented soil could be ascribed
to the fact that these organisms were taken from liquid culture. Such bacteria
taken from a single-phase (liquid) system possibly do not produce the biosurfactants needed to solubilize hydrocarbon from soil surfaces (two-phase system)
(Oberbremer & Muller-Hurtig 1989; Jain et al. 1992). Water content at field water
capacity (in this case it would be more accurate to refer to container capacity)
and below did not seem to affect biodegradation in this investigation. Saturated
conditions, however, led to anaerobiosis and inhibited hydrocarbon catabolism,
as can be seen from the two anaerobic treatments (*Sat[SO4]* and *Sat[NO3]*). Dry
soil, much below field water capacity, although probably more aerated, could
inhibit microbial catabolism due to too low a water activity. Although biodegradation in the anaerobic treatments was much less than in the aerobic columns,
microbial activity was evidenced by the detection of H_2S and FeS as described
earlier. The increased biodegradation in the soil supplemented with ash *(Ash)*
was ascribed to the macroporosity of the soil mixture, although the higher porosity was not reflected in a higher bulk density (data not shown), possibly due
to the greater particle density of the coarse ash. The total hydrocarbon content
for this treatment (without inoculum) was reduced from 4.4 (w/w) to 1.7 (w/w).
Although hydrocarbons of relatively small carbon sizes and concentrations were

detected in the vapor traps (chromatograms not shown) they did not seem to have much effect on the Biodegradation Index. Contaminated soils with a high proportion of hydrocarbons in the < 10 carbon range could, however, be significantly affected by air sparging.

Analysis of the column leachate chromatograms revealed the presence of hydrocarbons, although not only from the lower carbon range (more water soluble) but also from the higher carbon range (> C_{20}). The presence of > C_{20} hydrocarbons appeared to be unusual because of the low water solubility of these compounds. Their presence in the leachate was ascribed to adsorption to microorganisms and mineral colloidal material in the leachate as detected by SEM. Hydrocarbons adsorbed to microorganisms or colloidal mineral material do not pose as great a risk to groundwater contamination (Gounaris et al. 1993) as do nonattached organic chemicals, because of the filtration influence of soils for these colloids due to decreasing average pore sizes with increased depth (Harvey & Garabedian 1991).

REFERENCES

Bonazountas, M., and D. Kallidromitou. 1993. "Mathematical Hydrocarbon Fate Modelling in Soil Systems." In: E. J. Calabrese and P. T. Kostecki (Eds.), *Principles and Practices for Petroleum Contaminated Soils*, pp. 131-322. Lewis, Boca Raton, FL.

du Plessis, C. A., C. Phaal, and E. Senior. 1995a. "Bioremediation Monitoring for Hydrocarbon and Heavy Metal Contaminated Soil: A Case Study." Submitted for publication.

du Plessis, C. A., C. Phaal, and E. Senior. 1995b. "Monitoring Technique for Hydrocarbon Biodegradation in Soil." Submitted for publication.

Englert, C. J., E. J. Denzie, and J. Dragun. 1993. "Bioremediation of Petroleum Products in Soil." In: E. J. Calabrese and P. T. Kostecki (Eds.), *Principles and Practices for Petroleum Contaminated Soils*, pp. 111-129. Lewis, Boca Raton, FL.

Gounaris, V., P. R. Anderson, and T. M. Holsen. 1993. "Characteristics and Environmental Significance of Colloids in Landfill." *Environmental Science and Technology* 27: 1381-1387.

Harvey, R. W., and S. P. Garabedian. 1991. "Use of Colloid Filtration in Modelling Movement of Bacteria through a Contaminated Sandy Aquifer." *Environmental Science and Technology* 25: 178-185.

Jain, D. K., H. Lee, and J. T. Trevors. 1992. "Effect of Addition of *Pseudomonas aeruginosa* UG2 Inocula or Biosurfactants on Biodegradation of Selected Hydrocarbons in Soil." *Journal of Industrial Microbiology* 10: 87-93.

Labauve, J. M., J. Kotubyam, and R. P. Gambrell. 1988. "The Effect of Soil Properties and a Synthetic Municipal Landfill Leachate on the Retention of Cd, Pb, and Zn in Soil and Sediment Materials." *Journal of Water Pollution Control* 60: 379-385.

Oberbremer, A., and R. Muller-Hurtig, R. 1989. "Aerobic Stepwise Hydrocarbon Degradation and Formation of Biosurfactants by an Original Soil Population in a Stirred Reactor." *Applied Microbiology and Biotechnology* 31: 582-586.

Steam Injection and Enhanced Bioremediation of Heavy Fuel Oil Contamination

Jay Dablow, Ronald Hicks, and David Cacciatore

ABSTRACT

Steam injection has been shown to be successful in remediating sites impacted by heavy fuel oils. Field demonstrations at both pilot and full scale have removed No. 2 diesel fuel and Navy Special Fuel Oil (No. 5 fuel oil) from impacted soils. Removal mechanisms include enhanced volatilization of vapor- and adsorbed-phase contaminants and enhanced mobility due to decreased viscosity and associated residual saturation of separate- and adsorbed-phase contaminants. Laboratory studies have shown that indigenous biologic populations are significantly reduced, but are not eliminated by steam injection operations. Populations were readily reestablished by augmentation with nutrients. This suggests that biodegradation enhanced by warm, moist, oxygenated environments can be expected to further reduce concentrations of contaminants following cessation of steam injection operations.

INTRODUCTION

Soil vapor extraction (SVE) has been widely used to remove volatile organic compounds (VOCs) from the vadose zone and in conjunction with air sparging to remove VOCs in the saturated zone. However, SVE applicability is limited to contaminants with vapor pressures of greater than 1.0 mm Hg at ambient conditions. A large class of contaminants, heavy fuel oils (No. 2 diesel fuel to No. 6 fuel oil), which are encountered at many sites, have vapor pressures considerably lower than these limits at ambient temperatures. Additionally, these materials are highly viscous and have high residual saturation in the vadose zone which makes removing the adsorbed phase and pumping the separate phase difficult by conventional techniques.

The use of steam injection to heat the subsurface and manipulate the volatility, viscosity, and residual saturation of heavy fuel oils has been shown to effectively remediate these materials. In addition, some of the factors that affect biodegradation rates can be optimized immediately following cessation of steam injection, allowing enhanced bioremediation to act as an effective polishing technology for heavy fuel oils.

THE EFFECT OF TEMPERATURE ON HEAVY FUEL OILS

The process of injecting heat into the subsurface changes several key physical characteristics of heavy fuel oils, including vapor pressure, viscosity, and residual saturation. In addition and within limits, the biodegradation rates of indigenous bacterial colonies are greatly increased as the temperature of the soil increases.

By manipulating these characteristics, substantial improvements to heavy fuel oil remediation efficiency can lead to shorter cleanup duration and reduced remediation costs. Temperature increases in the soil are affected by the heat capacity of the various lithologic units in the subsurface, the heat content of the heat transfer fluid (air or steam), and the volume of the soil to be heated. The total heat energy required during the remediation process is a function of the heat energy necessary to initially heat the contaminated soil volume to the target temperature plus the heat energy necessary to sustain that soil temperature.

As the soil temperature rises, the vapor pressure of the vapor- and adsorbed-phase heavy fuel oils increases, resulting in volatilization of the volatile and semivolatile compounds of the oils. Vapor pressure increases of several orders of magnitude are possible by raising the temperature from ambient to steam temperature (100°C).

Viscosity, the tendency of a fluid to resist a shearing force, is the key factor affecting the mobility of heavy fuel oils in the subsurface. As seen in Table 1,

TABLE 1. Kinematic viscosity of selected petroleum products at 10°C and 100°C.[a]

Product	Kinematic Viscosity @ 10°C (centistokes)	Kinematic Viscosity @ 100°C(centistokes)
Gasoline	0.61 - 0.85	≤0.40
JP-4	1.1 - 1.8	0.47 - 0.64
No. 1 Fuel Oil	2.2 - 4.2	0.7 - 1.0
No. 2 Fuel Oil	3.0 - 8.0	0.85 - 1.3
No. 4 Fuel Oil	30 - 100	2.5 - 4.8
No. 5 Light Fuel Oil	130 - 400	5.5 - 8.0
No. 5 Heavy Fuel Oil	500 - 1,200	9.0 - 13
No. 6 Fuel Oil	1,500 - 30,000	15 - 50

(a) Perry and Chilton (1973), pp. 9-11.

kinematic viscosity of heavy fuel oils varies over several orders of magnitude at 10°C, with No. 5 and No. 6 fuel oils having viscosity as high as 30,000 centistokes. However, at 100°C, the viscosity of nearly all the referenced oils is reduced to levels at or below those of No. 2 diesel fuel.

A viscosity-related characteristic of heavy fuel oils, which greatly affects the adsorbed-phase oils is the residual saturation concentration. Heavy oils such as No. 6 fuel oil have very high residual saturation concentrations, as shown in Table 2. However, in conjunction with the decrease in viscosity of oils, the residual saturation concentrations of the adsorbed-phase oils decrease significantly. A comparison of kinematic viscosity and residual saturation at varying temperatures is shown in Figure 1. The combination of viscosity and residual saturation reductions results in substantial volumes of oil being desorbed from the soil and transferred to the separate phase in the soil pores, where it can be readily removed by standard pumping systems.

In addition to physical property changes, the factors affecting biologic activity and biodegradation rates are impacted by increases in soil temperature. The biodegradation rate has been observed to double for every 10°C rise in the soil temperature (Smith and Hinchee 1993). Also, when steam injection is the means of soil heating, moisture content and oxygen availability are significantly increased, enhancing the bioremediation process.

ENHANCED VOLATILIZATION OF DIESEL FUEL

Due to the latent heat of condensation, steam injection can be an efficient means of heating large soil masses. At the initiation of the steam injection process, steam exiting from an injection well contacts the soil and immediately condenses. During the condensation process, heat energy is transferred to the soil by convection and conduction. A cylindrical zone of heated soil with a condensation front at the outer perimeter expands radially outward from the injection well.

TABLE 2. Residual saturation for petroleum products in soil (mg/kg).

Soil Type	Gasoline[a]	No. 2 Fuel Oil[b]	Lube Oil[b]	No. 6 Fuel Oil[c]
Coarse gravel	—	800	1,600	—
Gravel to coarse sand	—	1,600	3,200	—
Coarse to medium sand	—	2,800	5,600	—
Medium to fine sand	2,000	4,800	9,600	60,000
Fine sand to silt	—	8,000	16,000	—

(a) Brown (1989).
(b) *Hazardous Waste Consultant*, March/April, 1992, pp. 1/19-20.
(c) Fogel et al. (1990).

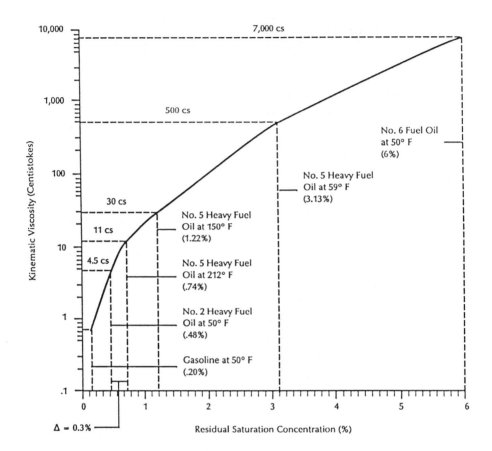

FIGURE 1. Residual saturation concentration versus kinematic viscosity of selected heavy fuel oils and gasoline.

Steam injection was selected to remediate a waste transfer station site in Huntington Beach, California, underlain by interbedded fine to medium sand, silt, and minor clay, where diesel fuel from a ruptured product delivery pipeline impacted soils and perched water to a depth of 13 m. Between 190,000 and 400,000 L of diesel fuel leaked over a 2-year period and impacted a sand lens at a depth of 12 to 13 m. The areal extent of impacted soils comprises approximately 0.9 ha and underlies the majority of the operational area of the site.

Steam injection pressure at the wellheads varied from 3,500 to 14,000 kg/m² with steam temperatures of approximately 120°C. Steam flowrates of 7,200 kg/h were required during the initial soil heating phase. Once the soil temperature was raised to 100°C, the flowrate required to maintain the soil temperature was approximately 3,600 kg/h.

The progress of the remediation was monitored primarily by thermocouples installed at various depths around the perimeter and within the plume of contaminated soils. Temperature measurements were compiled routinely throughout the duration of the remediation. Large temperature gradients were observed at the base of the steam injection zone and around the perimeter of the injection zone. Temperatures in the silty clay aquiclude underlying the steam injection zone were approximately 50°C lower than in the steam injection zone. Thermocouples installed 3 to 5 m outside the perimeter steam injection wells measured a temperature increase of only 3 to 6 degrees over the ambient soil temperatures.

Steam injection was terminated after 22 months. Approximately 113,000 L of diesel fuel were removed during the life of the project. The fact that 98% of the diesel fuel was recovered as vapor indicates that volatilization of the diesel fuel was the dominant mass transfer mechanism.

MOBILIZATION OF HEAVY FUEL OIL

Because the kinematic viscosity and the residual saturation concentration can be reduced significantly by heating of the soil, the mobility of heavy fuel oils can be increased to the point where pumping by standard pumping systems becomes a viable remediation option.

At a site in Yorktown, Virginia, a pilot test was conducted to evaluate three technologies to remove Navy Special Fuel Oil (NSFO), an oil similar to No. 5 heavy fuel oil, which leaked from large-capacity underground storage tanks. These technologies include standard pumping at ambient temperatures, hot water flooding, and steam injection in three separate test areas with individual recovery wells. A submersible pump was used in each well to recover any mobilized NSFO.

As can be seen in Figure 2, oil recovery in the vicinity of the steam injection system was two orders of magnitude greater than the hot water flood or ambient temperature pumping systems. Although hot water flooding was expected to be more efficient, the injection of hot water caused an oil/water density inversion that blocked oil from the recovery well.

ENHANCED BIOREMEDIATION
LABORATORY STUDIES

A series of respirometry and microbiologic enumeration tests were conducted to determine the effect of the high temperatures associated with steam injection on indigenous bacteria colonies. The results of the microbiological analyses indicated that populations of 10^6 to 10^7 colony-forming units per gram (cfu/g) were found in the presteam treatment samples; however, the poststeam and post-thermal treatment samples showed populations < 100 cfu/g. Although the population level was significantly reduced during the steam treatment, it was not eliminated. Therefore, a microbial enhancement by nutrient augmentation study was conducted to see if a longer equilibration time of the soil in a favorable environment could elevate the population density to pretreatment levels.

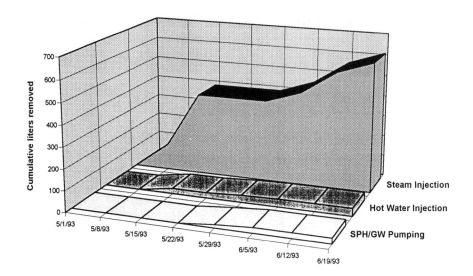

FIGURE 2. The effect of steam injection and hot water injection on separate-phase hydrocarbon (SPH) removal by SPH/groundwater (GW) pumping.

Microbial enhancement testing was performed on pretreatment and posttreatment samples. Nutrient-amended systems were prepared along with systems without nutrients as a control for the effect of the nutrient augmentation.

After 2 hours of incubation in the nutrient solution, the pretreatment samples showed bacteria populations of 10^6 cfu/g, consistent with the bacterial enumerations of the soil directly. The poststeam treatment samples showed bacteria populations of 10^5 to 10^7 cfu/g, compared to low populations found in the plating of the soil directly. The control system prepared from the poststeam treatment soil also showed bacteria populations of 10^5 cfu/g after slurrying in water alone. The postthermal treatment samples did not show any bacteria populations after the 2-hour incubation period.

After 1 week of incubation, all of the nutrient-amended systems and the control system prepared from the poststeam treatment soil showed large bacteria populations. However the control system prepared from the postthermal treatment soil still showed no bacteria populations. Although the bacteria are present, nutrients appear to be required to stimulate the bacteria to growth in the postthermal treatment sample.

These results show that the bacteria are still present in the poststeam and postthermal treatment samples. Given time, the bacteria present in the posttreatment soils will revitalize. The subsurface environment may need to be amended with nutrients, water, and oxygen to aid the bacteria back to growth. Although these results do not confirm that the surviving microbial populations can degrade the contaminant, they do suggest that steam injection does not, in itself, prevent the subsequent use of bioremediation. Further studies are being planned to determine if surviving microbial populations can degrade the remaining heavy oils.

DISCUSSION

The use of steam injection to manipulate physical parameters of heavy fuel oils and enhance remediation by vapor extraction and separate phase pumping has been documented in pilot tests and full-scale applications. The vapor pressure, viscosity, and residual saturation concentration of heavy fuel oils all can be changed by temperature effects associated with steam injection, so that removal efficiencies are improved by orders of magnitude. Reducing the cleanup duration leads to substantial reductions in the overall cost of remediation.

An added benefit of steam injection is the potential for enhancing biodegradation rates after cessation of steam injection. Temperature, moisture content, and oxygen availability can be optimized to fit the indigenous bacteria populations. A major concern, colony mortality due to steam injection, has been shown to be unfounded in laboratory tests. Bacteria that become dormant during steam injection can be reactivated by nutrient augmentation, allowing bioremediation to further reduce heavy fuel oil concentrations toward cleanup goals.

REFERENCES

Brown, R. A. 1989. "Oxygen Sources for Biotechnological Applications." Presented at the Biotechnology Work Group sponsored by the U.S. Navy Civil Engineering Laboratory and the U.S. Army Construction Engineering Laboratory, Monterey, CA.

Fogel, S., M. C. Leahy, R. Butts, and M. Jones. 1990. "Bioremediation of a No. 6 Fuel Oil Spill: Comparison of Laboratory Treatability Data with Field Remediation Data." Presented at 5th Petroleum-Contaminated Soil Conference, Amherst, MA.

Perry, R. H., and C. H. Chilton. 1973. *Chemical Engineers' Handbook*, 5th ed. McGraw-Hill, New York, NY.

Smith, L. A., and R. E. Hinchee. 1993. *In Situ Thermal Technologies for Site Remediation.* Lewis Publishers, Boca Raton, FL.

Nitrate-Based Bioremediation of JP-4 Jet Fuel: Pilot-Scale Demonstration

Stephen R. Hutchins, Dennis E. Miller, Frank P. Beck, Alison Thomas, Stephen E. Williams, and Guy D. Willis

ABSTRACT ──────────────────────────────

Data are presented for the first 4.5 months of operation of a pilot-scale treatment demonstration on nitrate-based bioremediation at Eglin Air Force Base, Florida. Two 30-m × 30-m treatment cells were delineated for treatment, one of which receives recharge amended to yield 10 to 20 mg/L NO_3-N and the other which receives no amendments. Application is by sprinklers at 11 gpm/cell. Movement of tracers and nitrate were monitored routinely through the use of both fully-penetrating wells and cluster wells. In the centers of both treatment cells, the tracers have penetrated to beneath the lower contaminated regions located 3 m beneath ground surface, 2.1 to 2.4 m below the water table. In the nitrate treatment cell, nitrate has also penetrated to this depth, but concentrations have decreased rapidly relative to the tracer at all depths. Lysimeter data show that about half of the applied nitrate is contacting the contaminated zone. Although total contaminant concentrations have not declined with nitrate addition to date, water quality analyses show some preferential degradation of labile compounds in the nitrate cell. Radiolabel microcosm studies confirm mineralization of toluene and *m*-xylene under denitrifying conditions. Part of the system has been modified to minimize vegetative uptake of nitrate.

INTRODUCTION

Although aerobic bioremediation has been successfully applied to fuel-contaminated aquifers (Lee & Raymond 1991; Bell & Hoffman 1991), difficulties relating to aquifer plugging and oxygen mass transport are often encountered (Barker et al. 1987; Aggarwal et al. 1991). Nitrate can also serve as an electron acceptor and results in anaerobic biodegradation of organic compounds via dissimilatory nitrate reduction and denitrification. Because nitrate is less expensive and more soluble than oxygen, it may be more economical to remediate fuel-contaminated aquifers using nitrate rather than oxygen. Previous field work at the U.S. Coast Guard Facility in Traverse City, Michigan, had shown that alkylbenzenes in an aquifer contaminated with JP-4 jet fuel could be degraded by the indigenous microorganisms under denitrifying conditions (Hutchins et al. 1991). However, the lack of a suitable control site precluded a direct assessment of the benefits of nitrate addition relative to infiltration recharge without nitrate amendments. Without such a comparison, the economics of nitrate-based bioremediation versus pump-and-treat methods could not be determined. The following research was therefore undertaken to provide a direct comparison through operation of a pilot project at a JP-4 jet fuel-contaminated sand-and-gravel aquifer at Eglin AFB, Florida. This report briefly describes the initial operation of the pilot system and highlights results of an interim performance evaluation based on the first 4.5 months of operation.

SITE DESCRIPTION

Extensive site characterizations by other groups have been published elsewhere and are available (EA Engineering 1987). In brief, a leak in an underground jet fuel pipeline was detected by Air Force personnel in April 1984. Operation of a pilot demonstration project on enhanced in situ biodegradation using hydrogen peroxide resulted in problems with both hydrogen peroxide stability and loss of infiltration capacity, reducing delivery of oxygen to the subsurface (Hinchee et al. 1989). The site was therefore considered for nitrate-based bioremediation. Researchers from the Robert S. Kerr Environmental Research Lab (RSKERL) and Rice University conducted a comprehensive site investigation to characterize site hydrogeology, determine the horizontal and vertical extent of contamination in aquifer core samples, provide vertical resolution of water quality, and conduct treatability studies (Thomas et al. 1994) to provide information for design and operation of the nitrate-based pilot demonstration system.

PILOT PROJECT DESIGN AND OPERATION

Figure 1 shows the location of the pilot treatment cells relative to the residual benzene, toluene, ethylbenzene, xylene, and trimethylbenzene (BTEXTMB) mass, based on core analyses. Two 30-m × 30-m treatment cells were delineated for treatment, one of which receives groundwater recharge amended to yield 10 mg/L NO_3-N and the other which receives no amendments. Nutrients are not added, because microcosm tests indicated that they were not required for this near-surface soil (data not shown). Application is by sprinkler at 11 gpm/cell continuously. Each cell contains monitoring wells, both in the center and at one edge (Figure 1). Monitoring wells consist of both conventional 5-cm ID PVC wells screened 0.3 to 3.4 m below ground surface, as well as cluster wells constructed

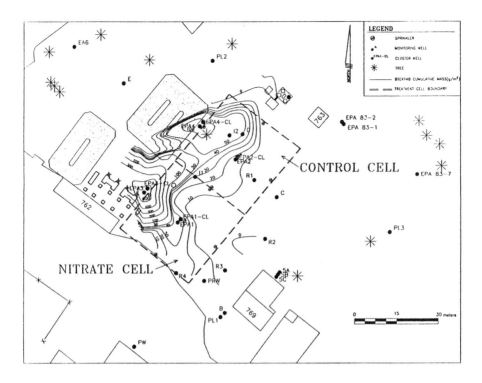

FIGURE 1. Site map of pilot demonstration project on nitrate-based bio-remediation of fuel-contaminated aquifer, Eglin AFB, FL.

of 6-mm OD polyethylene tubing with 5-cm stainless steel screens. Cluster wells were located at 1.2 m, 1.5 m, 2.0 m, 2.6 m, and 3.4 m below ground surface. Separate tracers were added to the sprinkler recharge waters for each of the two treatment cells during the first 2-week interval, and movement of tracers and nitrate were monitored routinely through the use of both fully penetrating wells and cluster wells with 5-cm screens. Operation began April 1994.

INTERIM PERFORMANCE EVALUATION

An interim performance evaluation was conducted in August 1994. Core samples had been initially taken to delineate the lateral and vertical extent of contamination at the site, and core samples were again obtained using a Giddings probe modified for acquisition and extrusion of saturated aquifer material. A geoprobe was used to drive a screened rod to three selected depths at several locations to obtain water samples for correlating water quality information with core analyses. Water samples were collected at three depths (1.1 to 1.5, 2.0 to 2.4, and 2.9 to 3.3 m below ground surface) from four locations within each cell (Figure 2). Samples were analyzed on site for pH, dissolved oxygen, and soluble

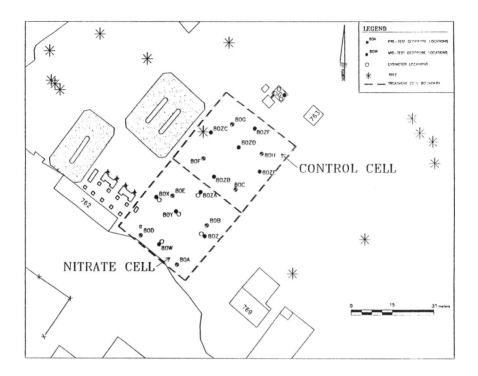

FIGURE 2. Geoprobe, lysimeter, and core locations in treatment cells.

Fe, and shipped back to RSKERL for analysis of inorganics (NO_3-N, NO_2-N, SO_4, NH_4-N, Br, Cl, PO_4), dissolved gases (N_2, CH_4, CO_2, and N_2O), TOC, and BTEXTMB. An attempt was made to quantify the amount of nitrate passing the root zone (0.0 to 0.2 m below ground surface) by installing suction lysimeters in the underlying vadose zone. The sprinkler system was shut down prior to installation of the lysimeters to avoid channelling of infiltrate down the casings. In addition, the holes were backfilled with bentonite. Five lysimeters were initially installed 0.4 to 0.5 m below ground surface (Figure 2). However, we were unable to obtain water samples from three locations and therefore these lysimeters were reinstalled 0.7 to 0.8 m below ground surface.

Microcosms were constructed using core samples aseptically collected 1.0 to 2.1 m below ground surface at Location 80ZA and groundwater from the three deepest cluster wells at Location EPA1-CL to evaluate biodegradation potential. Triplicate sets were spiked with nitrate and either radiolabeled benzene, toluene, *m*-xylene, or *o*-xylene; these were incubated anaerobically at 25°C and sampled as previously described (Hutchins 1993). It should be noted that this assay accounts for distribution of the radiolabel in the aqueous phase alone, and represents the extent of biodegradation of available soluble substrate. One set did not receive nitrate and served as a positive control.

RESULTS

During initial pilot operation, breakthrough of bromide in the center of the nitrate cell followed in sequence with depth, except for the lower two levels (Figure 3). In contrast, nitrate was removed after a transient breakthrough (Figure 4). Nitrate concentrations were generally less than 0.5 mg/L in the cluster wells during the next several months, and the influent nitrate level was therefore increased to 20 mg/L on July 15 1994. Based on the lysimeter data, breakthrough of nitrate varied significantly across the nitrate cell, being 50 to 60% in two locations and 4 to 6% in three others. In each location, nitrate concentrations decreased with time and ammonium concentrations (except for location 80W) increased with time (data not shown). This trend is consistent with the hypothesis that nitrate reduction to ammonium is occurring. Also, the three locations with the lowest nitrate concentrations had the highest NH_4-N concentrations. If the ammonium nitrogen arises from dissimilatory nitrate reduction, then the total nitrogen breakthrough more accurately depicts the percentage of nitrate not being taken up by the vegetation. In this case, nitrogen breakthrough increases to 50 to 70% in two locations and 15 to 20% in the other three. These data support the premise that a significant percentage of the applied nitrogen is being transported to the contaminated intervals.

Groundwater throughout the site is still contaminated, with dissolved BTEXTMB concentrations generally increasing in the lower depths (data not shown). This is probably due to the increased vertical hydraulic gradient brought

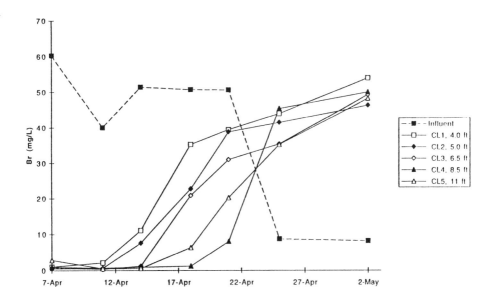

FIGURE 3. Breakthrough of bromide tracer in EPA-1 cluster wells, center of nitrate treatment cell.

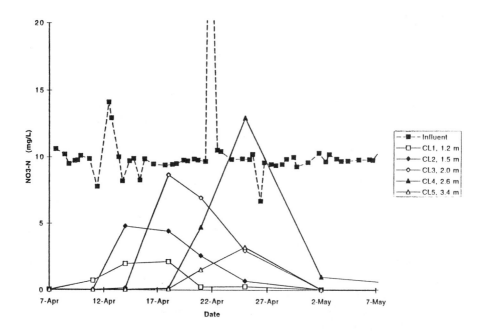

FIGURE 4. Removal of nitrate in EPA-1 cluster wells, center of nitrate treatment cell.

about by sustained infiltration, causing the leaching of aqueous BTEXTMB from the upper contaminated zones. These data were compared with those from the geoprobe samples taken prior to start-up of the pilot test to evaluate whether nitrate addition has caused any effect on aqueous BTEXTMB concentrations. This was done by averaging total BTEXTMB concentrations for a given level across either the nitrate cell or the control cell. This is by necessity a rough comparison, since geoprobe locations do not match up exactly with those done earlier. There was an average removal of about 83% of total dissolved BTEXTMB at each level, except for the upper two levels in the nitrate cell (Table 1). These data show that nitrate addition has not yet enhanced BTEXTMB removal relative to the control cell. This is not as expected, but the data are extremely variable, with coefficients of variation (standard deviation/mean) averaging 100%. Therefore, site variability should render this conclusion somewhat suspect.

The previous analysis was done to provide a direct comparison of water quality between the treatment cells, and represents a conventional approach. A better way to evaluate the data would be to examine changes in mass ratios of selected components. This would eliminate some of the variability induced by "pockets" of contamination dispersed across given levels. This was done for mesitylene (1,3,5-trimethylbenzene) and 1,2,3-trimethylbenzene. Both isomers are similar with respect to physical chemistry, but mesitylene is generally degraded under denitrifying conditions whereas 1,2,3-trimethylbenzene is recalcitrant (Hutchins,

TABLE 1. Average aqueous BTEXTMB concentrations in pilot cells, before and after 4.5 months of treatment.

Time Period	Pilot Cell	Screened Interval (m from ground surface)	Mean BTEXTMB (µg/L)	Standard Deviation (µg/L)	Coefficient of Variation (%)
		1.1 to 1.5	1,810	2,300	127
	Nitrate Cell	2.0 to 2.4	1,750	629	36
		2.9 to 3.3	1,730	2,230	129
Before Treatment (3/93 Data)		1.1 to 1.5	962	803	84
	Control Cell	2.0 to 2.4	5,440	2,970	55
		2.9 to 3.3	6,730	11,600	173
		1.1 to 1.5	207	181	87
	Nitrate Cell	2.0 to 2.4	1,960	3,260	166
		2.9 to 3.3	1,300	1,090	83
After Treatment (8/94 Data)		1.1 to 1.5	195	293	150
	Control Cell	2.0 to 2.4	1,300	1,130	87
		2.9 to 3.3	932	334	36

unpublished data). Mass ratios were calculated by dividing the concentrations of each isomer by the concentration of total BTEXTMB; coefficients of variation averaged 60% using this approach. Considering all of the data at all of the levels, the average ratio of mesitylene/1,2,3-trimethylbenzene was found to be 0.91±0.32 for the nitrate cell and 0.77±0.14 for the control cell before the pilot test. After 4.5 months operation, the ratio dropped to 0.49±0.46 for the nitrate cell and remained at 0.84±0.38 for the control cell. Preferential microbial degradation of mesitylene is the most likely explanation. It should be emphasized that the underlying mechanism for enhanced degradation cannot be discerned; enhanced degradation through other processes such as sulfate reduction could possibly contribute just as much as that through denitrification. However, the radiolabel microcosm test shows that biodegradation of toluene and m-xylene occurs when nitrate is added as the electron acceptor, but not in the absence of nitrate or in poisoned controls (Table 2). About 53% and 85% of the toluene and m-xylene were mineralized, respectively. Benzene and o-xylene were recalcitrant in this test under these conditions.

CONCLUSIONS

These data support the hypothesis that nitrate addition in the pilot test is enhancing biodegradation of selected compounds. However, it has not been

TABLE 2. Biodegradation and mineralization of test compounds (mean and standard deviation of three replicates).

Compound	Parameters	Time (days)	No Nitrate Added Mean	Std. Dev.	Nitrate Added Mean	Std. Dev.	Poisoned Controls Mean	Std. Dev.
Benzene	Concentration (mg/L)	0	2.01	0.53	1.45	0.07	1.52	0.05
		21	1.75	0.21	1.61	0.10	1.74	0.22
	% Mineralized	21	<2	<2	<2	<2	<2	<2
Toluene	Concentration (mg/L)	0	1.49	0.54	1.13	0.11	1.13	0.06
		21	1.79	0.67	0.00	0.00	1.47	0.17
	% Mineralized	21	<2	<2	52.1	4.2	<2	<2
m-Xylene	Concentration (mg/L)	0	1.11	0.08	6.15	4.51	4.14	4.91
		21	1.49	0.44	0.00	0.00	1.38	0.26
	% Mineralized	21	<2	<2	83.2	6.9	<2	<2
o-Xylene	Concentration (mg/L)	0	2.02	0.98	6.26	0.20	6.76	1.23
		21	2.23	0.40	2.19	0.16	2.12	0.08
	% Mineralized	21	<2	<2	<2	<2	<2	<2

possible to quantitate the extent of nitrate utilization due to vegetative growth relative to denitrification based on biodegradation of petroleum hydrocarbons. To address this, a 10-m × 10-m plot within each cell has been stripped of vegetation and overlain with a permeable barrier. Core samples will again be taken May 1995 to provide a final assessment of the efficacy of nitrate addition for bioremediation of fuel-contaminated aquifers.

ACKNOWLEDGMENTS

Although the research described in this paper has been funded wholly or in part by the U.S. EPA and the U.S. Air Force (MIPR N92-65, AL/EQ-OL, Environmental Quality Directorate, Armstrong Laboratory, Tyndall Air Force Base), it has not been subjected to Agency review and therefore does not necessarily reflect the views of the Agency, and no official endorsement should be inferred.

REFERENCES

Aggarwal, P. K., J. L. Means, and R. E. Hinchee. 1991. "Formulation of Nutrient Solutions for In Situ Biodegradation." In R. E. Hinchee and R. F. Olfenbuttel (Eds.), *In Situ Bioreclamation: Applications and Investigations for Hydrocarbon and Contaminated Site Remediation.* Butterworth-Heinemann, Stoneham, MA. pp. 51-66.

Barker, J. F., G. C. Patrick, and D. Major. 1987. "Natural Attenuation of Aromatic Hydrocarbons in a Shallow Sand Aquifer." *Ground Water Monitor. Rev.* 7:64-71.

Bell, R. A., and H. A. Hoffman. 1991. "Gasoline Spill in Fractured Bedrock Addressed with In Situ Bioremediation." In R. E. Hinchee and R. F. Olfenbuttel (Eds.), *In Situ Bioreclamation: Applications and Investigations for Hydrocarbon and Contaminated Site Remediation.* Butterworth-Heinemann, Stoneham, MA. pp. 437-443.

EA Engineering, Science, & Technology, Inc. 1987. *Site Characterization of the POL Area, Floating Fuel Recovery and Residual Cleanup Site, Eglin AFB, Florida.* EA Project Report DAF 71A, Atlanta, GA.

Hinchee, R. E., D. C. Downey, J. K. Slaughter, D. A. Selby, M. S. Westray, and G. M. Long. 1989. *Enhanced Bioreclamation of Jet Fuels — A Full-Scale Test at Eglin AFB FL.* Air Force Engineering & Services Center, Tyndall Air Force Base, FL.

Hutchins, S. R., W. C. Downs, J. T. Wilson, G. B. Smith, D. A. Kovacs, D. D. Fine, R. H. Douglass, and D. J. Hendrix. 1991. "Effect of Nitrate Addition on Biorestoration of Fuel-Contaminated Aquifer: Field Demonstration." *Ground Water* 29:571-580.

Hutchins, S. R. 1993. "Biotransformation and Mineralization of Alkylbenzenes under Denitrifying Conditions." *Environ. Toxicol. Chem.* 12:1413-1423.

Lee, M. D., and R. L. Raymond, Sr. 1991. "Case History of the Application of Hydrogen Peroxide as an Oxygen Source for In Situ Bioreclamation." In R. E. Hinchee and R. F. Olfenbuttel (Eds.), *In Situ Bioreclamation: Applications and Investigations for Hydrocarbon and Contaminated Site Remediation.* Butterworth-Heinemann, Stoneham, MA. pp. 429-436.

Thomas, A. T., S. R. Hutchins, P. B. Bedient, C. H. Ward, M. Wiesner, J. A. Bantle, and S. Williams. 1995. "Pilot-Scale Design for Nitrate-Based Bioremediation of Jet Fuel." In R. E. Hinchee, J. A. Kittel, and H. J. Reisinger (Eds.), *Applied Bioremediation of Petroleum Hydrocarbons,* pp. 133-141. Battelle Press, Columbus, OH.

Pilot-Scale Design for Nitrate-Based Bioremediation of Jet Fuel

Alison Thomas, Stephen R. Hutchins,
Philip B. Bedient, C. Herb Ward, Mark Wiesner,
John A. Bantle, and Stephen Williams

ABSTRACT

Extensive site characterization of a shallow fuel-contaminated aquifer was performed to define the design parameters for a nitrate-based bioremediation treatment system at Eglin Air Force Base (AFB), Florida. Core samples were obtained to delineate the distribution of aqueous-phase benzene, toluene, ethylbenzene, and xylenes (BTEX) and residual saturation in three dimensions at the site; examined to characterize the microbial populations; and assessed for toxicity of the fuel-contaminated solids. Treatability studies indicated that microbial populations can degrade alkylbenzenes under denitrifying conditions. Infiltration and tracer studies, combined with modeling efforts, were conducted to evaluate whether sprinkler irrigation would suffice to provide nitrate to contaminated regions below the water table. Laboratory column studies indicated that recirculation of recharge water could lead to plugging problems, and therefore a one-pass system was designed. The test areas consist of two adjacent 30-m by 30-m treatment cells, one of which receives potassium nitrate-amended water (test cell) and the other unamended water (control cell). Recharge water is applied via sprinklers at a rate of 11 gal/min (42 L/min) per cell. Operation began April 1994, and tracer studies indicate that the system is operating as predicted by the modeling, with active denitrification occurring.

INTRODUCTION

A nitrate-based bioremediation field study is being conducted at a ground-water fuel-contaminated site located at Eglin AFB, Florida. The objectives of this research are to provide a thorough site characterization to delineate contaminant distribution and microbial activity in the aquifer; conduct field and laboratory tests to provide design parameters for a pilot-scale treatment system; and design, construct, and operate the treatment system to provide a direct comparison of the effects of recharge with and without nitrate amendments for a 14-month period. Core and water data will be used to compare the extent of benzene, alkylbenzene, and JP-4 degradation in the two treatment plots; and changes in microbial populations and sediment toxicity will be evaluated as a result of nitrate-based bioremediation. This report briefly describes the site characterization, treatability studies, column tests, and infiltration/tracer tests conducted to determine the potential for nitrate-based bioremediation and the design parameters of a field treatment system. Performance data for the first 4.5 months of operation indicate that nitrate addition in the test plot is enhancing biodegradation of selected compounds (Hutchins et al. 1994).

SITE CHARACTERIZATION

In 1984, approximately 40,000 gal of JP-4 leaked from underground transit piping at the Petroleum, Oils and Lubricants (POL) yard at Eglin AFB, Florida. The geology of the site consists of 9- to 12- m-thick sand and gravel aquifer with underlying Pensacola clay. The groundwater table is located at 1.2 to 1.5 m. Site investigations have been previously conducted at the site to prepare for installation and operation of a hydrogen peroxide pilot-scale study (EA Engineering 1987). Data from this study identified significant problems with the use of hydrogen peroxide, including reduced aquifer permeability. The site remains contaminated with concentrations of BTEX in excess of regulatory limits. Because nitrate-based bioremediation has been proposed for remediation on monoaromatic hydrocarbons, it was considered for the remaining hydrocarbon contamination.

To determine the potential for nitrate-based bioremediation, researchers at the U.S. Environmental Protection Agency (U.S. EPA) Robert S. Kerr Environmental Research Laboratory (RSKERL) and Rice University conducted a comprehensive site investigation in March and July 1993. Field activities involved the use of a cone penetrometer, geoprobe, and drilling rigs. The cone penetrometer was used to delineate areas of BTEX contamination, as well as to characterize the hydrogeologic properties of the subsurface at the site. Collected samples were analyzed for BTEX on a real-time basis using a portable gas chromatograph (GC). For quality control, split samples were preserved and shipped to RSKERL for GC/mass spectroscopic (MS) analysis. Water table elevations determined by the cone penetrometer provided data for a potentiometric map, indicating that the groundwater flow generally follows land surface contours. The cone typically identified sand from ground surface to depth of penetration (5 to 6 m). Clay lenses were detected at 5-m depth in several locations. Interpretation of the cone logs suggest that the hydraulic conductivity of the sand ranges from 0.010 to 0.045 cm/s.

Water quality samples were obtained from groundwater monitoring wells and a geoprobe. The geoprobe was used to obtain a better vertical resolution of water quality, because monitoring well data provide only a general picture of the state of the aquifer. A screened stainless steel rod was driven to three selected depths at several locations to obtain water samples for correlating water quality information with the core analyses. Several parameters were monitored to provide an extensive characterization of water quality and indicated the types of microbial processes that may have been occurring in the subsurface. Flowthrough systems were used to minimize contact with air so that samples could be analyzed in the field for dissolved oxygen (DO) and pH using electrodes. In addition, samples were analyzed immediately for soluble iron using Chemetrics®. To evaluate volatile aromatic hydrocarbons, samples were analyzed for BTEX and the trimethylbenzenes (BTEXTMB). A maximum BTEX level of 4,500 µg/L was detected, with levels decreasing to approximately 10 µg/L over a distance of 90 m downgradient of the spill (Figure 1). Samples were also analyzed for bromide, chloride, sulfate, aqueous nitrate, nitrite, ammonia, orthophosphate, and total organic carbon (TOC).

Water quality data confirmed an anaerobic aquifer with oxygen concentrations less than 1 mg/L, nitrate concentrations less than 0.1 mg/L as NO_3-N, and methane concentrations up to 15 mg/L. Methanogenesis is occurring, with higher methane concentrations located just below the contaminated zone.

Nitrate and nitrite concentrations are low, but nutrients such as ammonia-nitrogen and phosphate are relatively high. Benzene concentrations range from 0 to 300 µg/L. Benzene concentrations are reduced relative to the other constituents, probably as a result of weathering and the hydrogen peroxide pilot study, and therefore may not present a significant problem to nitrate-based bioremediation due to its recalcitrance under denitrifying conditions.

Core samples were taken to delineate the lateral spread and vertical extent of contamination at the site and to provide mass estimates. This information was also used to help define the locations of the proposed treatment cells. Core samples were obtained using a drill rig modified for acquisition and extrusion of saturated aquifer material; 20 locations were designated for the acquisition of continuous cores, including two that extended from ground surface to 6 m below grade. The location of these cores is shown in Figure 2. Core locations 80A-80J also correspond to the location used for taking geoprobe samples, thus providing a direct comparison between core samples and water quality analyses. For each core location, concentrations of BTEXTMB and JP-4 in the individual subsamples were weighted for the sampled interval and summed to provide a total cumulative mass estimate in g/m^2 for that location.

A contour plot of the cumulative mass of JP-4 (g/m^2) and location of treatment cells is shown in Figure 3. The source is located in the proximity of 80N-80S, adjacent to the fuel tank, and the resultant residual saturation is distributed fairly evenly across an area downgradient. The residual saturated contaminated interval is 1.5 m thick, located at and below the groundwater table.

In terms of organic analyses, the aromatic hydrocarbons were considered both individually and as a combined fraction. The combined fraction, designated at BTEXTMB, comprised about 25% of the total mass of monoaromatic hydrocarbons in the weathered cores. The monoaromatics comprised about 14% of the residual JP-4 (Hutchins, unpublished data).

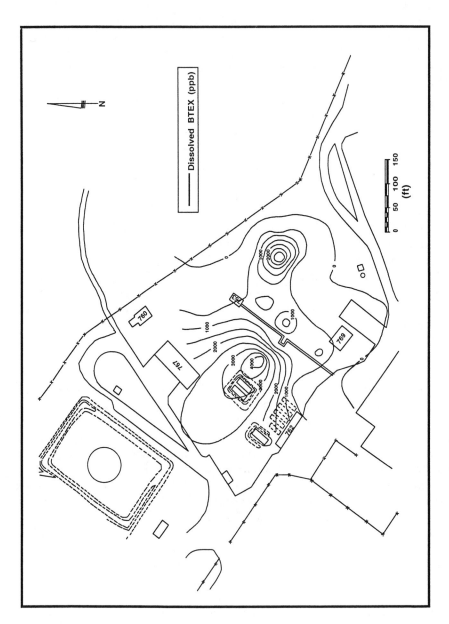

FIGURE 1. Dissolved BTEX concentrations in ppb (1 ft = 0.3 m).

TREATABILITY STUDIES

Microbial characterization included determination of direct counts, viable counts, most probable number (MPN) of total and JP-4 degrading denitrifiers, MPN of aerobic and anaerobic protozoa, and diversity. Aquifer sediments at the site contained variable, but generally high numbers of denitrifying bacteria, many of which can grow using constituents of JP-4 as carbon sources. Both aerobic and anaerobic protozoa were detected, indicating that grazing pressure may be exerted during remediation, serving to limit excess biomass and maintain hydraulic permeability in the formation. Batch microcosm tests were conducted to examine BTEXTMB degradation under denitrifying conditions. Microcosms were prepared aseptically in an anaerobic glovebox to preclude intrusion of oxygen. The rates of alkylbenzene biodegradation and nitrate (NO_3-N) consumption were 1.2 mg/L/d and 2 to 3 mg/L/d, respectively; i.e., lower than observed at other field sites (Hutchins et al. 1991; Hutchins and Wilson 1993).

To assess the success of remediation based on the toxicity of the core samples, the toxicity of JP-4-contaminated sediments will be determined using the standard Frog Embryo Teratogenesis Assay-*Xenopus* (FETAX; ASTM 1991) before and after nitrate-based bioremediation. In addition to this standard developmental assay, reproductive toxicity testing will be used to assess the toxicological effects throughout the complete reproductive cycle.

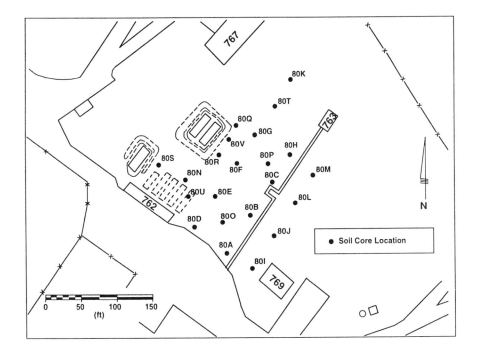

FIGURE 2. Soil core locations (1 ft = 0.3 m).

COLUMN TESTING

Reduced permeability during the hydrogen peroxide pilot study at the Eglin POL site inhibited delivery of nutrients and oxygen. This reduced permeability was attributed to plugging from iron and/or phosphate precipitation. Because the same problems could adversely affect the nitrate-based pilot study, laboratory column tests were undertaken to identify the likely cause of reduced permeability. Laboratory experiments were conducted using the soil and both filtered and unfiltered groundwater samples. Raw groundwater contained a total iron concentration of 0.03 mg/L, and ferrous was not detected. After the groundwater was acidified and filtered, the total iron concentration was higher (1.01 mg/L) with a slight ferrous concentration (0.01 mg/L).

To investigate the effect of precipitation of calcium and/or iron phosphate salts, the nutrient solution used in the previous pilot study was simulated and added to the filtered groundwater at a concentration of 1,000 mg/L and pH of 6.69. After initial decline due to rearrangement of fines, data showed no further reduction in permeability. Results indicated that any interaction occurring between the nutrient solution (ammonium and phosphate salts) and the soil in the column did not affect the permeability of the sandy porous medium.

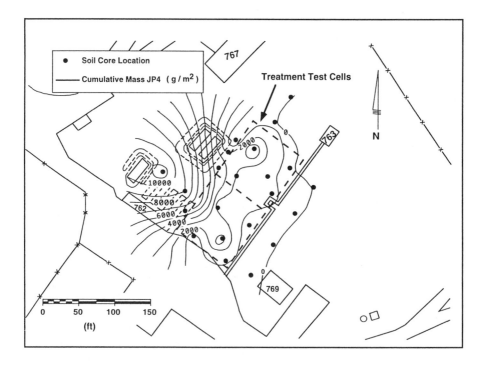

FIGURE 3. Contour plot of cumulative mass of JP-4 (g/m²) and cell boundaries for nitrate project (1 ft = 0.3 m).

The groundwater appeared rather turbid, implying a high content of suspended particles about 0.5 to 2.0 µm in size. Column tests using dynamic light scattering experiments were conducted on raw water and water that had been allowed to stand for 5 days to allow some of the larger particles to settle. Dynamic light scattering measurements found no particles in the effluents in both cases, evidence that all suspended particles in the inlet water were retained in the aquifer soil within the column. The column tests suggested that particles smaller than 1 µm, which do not settle easily, are primarily responsible for the reduced permeability. Therefore, even in the absence of hydrogen peroxide and nutrients, recirculation of the shallow groundwater would require an aboveground water treatment unit capable of removing particles in the submicron range.

INFILTRATION TESTING AND MODELING

Infiltration/tracer tests were conducted at the site to evaluate the feasibility of surface application as a means of supplying nitrate for the pilot-scale study. An infiltration test was designed to characterize the infiltration characteristics of the site and to provide site-specific information about the formation of groundwater mounds in response to surface application. The conservative tracer test simulated vertical transport of nitrate under field conditions through the use of sodium bromide. The infiltration test and tracer study were conducted at two test plots measuring 4.5 m by 3.0 m installed with multilevel cluster wells.

Modeling of the hydraulics of mound formation and dissipation with the two-dimensional groundwater numerical model BIOPLUME II (Rifai et al. 1987) was conducted to achieve three objectives: (1) to calibrate the model to the results obtained during the infiltration test; (2) to estimate hydrogeologic parameters for predictive modeling; and (3) to predict groundwater mounding response to various scenarios for the larger pilot-scale treatment cells. Infiltration of unamended tap water at an average application rate of 36 in. (91 cm)/d produced groundwater mound formations in both test plots, and data were used to calibrate the BIOPLUME II model. Modeling of the observed response of the water table during the test plot infiltration test provided estimates of the site-specific hydrogeologic parameters necessary for predictive modeling of the pilot-scale system. Predictive modeling runs were used to anticipate the extent of water-table mounding under a variety of surface application schemes necessary to create the vertical hydraulic gradient to force the nitrate into the subsurface. Based on the predictive modeling, an optimal hydraulic surface application rate of 2.88 in. (7.31 cm)/d was computed as the design flowrate.

The groundwater mounds formed at the test plots provided favorable hydraulic conditions for vertical transport of the sodium bromide tracer. Complete breakthrough of the tracer was detected at the deepest cluster well in each plot, indicating that a vertical hydraulic gradient was created. This suggested that conditions were favorable for transport of chemicals from the surface to the contaminated zone of the subsurface.

PILOT-SCALE DESIGN

Based on the site characterization data, infiltration/tracer tests, and predictive modeling of a pilot-scale nitrate-based bioremediation study, a surface application treatment system was designed to deliver 10 mg/L NO_3-N amended water at a flowrate of 11 gpm to the test cell and an equal amount of unamended water to the control cell. Each cell measures 30 m by 30 m. The recharge water produces a groundwater table rise of approximately 0.76 m. The system has the flexibility to increase or decrease the flowrate uniformly across the individual treatment cells.

CONCLUSIONS

The site characterization data and treatability studies indicated that nitrate-based bioremediation is feasible for this site, and the requisite microbial activity is distributed throughout the treatment region. Column studies and infiltration/tracer tests indicated a one-pass system, and surface application of nitrate was feasible for a remediation system design. Surface application offers an inexpensive, noninvasive alternative to injection wells and infiltration galleries for in situ bioremediation applications. Design of a surface application system does require significant characterization of site hydrogeology and an understanding of site-specific infiltration and water-table mounding characteristics. The technology employs artificial recharge as well as favorable hydraulic conditions for mixing and vertical transport of supplemental electron acceptors and nutrients. A test plot infiltration test and a conservative tracer test at Eglin AFB, Florida, indicated the feasibility of transporting solutes to the subsurface via recharge water. Modeling of the experiments provided quantitative estimates of site-specific hydrogeologic and transport parameters. Tracer tests confirmed that surface application can adequately transport nitrate and nutrients to the subsurface.

REFERENCES

ASTM. 1991. "Standard Guide for Conducting the Frog Embryo Teratogenesis Assay-Xenopus (FETAX)." *American Society for Testing and Materials*, ASTM Designation E 1439-91.

EA Engineering, Science, & Technology, Inc. 1987. *Site Characterization of the POL Area, Floating Fuel Recovery and Residual Cleanup Site*, Eglin AFB, Florida, EA Project Report DAF 71A, Atlanta, GA.

Hutchins, S. R., W. C. Downs, J. T. Wilson, G. B. Smith, D. A. Kovacs, D. D. Fine, R. H. Douglass, and D. J. Hendrix. 1991. "Effect of Nitrate Addition on Biorestoration of Fuel-Contaminated Aquifer: Field Demonstration." *Groundwater* 29:571-580.

Hutchins, S. R., D. E. Miller, F. P. Beck, A. Thomas, S. E. Williams, and G. D. Willis. 1995. "Nitrate-Based Bioremediation of JP-4 Jet Fuel: Pilot-Scale Demonstration." In R. E. Hinchee, J. A. Kittel, and H. J. Reisinger (Eds.), *Applied Bioremediation of Petroleum Hydrocarbons*, pp. 123-131. Battelle Press, Columbus, OH.

Hutchins, S. R., and J. T. Wilson. 1993. "Nitrate-Based Bioremediation of Petroleum-Contaminated Aquifer at Park City, Kansas: Site Characterization and Treatability Study." In R. E. Hinchee and R. F. Olfenbuttel (Eds.), *In Situ Bioreclamation: Applications and Investigations for Hydrocarbon and Contaminated Site Remediation*, pp. 429-436. Butterworth-Heinemann, Stoneham, MA.

Rifai, H. S., P. B. Bedient, R. C. Borden, and J. F. Haasbeek. 1987. *BIOPLUME II — Computer Model of Two-Dimensional Transport under the Influence of Oxygen Limited Biodegradation in Groundwater*, User's Manual, Version 1.0. Rice University, Houston, TX.

In Situ Bioremediation of a Pipeline Spill Using Nitrate as the Electron Acceptor

Stephen R. Hutchins, John T. Wilson, and Don H. Kampbell

ABSTRACT

The Robert S. Kerr Environmental Research Lab (RSKERL) is monitoring the progress of nitrate-based bioremediation at Park City, Kansas, where recharge water is being applied to a heterogeneous petroleum-contaminated aquifer through numerous injection wells. The remediation system provides recharge amended with nitrate and nutrients to two cells and nutrients without nitrate to one cell. One recovery well recirculates groundwater and another provides hydraulic control. Treatability studies demonstrated that the requisite microbial activity is distributed throughout the site. A total of 15 m of recharge containing 700 kg NO_3-N was applied to two combined cells (5,800 m^2). Denitrification was evidenced by transient production of both nitrite and nitrous oxide during operation. However, petroleum hydrocarbons are still being leached from the contaminated intervals. Core analyses reveal that certain zones are being remediated, whereas others are not. Although site heterogeneity precludes an accurate assessment of the extent of remediation at this time, analyses of ratios of various components indicate that bioremediation is occurring.

INTRODUCTION

Fuel-contaminated aquifers are often difficult to remediate aerobically because of problems relating to aquifer plugging and oxygen mass transport (Aggarwal et al. 1991). Several investigators are evaluating in situ biorestoration under anaerobic conditions, specifically with nitrate as an alternative electron acceptor. These processes have been evaluated in the field at pilot scale (Hutchins et al. 1991; Hilton et al. 1992), but there are few documented full-scale projects that demonstrate the applicability of nitrate-based bioremediation. An aquifer contaminated with petroleum hydrocarbons at Park City, Kansas, offers such an opportunity and is being treated by nitrate-based bioremediation. RSKERL was requested to assist with the design of the operation and to provide an interim performance evaluation based on water quality and core analyses. Although the full study will be published at a later date, this paper describes selected details of the evaluation and focuses on (1) the microbial treatability studies for assessing the potential for nitrate-based bioremediation, (2) the water-quality monitoring conducted to gain insight into biological mechanisms, and (3) the interim performance assessment based on core sampling.

SITE DESCRIPTION

The site is located in the Little Arkansas River Valley northwest of Wichita, Kansas and overlies the Equus Beds aquifer. The aquifer is approximately 14 m thick in the study area and is comprised of sand and gravel interlaced with silt and clay lenses and capped by clay overburden. Depth to water is 5 to 6 m, and the hydraulic conductivity ranges from 0.12 to 0.36 cm/sec. Additional site information has been published (Kennedy & Hutchins 1992). The aquifer became contaminated with a mixture of petroleum hydrocarbons that leaked slowly during the late 1970s from a pipeline carrying a variety of refined products, including gasoline and diesel. A subsurface injection system, consisting of 530 injection wells, 5.5 m in depth, screened over a 1-m interval, and spaced 6 m on center, was installed in the sandy vadose zone below the clay layer but just above the water table. During a 1-month test period, air was injected into the formation. However, a continued loss in injection capability was observed, due primarily to air entrainment and secondarily to iron precipitation (L. Kennedy, personal communication). Based on these results, a decision was made to evaluate nitrate-based bioremediation for anaerobic treatment of the aquifer.

TREATABILITY STUDIES

Initial treatability studies had demonstrated that nitrate removal occurred in 20 out of 21 continuous cores from 2.5 to 7.7 m below ground surface at one location (Hutchins et al. 1993), and that aquifer microorganisms from two aquifer cores could degrade selected alkylbenzenes under denitrifying conditions (Hutchins & Wilson 1994). However, additional treatability studies were needed to determine whether this activity was prevalent throughout the aquifer. Therefore, core samples from six to seven discrete depth intervals were obtained from five locations (A, B, D, E, and F), shown in Figure 1. The total depth interval ranged from 2.6 to 8.4 m below ground surface.

Microcosm Preparation

Microcosms were prepared in an anaerobic glovebox as described previously (Hutchins 1993) to assess biodegradation of benzene, toluene, ethylbenzene, xylenes, and trimethylbenzenes (BTEXTMB). In brief, triplicate microcosms for each core sample were constructed with 10 g aquifer material in 60-mL serum bottles, and each was amended with nutrients and nitrate to provide final solution concentrations of 30 mg/L NO_3-N, 10 mg/L NH_4-N, and 10 mg/L PO_4-P. For

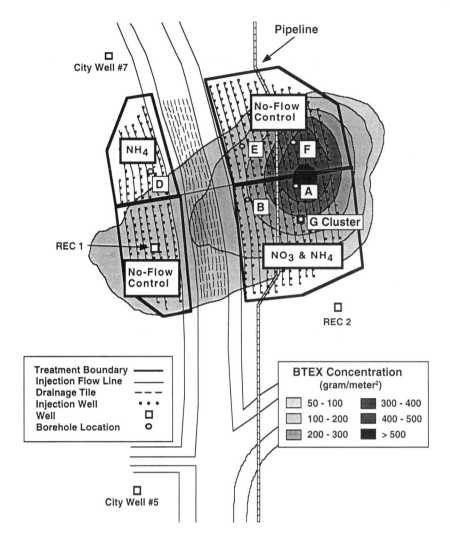

FIGURE 1. Site map showing location of treatment cells, core samples, cluster wells, and recovery wells.

Location F, a live control was prepared for each core sample by omitting nitrate addition. For all core samples, a corresponding poisoned control was amended with biocides to provide solution concentrations of 250 mg/L mercuric chloride and 500 mg/L sodium azide. Microcosms were spiked with mixed BTEXTMB, sealed without headspace using Teflon™-lined butyl rubber septa, and incubated in the glovebox at room temperature. Microcosms were repetitively sampled in the glovebox at designated time intervals by removing the septum and obtaining 3.0-mL aqueous samples using glass syringes. The removed volume was replaced using sterile 2-cm^3 glass rods and the microcosm was resealed without headspace, mixed, and incubated as before.

When this test was completed, supernatants were aseptically decanted from the microcosms and the glass rods were removed. The microcosms were then respiked with nutrients and/or biocides as previously described, and amended with UL-^{14}C-*m*-xylene instead of BTEXTMB to assess the extent of biodegradation of a target compound. Distribution of the radiolabel was assessed using a modification of the procedure used by Grbic-Galic and Vogel (1987). It should be noted that this assay accounts for distribution of the radiolabel in the aqueous phase alone, and represents the extent of biodegradation of available soluble substrate. Three different measurements were done on each sample.

For total ^{14}C activity, 0.5 mL of sample were injected directly into a mixture of 9 mL Beckman EP scintillation cocktail and 1 mL 1 N NaOH. This serves to contain the radiolabeled parent compound as well as any nonvolatile intermediates of metabolism. Next, 0.5 mL of sample were injected into 1 mL NaOH. This was purged with nitrogen gas at 250 mL/min for 5 min, followed by the addition of 9 mL scintillation cocktail. This measurement represents both $^{14}CO_2$ and nonvolatile intermediates. Finally, 0.5 mL of sample were injected into 1 mL 1 N HCl and similarly purged. This represents the nonvolatile intermediates only, and $^{14}CO_2$ was calculated by the difference between this sample and the NaOH-treated sample. Additional details of the method have been described elsewhere (Hutchins 1993).

Microcosm Results

A complete description of the microcosm data set is beyond the scope of this paper; representative data are shown for Location F in Figure 2. The upper graph shows removal of the individual hydrocarbons at 5.5 m below ground surface. The hydrocarbon concentrations in the corresponding control decreased by 14 to 23% (unpublished data). The middle graph in Figure 2 shows removal of all of the hydrocarbons, summed as BTEXTMB, for each of the depth intervals relative to both poisoned and live controls. The average BTEXTMB removal, corrected for loss in controls, was 54 ± 19% for all 34 core samples. Other research has shown that benzene, *o*-xylene, and 1,2,3-trimethylbenzene, which account for 37% of the total BTEXTMB mass, are generally recalcitrant under denitrifying conditions (Hutchins 1993, unpublished data). These data therefore indicate that most of the labile compounds are degraded by the native aquifer microbiota. Mineralization of at least one target compound, *m*-xylene, was confirmed for each depth interval at Location F (Figure 2, lower graph). The average extent of *m*-xylene mineralization was 89 ± 7% for all 34 core samples. These data show that the requisite microbial activity is distributed throughout the site.

PROJECT DESIGN AND OPERATION

The remediation system was designed to provide recharge amended with nitrate (10 mg/L NO_3-N) and nutrients (5 mg/L NH_4-N) to two combined cells (5,800 m^2) and nutrients without nitrate to one cell (2,700 m^2). Other cells served

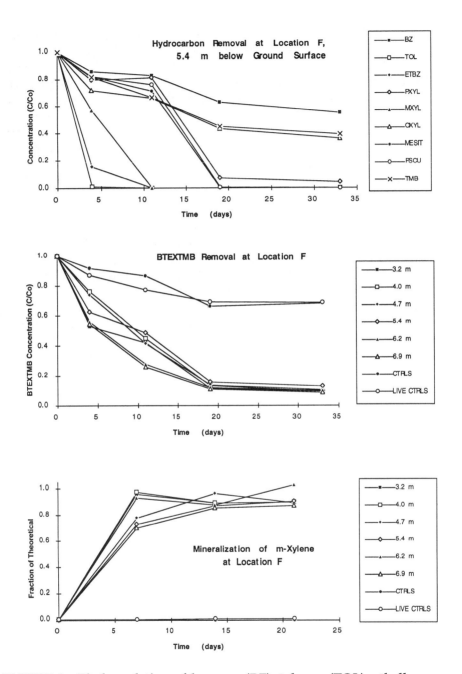

FIGURE 2. Biodegradation of benzene (BZ), toluene (TOL), ethylbenzene (ETBZ), *p*-xylene (PXYL), *m*-xylene (MXYL), *o*-xylene (OXYL), 1,3,5-tri-methylbenzene (MESIT), 1,2,4-trimethylbenzene (PSCU), and 1,2,3-tri-methylbenzene (TMB) in microcosms. Other graphs show biodegradation of cumulative BTEXTMB and mineralization of *m*-xylene. Mean of three replicates.

as no-flow controls. One recovery well (REC1) is pumped at 200 gpm to provide recharge for recirculation and another (REC2) is pumped at 100 gpm for hydraulic control, with the discharge treated by air stripping (Figure 1). A tracer study demonstrated that operation of the injection wells results in a strong vertical gradient, which allows delivery of tracer (or nitrate and nutrients) through the contaminated region (Johnson et al. 1994). Other details on operation have been published (Hutchins and Wilson 1994). Operation commenced June 1, 1993, with water recharge only at a rate of 70 gpm/cell, and nutrient and nitrate injection began August 5, 1993.

Water quality was monitored monthly for the 2 recovery wells and for 11 fully-penetrating wells and 2 groups of 5 cluster wells. Samples were analyzed on site for pH, dissolved oxygen, and temperature and shipped back to RSKERL for analysis of inorganics (NO_3-N, NO_2-N, SO_4, NH_4-N, PO_4-P, Br, Cl), dissolved gases (N_2, CH_4, CO_2, and N_2O), total organic carbon (TOC), and BTEXTMB. Core samples were taken again on February 18, 1994, to assess field performance after 9 months of operation. Duplicate locations, 1.5 m apart, were sampled adjacent to Locations A, D, F, and G (Figure 1). Discrete 15-cm cores were obtained over continuous lengths from 3 to 10 m below ground surface to define the vertical extent of contamination, using methods described previously (Hutchins et al. 1991). These sampling locations were approximately 1.5 to 2.5 m away from locations that had been sampled prior to startup of the project.

PERFORMANCE EVALUATION

Injection capacity dropped significantly in all treatment cells after 6 months of operation, despite the absence of oxygen (<0.6 mg/L) in the recirculated water. Although not verified, it is suspected that this loss resulted from recirculation and deposition of fine particulates. Despite this decline, a total of 15 m of recharge was applied to all three cells, with the nitrate treatment cells receiving 700 kg NO_3-N. BTEXTMB levels rose initially in many of the monitoring wells, due to the elevation of the water table, which resulted in additional contact with residual saturation in the vadose zone (unpublished data). BTEXTMB levels dropped steadily from 1,500 µg/L to 700 µg/L in REC1, whereas levels in REC2 increased initially from 1,600 µg/L to 4,800 µg/L by October 1993, and then decreased steadily to 1,400 µg/L by February 1994. Although the levels in most monitoring wells have dropped relative to the initial values, the contaminated sediments continue to leach BTEXTMB to the infiltration recharge. By February 1994, aqueous BTEXTMB levels were 2,200 µg/L in the nitrate cell (Well A, screened 4.0 to 7.0 m below ground surface) and 11,900 µg/L in the no-flow control cell (Well F, screened 3.7 to 6.7 m below ground surface).

Because of the strong vertical hydraulic gradient, Cluster Well G was used to evaluate denitrification in flowpaths to REC2 during operation (Figure 1). Screened intervals, relative to ground surface, were 4.6 to 6.1 m for G-1, 6.1 to 7.6 m for G-2, 7.6 to 9.1 m for G-3, 9.1 to 10.7 m for G-4, and 10.7 to 12.2 m for

G-5. After nitrate injection began in August 1993, there was a transient break-through of nitrate during the next two months (Figure 3). Denitrification was evidenced by transient production of both nitrite and nitrous oxide in the upper cluster wells. The average dissolved oxygen concentration in the cluster wells was 0.4 ± 0.3 mg/L during this time. Nitrate and nitrite levels have remained below 0.5 mg/L in REC2 throughout the study, indicating nitrate removal. Although these data provide strong evidence for denitrification, this does not confirm that petroleum hydrocarbons are being used as the carbon source. However, given the demonstrated ability of the native aquifer bacteria to degrade alkylbenzenes under denitrifying conditions, this would be consistent with the premise of nitrate-based bioremediation.

Core analyses reveal that certain zones are being remediated, whereas other zones are not. Example data are shown for core concentrations of benzene and toluene at Location A in the nitrate cell before (60A, 60AA) and after (60AB, 60AC) treatment (Figure 4). In 60AB, these components are highly weathered, whereas weathering is restricted to the water table smear zone in 60AC. Site heterogeneity therefore precludes an accurate assessment of the extent of remediation based on direct core analyses. However, the effects of site heterogeneity can be reduced by calculating the ratios of the components to the total petroleum hydrocarbons (TPH). This was done for all of the cores at locations A, G, and F, generating a cumulative mass ratio representing the entire continuous core length for the duplicate boreholes (Figure 5). Mass ratios have not changed substantially at Location F, the no-flow control. However, benzene, toluene, and ethylbenzene are reduced to a much greater extent at both locations in the nitrate cell (Figure 5). This probably results from both leaching and biological activity, and again does not confirm that biodegradation is responsible for contaminant mass reduction. However, biodegradation is implied by the xylene data, because *m*-xylene and *o*-xylene are reduced in the nitrate treatment cell relative to *p*-xylene.

Each isomer would be expected to behave similarly if leaching were the only removal mechanism, and in fact one would expect a similar or higher mass loss of *p*-xylene relative to the other two isomers based on its higher vapor pressure; *m*-xylene is easily degraded under denitrifying conditions by the aquifer bacteria, and this observation would again be consistent with nitrate-based bio-remediation. Other researchers have observed preferential biodegradation of *o*-xylene relative to *p*-xylene under anaerobic conditions (Evans et al. 1991). However, *o*-xylene is generally recalcitrant under denitrifying conditions with these sediments, which indicates that other processes may be operative.

CONCLUSIONS

These data have shown that active denitrification is occurring in the con-taminated aquifer and that certain areas are being remediated whereas others are still highly contaminated. Although these observations, in conjunction with the treatability studies, substantiate biological activity as a removal process in

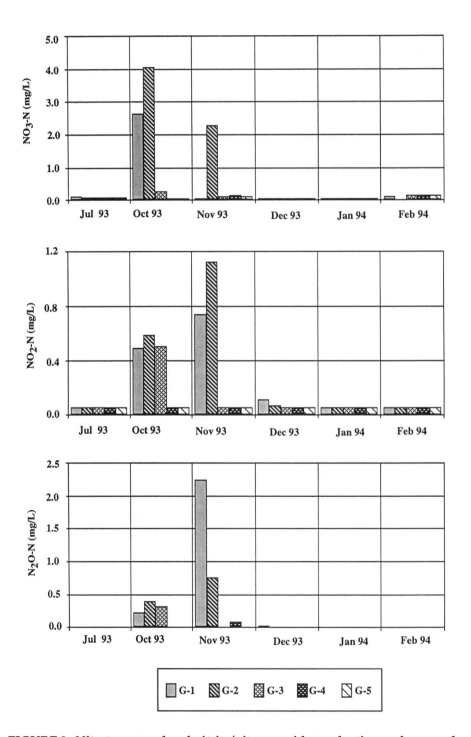

FIGURE 3. Nitrate removal and nitrite/nitrous oxide production and removal in G cluster well. Nitrate added August 1993.

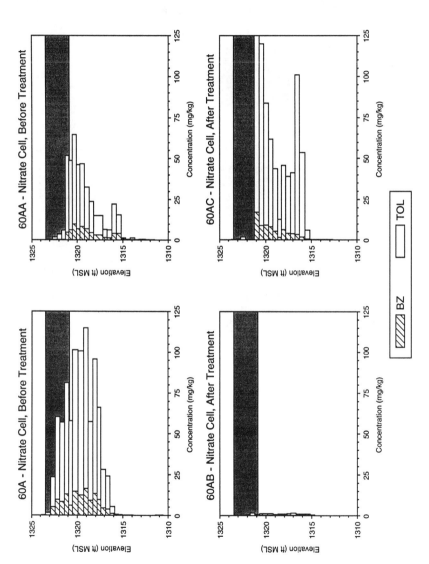

FIGURE 4. Core concentrations of benzene (BZ) and toluene (TOL) in nitrate cell before and after treatment. Shaded area represents water table smear zone.

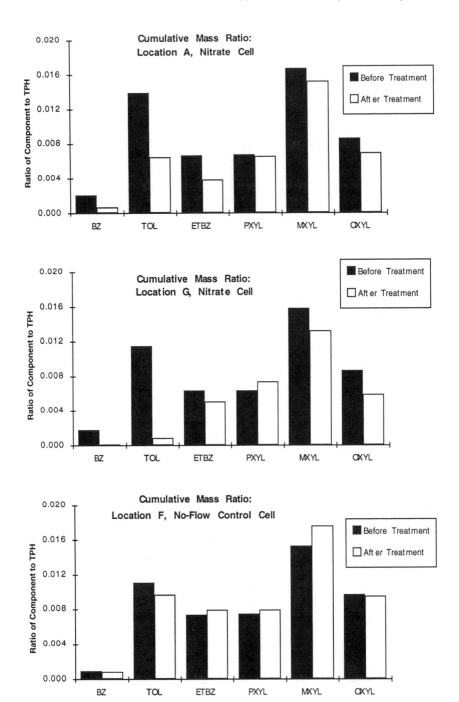

FIGURE 5. Cumulative mass ratios of selected components in Locations A, G, and F, before and after treatment. Ratios are based on duplicate continuous cores through the contaminated zone.

this field system, the relative contribution of denitrification to biodegradation of specific petroleum contaminants can be inferred but not ascertained. The data show promise for application of nitrate-based bioremediation to other sites. However, as with most in situ processes, preferential flowpaths can create a problem, and better methods need to be developed for cost-effective assessment of the extent of bioremediation in heterogeneous systems.

ACKNOWLEDGMENT

Although the research described in this paper has been funded wholly or in part by the U.S. Environmental Protection Agency, it has not been subjected to Agency review and therefore does not necessarily reflect the views of the Agency, and no official endorsement should be inferred.

REFERENCES

Aggarwal, P. K., J. L. Means, and R. E. Hinchee. 1991. "Formulation of Nutrient Solutions for In Situ Biodegradation." In R. E. Hinchee and R. F. Olfenbuttel (Eds.), *In Situ Bioreclamation: Applications and Investigations for Hydrocarbon and Contaminated Site Remediation.* Butterworth-Heinemann, Boston, MA. pp. 51-66.

Evans, P. J., D. T. Mang, and L. Y. Young. 1991. "Degradation of Toluene and *m*-Xylene and Transformation of *o*-Xylene by Denitrifying Enrichment Cultures." *Appl. Environ. Microbiol.* 57:450-454.

Grbic-Galic, D., and T. M. Vogel. 1987. "Transformation of Toluene and Benzene by Mixed Methanogenic Cultures." *Appl. Environ. Microbiol.* 53:254-260.

Hilton, J., B. Marley, T. Ryther, and J. Forbes. 1992. "Pilot Test of Nitrate-Enhanced Bioremediation in a Moderate- to Low-Permeability Aquifer." In NGWA/API (Eds.), *Proceedings, Petroleum Hydrocarbons and Organic Chemicals in Ground Water: Prevention, Detection, and Restoration.* Water Well Journal Publishing, Dublin, OH. pp. 527-540.

Hutchins, S. R., W. C. Downs, J. T. Wilson, G. B. Smith, D. A. Kovacs, D. D. Fine, R. H. Douglass, and D. J. Hendrix. 1991. "Effect of Nitrate Addition on Biorestoration of Fuel-Contaminated Aquifer: Field Demonstration." *Ground Water* 29:571-580.

Hutchins, S. R. 1993. "Biotransformation and Mineralization of Alkylbenzenes under Denitrifying Conditions." *Environ. Toxicol. Chem.* 12:1413-1423.

Hutchins, S. R., D. H. Kampbell, M. L. Cook, F. M. Pfeffer, R. L. Cosby, J. T. Wilson, B. Newell, J. A. Johnson, V. Ravi, and J. K Rumery (Eds.). 1993. *Combining Treatability Studies and Site Characterization for Rational Design of In Situ Bioremediation Using Nitrate as an Electron Acceptor.* Technical Report, EPA 600/R-93/054. U.S. Environmental Protection Agency, R.S. Kerr Environmental Research Laboratory, Ada, OK.

Hutchins, S. R., and J. T. Wilson. 1994. "Nitrate-Based Bioremediation of Petroleum-Contaminated Aquifer at Park City, Kansas: Site Characterization and Treatability Study." In R. E. Hinchee, B. C. Alleman, R. E. Hoeppel, and R. N. Miller (Eds.), *Hydrocarbon Bioremediation.* Lewis Publishers, Ann Arbor, MI. pp 80-92.

Johnson, J. A., V. Ravi, and J. K. Rumery. 1994. "Estimation of Solute Concentrations Using the Pathline Counting Method." *Ground Water* 32:719-726.

Kennedy, L., and S. R. Hutchins. 1992. "Applied Geologic, Microbiological, and Engineering Constraints of In-Situ Bioremediation." *Remediation J.* 3:83-107.

Nitrate as Electron Acceptor in In Situ Abandoned Refinery Site Bioremediation

Gerhard Battermann and Matthias Meier-Löhr

ABSTRACT

The aquifer beneath an abandoned refinery site is highly polluted with benzene, toluene, ethylbenzene, and xylenes (BTEX). After removal of the free phase by hydraulic measures until 1986, the immobile residual concentration located 6 to 10 m beneath the surface is still present and causes hydrocarbon concentrations from 10 to 100 mg/L in the groundwater. Laboratory tests proved the biodegradability of the hydrocarbon compounds under denitrifying conditions. Based on the results of the pilot study, large-scale bioremediation covering an area of about 20 ha was initiated. About 500 m³/h of groundwater were extracted, and 400 m³/h were recharged. The large-scale plant has been operating since 1991. Nitrate as an electron acceptor has been used since 1992. About 300 metric tons (MT) of hydrocarbons have been removed to date (80% by biodegradation and 20% by flushing). The area of groundwater pollution is diminished by a factor of about two. More than 60% of all groundwater observation wells are now free of dissolved hydrocarbons. In addition, the decrease of biological nitrate consumption gives evidence of advanced bioremediation of the soil.

INTRODUCTION

Some 10 years ago remediation of a hydrocarbon spill was generally considered successful once the light, nonaqueous-phase liquid (LNAPL) contaminants in free phase at the surface of the groundwater had been removed. Groundwater pollution, however, which was caused by the remaining hydrocarbons binding to the soil (immobile residual saturations), can still endanger the water supply. Today, advanced requirements necessitate additional measures to speed up removal of these residual saturations. Considering the plurality of technical solutions, understanding the benefits and limitations of the different systems is essential. Being the most economic technology at the investigated site, a large-scale in situ bioremediation with nitrate as the alternative electron acceptor was designed and put into operation.

HYDROGEOLOGIC CONDITIONS
AND GROUNDWATER CONTAMINATION

The site subsurface consists of flood-originated loam of 0.5- to 1-m thickness. A mixture of sand, gravelly sand, or sandy gravel with a thickness of about 20 m is located underneath. This layer is intersected at different depths with patchy silt layers of small areal extent. The permeability ranges from 7×10^{-4} to 2×10^{-3} m/s. Lower aquifers are separated by a hydraulically effective aquiclude. The depth to groundwater ranges from 5 to 6 m.

The discharged mixture of hydrocarbons was an intermediate of gasoline production consisting mainly of BTEX aromates. Its solubility in water is relatively high; measurements show about 250 mg/L. Upon recognition of the spill in 1974, hydraulic cleanup measures were implemented immediately to prevent the LNAPL pollution from spreading. The free oil at the groundwater surface had been almost completely removed in 1986, with a recovery of about 2,000 MT of oil.

Only the immobile residual saturation of oil in the pore volume remained in the subsurface. At a depth between 6 to 10 m, limited to the saturated zone, the contamination covered an area of about 7 ha. The vadose zone was not contaminated. With average concentrations of about 1 g/kg, the total amount of oil is estimated to be about 500 MT in 500,000 MT of polluted soil. Concentrations of hydrocarbons in the groundwater varied from 10 to 100 mg/L, spread over an area of about 20 ha. Inside the contaminated area the redox potential was reduced to less than minus 200 mV. Outside the groundwater contains 3 to 5 mg/L of oxygen.

REMEDIATION STRATEGY

In view of the specific conditions at the site, especially the geologic characteristics, the properties of the contaminants and the existing infrastructure, in situ bioremediation with nitrate as an alternative electron acceptor promised to be the most cost-effective technology. The successful application of nitrate for bioremediation of hydrocarbons in the saturated zone had already been reported several times (Battermann 1986; Hutchins et al. 1991, 1994). The decisive benefits of nitrate as a substitute for oxygen are primarily seen in its good solubility and stability in water, and the low price. In contrast to nitrate, the proven means of supplying oxygen (aeration, sparging with oxygen, or addition of H_2O_2) are relatively expensive to implement and operate in sufficient quantities across a large site.

The quantity of water to be circulated, required for the application of the different electron acceptors in the aquifer, may clarify the opportunities and the expenditures (hydraulic equipment, energy, etc.) to be expected. For complete degradation of 1 g of hydrocarbons to carbon dioxide, 4 to 5 g of nitrate or 3 to 3.5 g of oxygen are necessary. Subject to an initial concentration of 4 g hydrocarbons per kilogram of soil, in the case of nitrate (with a concentration in water of 500 mg/L) only 80 m^3 of injection water are required for bioremediation of 1 m^3 of soil. In the case of oxygen, regardless of the source, the solubility is determined by its partial pressure in accordance with Henry's law. Outgassing and loss of oxygen can already occur at very low concentrations (e.g., 10 mg/L and normal pressure). Thus, the quantity of water required for remediation of 1 m^3 of soil comes to about 3,000 m^3. Furthermore, the cost of the same amount of electron acceptor oxygen decomposed from hydrogen peroxide is up to five times higher than that of nitrate.

On the other hand, some limitations can be observed in the use of nitrate. A few laboratory studies, but not all (Major et al. 1988), indicate no initial cleavage of benzene without oxygen. The velocity of microbial degradation under denitrifying conditions is considerably slower.

Limited scaling up from laboratory studies and reservations about nitrate required a pilot-scale field test to prove the efficiency of bioremediation at the site. The overall result of these field experiment (Battermann et al. 1994) with regard to the applicability of nitrate and hydrogen peroxide for in situ bioremediation of the contaminants at this specific site showed that only nitrate is efficient enough and can be distributed over all contaminated areas. In contrast, hydrogen peroxide is efficient only in the vicinity of the infiltration due to its rapid catalytic decomposition and outgassing of the released oxygen. According to the mass balance, a degradation rate of 1 to 2 g of hydrocarbons per cubic meter of soil per day was calculated for normal groundwater temperatures. The measurements indicated doubling of this rate by raising the groundwater temperature 20°C. A rough calculation based on the data provided from the test field shows that, for degradation of all bioavailable hydrocarbons at the site, about 5 years of operation time are necessary.

LARGE-SCALE REMEDIATION

Installations

The location map (Figure 1) shows the initial areal extent of contamination in soil and groundwater and the flushing system. About 500 m^3/h of groundwater are extracted by 16 wells and 400 m^3/h are recharged via infiltration ditches within the 20 ha area of bioremediation. The average residence time of the circulating water in the remediation area ranges from 40 to 60 days. Protection against spreading pollution into surrounding areas requires a net discharge of 100 m^3/h.

The discharged water had to be treated before reinfiltration to remove hydrocarbons, iron, manganese, and bicarbonate. The concentrations of these compounds are so high that they would cause a damaging reduction of recharge capacity in the infiltration ditches due to precipitation and biomass production.

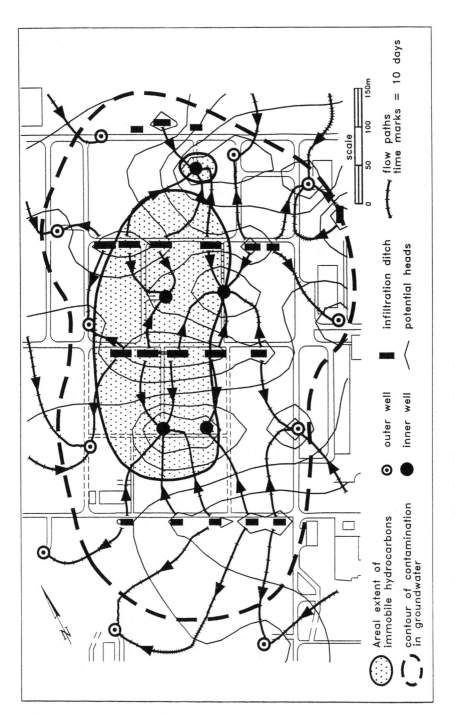

FIGURE 1. Contamination and hydraulic system location map.

The enhancement of bioremediation in the groundwater depends on the increase of available electron acceptors and nutrients. Because of the large amount of contaminants at the site, the dissolved oxygen in the water reinjection is not sufficient, and as a result of the field test, nitrate was chosen as an additional and effective electron acceptor.

As a complementary measure to increase the degradation rate, the groundwater was warmed between 20 and 24°C. It was proven by the field test that a higher temperature has a beneficial effect on the biodegradation rate.

Operation

The large-scale plant has been operating for 3 years with a capacity of about 500 m³/h circulation water. The hydraulic conditions largely correspond with the groundwater flow model calculations. To verify the model based on assumptions, a tracer test was performed over the entire area. Flow conditions and the efficiency of the hydraulic measures as assumed could be proven. The detection of sodium fluorescein, which was used as a tracer, at the partly multilevel observation wells in the upper groundwater layer facilitates a realistic prediction of the overall spreading of nitrate in the circulating groundwater flow.

The next step was to increase nitrate as electron acceptor and inorganic growth factors (phosphate) in the water to be reinjected into the subsurface to enhance bioactivity.

Due to the decrease of recharge capacity of the infiltration ditches after 6 months of operation, the process of remediation was slightly delayed. The cause of the capacity loss could not be determined, but intensive investigations showed that biological processes could be excluded. The problem was overcome by drilling 9-m-deep holes in the infiltration ditches and filling them up with coarse gravel. To exclude one of the possible causes, the P-compound (pyrophosphate) added to the system was changed to a more stable one (hexametaphosphate). In the following years of operation, only slight decreases of infiltration capacity were observed. The time of operation is counted after full infiltration capacity could be ensured. Therefore, only 2 years of full operation time are presented.

The development of significant parameters of groundwater quality in the inner flushing circuit is shown in Figure 2. For a representative interpretation, no spatial differentiation according to the flow to each well is given. The figure shows average values for the 5 inner wells (marked in Figure 1). The other wells partly receive flow from outside the region with immobile saturations. To evaluate the locally differentiated conditions in the whole area of remediation, all measurements of the 16 wells and the approximately 200 observation wells had to be considered.

The concentration of nitrate (not shown in Figure 2) as a function of time depends mainly on the various input concentrations and microbiological depletion. For the first year of full operation, with an input concentration of about 150 mg/L, an average of 100 mg/L of nitrate was degraded. The rate descends to 70 mg/L in the second year. The beginning of the third year shows 60 mg/L. Most probably, this decrease is caused by the diminished area of contamination.

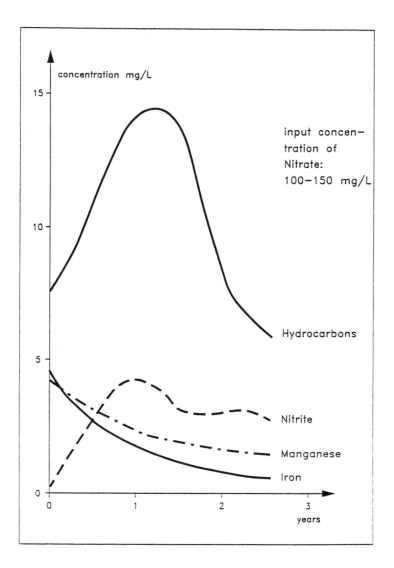

FIGURE 2. Groundwater quality of the inner wells.

According to the result of the field test, the concentrations of nitrite are relatively small and do not exceed 4 mg/L NO_2 (Figure 2). After 1 year of full operation, the maximum is observed. After 2 years, a level of 3 mg/L is established, probably resulting from the more homogeneous degradation.

Depending on the increase of redox potential by nitrate, the initial iron concentrations of 4 mg/L Fe are diminished to 0.5 mg/L. The decrease as a function of time is much slower than observed in the pilot test. This shows the influence of the average passage time (50 days as opposed to 5 days) and the effects of higher macroscopic dispersion by scaling up. The concentrations of manganese are diminishing less rapidly. According to the redox potential defined by nitrate, there is no complete reduction; 1.5 mg/L Mn is observed after 2 years of operation.

The development of hydrocarbon concentrations differs significantly from the observations during the field test. Instead of decreasing, the concentrations are doubled in the first year of full operation. Lower concentrations are not reached until the second year. Therefore, an unexpectedly high amount of hydrocarbons (50 MT in 2 years) extracted with the circulating water could be determined. Similar mobilizing effects, probably caused by the formation of biosurfactants, were observed in several laboratory investigations (Francy et al. 1991). To date, the mobilizing effects still seem to be active. After 2 years of full operation the hydrocarbon concentrations are much higher, as observed after 2 weeks in the field test.

The trend of development can also be drawn from the spatial distribution of hydrocarbons in the groundwater as shown in Figure 3, based on measurements in about 200 observation wells. The number of wells with very low concentrations have increased from 17% to more than 50%. Hydrocarbons are removed in the major part of the area after 2 years of full operation. Today the hot spots of residual saturation can be more exactly localized requiring an adaptation of the hydraulic system.

Balance of Remediation

Economic concerns prohibit a representative investigation of the soil. The amount of hydrocarbons attached to the soil at the beginning of bioremediation and today is only known from estimates. All balances are determined by measurements in the groundwater and the water treatment.

The stoichiometric relationship of equation 1 in Figure 4 assumes complete mineralization whereas equation 2 describes incomplete mineralization with formation of biomass (approximated by the term $C_5H_7O_2N$) and of metabolites (given as dissolved organic carbon [DOC] by the term CH_3COO^-). Measured parameters in the diagram are the net consumption of nitrate and oxygen and the net production of inorganic carbon (dissolved bicarbonate and carbon dioxide). All terms are calculated as mean concentrations in the circulating water.

Assuming complete mineralization as given by equation 1, in the first year of full operation the measured and computed concentrations of inorganic carbon corresponded within a 10% range of validity. Afterwards an increasing discrepancy between measured and calculated inorganic carbon is observed. Using equation 1 gives a disproportion of about a factor of two, as shown in the diagram of Figure 4. Incomplete mineralization according to equation 2 fits better. About 15 mg/L of dissolved metabolites and about 35 mg/L of biomass give a good adjustment to the measured quantities of inorganic carbon. The rate of hydrocarbon removal is increased about two times in comparison to complete mineralization. This assumption is supported by special analytical investigations showing hydrophilic metabolites of various types in total quantities of some 10 mg/L in the extracted water. Under these conditions, more hydrocarbons are removed per unit input of nitrate and oxygen.

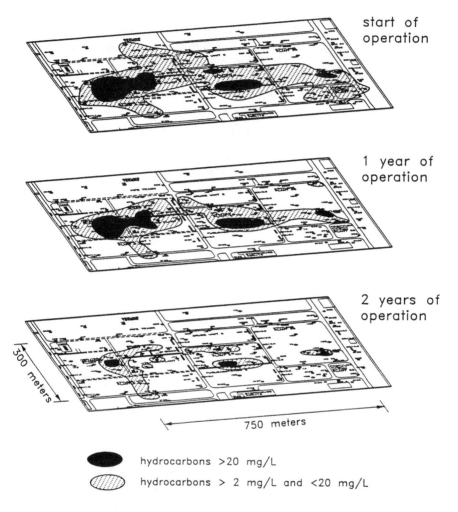

start of
operation

1 year of
operation

2 years of
operation

300 meters

750 meters

⬤ hydrocarbons >20 mg/L

▨ hydrocarbons > 2 mg/L and <20 mg/L

FIGURE 3. Spatial distribution of hydrocarbons in groundwater.

CONCLUSIONS

In situ bioremediation with nitrate as an alternative electron acceptor is a cost-effective technology under the specific conditions at the site. Electron acceptors are available in adequate quantities within the aquifer at any time. Although the degradation rate determined by the pilot-scale field test could not be achieved, large-scale remediation speeds up removal and degradation of hydrocarbons. Furthermore, disadvantageous growth of biomass and outgassing clogging the aquifer may be avoided.

The economic advantages of nitrate are determined by minor rates of circulating water with less expenditure for water treatment and hydraulic installations

Stoichiometric Relationships:

$$(1) NO_3^- + 0.41\ O_2 + 0.19 C_7 H_8 \longrightarrow 0.29\ CO_2 + 1.00\ HCO_3^- + 0.5\ N_2 + 0.24\ H_2O$$

$$(2) NO_3^- + 0.41\ O_2 + 0.46 C_7 H_8 \longrightarrow 0.42\ CO_2 + 0.51\ HCO_3^- + 0.37\ N_2 - 0.06\ H_2O +$$
$$0.26\ C_5 H_7 O_2 N + 0.49 CH_3 COO^-$$

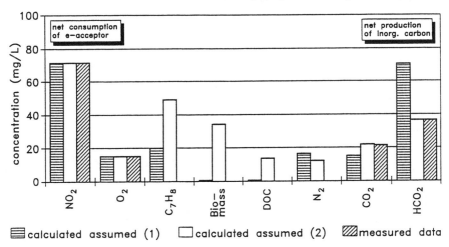

FIGURE 4. Mass balance of bioremediation.

and operation, as well as the low price compared with oxygen. Therefore, large-scale in situ bioremediation of aromatic hydrocarbons in particular often is only feasible by application of nitrate. On the other hand, the use of an oxygen source for remediation may only be considered for parts of sites requiring rapid degradation to reduce loss of time.

REFERENCES

Battermann, G. 1986. "Decontamination of Polluted Aquifers by Biodegradation." In J. W. Assink and W. J. van den Brink (Eds.), *Contaminated Soil*. Martinus Nijhoff Publishers, Dordrecht, Netherlands. pp. 711-722.

Battermann, G., R. Fried, M. Meier-Löhr, and P. Werner. 1994. "Application of Nitrate as Electron Acceptor at an In Situ Bioremediation of an Abandoned Refinery Site: Pilot Study and Large-Scale Operation." In R. E. Hinchee et al. (Eds.), *Hydrocarbon Remediation*. Lewis Publishers, Boca Raton, FL. pp. 93-99.

Francy, D. S., J. M. Thomas, R. L. Raymond, and C. H. Ward. 1991. "Emulsification of Hydrocarbons by Subsurface Bacteria." *J. Ind. Microbiol.* 8:237-246.

Hutchins, S. R., and J. T. Wilson. 1991. "Laboratory and Field Studies on BTEX Biodegradation in a Fuel-Contaminates Aquifer under Denitrifying Conditions." In R.E. Hinchee and R.F. Olfenbuttel (Eds.), *In Situ Bioreclamation*. Butterworth-Heinemann, Stoneham, MA. pp. 157-172.

Hutchins, S. R., and J. T. Wilson. 1994. "Nitrate-Based Bioremediation of Petroleum-Contaminated Aquifer at Park City, Kansas: Site Characterization and Treatability Study." In R. E. Hinchee et al. (Eds.), *Hydrocarbon Remediation*. Lewis Publishers, Boca Raton, FL. pp. 80-92.

Major, D. W., I. C. Mayfield, and J. J. Barker. 1988. "Biotransformation of Benzene by Denitrification in Aquifer Sand." *Groundwater* 26:8-14.

In Situ Bioremediation: Confined Aquifer Contaminated With MGP Wastes

G. L. Nelson, Barry Harrison,
Daniel J. Fetter, and Don E. Richard

ABSTRACT

A field-scale pilot study was conducted at a former manufactured gas plant (MGP) site to evaluate the feasibility of using in situ bioremediation to reduce the concentrations of organic contaminants in the groundwater. The study area was a 3- to 4-m-thick confined silty sand aquifer. The study began with injection of a bromide tracer slug, followed by continuous injection of oxygenated tap water. The injected water was oxygenated using gas-transfer technology for air removal/oxygen dissolution. Long-term trends in groundwater quality have been monitored in downgradient wells to evaluate changes resulting from biological activity. Preinjection measurements of the hydraulic conductivity of the aquifer near the injection well were conducted for comparison with future post-injection testing to quantify potential irreversible fouling of the aquifer by inorganic precipitates of biological fouling. The injection of the oxygenated water began June 7, 1994, and is expected to continue for at least 1 year. Preliminary results indicate that the injected oxygen has been consumed in situ.

INTRODUCTION

The field-scale in situ bioremediation pilot study is being conducted at the Peoples Natural Gas site in Dubuque, Iowa. The pilot study has consisted of baseline groundwater quality monitoring and ongoing groundwater quality monitoring during continuous injection of oxygenated water into a confined silty sand aquifer. Baseline groundwater samples were collected on May 26, 1994. The injection of the oxygenated water began on June 7, 1994.

STUDY AREA

The silty sand aquifer, the area of focus for this study, occurs sandwiched between upper and lower confining clay units as shown on Figure 1. The

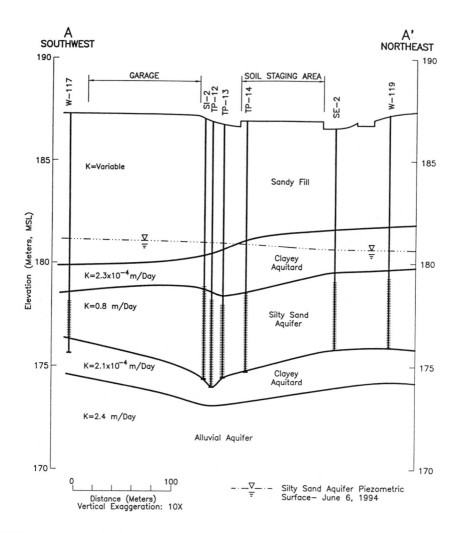

FIGURE 1. Study area geologic cross section.

composition of the silty sand aquifer varies from silty sand to poorly graded sand with silt. The silty sand aquifer is under confined conditions. Water-level data from monitoring wells finished in the silty sand aquifer indicate that the piezometric level may rise 1.5 to 3 m above the top of the aquifer. The direction of groundwater flow is northeasterly at a rate of about 0.8 m/d.

PILOT STUDY LAYOUT

The pilot study layout includes an injection well (SI-2), an existing upgradient monitoring well (W-117), five new temporary downgradient monitoring wells

(TP-12 through TP-16), and a water supply and oxygen dissolution system. All wells are screened across the entire thickness of the silty sand unit. The pilot study layout is shown on Figure 2. Placement of the monitoring well network was guided with the development of a Multiple-Layer Analytic Element Method groundwater model for the site (Strack 1989). Wells were located in an effort to (1) characterize upgradient water quality, (2) provide locations for observing the bromide tracer as it migrated downgradient from the injection well, and (3) provide locations for monitoring groundwater quality and groundwater-level data in the area that potentially could be affected by the injection of the oxygenated water.

A Membran Corporation degassing and oxygen dissolution system was used to boost the dissolved oxygen concentration of tap water from 7 mg/L to approximately 25 mg/L at 17°C. The main features of the system included the potable water supply line from the city water service, a 1,000-L mixing tank with a

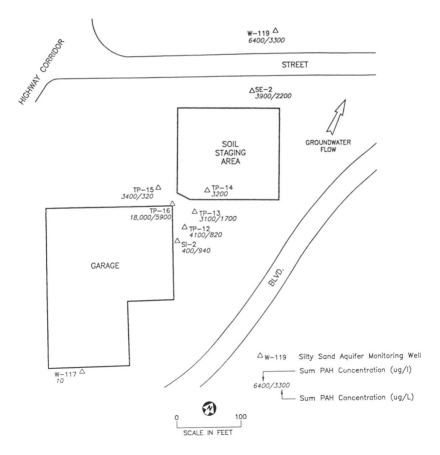

FIGURE 2. Study area monitoring well layout and baseline concentrations for contaminants of concern in groundwater.

degassing unit, a 1,000-L mixing tank with an oxygen dissolution unit, flow metering and control, and a gravity discharge line to well SI-2. This two-step process was used so that the oxygen concentration could be increased to 25 mg/L without exceeding a total gas pressure of 1 atm.

ACTIVITIES COMPLETED

The activities completed during the pilot study, to date, include source material characterization, baseline groundwater quality testing, baseline hydraulic conductivity testing of the silty sand aquifer (not discussed in this report), a bromide tracer test, and ongoing monitoring of hydraulic performance and groundwater quality during continuous injection of oxygenated water into the silty sand.

RESULTS

Source Material Characterization

During installation of the pilot study monitoring well network, oily soils were observed in the silty sand. Nonaqueous-phase liquid (NAPL) saturations appeared to be highest near the top and bottom of the unit. Soils that were reported to have identifiable accumulations of liquid NAPL (LNAPL) were encountered during the installation of wells TP-13, TP-14, and TP-16 (thicknesses of 0.7 m, 1.1 m, and 0.1 m, respectively). Soils with visible accumulations of dense NAPL (DNAPL) were reported in the samples observed during the installation of wells TP-13 and TP-14 (thicknesses of 0.6 m and 1.0 m). Soil samples with an oil sheen were observed during installation of well SI-2.

During the first month of groundwater monitoring, NAPLs were not observed in the monitoring wells. During the second month, an LNAPL thickness of about 0.03 m and a DNAPL thickness of 0.003 m accumulated in the top and bottom, respectively, of well TP-12. At that time, a DNAPL accumulation of about 0.15 m was measured in the bottom of the injection well (SI-2). The observed thickness of LNAPL and DNAPL in well TP-12 has remained fairly constant during the three subsequent monthly monitoring events.

Laboratory analysis of NAPL samples is presented in Table 1. The DNAPL analysis was conducted on a soil sample from well TP-14 that appeared saturated with coal tar. The LNAPL sample was collected from well TP-12 on July 20, 1994.

Baseline Groundwater Quality

The contaminants of concern for this study are benzene, toluene, ethylbenzene, and xylenes (BTEX) and polycyclic aromatic hydrocarbons (PAHs) as defined by the remediation goals for groundwater (U.S. EPA 1992). The baseline (prior to injection) concentrations of these parameters in the silty sand aquifer

TABLE 1. Source material analytical results[a].

Analyte	LNAPL TP-12 07/20/94	DNAPL-Saturated Soil TP-14D 05/12/94
Volatiles		
Benzene	5.4	<0.5
Ethylbenzene	32	<0.5
Toluene	16	<0.5
Xylenes	43	0.5
Carcinogenic PAHs		
Benzo(a)anthracene	<2,000	<6.6
Benzo(b)fluoranthene	<2,000	<6.6
Benzo(k)fluoranthene	<2,000	<6.6
Benzo(a)pyrene	<2,000	<6.6
Carbazole	—	<6.6
Chrysene	<2,000	<6.6
Dibenzo(a,h)anthracene	<2,000	<6.6
Indeno(1,2,3,cd)pyrene	<2,000	<6.6
Noncarcinogenic PAHs		
Acenaphthene	<2,000	8.2
Acenaphthylene	6,200	24
Anthracene	<2,000	9.5
Benzo(g,h,i)perylene	<2,000	<6.6
Dibenzofuran	<2,000	<6.6
Fluoranthene	2,000	10
Fluorene	2,400	14
2-Methylnaphthalene	25,000	80
Naphthalene, semivolatiles	31,000	87
Phenanthrene	7,000	32
Pyrene	3,500	14
Sum of Total PAH Compounds	71,000	280
Total Chromatographable Organics	630,000	1,600
Density, g/cc	0.99	NA[b]

(a) Concentrations in mg/kg, unless noted otherwise.
(b) NA = not analyzed.

are presented on Figure 2. Table 2 presents baseline groundwater data for the silty sand aquifer at wells W-117 and TP-12 for a more extensive list of parameters. The baseline analysis of the major chemical components of silty sand groundwater indicated that the groundwater appeared to be suitable for microbial growth. Contaminants and macronutrients (orthophosphate and ammonia-nitrogen) were detected in sufficient concentrations to support microbial growth.

TABLE 2. Baseline groundwater quality analytical results[a].

Analyte	W-117	TP-12
Contaminants of Concern		
Sum of BTEX	9.2	4,100
Sum of Total PAH Compounds	11	820
Field Parameters		
Redox, mV	−109.4	−43.5
Temperature, °C	14.5	14.8
pH, standard units	7.09	6.60
Specific Conductance @ 25°C	4,300	5,840
Dissolved Oxygen, mg/L	1.84	2.15
Nutrients		
Orthophosphate-P, Total, mg/L	1.59	0.42
Nitrite, mg/L	<0.05	0.07
Nitrate, mg/L	0.06	<0.05
Ammonia Nitrogen, mg/L	125	94.9
Total Kjeldahl Nitrogen, mg/L	151	106
Other Inorganic Parameters		
Total Alkalinity, mg/L	698	893
Bicarbonate Alkalinity, mg/L	698	893
Calcium, filtered, mg/L	213	331
Chloride, mg/L	900	1,210
Chemical Oxygen Demand, mg/L	75	163
Fluoride, mg/L as F	0.58	0.37
Iron, filtered, mg/L	17.8	26
Potassium, filtered, mg/L	9.02	6.52
Magnesium, filtered, mg/L	85.2	152
Manganese, filtered, mg/L	8.32	19.4
Sodium, filtered, mg/L	247	569
Sulfate, mg/L	262	782
Other Organic Parameters		
Total Organic Carbon, mg/L	11.4	42.0
Total Chromatographable Organics	0.51	12
Total Heterotrophic Bacteria, CFUs/mL[b]	<1,000	43,000
Naphthalene-Acclimated Bacteria, CFUs/mL	<1,000	17,000

(a) Concentrations in μg/L, unless noted otherwise.
(b) CFU = colony-forming unit.

However, because the concentrations of bacteria and dissolved oxygen in the groundwater were relatively low, oxygen was believed to be the rate-limiting factor for microbial activity. A relatively depressed redox potential (about −100 mV), coupled with a relatively high chemical oxygen demand (about 100 mg/L), were also indicative of an oxygen-depleted subsurface environment.

Bromide Tracer Study

The bromide tracer slug that was injected into well SI-2 was observed passing through all the downgradient wells (TP-12 through TP-16) in the pilot study area. The breakthrough curves for the bromide plume and the groundwater velocity results from the tracer test for the axial wells (TP-12 through TP-14) are shown on Figure 3. The results of the tracer study demonstrated that all the downgradient wells are hydraulically connected to the injection well. The principal direction of groundwater flow was confirmed to be in a northerly direction. The tracer test indicated hydraulic residence times from the injection well to TP-12, TP-13, and TP-14 to be on the order of 9, 12, and 37 days, respectively (based on center of mass). The average velocity of the plume was approximately 1 m/d. This estimate is in good agreement with that obtained using the hydraulic conductivity calculated from a pump test conducted in well SI-2 prior to injection.

Ongoing Monitoring Activities

Groundwater Elevations. Groundwater elevations in the pilot study wells have been monitored during injection of oxygenated water to (1) quantify the gradients that were present in the silty sand aquifer, and (2) verify that the aquifer near injection well SI-2 did not become fouled. The groundwater elevation at well SI-2 has not exhibited a significant rise relative to other silty sand wells and the nearby Mississippi River, indicating that biological or inorganic fouling of the aquifer has not occurred. Figure 4 presents a comparison of the groundwater elevations at well SI-2 and the elevation of the Mississippi River at the Dubuque gauging station.

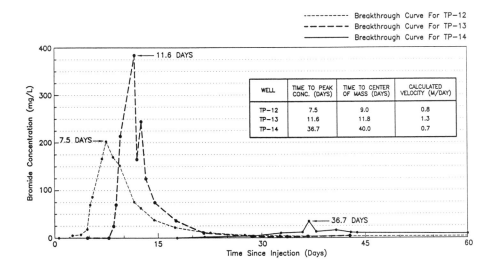

FIGURE 3. Bromide tracer test results.

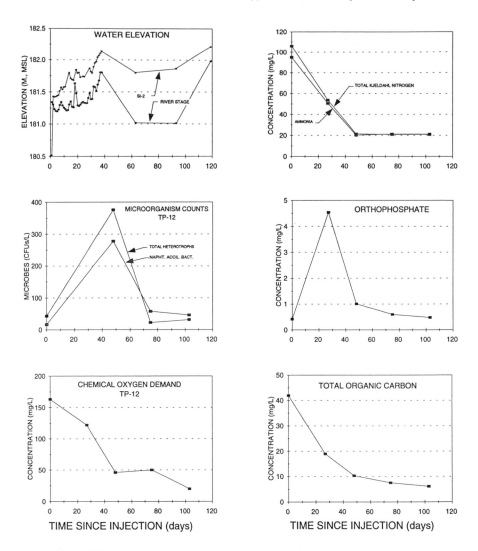

FIGURE 4. Observed trends in system monitoring parameters.

Biological Indicator Parameters. The dissolved oxygen concentration in the pilot study wells (TP-12 through TP-16) downgradient of injection well SI-2 has remained nearly constant at less than 1 mg/L after 4 months of injection. Oxygen breakthrough has not been observed in any of the monitoring wells downgradient of the injection well. Therefore, groundwater monitoring for other indicator parameters has focused on well TP-12 (first downgradient well of injection well SI-2).

Figure 4 also presents the trends of laboratory microbial enumerations of total heterotrophic bacteria and naphthalene-acclimated bacteria, chemical oxygen demand (COD), total Kjeldahl nitrogen, and orthophosphate at TP-12.

CONCLUSIONS

The site hydrogeology appears to be favorable for in situ bioremediation. Indigenous microbial populations have been present in the groundwater at all the monitoring wells. The injection of oxygenated waters into the reduced subsurface environment does not appear to have impaired the permeability of the silty sand unit, and the dissolved oxygen is being consumed during its hydraulic travel from the injection well to TP-12.

The baseline contaminant concentrations and the trends in indicator parameters compiled during the first 4 months of the pilot test suggest that if a zone of biological activity has formed, it is probably still too far upgradient of the first downgradient monitoring well (TP-12) for meaningful changes to be observed in dissolved O_2, contaminant concentrations, and microbial populations. The downward trend in ammonia is believed to be the result of microbial utilization and decreases associated with development of a mound of relatively clean injected water in the vicinity of injection well SI-2. Any decreases that may be occurring in aqueous-phase contaminant concentrations in the zone of bioremediation are likely being diminished between the zone of activity and TP-12 by dissolution of additional contaminants. It is possible that the zone of bioremediation could be advancing downgradient more rapidly along the middle elevations of the silty sand, which are vertically distant from the free-phase NAPLs. In that case, oxygen breakthrough at TP-12 could precede removal of all the source material. The downward trend in COD at TP-12 may be an indicator of this situation.

REFERENCES

Strack, O.D.L. 1989. *Groundwater Mechanics*, Prentice-Hall Inc., Englewood Cliffs, NJ.
U.S. EPA. 1992. *Consent Decree*. Signed by U.S. EPA and settling defendants, May 1992.

In Situ Aquifer Bioremediation of Organics Including Cyanide and Carbon Disulfide

Jacqueline A.M. Abou-Rizk, Maureen E. Leavitt, and Duane A. Graves

ABSTRACT

Low levels (<1 mg/L) of acetone, cyanide, phenol, naphthalene, 2-methylnaphthalene, and carbon disulfide from an inactive industrial landfill were found above background levels in a shallow aquifer at an eastern coastal site. In situ biodegradation was evaluated for treatment of these contaminants. Two soil samples and three groundwater samples were taken from the site for a laboratory bioassessment and a biotreatability test. The positive results of the bioassessment suggested moving forward with biotreatability testing. Biotreatability test results indicated suitable site conditions for bioremediation and that all the contaminants of concern at the site could be biodegraded to nondetect or very low levels (<50 µg/L) with oxygen only; i.e., addition of nutrients was not required. Pilot-scale testing was undertaken on site to provide information for full-scale design, including oxygen requirements and air injection well spacing. This report describes the approach, the results, and their impact on the full-scale remediation system.

INTRODUCTION

Groundwater samples from a landfill's point of compliance (POC) wells (Figure 1) at an eastern coastal site contain slightly elevated concentrations of acetone, naphthalene, 2-methylnaphthalene, phenol, cyanide, and carbon disulfide compared to background well samples. Site characteristics indicated that this site would be ideal for in situ bioremediation. The soil is sandy and permeable, nitrogen and phosphorus are available in the groundwater and soil, the aquifer is shallow and well characterized, and the climate is temperate. Although a literature review provided evidence that all constituents of concern can be biodegraded if conditions are conducive, field parameters were evaluated and biotreatability testing was undertaken to demonstrate that the constituents of concern would biodegrade at the low levels observed on site (less than 1 mg/L).

Additionally, BIOPLUME II was used to estimate field oxygen requirements and to predict treatment effectiveness under site hydrogeologic conditions.

EXPERIMENTAL PROCEDURES AND MATERIALS

A site visit was made to gather field data and samples of soil and groundwater for bioassessment and biotreatability studies. Visual observations were

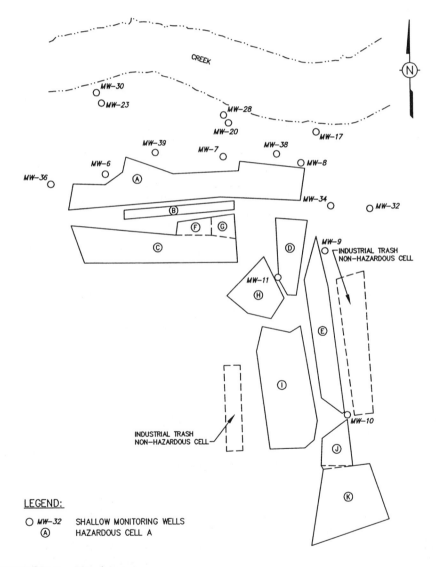

FIGURE 1. Site layout.

made, odors were noted, and redox potential and pH values of purged well samples were measured. Groundwater samples were analyzed for the constituents of concern at an off-site laboratory using U.S. Environmental Protection Agency SW846 Methods for Analysis of Solid Waste (Methods 8240, 8270 and 9012). Experimental work consisted of the bioassessment and the biotreatability study. Additionally, a field pilot-scale test was undertaken.

Bioassessment

The bioassessment was completed to define the parameters that influence the successful application of bioremediation. Three groundwater samples and two soil samples were used in the assessment. Background nutrients, ammonia and orthophosphate, were quantified using an ammonia-specific electrode and spectrophotometry, respectively. Chloride was measured in water samples only using a HACH kit method. Bacterial density was measured using a modification of the spread plate method. Heterotrophs were defined as colonies grown on dilute nutrient agar. Contaminant degraders were defined as colonies grown on mineral salt agar supplemented with phenol, naphthalene, and acetone. Microbial response to nutrient addition was completed using Restore 375® mixed with soil and water samples. The response was quantified by the change in bacterial density as measured by plate counts.

Biotreatability Study

In the biotreatability study, 5 L of groundwater collected from three wells, MW-6, MW-7, and MW-39 (Figure 1), were composited to perform a respirometer and vial microcosm study to determine the biotic and abiotic loss of target compounds over a 24-day incubation period. Solids were not included in the study because of complications typically associated with sampling two matrices within one sample. The lack of solids in each sample did not impact the goal of the study, which was to determine if the compounds could be biodegraded by indigenous organisms. The composite was divided into eleven 2-L bottles and six 40-mL vials. Each treatment described in Table 1 was tested in duplicate. Four sets of composites were used to distinguish among untreated, biologically inhibited, oxygen enhancement, and oxygen plus nutrient enhancement. Untreated samples were sealed and incubated at 4°C for the duration of the study. Biologically inhibited samples were treated with mercuric chloride. Active samples were either aerated or aerated and supplemented with nutrients. Sealed composited samples were spiked with the contaminants of concern so that the final concentration of each was approximately 1 mg/L, except cyanide, which was spiked to a final concentration of approximately 0.1 mg/L. The 2-L bottles were maintained on a computerized respirometer (N-CON, Larchmont, New York) and the oxygen consumption of each bottle was recorded every 2 hours (Figure 2). The 40-mL vials were sealed and maintained on a shaking table. Both the 40-mL vial samples and the untreated controls remained unopened for the duration of the study.

TABLE 1. Biotreatability study treatment scheme and results of constituent analyses.

Treatment	Constituent Concentration (ppb)					
	Phenol	Naphthalene	Methyl-naphthalene	Acetone	Carbon Disulfide	Cyanide
Initial Composite	400	6(J)	5(J)	2100	94	210
Untreated - A	540	7(J)	4(J)	1600	250	340
Untreated - B	490	5(J)	U(15)	1600	300	370
Biologically-Inhibited - 1	U(15)	5(J)	20(J)	1100	U(5)	200
Biologically-Inhibited - 2	470	5(J)	U(15)	1000	U(50)	240
Oxygen-Enhanced - 3	U(15)	U(15)	U(15)	42	U(5)	U(10)
Oxygen-Enhanced - 4	U(15)	U(15)	U(15)	35	U(50)	U(10)
Oxygen-Enhanced plus Nutrients - 5	U(15)	U(15)	U(15)	30	U(5)	U(10)
Oxygen-Enhanced plus Nutrients - 6	U(15)	U(15)	U(15)	37	U(50)	30

(U) = Below method detection limit.
(J) = Value is below detection limit, value is estimated.

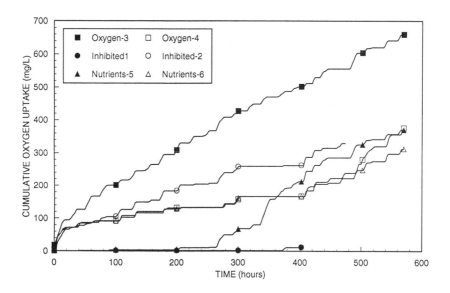

FIGURE 2. Oxygen consumption in biotreatability samples.

At the completion of the biotreatment study, the liquid samples from both the 2-L respirometer bottles and the 40-mL vials were analyzed for the constituents of concern.

BIOPLUME II Modeling

To begin characterizing the contaminant patterns at the site, it was discovered that many of the species were sporadic and inconsistent from one sample point to the next. Two exceptions were acetone and sulfide, each of which was prevalent at many locations and at the same locations from one sampling event to the next. Because of the limited data, all modeling was completed using acetone as the model compound representing contamination in the groundwater. Constituent data were contoured to produce an acetone plume map and a sulfide plume map (Figure 3). These plumes roughly coincide. From this information, a remediation scheme was simulated using a groundwater flowrate of 88 ft (26.8 m)/y, 5 mg/L oxygen, no oxygen recharge, an acetone source at 2 mg/L beneath the landfill, a 1-year anaerobic half-life of acetone, and oxygen injection wells at 0.01 and 0.001 cfs (0.0003 and 0.00003 m^3/s) airflow.

Field Pilot-Scale Testing

An air injection well, an upgradient reference well, and three downgradient progress wells (east, west, and north of the injection well) were installed. Wells were drilled to a depth of approximately 30 ft (9.2 m) (approximately 15 ft [4.6 m] into the water table) for the pilot test. The air injection well has a 1-ft (0.3-m) screen, whereas the other wells have 10-ft (3-m) screens. The injection well is

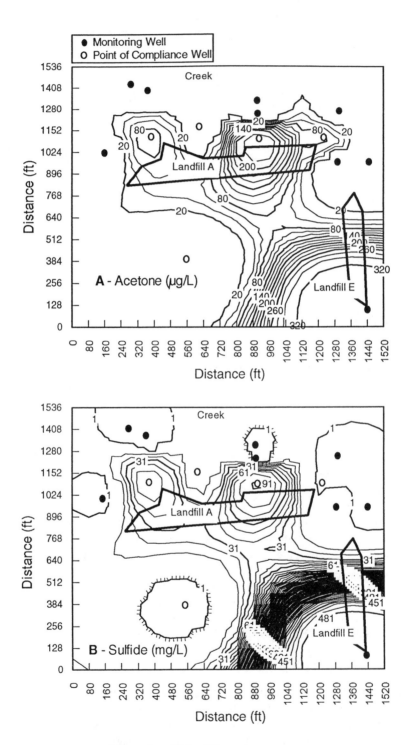

FIGURE 3. Acetone (A) and sulfide (B) contour maps.

connected to a solar-powered blower system consisting of two ⅛-hp compressors that discharge 2 to 4 cfm (0.06 to 0.12 m³/min) at up to 10 psi. The system currently operates at approximately 6 psi, which renders an airflow rate of approximately 2.5 scfm.

Continuous operation of the compressors is ongoing with weekly monitoring of the pH and redox potential of the groundwater. The redox potential has increased to positive values in the progress wells, whereas the reference well redox remains negative. Monthly sampling and analysis of reference well and progress wells will indicate whether the constituents of concern are being treated.

RESULTS

During the site visit, sulfide production was apparent in all locations except the background well, MW-1, based on visual observations (gray tint in water), odor, and redox potential values (ranged from –163 to –264 mV in impacted POC wells) of purged-well samples. Field groundwater samples had acidic pH values ranging from 3.9 to 6.1 (data not shown).

Bioassessment testing determined that nutrients are present in adequate concentrations for biodegradation and that bacteria are present and can be stimulated by addition of oxygen. Ammonia ranges from 16 to 39 mg/L in the groundwater; orthophosphate is below detection limits (<0.5 mg/L) in the groundwater and ranges from 910 to 3,300 mg/kg in the soil (data not shown). Chloride content of the groundwater is low (less than 38 mg/L), indicating little influence from the estuarine receiving water body. Bacterial concentrations were on the low end of the typical range of values in the groundwater samples, ranging from 10^3 to 10^4 colony-forming units (CFU)/mL, but the soil contained up to 10^5 CFU/g. After stimulation with oxygen and nutrients, four of the seven samples showed at least one to two orders of magnitude increase in heterotrophic bacterial density. The contaminant degraders responded with at least one order of magnitude increase in three samples, but the others remained below detection (Table 2). The lack of response may be due to a lack of organic carbon to sustain higher bacterial densities.

The biotreatability study provided evidence that native bacteria could degrade the constituents of concern in the groundwater under untreated and enhanced conditions. Oxygen was consumed in the oxygen-enhanced and in the oxygen- and nutrient-amended samples. Consumption never completely plateaued in any sample, suggesting that biodegradation was slowly ongoing. With one exception, all constituents were brought to below the detection limit in the oxygen-enhanced and the oxygen-enhanced/nutrient-amended samples. The exception was acetone, whose concentration was reduced more than 98% (Table 1). Some acetone reduction occurred in the untreated controls, but acetone can be degraded anaerobically. Final concentrations were from 30 to 42 μg/L and may have fallen to below detection if the study had continued.

Carbon disulfide was completely degraded in the active samples. The initial composite had 94 μg/L and 275 μg/L was the average in the untreated controls.

TABLE 2. Stimulation of the growth of site microbes by enhanced oxygenation and nutrient augmentation.

Sample No.	Total Heterotrophs			Contaminant Degraders		
	Initial (CFU/g)	Oxygen[a] (CFU/g)	Restore[b] (CFU/g)	Initial (CFU/g)	Oxygen (CFU/g)	Restore (CFU/g)
MW-6	3.1×10^3	4.1×10^4	6.8×10^3	$<1.0 \times 10^1$	$<1.0 \times 10^2$	$<1.0 \times 10^2$
MW-7	4.1×10^4	5.9×10^4	5.0×10^2	$<1.0 \times 10^1$	$<1.0 \times 10^2$	$<1.0 \times 10^2$
MW-7-South	1.2×10^3	1.0×10^2	1.0×10^2	$<1.0 \times 10^1$	$<1.0 \times 10^2$	$<1.0 \times 10^2$
MW-7-North	1.0×10^2	6.6×10^4	7.8×10^5	$<1.0 \times 10^1$	$<1.0 \times 10^2$	$<1.0 \times 10^2$
MW-39	4.6×10^4	7.2×10^6	3.8×10^7	3.2×10^4	1.5×10^6	9.5×10^5
MW-7,15-17	8.5×10^6	4.9×10^6	7.6×10^7	3.4×10^5	3.1×10^5	1.1×10^7
MW-7, 18-20	5.2×10^4	$>3.0 \times 10^9$	3.9×10^8	6.6×10^3	1.6×10^6	6.8×10^6

(a) The control treatment was vigorously shaken to provide oxygen to the microbes, but no nutrients were added in addition to those present in the sample material.
(b) Restore treatments are oxygenated and nutrient augmented with 100 mg/kg of the microbial nutrient formulation Restore 375®.

No carbon disulfide was detected in any of the active vessels or the inhibited controls (method detection limit 5 to 500 µg/L). Because no volatilization was noted in the untreated controls, it is likely that the carbon disulfide was transformed in the inhibited controls.

Cyanide was completely degraded in three of the four active vessels and more than 85% degraded in the fourth active vessel. The initial composite averaged 210 µg/L. All of the control vessels had similar concentrations, ranging from 200 to 370 µg/L. Final concentrations ranged from nondetect (method detection limit 10 µg/L) to 30 µg/L.

BIOPLUME II modeling suggests that anaerobic biodegradation is currently reducing contaminant concentrations as the water flows toward the POC wells (Figure 4), but it is occurring slowly and may not protect the receiving water body. However, oxygen enhancement at a minimal rate will provide ample oxygen to degrade the chemicals of concern in the groundwater at a rate that will protect the receiving water body.

Field pilot-scale results were not available at the time this paper was written, but will be presented.

DISCUSSION

The site is an excellent candidate for in situ bioremediation. It has high permeability, sandy soil, available nitrogen and phosphorus in the groundwater and soil, shallow groundwater, temperate climate, biodegradable constituents

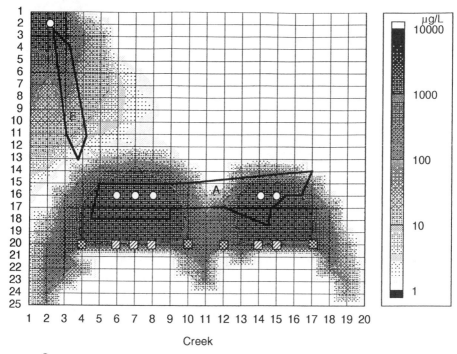

Creek

○ Acetone Leak, 0.01 cfs @ 2,000 ppb

▨ Air sparge unit, 0.01 cfs @ 10,000 ppm

▩ Air sparge unit, 0.001 cfs @ 10,000 ppm

FIGURE 4. Effect of oxygen enhancement on acetone distribution.

of concern, and a resident bacterial population capable of degrading these constituents.

Field analyses and observations and BIOPLUME II modeling results indicate that anaerobic activity is prevalent in the saturated zone; however, the bioassessment testing and the biotreatability study results indicate that adequate nutrients are available for bacterial growth and, under oxygen-enhanced conditions, the constituents of concern can be degraded at a rate adequate to protect the receiving water body.

BIOPLUME II modeling results indicate that minimal oxygen enhancement will reduce constituent concentrations to bring the groundwater into compliance, and that in situ biotreatment will protect the downgradient receiving water body.

No. 6 Fuel Oil Bioremediation in Fractured Bedrock

A. Laszlo Kovacs and Michael C. Landsman

ABSTRACT

No. 6 fuel oil was released from underground storage vessels that were installed in 1968 at a prominent university in Washington, DC. Initial remedial efforts consisted of excavating contaminated soil and saprolite to bedrock. Bioremediation and free-product recovery were chosen as the most feasible alternatives to the remediation of residual impacts. A bioleachate field consisting of a gravel bed covered by plastic sheeting with oxygen and nutrient distribution piping was constructed in the excavated pit. The leachate field was reconstructed following installation of a new tank field to serve as a permanent structure. The long-term in situ microbial degradation portion of the project was developed to reduce total petroleum hydrocarbon (TPH) levels in both the groundwater and the impact zone. A biotreatability bench study has shown a viable microbial population in the subsurface that may be adapted to degrade no. 6 fuel oil. A 1-month-long pilot study, consisting of full-scale nutrient augmentation and air sparging, was implemented. Results from air and water monitoring indicate that stimulation of microbial activity in the vadose and saturated zones is occurring. The bench-scale and field pilot studies indicate a reasonable chance for project success.

INTRODUCTION

The operation and process chosen to remedy no. 6 fuel oil-impacted saprolite and fractured bedrock in northwest Washington, DC, exemplify a synergy of economics and ecology. Based on the physics of wastewater engineering, the system combines physical methods of treatment (unit operation) with a method of treatment in which the removal of the contaminant is brought about by biological reactions (unit process). The unit operation consists of a downgradient groundwater/product recovery well equipped with an automated recovery system. The unit process consists of a leaching field equipped with air and nutrient injection lines and the target area; it follows the approach of letting the treatment find the impacts via the original, naturally occurring flow paths. The leaching field is presented in two parts:

1. Leaching field #1 was built in April 1993 and destroyed in July 1994. It served as a disposable part of the system startup prior to final construction of the tank field (Figure 1).
2. Leaching field #2 was constructed in August 1994 along with the new tank field and is a permanent structure (Figure 2).

The system design takes into account the geologic and structural constraints of the site and provides a low-cost solution for reducing TPH levels.

SITE DESCRIPTION

The site is located in the eastern edge of the Piedmont physiographic province of eastern North America in northwest Washington, DC. During the preliminary environmental site assessment, 38 soil borings were completed to depths ranging from 5 to 25 ft (1.5 to 7.6 m) below the surface using a drill rig; 2-ft (0.6-m) split-spoon samples were collected at 5-ft (1.5-m) intervals; 56 hand auger borings also were advanced to depths of 1 to 10 ft (0.3 to 3.0 m).

Groundwater from seven monitoring wells was analyzed for the presence of benzene, toluene, ethylbenzene, and xylenes (BTEX) and TPH. Soil and groundwater contamination was found to be restricted to a localized area immediately surrounding the tanks (Figure 3). Approximately 100,000 ft^3 (353 m^3) of soil have been impacted by the release of an estimated 5,000 gal (19,000 L) of no. 6 fuel oil over a period of roughly 10 years. Weathered bedrock (saprolite) in this area comprises the upper 15 to 20 ft (4.6 to 6.1 m) above the unweathered bedrock. Depth to groundwater ranges approximately 25 to 32 ft (7.6 to 9.8 m) below grade. Vadose soil samples were characterized as sandy silt to silt; the expected hydraulic conductivity (k) value is on the order of 1.04×10^{-4} darcy (10^{-9} m/s).

Porosities of unfractured plutonic igneous and metamorphic rocks are rarely larger than 2%, resulting in extremely small primary permeabilities [(0.00019 millidarcy) (10^{-11} to 10^{-13} m/s) (Stuart et al. 1954)]. The bedrock at the site generally has a very low porosity except in the open joints and fractures; the hydraulic conductivity in the fractures (secondary porosity) is estimated at 0.0364 darcy (3.5×10^{-7} m/s). Depending on fracture characteristics (i.e., apertures and density), the hydraulic conductivity of fractured igneous rocks ranges from one to 10^2 m/day (Todd 1980). In the bedrock, the primary contaminant migration is along fractures.

A field study mapped unmineralized joints and open fractures, the most common mesoscopic structural features in the local bedrock. A total of 104 strike-and-dip measurements (data points) were collected from 10 outcrops using a Brunton compass. Stereographic representation of the data points showed two preferred joint and fracture orientations. One joint set is vertical, tightly spaced (less than 30 cm), and oriented southeast to northwest. The conjugate set is similar, but is oriented to the southwest to northeast. Groundwater level measurements show a

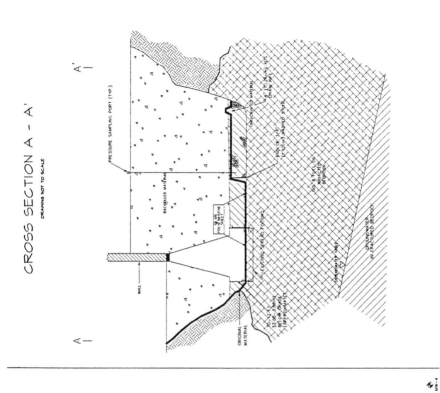

FIGURE 1. Leaching field #1.

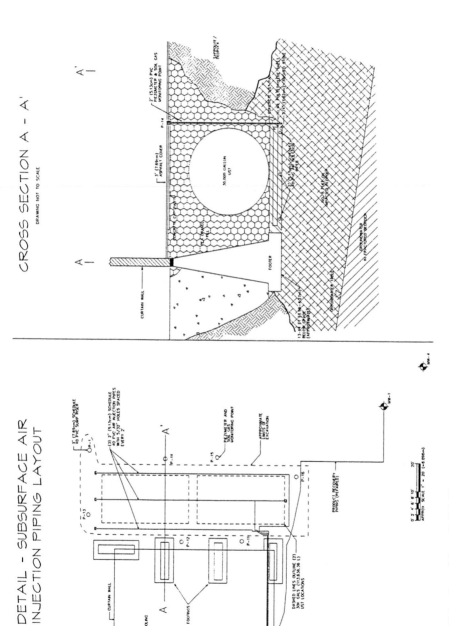

FIGURE 2. Leaching field #2.

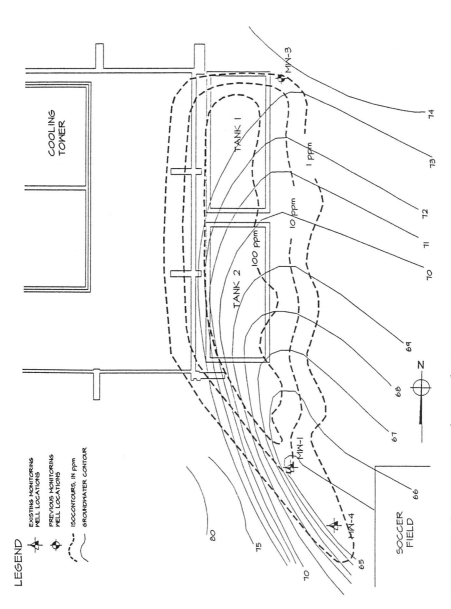

FIGURE 3. Isocontours and groundwater contours.

southeast flow direction. Based on the field study, there is a high probability that monitoring wells MW-1 and MW-4 intercepted joints in the preferred groundwater flow direction. An air injection/vapor extraction study confirmed the connectedness of the two downgradient monitoring wells with the leach gallery.

The presence of more than 10^4 colony-forming units (CFU)/gm of petroleum-degrading heterotrophs in several samples was a positive indicator for biological activity (Envirogen Inc. 1993, unpublished data). Orthophosphate and nitrogen were not detected above the instrument detection levels, 0.5 mg/kg and 5 m/kg, respectively, and nitrate was not detected in half of the samples. The pH values ranged from 6.0 to 8.0 (typical remedial designs range from 6.5 to 8.0). A 5-month bench-scale study showed that a nutrient-amended sample with total viable CFU/gm soil ranging from 2.3×10^5 to 8.8×10^6 and contaminant-specific CFU/gm soil ranging from 9.2×10^4 to 3.1×10^6 decreased TPH concentration by 61% (initial concentration of 5,700 mg/kg to final concentration of 2,200 mg/kg).

SYSTEM DESIGN

The remedial system design incorporates two methods: a unit operation involving the removal of free product from the groundwater table, and a unit process in which biological reactions are accelerated to reduce TPH levels in the groundwater. The main components of the system are listed in Table 1.

The leaching field design takes advantage of the perched water forming in the tank pit. The perched water results from the hydraulic conductivity differential between the gravel fill in the tank field and the fractured bedrock (Figure 4). The air injection lines are situated within the saturated zone of the perched "pond" and surrounded by gravel to provide a porosity percent range of approximately 30% (Morris and Johnson 1967).

The leaching gallery serves as a nutrient-enriched aeration pond. Oxygen- and nutrient-enriched water percolates through the unsaturated impacted zone to the aquifer following the paths taken by the no. 6 fuel oil.

Nutrients, in the form of a commercially available product (Microcat NP, by Bioscience, Inc.), are dissolved manually at the surface in 55-gal (208.2-L)

TABLE 1. System components.

Unit Operation	Unit Process
• Compressor	• Explosion-proof regenerative blower (2.0 HP, 160 SCFM max. flow)
• Air Regulator	
• Electronic Controller	• Air/nutrient distribution lines (2 in. [5.1-cm] schedule 40 PVC with ball valves and pressure gauges)
• Pneumatic Pump	• Leaching field (pond in gravel bed)

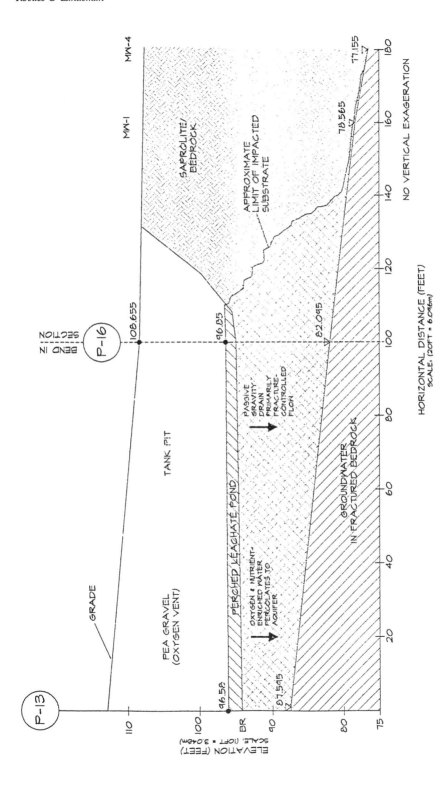

FIGURE 4. Cross section of leaching field and impacted zone.

steel drums and introduced into the leachate gallery via the piezometers. The elemental breakdown of the nutrient product is nitrogen, 33%; phosphorus, 12%; hydrogen, 7%; oxygen, 42%; and carbon, 6%. Nutrient amendments are made using a mixture of approximately 1,200 gal of H_2O per pound (10,021 L per kg) of nutrient product. A maximum nitrate concentration of 10 mg/L is maintained at the recovery wells in order to comply with U.S. Environmental Protection Agency (EPA) drinking water criteria.

MONITORING STRATEGY

The various parameters monitored in the soil gas and water (leachate field and groundwater) are listed in Table 2. The presence of nutrients in water increases the electrical conductivity. The presence of nutrients, migrated vertically and laterally from the leaching gallery, is expected to appear as an increase in electrical conductivity and total dissolved solids. Relatively inexpensive colorimetric field test kits are also used to monitor nutrient concentrations.

Typical exothermic biochemical reactions (those that release energy) have the following basic stoichiometric equations:

$$C_6H_{12}O_6 + 6O_2 \rightarrow 6CO_2 + 6H_2O \tag{1}$$

for heterotrophic, aerobic; and

$$C_6H_{12}O_6 \rightarrow 3CH_4 + 3CO_2 \tag{2}$$

for heterotrophic, anaerobic (Metcalf and Eddy, Inc. 1979).

Microbial degradation of the hydrocarbons is expected to be manifested in a decrease in biochemical oxygen demand (BOD) and TPH in the water and an increase in CO_2 and CH_4 in the soil gas, as well as an increase in dissolved CO_2 in the water.

TABLE 2. Parameters monitored.

Soil Gas	Water
• Oxygen (O_2)	• Dissolved oxygen (DO; %)
• Carbon dioxide (CO_2)	• Dissolved carbon dioxide (CO_2; ppm) mg/L
• Methane (CH_4)	• Conductivity (μS)
	• pH
	• Temperature (°C)
	• Ammonia nitrogen (ppm) mg/L
	• Nitrate (ppm) mg/L
	• Phosphate (ppm) mg/L

SYSTEM STARTUP/PILOT STUDY

Operation of the free product recovery system was initiated on June 18, 1993, and, except for temporary shutdowns for adjustments, it continues to operate. The first leaching gallery (leaching field #1), part of the unit process, was constructed in April 1993 at the time of backfilling of the old tank pit. System loading was initiated on March 10, 1994, with the injection of approximately 200 lb (90.7 kg) of nutrient product over a 4-week period and air sparging in the leaching gallery following approval by Washington, DC, Regulatory Affairs of the bioremediation pilot study. Water used to dissolve the nutrient product was extracted from the upgradient riser in the leaching field and injected into downgradient piezometers.

Biological activity and nutrient distribution were evaluated by monitoring soil gas and water quality characteristics in the leaching field (Figures 5 through 7). Initial values represent average pretreatment baseline measurements.

Oxygenation of up to 7.42 mg/L dissolved oxygen was achieved by sparging atmospheric air through the Advanced Drainage Systems (ADS) drainpipe and into the saturated gravel bed of the leaching field using a regenerative blower with a pressure capacity of 80 scfm (2.3 m^3/min) at 62 in. of water (2.375 psi). The regenerative blower was operated continuously at 30 in. (76.2 cm) of water pressure during the course of the study and produced an airflow into the leaching field of approximately 110 ft^3/min (3.1 m^3/min).

SYSTEM OPERATION/BIOVENTING TESTS

Biorespiration tests were conducted following initiation of bioventing on June 1, 1994, marking the full-scale startup of the unit process. The respiration tests consisted of periodic monitoring of oxygen (O_2) and carbon dioxide (CO_2) levels in the leaching field over a 4-day period following blower shutdown. Soil gas samples collected from the piezometer were analyzed in the field using a portable electrical gas monitor. Declining levels of O_2 and slightly increasing levels of CO_2 were interpreted as indirect evidence of biodegradation. Figures 8 and 9 present data from the biorespiration tests. Indirect methods of testing the efficiency of biodegradation are being employed because direct evidence of the magnitude of no. 6 fuel oil conversion to bacterial cells is not feasibly obtainable.

CURRENT DEVELOPMENTS

Construction of the new leaching gallery (see Figure 2) was completed in August 1994, together with the new tank field. The new design was developed to maximize utility while conforming to limits posed by the tank field. Air sparging capabilities were improved with three air/nutrient distribution lines below the

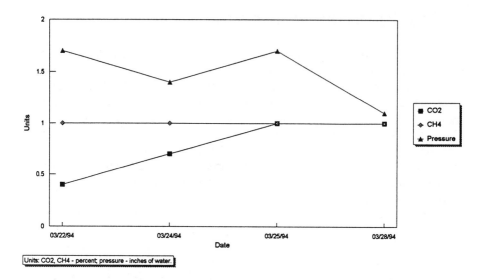

FIGURE 5. Soil gas measurements (MW-4).

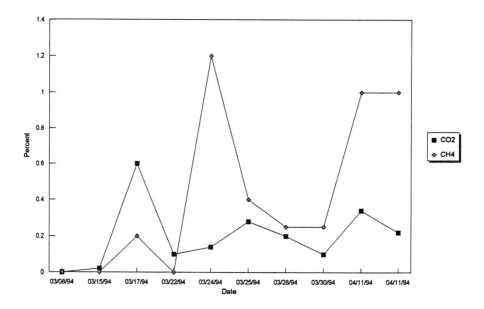

FIGURE 6. Average soil gas measurements.

tank slab. The leaching gallery refilled with rainwater and water from the unsaturated zone (water column not exceeding 25 in. [63.5 cm] and above the bedrock surface). Performance of the new leaching field has been monitored by measuring dissolved oxygen levels. Figure 10 shows a favorable trend. Increased CH_4 and

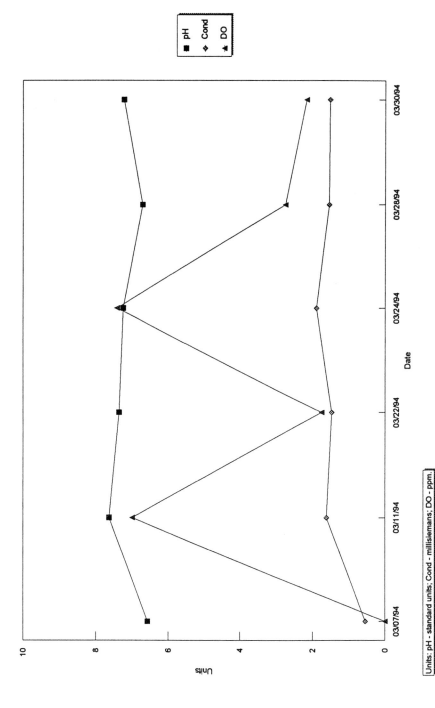

Units: pH - standard units; Cond - millisiemans; DO - ppm.

FIGURE 7. Average water measurements.

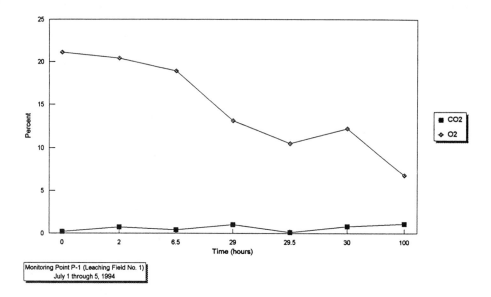

FIGURE 8. Bioventing test, monitoring point P-1 (leaching field #1).

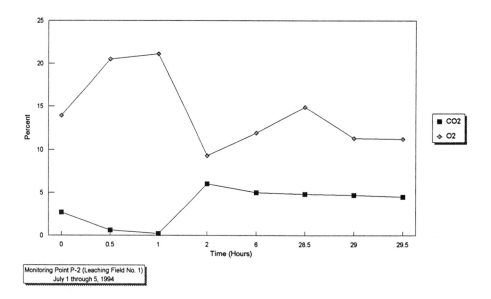

FIGURE 9. Bioventing test, monitoring point P-2 (leaching field #1).

CO_2 in soil gas monitored in MW-1 and MW-4 are positive indicators of microbial degradation of the hydrocarbons (see Figures 11 and 12).

The new tanks operate with heated fuel oil (180°F [82.22°C]). Heat from the tanks is transferred to the leaching pond. Temperatures in the leaching pond

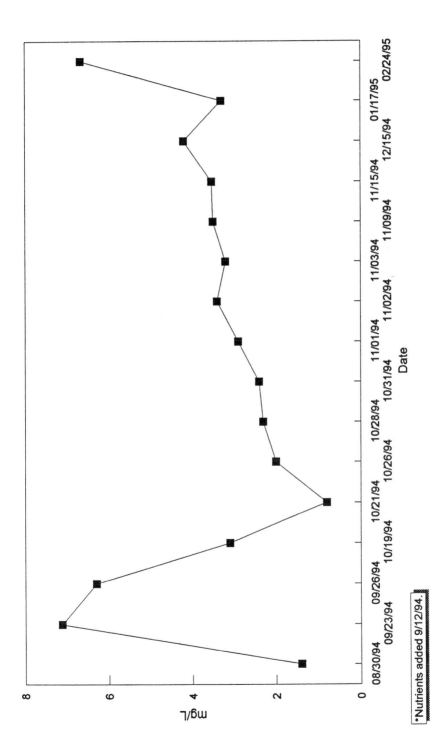

FIGURE 10. Average dissolved oxygen (leaching field #2).

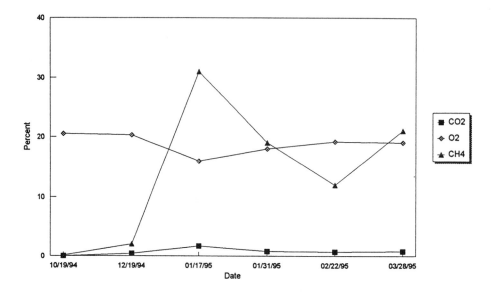

FIGURE 11. Soil gas measurements, MW-1.

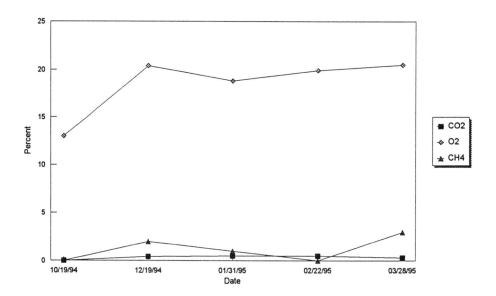

FIGURE 12. Soil gas measurements, MW-4.

range from 40 to 45°C. The rate of reaction for microorganisms increases with increasing temperature, doubling with about every 10°C rise in temperature until some limiting temperature is reached (Metcalf and Eddy 1979). Mesophilic bacteria function best in a temperature range of 20 to 45°C. The optimum range is 25°C to 40°C (Metcalf and Eddy 1979). Heat loss is expected to occur in the unsaturated zone as the heated nutrient and oxygen-enriched pond water percolates downward. Heated water and bedrock may also act to lower the viscosity of entrained no. 6 fuel oil. A few days after the pond water reached a maximum heat of 45°C, a product thickness increase was detected in MW-1 from a sheen to 0.05 ft (1.5 cm). A drastic increase in product thickness to 1.12 ft (34.1 cm) was detected in MW-1 in March 1995 coupled with an increase in TPH and BTEX

TABLE 3. Groundwater analytical data.

Monitoring Well Number	Sample Date	TPH (mg/L)[a]	Detection Limit (mg/L)	Total BTEX (µg/L)[b]	Detection Limit (mg/L)
MW-1	3/22/95	220	50	21.9	1
	12/9/94	48	5.0	6.7	1
	9/8/94	ND[c]	0.5	5.6	1
	6/8/94	12	0.5	13.1	1
	4/14/94	130	0.5	ND	1
	3/30/94	18	0.5	ND	1
	3/11/94	48	0.5	ND	1
	12/28/93	13	0.5	24.9	1
	11/30/93	100	5.0	39	1
	10/26/93	NS[d]	NS	106	1
	10/28/93	7.2	0.5	NS	NS
	9/24/93	180	1.0	43	1
	8/9/93	102	0.5	110	10
	7/9/93	16	0.5	<1	1
	6/9/93	6.7	1.0	12	1
MW-4	3/22/95	28	5	3.3	1
	12/9/94	11	0.5	2.7	1
	9/8/94	36	0.5	1.3	1
	6/8/94	2.2	0.5	3.7	1
	4/14/94	20	0.5	5.4	1
	3/30/94	67	0.5	ND	1
	3/11/94	43	0.5	ND	1
	12/28/93	2.2	0.5	3.6	1
	11/30/93	11	0.5	12	1
	10/26/93	NS	NS	<1	1
	10/28/93	<0.5	0.1	NS	NS
	9/24/93	22	0.5	2	1
	8/9/93	28	0.5	3	1
	7/9/93	0.88	0.5	<1	1
	6/9/93	<1.0	1.0	<1	1

(a) mg/L = milligrams/liter (approximately equal to parts per million).
(b) µg/L = micrograms per liter (approximately equal to parts per billion).
(c) ND = compound not detected at or above the detection limit.
(d) NS = not sampled.

levels in groundwater (Table 3). The hydrocarbon spike occurred following an increase in CH_4 and CO_2 and is believed to result from the desorption of residual hydrocarbons brought on by emulsifying agents produced by the oil-degrading microorganisms in the target area.

CONCLUSIONS

Overall the biodegradation system appears to be operating favorably. Contaminant values are expected to decrease over the next 3 years. Monitoring will continue until that time. Soil gas measurements in MW-1 are expected to exhibit increased CO_2 and CH_4 values as the treatment moves downgradient.

ACKNOWLEDGMENTS

Personnel instrumental in the success of this project include Michael Vandemark, Kevin O'Brien, Larry Deschaine, Matthew Van Patten, Kent Campbell, and Vincent DiRenzo. Also acknowledged is the support of Aurora Morris and Sheila White. This remedial program has been made possible by the environmentally conscious efforts and cooperation of Georgetown University and the Washington, DC, Department of Consumer and Regulatory Affairs.

REFERENCES

Metcalf and Eddy Inc. 1979. *Wastewater Engineering: Treatment, Disposal, Reuse*, p. 401. McGraw-Hill Inc., Boston, MA.

Morris, D. A., and A. I. Johnson. 1967. *Summary of Hydrologic and Hydrologic and Physical Properties of Rock and Soil Materials, as Analyzed by the Hydrologic Laboratory of the U.S. Geological Survey 1948-60*. U.S. Geological Survey Water-Supply Paper 1938-D, 42 pp.

Stuart, W. T., E. A. Brown, and E. C. Rhodehamel. 1954. *Groundwater Investigations of the Marquette Iron-Mining District*. Michigan Geological Survey Tech. Report 3.

Todd, D. K. 1980. *Groundwater Hydrology*, 2nd ed. John Wiley & Sons, Inc., New York, NY.

Bioremediation of Oil on Shorelines With Organic and Inorganic Nutrients

Per Sveum and Svein Ramstad

ABSTRACT

Two experiments to study the mechanisms associated with nutrient-enhanced biodegradation of oil (Statfjord crude oil)-contaminated shorelines were done in continuous-flow seawater exchange basins with simulated tides. The fertilizers included fish meal pellets, stick water pellets, and two concentrations of Max Bac: standard and five times higher. Both one-time and repeated additions of fish meal were studied. The number of oil-degrading bacteria in the sediment increased by three to four orders of magnitude after adding oil and fertilizer, and repeated fertilization had little effect. Oil degradation was found to be extensive with all treatments in both experiments, which lasted 35 or 98 days. Polycyclic aromatic hydrocarbon degradation seems to be most extensive in the sediments with repeated application of fish meal. The relation between accumulated total soluble nitrogen in interstitial water and nC_{17}/pristane differs between the sediments treated with Max Bac and the organic additives, and indicates that this concentration cannot be used as a sole indication of the oil degradation rate if organic nutrients are used. The relation between accumulated CO_2 production and nC_{17}/pristane ratio indicates a diauxic use of the two different sources of carbon present, without being absolute. Repeated fertilization with organic additives is neither beneficial nor detrimental to the oil degradation activity.

INTRODUCTION

Although bioremediation of oil-contaminated shorelines through addition of fertilizers has proven to be an effective cleaning method (Bragg et al. 1994), the technique is still in its infancy. Enhancement of biodegradation by fertilizer addition relies on the well-accepted fact that essential nutrients such as nitrogen, phosphorous, and iron are limiting to oil-degrading microbes (Atlas and Bartha 1972; Dibble and Bartha 1976). These nutrients can be added as fertilizer mixtures (e.g., Atlas and Bartha 1973; Bragg et al. 1994; Ladousse and Trainer 1991; Olivieri et al. 1976), although only a few fertilizers especially designed for use on shorelines are commercially available. Bragg et al. (1994) demonstrated that differences in biodegradation rates resulted from different levels of soluble nitrogen in sediment pore waters. Since the fate of the nutrients after addition will determine whether sufficiently high levels can be maintained for successful bioremediation, it is possible that the form of the limiting nutrients in the fertilizer is important.

Shorelines are characterized by several dynamic processes, of which the water filtering through the sediment is a major physical process of deterministic importance for oil biodegradation. The water filtered through the intertidal interstices of beach sediments depends on the sediment characteristics, as well as the beach topography and the tide, and can exceed more than 18 $m^3 \cdot m^{-1} \cdot day^{-1}$ (McLachlan 1982; Riedl 1971). It affects biodegradation of oil by enhancing the physical self-cleaning of the sediment via flushing (Sveum and Bech 1994), and simultaneously decreases the effect of the bioremediation by removing added fertilizers or their dissolved products and bacteria.

The adaptation of the indigenous bacterial community to the contaminating oil and the added nutrients is the key parameter for successful bioremediation. It is therefore of considerable interest to understand interactions between the nutrients, their behavior, and the microbial community.

The goal of the present paper is to discuss mechanisms and interactions connected to the use of organic additives as fertilizers for oil-contaminated shorelines.

MATERIALS AND METHODS

Mesoscale experiments were done in continuous-flow seawater exchange basins (Sveum et al. 1995) measuring h × w × l = 1 × 2 × 4 (m). The shorelines (h × w × l = 0.9 × 2.0 × 2.2 [m], i.e., the slope was 0.4) consisted of initially pristine sand and gravel beach material of marine origin. Basin seawater levels varied according to a normalized tidal cycling. The seawater exchange rate was 1,200 L/h and the average seawater temperature was approximately 10°C.

The basins were operated with tidal variation, generated waves, and seawater exchange for 7 days prior to oil application to establish marine conditions in the sediment. Statfjord crude oil (150+) (2080 mL·m^{-2}) was added at high tide on the water surface and allowed to inundate and contaminate the beach as the water level fell.

Additives were added either once, one day after oiling (Experiment 1), or at regular intervals beginning one week after oiling (Experiment 2). The treatments are summarized in Table 1, and the composition of the three additives is given in Table 2.

Sediment samples from the intertidal part of the shoreline were taken according to a randomized and stratified strategy. The shoreline was stratified into four 60-cm sections. A 10 × 10-cm sample was taken from each section according to a random number system. For oil analysis, three samples were taken from the

TABLE 1. Experimental design in the two experiments in the continuous-flow seawater exchange basin.

Experiment	Basin	Treatment	Time of Treatment	Added Amount (grams)
1	A	Stick water pellets (3 mm)	Start of experiment	1,680
	B	Max Bac	Start of experiment	1,340
	C	Fish meal pellets (3 mm)	Start of experiment	1,680
	D	Max Bac	Start of experiment	6,700
2	A	Fish meal pellets (3 mm)	Start of experiment	1,680
	B	Fish meal pellets (3 mm)	Every week	1,680 + 252[a]
	C	Fish meal pellets (3 mm)	Every third week	1,680 + 252[b]
	D	Max Bac	Start of experiment	1,340

(a) 252 g added every week after initial addition of 1,680 g.
(b) 252 g added every third week after initial addition of 1,680 g.

upper 3 cm, with a steel sampling box. Particles with a diameter above 10 mm were discarded. Samples for nutrient and microbial analysis were taken from the upper 3 cm of the sediment with a spatula.

Total heterotrophic respiration in the sediment was measured as the total CO_2 produced using a Siemens Ultramat 10 Infrared Gas Analyzer modified for

TABLE 2. Composition of the additives used in the two continuous-flow seawater exchange basin experiments.

Name	Description	N(%)	P(%)	C(%)	Other Comp.
Fish meal	Protein	10.5[a]	2.0[b]	46.8[a]	40[c]
Stick water	Protein	11.3[a]	1.4[b]	41.8[a]	45[d]
Max Bac	NH_4NO_3, $Ca_3(PO_4)_2$, $(NH_4)_3PO_4$	28.0[b]	3.5[b]	—	[e]

(a) Analyzed on a Carlo Elmer element analyzer.
(b) Data given by the supplier.
(c) Fat (12%), water (10%), minerals and vitamins (11%).
(d) Water (30%), minerals and vitamins.
(e) Grains encapsulated in polymerized vegetable oil.

septum injection. CO_2 from samples contained in sealed bottles at 20°C was measured three times during 4 h of incubation.

The number of oil-degrading bacteria was determined by the Sheen Screen most probable number (MPN) method (Brown and Braddock 1990). Statfjord crude oil (150+) was used as the hydrocarbon source. The sediment samples (approximately 2 g) were mixed with filtered seawater (10 mL) for 30 min on a rotary mixer in sterile test tubes. The MPN plates were read after 7 and 14 days.

The total number of heterotrophic bacteria was enumerated after staining with 4,6-diamino-2-phenylindole (DAPI) (Porter and Feig 1980): the sediment sample (approximately 1 g) was suspended in a proteose peptone (1 g/L) and sodium hexametaphosphate solution (2 g/L), mixed on a Whirl mixer for 1 min, and filtered through a black band filter (Schleicher & Schuell no. 589) to remove oil and other particles. The filtrate (100 µL) was diluted in filter-sterilized distilled water (9.9 mL) and mixed well with DAPI solution (600 µL). The sample was allowed to settle for 5 minutes before filtration. The cells were collected on a prestained (black) polycarbonate filter (Costar no. 110656, 0.22 µm) and counted in a Leitz Dialux 20 Research Microscope equipped with a fluorescence Ploemopac device (UV-filter A).

Nitrogen and phosphorus were determined colorimetrically on an automatic nutrient analysis system (Aquatec, Tecator AB, Höganäs, Sweden). Both sediment samples and water samples from the interstitial pore volume were analyzed. The water samples were analyzed for ammonium, nitrite/nitrate, total oxidized nitrogen, phosphate, and total phosphorus. The total amount of ammonia and organic nitrogen in sediment samples was determined as ammonia after digestion with a modified Kjeldahl method with a selenium catalyst in the digester unit (Tecator AB, Hugeness, Sweden).

Oxygen concentrations in the interstitial water were measured in samples from the perforated wells (15 cm deep) in the shoreline. The samples were taken from the well, after removal of approximately two well-volumes of water, when the water level in the basin was at the top of the well, and transferred to a flask with limited exposure to air. The oxygen content was measured with a polarographic oxygen electrode (Schott Gerate 9002/2). Control experiments directly in the well gave similar results.

Hydrocarbons in sediment samples were extracted with *n*-hexane using a Soxtec System HT6 (Tecator AB, Hugeness, Sweden) at 140°C for 2 h. The resulting oil-hexane solution was filtered through a 0.22-µm filter before analysis on a Hewlett Packard 5890 Series II gas chromatograph equipped with flame ionization detector and a splitless injector. Oil biodegradation was evaluated from the nC_{17}/pristane ratio. It should be noted that when the nC_{17}/pristane ratio of Statfjord crude is below approximately 0.6, it seems to underestimate biodegradation of the oil.

The sediment oil content was measured gravimetrically after soxhlet extraction. The extracted oil samples were separated into three fractions through solid-phase extraction (Bond Elute) with a method modified from Radke et al. (1980).

RESULTS AND DISCUSSION

Figures 1 and 2 show the nutrient concentrations measured in the Experiment 1 sediments. The sediments treated with the organic additives fish meal and stick water showed an initially high level of nutrients in the interstitial water, which gradually decreased during the experiment. Max Bac had a similar effect, although the decrease was more rapid and to a lower level. No statistically significant differences were found between nutrient concentrations for the treatments when tested (student's paired t-test). The initial high concentrations seen with Max Bac is probably due to release of nutrients from grains with damaged surfaces. The average weight loss of intact Max Bac grains was less than 10% during the experimental period, indicating that the release of the nutrients was very slow. This may be partly due to the fact that the grains were added at the beginning of the experiment (i.e., 1 day after application of the oil) when there was still oil on the water surface in the basin. As a result, oil stuck to the grain surface might have altered the nutrient-release properties of the fertilizer. The increase in total nitrogen concentration with time in the sediment fertilized with the highest concentration of Max Bac might then be due to biological degradation or physical removal of the oil covering the grain surface. In Experiment 2, similar trends were observed, but with a significant increase in the concentration of soluble nitrogen and ammonium in the basin with repeated addition of additives every third week and weekly (student's paired t-test, Abs(Dif)-LSD 0.16 and 0.13, and 0.29 and 0.25, respectively; cf. SAS 1989 for statistical details).

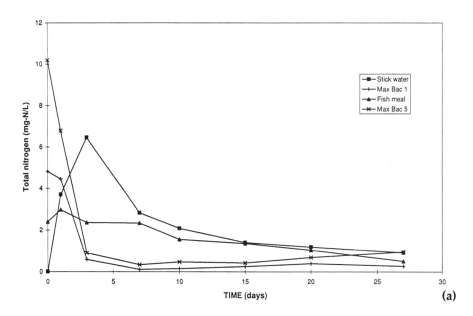

FIGURE 1. Concentration of soluble nitrogenous nutrients in the interstitial water from Experiment 1. (a) Total oxidized nitrogen.

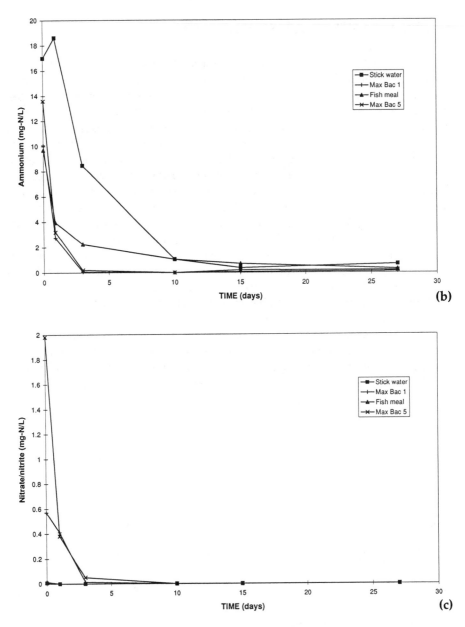

FIGURE 1 (continued). Concentration of soluble nitrogenous nutrients in the interstitial water from Experiment 1. (b) Ammonium. (c) Nitrate/nitrite.

The number of oil-degrading bacteria in the sediment increased by three to four orders of magnitude after the addition of oil and fertilizer (Figure 3). The sediments with one time and weekly addition of fish meal were significantly different from the basins with addition of fish meal every third week and with

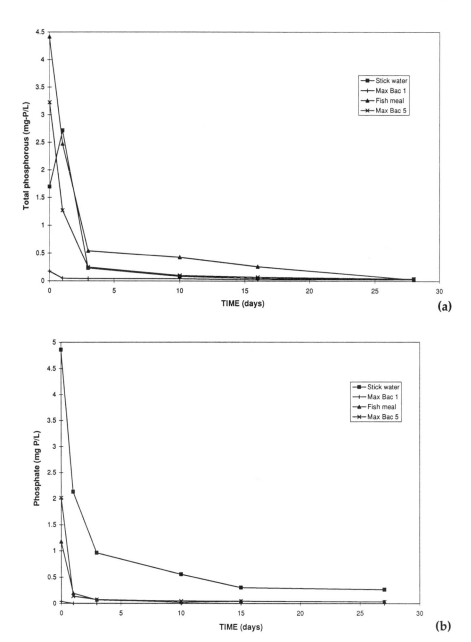

FIGURE 2. Concentration of soluble phosphorous nutrients in the interstitial
water from Experiment 1. (a) Total phosphorous. (b) Phosphate.

Max Bac (student's paired t-test, Abs(Dif)-LSD 1×10^7 and 3×10^6, respectively).
The differences indicate that repeated application of fertilizers might affect
the level of oil-degrading bacteria. In Experiment 1, significant differences were

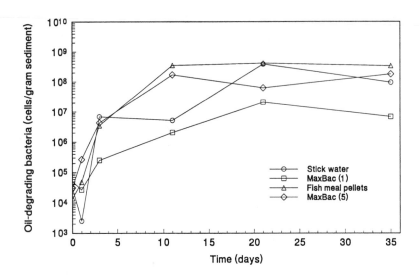

FIGURE 3. The number of oil-degrading bacteria in sediment samples from Experiment 1.

found between the basin treated with stick water and all the other treatments, and between the two levels of Max Bac (student's paired t-test, Abs(Dif)-LSD between 1.9×10^7 and 6×10^7, respectively). This indicates that the level of oil-degraders are influenced by the availability of essential nutrients, and not only by the concentration of hydrocarbons.

Figure 4 shows the oxygen concentration in the interstitial water of the basin treated with fish meal during Experiment 1. There is a general decrease following fish meal application, suggestive of increased microbial activity in the sediment. Indeed, the respiration rate in the sediment (under optimal conditions with excess oxygen; Figure 5) is significantly higher with organic than with inorganic additives (student's paired t-test, Abs(Dif)-LSD between 0.25 and 0.50 in Experiment 1, and between 0.22 and 0.48 in Experiment 2). This effect of fish meal is more pronounced lower in the beach, which is probably due to the lower wave intensity, and therefore oxygen supply, at low water levels. An alternative explanation is that, at lower water levels, the sediment was water saturated for longer, allowing the microorganisms to consume more of the oxygen in the interstitial water. Similar oxygen profiles were found with stick water and Max Bac, but with progressively less effect. The oxygen decrease might affect oil degradation, but this is very difficult to quantify. In experiments to be reported elsewhere, mechanical tilling of the sediment increased the rate of oil degradation with both Max Bac and fish meal.

There was substantial degradation of the oil in all the treated basins (Figures 6 and 7). In Experiment 1, the difference between the basin with the highest amount of added Max Bac and the two organic additives was not significant when based on the nC_{17}/pristane ratio. However, a significant difference was

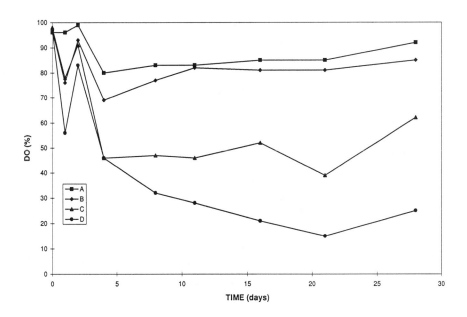

FIGURE 4. Oxygen concentration (DO is dissolved oxygen) in the experiment with fish meal pellets measured in four interstitial water sample wells, located along a gradient from the upper part of the beach (A) to the bottom (D).

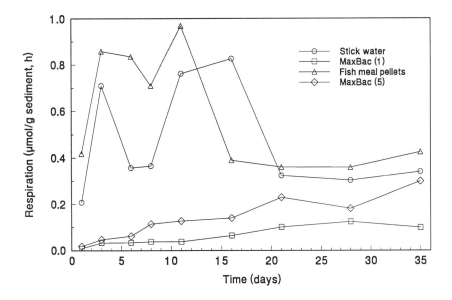

FIGURE 5. Total heterotrophic respiration in sediment samples from Experiment 1.

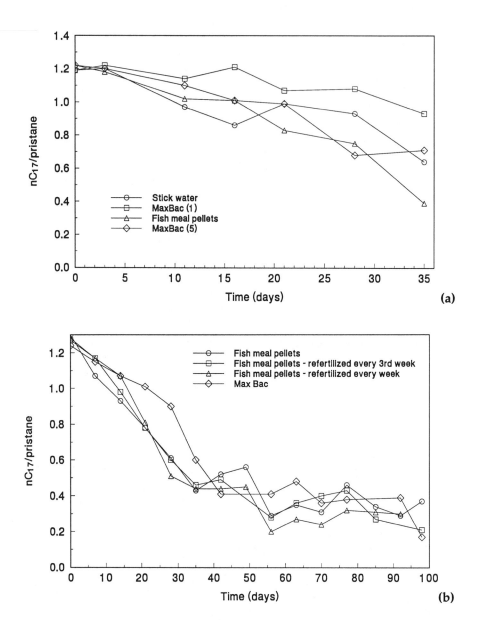

FIGURE 6. Oil degradation (expressed as nC$_{17}$/pristane). (a) Experiment 1.
(b) Experiment 2.

found between the basins with organic additives and the basin with the low
amount of Max Bac (student's paired t-test, Abs(Dif)-LSD 0.02 and 0.04). In
Experiment 2, the differences in the nC$_{17}$/pristane ratio was not statistically
significant, but it has been found that the ratio is valid for this specific crude
(Statfjord) only as long as it remains above approximately 0.6. If we assume
that the polar fraction acts as a conserved internal marker within the oil, Figure 7

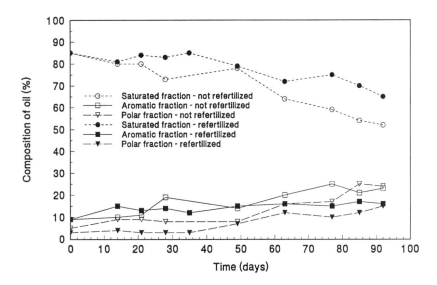

FIGURE 7. Saturated, aromatic and polar compounds in Experiment 1 basins treated once and every week with fish meal.

can be interpreted as indicating 45% degradation of the aromatics in all samples, and a more pronounced degradation of the saturate fraction in the basin with one application of fish meal (85% compared to 75%).

The composition of PAHs at the end of Experiment 2 is given in Figure 8. Assuming that hopane is not degraded at all (Prince et al. 1994b), we can see that fluorene, naphthalene, and alkylated-naphthalenes were very extensively degraded. The dibenzothiophenes and phenanthrenes were also extensively degraded, with a clear preference for the least alkylated forms (Elmendorf et al. 1994). Interestingly, PAH degradation seems to be most extensive in the sediments with repeated application of fish meal.

The oil degradation was considerably higher during the first week in the experiment, with 1 week between oil contamination and additive application, than in other experiments with only 1 day between contamination and application, probably because the microorganisms were more adapted toward hydrocarbon degradation before additive application. The concentrations of oil-degrading microorganisms are two to three orders of magnitude higher after a longer adaptation period. In addition, with longer time intervals between oil application and fertilization, only minor amounts of the oil remain at the water surface.

Oil Degradation and Interstitial Water Nitrogen Concentration

After the bioremediation cleanup operation following the *Exxon Valdez* incident, it was reported that the concentration of soluble nitrogen in the interstitial

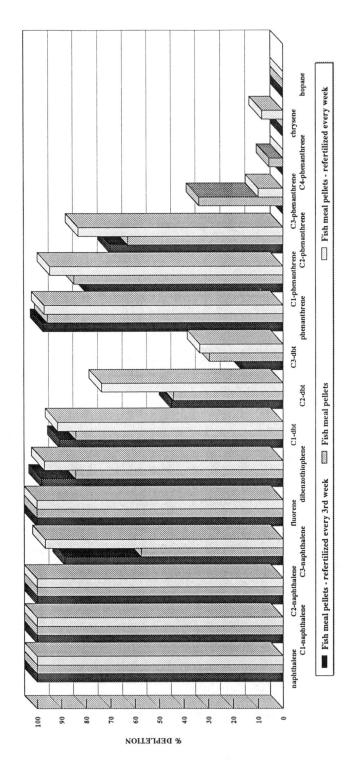

FIGURE 8. PAH composition measured at the end of Experiment 2 (i.e., after 98 days).

water correlated with the change in hydrocarbon composition (Bragg et al. 1994). For the results reported above, a correlation between the accumulated total nitrogen concentration in the interstitial water and the change in nC_{17}/pristane ratio is given in Figure 9. The nitrogen concentration is given as the accumulated nitrogen concentration in the interstitial water, which is proportional to the total nitrogen exposure to the microorganisms, calculated as the integrated area under the concentration curves after different times of the experiments. There seems to be a linear relationship between the degradation of oil measured as the change in the nC_{17}/pristane ratio and the nitrogen concentration (Figure 9a). In Experiment 1, basins with the two concentrations of Max Bac, the relation between nC_{17}/pristane and total nitrogen is similar, and differs significantly from the basins with fish meal and stick water. The difference in slope of the two lines indicate that the microorganisms are not able to use the high initial concentration of nitrogen in the interstitial water. In the basins with stick water, the relation between the degradation rate and soluble nitrogen is linear, whereas the line breaks in the basins with fish meal. In the first period, there is a slope similar to that found in the sediment treated with stick water; in the second period, there is a slope parallel to that found in the basins with Max Bac. Similar results were found in Experiment 2 for the longer duration and repeated fish meal study. A clearly different relation was found between the basins with Max Bac and the basins with fish meal (Figure 9b). With fish meal pellets, a slightly different slope was found in the sediment without repeated fertilization. These results demonstrate that the concentration of soluble nitrogen cannot be used as a sole indication of the oil degradation rate if organic additives are used.

Oil Degradation and Heterotrophic Respiration

Accumulated respiration (i.e., CO_2 production) was integrated by the same method as for soluble nitrogen for different times for Experiments 1 and 2 (Figure 10). In Experiment 1 the relation is similar for both concentrations of Max Bac (Figure 10a). With stick water, the relation is linear, but the slope is not as steep as for the basins with Max Bac. In the basins with added fish meal, the relation changes during the experiment. In the first period, the slope is similar to that found with stick water; in the last part, the slope is similar to that found for Max Bac. In the experiments with Max Bac, the hydrocarbon is the dominating carbon source, and the respiration rate is thus more or less proportional to the utilization of the hydrocarbons. With fish meal and stick water, another — and presumably more easily available — carbon source is introduced in addition to the hydrocarbons. The increased slope with fish meal at the end of the experiment indicates that the available carbon sources in the additives, denoted "external carbon" by Sveum et al. (1994), have been used by the microorganisms. When the external carbon has been consumed, the metabolism is directed toward hydrocarbons. The shift in metabolism is less distinct with stick water addition. This can be explained by a higher proportion of soluble components in stick water than in fish meal. It will therefore be more available to the microbes in

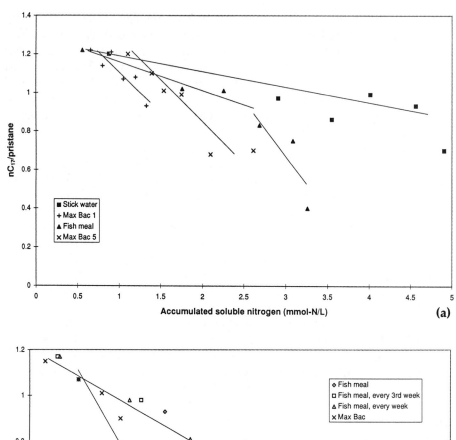

(a)

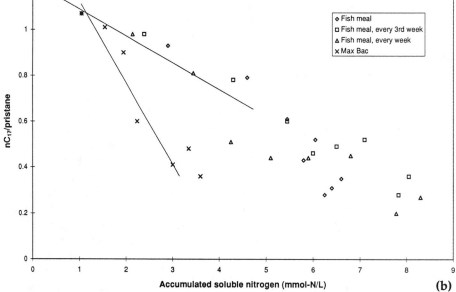

(b)

FIGURE 9. Oil degradation (expressed as nC_{17}/pristane) as a function of the accumulated total nitrogen concentration in the interstitial water. (a) Experiment 1. (b) Experiment 2.

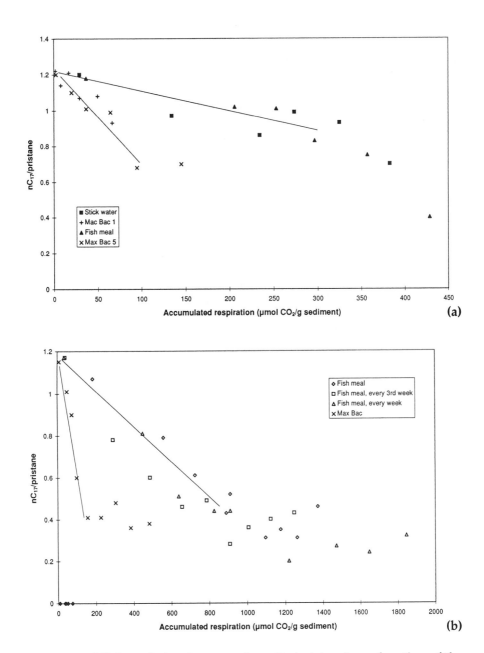

FIGURE 10. Oil degradation (expressed as nC_{17}/pristane) as a function of the accumulated CO_2 production. (a) Experiment 1. (b) Experiment 2.

the sediment. Similar relations were found in the long-time and repeated fertilization experiments (Figure 10b). The relation in the basin with Max Bac and the basins with fish meal differed clearly, and the relation between accumulated

CO_2 production and the change in the nC_{17}/pristane ratio in the basins with added fish meal were similar until the nC_{17}/pristane ratio dropped below 0.4. However, the respiration curves (Figure 5b) show that the CO_2 production decreased earlier in the basin without repeated fertilization; the basin with fertilizer added every week remained at a high level of CO_2 production during the entire experiment. This indicates that the microorganisms used both carbon sources (hydrocarbon and fish meal) throughout the experiment, that the shift in metabolism toward hydrocarbon utilization is dependent on the total amount of additives supplied to the sediment, and that the metabolism of both hydro-carbons and the additive takes place simultaneously but at different rates. Repeated fertilization with organic additives is neither beneficial nor detrimental to oil degradation activity. A diauxic utilization of the two different forms of carbon present is indicated, however, without being absolute, because biodegrada-tion of the oil can be observed even if the externally added carbon is present and is preferentially used.

Sveum et al. (1994) showed that the supply of external carbon in additives could be of importance for the assimilation and thereby the retention of essential nutrients in microbial biomass. Their conclusion was based on observations on the increased necromass, i.e., the difference between metabolically active biomass and the total biomass. Addition of complex organic fertilizers can thus be viewed as a tradeoff, where nutrient retention is increased, allowing for a one-time, rather than a repeated, fertilizer treatment with inorganic additives.

ACKNOWLEDGMENTS

This study is part of the Esso SINTEF Coastal Oil Treatment Program (ESCOST), which is supported by Esso Norge A/S. Special thanks are due to Dr. Roger Prince, Exxon Research and Engineering, and Mr. Geir Indrebø, Esso Norge A/S, for their continuous advice and support throughout the ESCOST program.

REFERENCES

Aquatec Manual no. 5000-3139, 9010, Tecator AB, Hugeness, Sweden.

Atlas, R. M., and R. Bartha. 1972. "Degradation and mineralization of petroleum in sea water: Limitation by nitrogen and phosphorus." *Biotechnol. Bioeng.* 14: 309-317.

Atlas, R. M., and R. Bartha. 1973. "Stimulated biodegradation of oil slicks using oleophilic fertilizers." *Environ. Sci. Technol.* 7: 538-541.

Bragg, J. R., R. C. Prince, E. J. Harner, and R. M. Atlas. 1994. "Effectiveness of bioremediation for the *Exxon Valdez* oil spill." *Nature* 368: 413-418.

Bragg, J. R., R. C. Prince, J. B. Wilkinson, and R. M. Atlas. 1992. *Bioremediation for Shoreline Cleanup Following the 1989 Alaskan Oil Spill: Exxon Company*, USA, Houston, TX.

Brown, J., and J. F. Braddock. 1990. "Sheen screen, a miniaturized most-probable-number method for enumeration of oil-degrading microorganisms." *Appl. Environ. Microbiol.* 56: 3895-3896.

Dibble, J. T., and R. Bartha. 1976. "Effect of iron on the biodegradation of petroleum in sea water." *Appl. Env. Microbiol. 31*: 544-500.

Elmendorf, D. E., C. E. Haith, G. S. Douglas, and R. C. Prince. 1994. "Relative rates of biodegradation of substituted polycyclic aromatic hydrocarbons." In R. E. Hinchee, A. Leeson, L. Semprini, and S. K. Ong (Eds.), *Bioremediation of Chlorinated and Polycyclic Aromatic Hydrocarbon Compounds*, pp. 188-202. Lewis Publishers, Boca Raton, FL.

Ladousse, A., and B. Trainer. 1991. "Results of twelve years of research in spilled oil bioremediation; Inipol EAP22™," *Proceedings of the 1991 International Oil Spill Conference*, 577-582. American Petroleum Institute, Washington, DC.

McLachlan, A. 1982. "A model for estimation of water filtration and nutrient generation by exposed sandy beaches." *Marine Environmental Research 6*: 37-47.

Olivieri, R., P. Bacchin, A. Robertiello, N. Oddo, L. Degen, and A. Tonolo. 1976. "Microbial degradation of oil spills enhanced by a slow-release fertilizer." *Appl. Environ. Microbiol. 31*: 629-634.

Olivieri, R., A. Robertiello, and L. Degen. 1978. "Enhancement of microbial degradation of oil pollutants using lipophilic fertilizers." *Marine Pollut. Bull. 9*: 217-220.

Porter, K. G., and Y. S. Feig. 1980. "The use of DAPI for identifying and counting aquatic microflora." *Limnol. Oceanogr. 25*: 943-948.

Prince, R. C. 1993. "Petroleum spill bioremediation in marine environments." *Critical Reviews Microbiology. 19*, 217-242.

Prince, R. C., J. R. Clark, J. E. Lindstrom, E. L. Butler, E. J. Brown, G. Winter, M. J. Grossman, R. R. Parrish, R. E. Bare, J. F. Braddock, W. G. Steinhauer, G. S. Douglas, J. M. Kennedy, P. J. Barter, J. R. Bragg, E. J. Harner, and R. M. Atlas. 1994a. "Bioremediation of the *Exxon Valdez* oil spill: Monitoring safety and efficacy." In R. E. Hinchee, B. C. Alleman, R. E. Hoeppel, and R. N. Miller (Eds.), *Hydrocarbon Bioremediation*, pp. 107-124. Lewis Publishers, Boca Raton, FL.

Prince, R. C., D. L. Elmendorf, J. R. Lute, C. S. Hsu, C. E. Haith, J. D. Senius, G. J. Dechert, G. S. Douglas, and E. L. Butler. 1994b. "17a(H),21b(H)-hopane as a conserved internal marker for estimating the biodegradation of crude oil." *Environ. Sci. Technol. 28*, 142-145.

Radke, M., H. Willsch, and D. H. Welte. 1980. "Preparative hydrocarbon group type determination by automated medium pressure liquid chromatography." *Anal. Chem. 52*: 406-411.

Riedl, R. J. 1971. "How much water passes through sandy beaches?" *Int. Revue Res. Hydrobiol. 56*: 923-946.

SAS. 1989. *JMP® User's Guide*. Version 2 of JMP.

Sveum, P., and C. Bech. 1994. "Bioremediation and physical removal of oil on shore." In R. E. Hinchee, B. C. Alleman, R. E. Hoeppel, and R. N. Miller (Eds.), *Hydrocarbon Bioremediation*, pp. 107-124. Lewis Publishers, Boca Raton, FL.

Sveum, P., and A. Ladousse. 1989. "Biodegradation of oil in the arctic: Enhancement by oil-soluble fertilizer application." *Proc. 20th Oil Spill Conference*, pp. 439-446. San Antonio, TX.

Sveum, P., L.-G. Faksness, and S. Ramstad. 1994. "Bioremediation of oil-contaminated shorelines: The role of carbon in fertilizers." In R. E. Hinchee, B. C. Alleman, R. E. Hoeppel, and R. N. Miller (Eds.), *Hydrocarbon Bioremediation*, pp. 163-174. Lewis Publishers, Boca Raton, FL.

Sveum, P., S. Ramstad, L.-G. Faksness, C. Bech, and B. Johansen. 1995. "Physical modeling of shoreline bioremediation: Continuous flow mesoscale basins." In R. E. Hinchee, G. S. Douglas, and S. K. Ong (Eds.), *Monitoring and Verification of Bioremediation*, pp. 87-96. Battelle Press, Columbus, OH.

Large-Scale Experience with Biological Treatment of Contaminated Soil

Volker Schulz-Berendt and Emmo Poetzsch

ABSTRACT

The efficiency of biological methods for the cleanup of soil contaminated with total petroleum hydrocarbons (TPH) and polycyclic aromatic hydrocarbons (PAH) was demonstrated by a large-scale example in which 38,000 tons of TPH- and PAH-polluted soil was treated on site with the TERRAFERM® degradation system to reach the target values of 300 mg/kg TPH and 5 mg/kg PAH. Detection of the ecotoxicological potential (Microtox® assay) showed a significant decrease during the remediation. Low concentrations of PAH in the ground were treated by an in situ technology. The in situ treatment was combined with mechanical measures (slurry wall) to prevent the contamination from dispersing from the site.

INTRODUCTION

The cleanup of contaminated soil from old industrial sites and dumps with different mixtures and concentrations of pollutants is one of the greatest challenges to environmental technologies. Biological treatment of these materials has been developed during the last 10 years and today is considered one of the best alternatives for special waste land disposal of volumes of hundreds up to several thousand cubic meters. The large-scale regeneration and recultivation of contaminated soils by microorganisms is based on the following principles: selection, adaptation, and optimization of microorganism consortia; selection of additives used to enhance the microbial activities; optimization of nutrient supply; preparation of the soil and mixing of the process components; construction and operation of biological treatment plants, and maintenance and control of the process.

Large-scale experience with ex situ and in situ treatment of TPH, PAH, and volatile chlorinated hydrocarbons has taught us that, depending on the kind of pollution, characteristics of the site, and the planned use of the cleaned soil, different technological solutions must be used (Schulz-Berendt 1993).

BIOLOGICAL REMEDIATION OF AN OLD SITE CONTAMINATED WITH TPH AND PAH

In the soil of the former repair plant of the German railway company (Deutsche Bundesbahn) near the Main River in Frankfurt, soil contaminations were detected during excavation. Concentrations of organic pollutants up to 20,000 mg/kg of TPH and 800 mg/kg of PAH were found by investigations to a depth of about 20 m. Because of the location of contaminants in different segments of the ground and the need for continuing the construction of the building, an integrated concept of ex situ and in situ treatments was carried out at this site (Baumann et al. 1994). Gravelly sand above and below the groundwater, polluted by TPH and PAH, was enclosed with a 5- to 10-cm-thick slurry wall made from Dyckerhoff-Solidur-Mixture (stone dust and cement mixture). It was then excavated and treated on site. Highly contaminated fine tertiary sand, polluted by PAH down to 21 m below grade, was also excavated. The holes were refilled with lean concrete. As a directly available and approved technique, biological on-site treatment with the TERRAFERM® system (Henke 1989) was chosen for soil cleanup. The remaining contamination of PAH in the groundwater and subsoil was treated by a combination of water treatment and in situ biology. For safety reasons, this region was enclosed by a second slurry wall.

We began working in March 1991, and by July 1991 38,000 tons of soil had been dug out and separated into contaminated and uncontaminated material by analytical assessment in a mobile laboratory on the site. Target values were set by the authorities at 300 mg/kg TPH and 5 mg/kg PAH. The soil with concentrations of pollutants above the target values was prepared for biological degradation by the TERRAFERM® process. The process diagram (Figure 1) shows the different steps of treatment. The first step involved separating out materials that cannot be degraded, such as plastics, iron, etc.; sieving of the soil (30 mm); and crushing stones and larger particles to a size below 30 mm. Then the fine soil together with the crushed material was homogenized in a special machine (the "Maulwurf") with high-speed rotating knives. Because of the sandy structure of the soil (only 12% <0.063 mm), no organic additives were necessary to improve soil structure. A solution containing mineral nutrients and bacteria isolated from the contaminated soil was spread in an amount of 10 L per m^3 of soil after passage through the Maulwurf.

Laboratory degradation studies with soil samples from the site had shown that a C:N:P ratio 100:20:10 gave the best results. Therefore, the solution contained nitrogen and phosphorus in these amounts, and additional small amounts of $Na_2SO_4 \times 10\ H_2O$, $MgCl_2 \times 6\ H_2O$, $CaCl_2 \times 2\ H_2O$, and trace-element solution. The processed soil was brought into four tents with a total area of 20 × 420 m and piled to a height of 2.50 m. The ground of the tents was prepared by different layers of sand, fleece, and hydrocarbon-resistant foil to prevent pollutants from being washed into the subsoil. Further treatment included regular turning of the soil (every 4 weeks) and the addition of water and nutrients. Water addition ensured that the water content of the soil would not drop below 15% of the dry substance. The nutrients were added to hold the above mentioned C:N:P

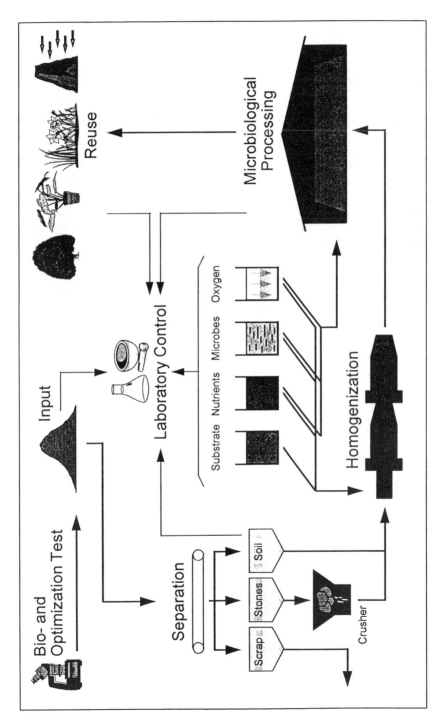

FIGURE 1. Biological soil treatment — TERRAFERM® process.

ratio of available nitrogen and phosphorus compounds. The bacteria were cultivated in the laboratory with an anthracene-oil-containing medium and identified
as a *Pseudomonas putida* sp. They were added in a concentration of 10^9 colony-
forming units (CFU)/L.

Average concentrations at the beginning of biological treatment were about
1,700 mg/kg of TPH and 100 mg/kg of PAH. Corresponding to these pollutant
values, toxicity was detected by the Microtox® assay (Ribo & Kaiser 1987). The
GL_{20} value (the diluting-factor for reaching an inhibition of bioluminescence below
20%) at the beginning of degradation was 23, which indicated a high degree
of toxicity.

From April 1991 to June 1992 the target values of TPH <300 mg/kg (Figure 2)
and PAH <5 mg/kg (Figure 3) were reached by biological breakdown of the
components. In relation to the reduction of the pollutants, the number of toxicity
equivalents detected by Microtox® assay also decreased (Figure 4), which means
that the remaining concentrations are acceptable for an unlimited use of the
cleaned soil for recultivation.

Although the target values corresponding to the existing regulations have
been reached, the use of biologically decontaminated soil is often restricted by
the authorities. The fear of dangerous metabolites or "hidden" contaminants
must be allayed by monitoring programs that can prove the fate of disappearing
compounds by a closed carbon balance, for example (Figure 5).

The in situ treatment was started in November 1994. The first results show
a good degradation rate at the water-treatment plant. It is too early to assess
the effect of biological activities underground.

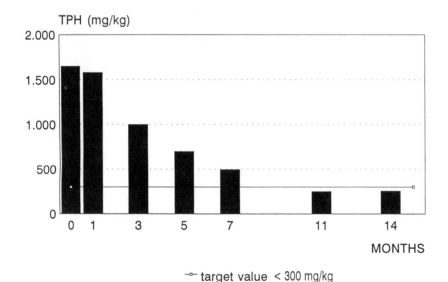

FIGURE 2. Deutsche Bundesbahn: Degradation of TPHs from April 1991
(month 0) to June 1992 (month 14).

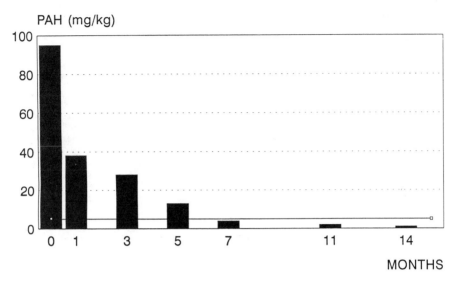

FIGURE 3. Deutsche Bundesbahn: Degradation of PAHs from April 1991 (month 0) to June 1992 (month 14).

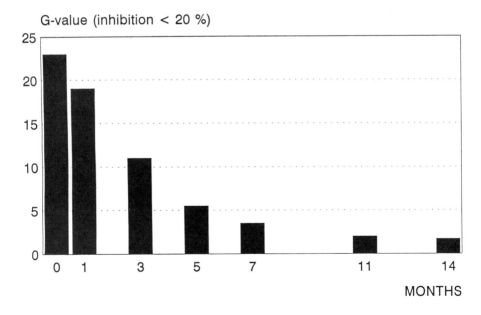

FIGURE 4. Deutsche Bundesbahn: Development of ecotoxicity measured by Microtox® assay (bioluminescence test) in soil extract during biological remediation of TPH and PAH pollution.

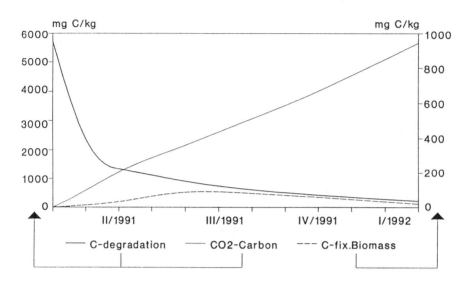

FIGURE 5. Carbon balance of TPH and PAH degradation (from Baumann et al. 1994, modified).

CONCLUSIONS

For compounds such as TPH and PAH, proven technologies such as the TERRAFERM® process for on-site and off-site treatment are widely accepted. For contaminations that require high expenditures for excavation or treatment because of their location in the ground or their volatility, in situ methods can be used. For safety reasons and to reduce the amount of contaminated water, in many cases the hydrologic approach must be supplemented by mechanical barriers that enclose the treatment area. Under these conditions, biological soil treatment is a safe, inexpensive, and well-accepted technology.

REFERENCES

Baumann, V., H.-G. Loewner, and V. Schulz-Berendt. 1994. "Sanierung eines Geländeteils des ehemaligen Ausbesserungswerkes der Deutschen Bundesbahn an der Idsteiner Straße in Frankfurt/Main." In Deutsche Gesellschaft für Geotechnik, *Vorträge der Baugrundtagung 1994 in Köln*, pp. 5-22.

Henke, G. A. 1989. "Experience Reports About On-Site Bioremediation of Oil-Polluted Soils." In K. J. Thomé-Kozmiensky (Ed.), *Recycling International. Volume 3*, pp. 2178-2183. EF-Verlag.

Ribo, J. M., and K.L.E. Kaiser. 1987. "*Photobacterium phosphoreum* — Toxicity Bioassay, I. Test Procedures and Application." *Toxicity Assessment*. 2: 305-323.

Schulz-Berendt, V. 1993. "Soil Bioremediation in Practice: Problems and Results." In H.J.P. Eijsackers and T. Hamers (Eds.), *Integrated Soil and Sediment Research: A Basis for Proper Protection*, pp. 559-576. Kluwer Academic Publishers, Dordrecht, Boston, London.

In Situ Closed-Loop Bioremediation: Rapid Closure in a Northern Climate

David F. Weymann and LeeAnn M. Hammerbeck

ABSTRACT

In situ closed-loop bioremediation was employed to achieve site closure at a former railyard in Minneapolis, Minnesota. Soil and groundwater were contaminated with gasoline. The closed-loop remediation system design incorporated three downgradient groundwater recovery wells and a low-pressure pipe infiltration gallery. Aboveground treatment of recovered groundwater was provided by a fixed-film bioreactor. The total reported benzene, toluene, ethylbenzene, and xylenes (BTEX)-removal efficiency of the bioreactor ranged from 98.8% to 100%. Concentrations of BTEX components in groundwater wells were reduced by 45% to 98%. The cleanup goals set by the Minnesota Pollution Control Agency were met within the first 6 months of treatment, and the remediation system was shut down after 20 months of operation. This project further demonstrates the effectiveness of reactor-based, closed-loop in situ bioremediation at sites with favorable conditions.

INTRODUCTION

Microbial respiration is strongly influenced by temperature; thus, the efficiency of in situ bioremediation may be questioned for cold weather climates. In situ closed-loop bioremediation was employed to achieve site closure at a former railyard in Minneapolis, Minnesota, where the soil and groundwater were contaminated with gasoline constituents. Bioremediation was selected based on its ability to treat both soil and groundwater (Alexander 1994; Thomas and Ward 1989) and on the proven performance of bioremediation systems at similar sites (Schmitt and Caplan 1987; Schmitt et al. 1991; Lieberman et al. 1989). The project was noteworthy for its success in achieving rapid cleanup in a climate characterized by extremely cold winter temperatures. The remediation effort represented an effective partnership between two environmental consulting firms and the Minneapolis Community Development Agency (MCDA).

SITE DESCRIPTION
AND FEASIBILITY TESTING

The site was located in a former railyard that is currently owned by the MCDA. In the source area, fill material dominated by a low hydraulic conductivity lean clay (average saturated hydraulic conductivity [Ksat] = 1.7×10^{-5} cm/s) and rubble was found from the surface to approximately 3 m below land surface (bls). High-permeability (average Ksat = 1.1×10^{-1} cm/s) alluvial sands extended from 3 m to 5.5 m bls and were underlain by glacial till (average Ksat = 4.1×10^{-3} cm/s). The water table fluctuated between 6.1 m and 7.6 m bls under the natural hydrologic cycle. Wells were screened primarily in the glacial till. The initial distribution of soil and groundwater contamination (reported July 1990) and the locations of the site wells and infiltration gallery are shown in Figure 1. The approximate area of the target plume was 2.0 acres (0.9 hectare). The portion of the plume beyond the treatment area boundary was addressed under a separate project. A maximum initial soil contaminant concentration of 220 mg/kg total hydrocarbons (THC) as gasoline was found in soil from boring MW-103 at a depth of 7.6 m bls. A maximum groundwater contaminant concentration of 240,000 µg/L THC as gasoline was also found in MW-103.

The results of the biofeasibility analysis (BFA) indicated conditions favorable to bioremediation. The groundwater pH was 7.1 and there was a moderate indigenous microbial population of 1.6×10^4 colony-forming units (CFU)/mL. No inhibition of an adapted microbial culture was observed in the groundwater toxicity assay. The soil pH of 8.8 was at the high end of the optimal range for bioremediation but did not appear to inhibit microbial respiration. Heterotrophic soil organisms were enumerated at 1×10^5 CFU/g. No toxic inhibition of microbial respiration in soil was indicated. The BFA results indicated that supplemental inorganic nutrients would be required to maintain optimal contaminant biodegradation. The results of the gasoline biodegradation experiment indicated a rapid reduction in contaminant concentrations as compared to the no-action control, suggesting the presence of a microbial population capable of degrading the target contaminants.

The surface air temperature ranged from a daily average of 1.6°C in winter to 11.2°C in summer. Groundwater temperature ranged from 10°C to 14°C over a year. The treatment system was installed in a building that was maintained at approximately 15°C in winter.

REMEDIATION SYSTEM DESIGN

The soil and groundwater treatment system featured the patented (U.S. Patent 4 992 174, 1991) PetroClean® Bioremediation System, consisting of an aboveground, fixed-film bioreactor coupled with a closed-loop in situ bioremediation component. The bioreactor volume was approximately 4,000 gal (15,150 L) with a media section volume of approximately 3,000 gal (11,400 L). The media section

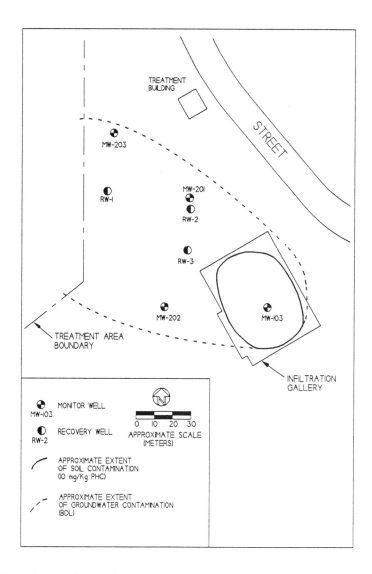

FIGURE 1. Contaminant distribution and location of site wells and infiltration gallery.

was packed with 288 ft³ (8.2 m³) of polyvinyl chloride (PVC) fixed-film media with a specific surface area of 42 ft²/ft³ (140 m²/m³). Influent was distributed at the surface of the media section and flowed under a weir into a clarifier section prior to discharge. Air was supplied to the reactor with a blower at a typical flowrate of 30 ft³/min (0.85 m³/min). A process schematic of the PetroClean system is shown in Figure 2. The subsurface components of the closed-loop design consisted of three groundwater recovery wells and a unique two-tiered, low-pressure pipe infiltration gallery installed over impacted soils. The objectives

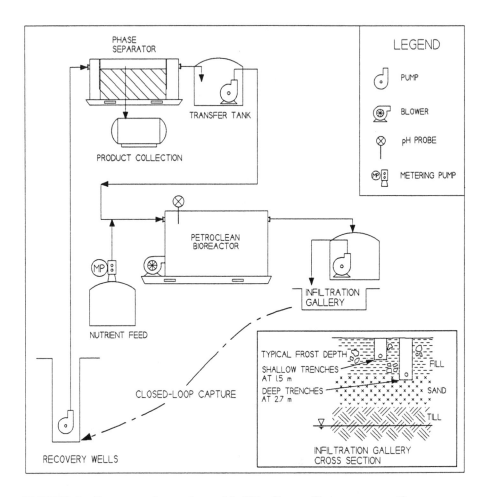

FIGURE 2. Process schematic and infiltration gallery cross section.

of the closed-loop component were to stimulate in situ microbial activity by delivering nutrients and oxygenated water while maintaining hydraulic capture. The closed-loop design was developed based on a computer modeling study, and hydraulic capture was confirmed by water-level data collected during the project. Nutrients were added to the bioreactor and to the treated groundwater prior to discharge to optimize subsurface nutrient availability. Nutrients consisted primarily of technical-grade diammonium phosphate and ammonium chloride salts. The ammonia-nitrogen concentration in the discharged water was limited by the regulatory agency to 20 mg/L.

The groundwater recovery rate ranged from 1.2 gal/min (4.5 L/min) to 8.0 gal/min (30.3 L/min) and averaged 5.22 gal/min (19.8 L/min). The system initially consisted of two bioreactors. However, due to the lower than expected recovery rate and high contaminant-removal efficiencies, the second reactor was eliminated. The hydraulic retention time ranged from approximately 8 h to 55 h. Treated water was stored and periodically dosed sequentially to each of the seven infiltration gallery subfields. The infiltration gallery was designed to provide uniform application of treated groundwater within the source area. The low-pressure pipe (LPP) infiltration gallery subfields were installed at two depths to account for differing hydraulic conductivities with depth, while ensuring uniform water distribution to target soils and providing sufficient hydraulic capacity. A gallery cross section is shown in Figure 2. The gallery pipe network consisted of 1.5-in. (3.8-cm)-diameter PVC pipe laterals with 5/32-in. (0.4-mm)-diameter holes drilled on a 2.7-m interval. The hole size and spacing were designed to achieve the target flowrate to the gallery subfields under the design pressure head. Laterals were installed in gravel-filled trenches.

RESULTS AND DISCUSSION

The THC removal efficiency was reported as 100% for all sampling dates after the fifth day of system operation. The total BTEX removal efficiency ranged from 99% to 100%, as did the removal efficiency of individual BTEX components. Removal efficiency was not affected by the stated range in hydraulic retention time. Contaminant concentrations in recovery and monitor wells generally increased after startup and then decreased steadily over time. The cleanup goals set by the Minnesota Pollution Control Agency were met within the first 6 months, and contaminant concentrations declined further with continued treatment. BTEX components were reduced to below their respective cleanup goals, and in most cases concentrations were reduced to below the state-recommended allowable limits (RALs) for drinking water. The negotiated cleanup goals of 100 times the RALs for specific compounds were based on groundwater use and exposure risk. For example, the state RAL for benzene is 10 µg/L; thus, the cleanup goal was set at 1,000 µg/L. Changes in contaminant concentrations in recovery wells and system influent are shown in Figure 3. Percent reductions from peak concentrations ranged from 83% in RW-3 to 97% in RW-2. The combined influent concentrations were dominated by the contribution of RW-1, which produced the most water.

Groundwater concentrations in selected monitor wells are shown in Figure 4. Trends in contaminant concentrations in MW-103 were characterized by an initial increase and stabilization, followed by a later decline. The initial increases in MW-103 and in recovery wells probably resulted from mobilization of sorbed contaminants from the vadose zone and aquifer. It is notable that after cessation of active remediation, groundwater concentrations rebounded only modestly in some wells and continued to decline thereafter. This suggests successful remediation of residual contamination in the source area and continued passive bioremediation in the groundwater plume. The regulatory agency did not require analysis for soil contaminants beyond the baseline sampling; thus, few data are available. It can only be assumed that physical flushing and biological attenuation resulted in a reduction in soil contaminant concentrations.

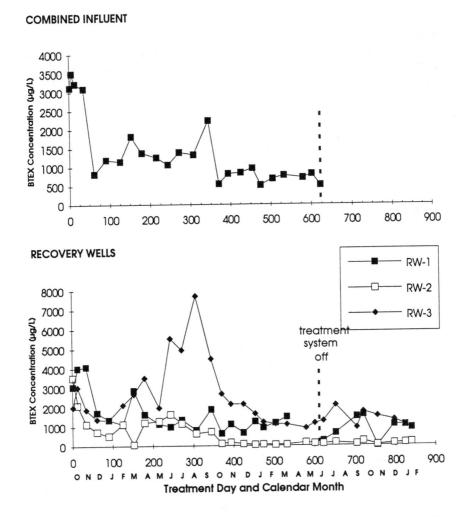

FIGURE 3. **Recovery well and system influent contaminant concentrations.**

Trends in the microbial population density suggest that the observed contaminant reductions were due, at least in part, to in situ biodegradation. Microbial counts (CFU/mL) increased by up to 3 orders of magnitude in recovery wells and combined influent (Figure 5). In addition, near-optimal conditions for biodegradation were established and maintained. The pH generally remained optimal and nitrogen species were detected in moderate concentrations. Phosphate concentrations were consistently below the analytical detection limit. However, the phosphate detection limit was relatively high (0.08 mg/L), and the phosphate requirement is relatively low. The observed dissolved oxygen (DO) concentrations were typical of those in contaminant plumes where biological attenuation is occurring, and DO concentration appeared to be strongly correlated with the

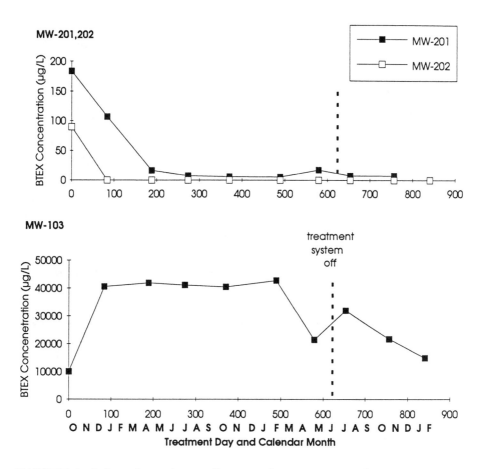

FIGURE 4. Selected monitor well contaminant concentrations.

contaminant concentration (Table 1). The depletion of DO suggests microbial consumption. However, the low DO concentrations detected appeared to be sufficient to support ongoing biodegradation.

The northern climate did not appear to affect the system performance. Although the surface air temperature dropped to very low temperatures during the winter months, the ambient groundwater temperature was moderated at the depths of interest. Installation of the bioreactor in a heated building prevented a significant drop in the temperature of recovered groundwater during winter such that a temperature favorable to biodegradation was maintained.

The described treatment system resulted in a rapid site closure, yet it is possible that cleanup could have been further accelerated. The high contaminant concentrations within the source area resulted in a depletion of DO that may have suppressed microbial activity. Biodegradation may have been enhanced by increasing the subsurface delivery of DO and nutrients, which was limited by the relatively low groundwater recovery and infiltration rates. Although DO

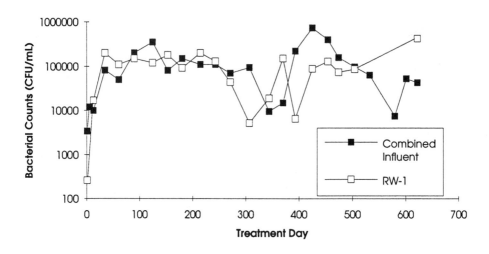

FIGURE 5. **Microbial population density in RW-1 and combined influent.**

was observed in most wells, concentrations were low. Subsurface aeration, such as air sparging, may have accelerated bioremediation by providing supplemental oxygen. The groundwater recovery rate declined significantly during the project. The reasons for the decline are unclear. Possible explanations include a local dewatering of the aquifer, a drop in well efficiency, or a drop in aquifer hydraulic conductivity due to migration of fine particles or microbial growth. Vacuum-enhanced groundwater recovery or infiltration of supplemental clean water may have improved both biodegradation and contaminant flushing.

CONCLUSIONS

The described project employed closed-loop in situ bioremediation to produce a significant closure at a petroleum-contaminated site in a cold climate. Bioremediation was selected for the site based on the favorable results of a biofeasibility analysis. The project provided a model application of bioremediation in the State of Minnesota and provided closure more quickly and at a lower cost than is typically possible with other remediation technologies. For these reasons, the project was recognized with a Grand Award for Engineering Achievement from the Consulting Engineers Council of Minnesota. Although this project was not implemented as a detailed research project, sufficient data were collected to indicate a significant microbiological response to the treatment program. Evidence of the enhanced subsurface conditions include a significant increase in the microbial population and favorable pH, nutrient status, and DO concentrations in the majority of the contaminant plume. Following cessation of active remediation, concentrations rebounded only modestly and continued to decline thereafter, suggesting ongoing passive bioremediation. This project further

TABLE 1. Dissolved oxygen readings in selected wells.[a]

Well	Location	Relative Contamination	DO (mg/L)
MW-103	source area below gallery	high	0.00
MM-201	near RW-2	low	0.38
PZ-3	upgradient from source	NA	1.98
MW-202	south edge of plume	BDL	1.98
MW-203	downgradient, plume edge	BDL	0.32
RW-1	330 ft from MW-103	moderate	0.72
RW-2	210 ft from MW-103	low	1.05
RW-3	180 ft from MW-103	moderate	0.24

(a) BDL = below detection limit; NA = not applicable.

demonstrates the effectiveness of reactor-based, closed-loop in situ bioremediation at sites with favorable conditions.

REFERENCES

Alexander, M. 1994. *Biodegradation and Bioremediation.* Academic Press, San Diego, CA.

Lieberman, M. T., E. K. Schmitt, J. A. Caplan, J. R. Quince, and M. P. McDermott. 1989. "Biorestoration of Diesel Fuel Contaminated Soil and Groundwater at Camp Grayling Airfield Using the PetroClean Bioremediation System." *Proceedings of the Conference on Petroleum Hydrocarbons and Organic Chemicals in Groundwater: Prevention, Detection, and Restoration.* Houston, TX.

Schmitt, E. K., and J. A. Caplan. 1987. "In Situ Biological Cleanup of Petroleum Hydrocarbons in Soil and Groundwater." *Proceedings of the Fifth Annual Hazardous Materials Management Conference.* Atlantic City, NJ.

Schmitt, E. K., M. T. Lieberman, and J. A. Caplan. 1991. "Bioremediation of Soil and Groundwater Contaminated with Stoddard Solvent and Mop Oil using the PetroClean Bioremediation System." In R. E. Hinchee and R. F. Olfenbuttel (Eds.), *In Situ Bioreclamation: Applications and Investigations for Hydrocarbon and Contaminated Site Remediation,* pp. 581-599. Butterworth-Heinemann, Stoneham, MA.

Thomas, J. M., and C. H. Ward, Jr. 1989. "In Situ Biorestoration of Organic Contaminants in the Subsurface." *Environmental Science and Technology* 23: 760-765.

In Situ Remediation of Hydrocarbon Contamination Using an Injection-Extraction Process

Arnold Ross, Charles Tremblay, and Charles Boulanger

ABSTRACT

Soil can be remediated using a variety of technologies. These are performed through physical, chemical, or biological processes either in situ (without excavation) or ex situ (with excavation). Écosite Inc. has developed a soil treatment technology to be applied in situ using an injection-extraction system (IES). This new restoration process uses custom-designed equipment for recovering free-phase hydrocarbons and for injection/recovery of different treatment solutions through cyclic manipulation of the water table level. Process development applied the basic principles of soil washing with improved distribution of the washing solution and improved hydraulic control using air sparging and vacuum capability. In this case study, free-phase recovery and soil washing have been used successfully to remediate the site. During the fall and winter of 1993-94, in situ restoration of soil contaminated with cutting oil below a machine shop was begun. The contamination extended from 1.83 to 4.27 m underneath the concrete slab. This represents a volume of 1,800 m^3 of oil-laden soil with concentrations reaching 200,000 mg/kg. Moreover, free-floating phase hydrocarbons up to 1 m thick were observed. To clean the site, 400 injection/recovery points were arranged into three networks. A data collection system was used to monitor the water table level. A total of 160,000 kg of oil was extracted from the subsoil in less than 110 days of operation.

INTRODUCTION

Many technologies can be used to remediate underground soil and water (U.S. EPA 1985). Remediation typically is based on off-site or in situ physical, chemical, or biological treatment of the contaminated material (Preslo et al. 1989). From all these approaches, we developed an in situ physico-chemical treatment technology involving hydraulic operations performed with equipment used specifically for the injection/recovery of various washing solutions.

Using the basic principles of soil flushing technology, we improved the technology of washing solution distribution and underground water control. With this approach, the contaminated zone is isolated and washing solutions are successively injected into contaminated soils and pumped out through a network of specially designed wells. In addition, this process greatly minimizes canalization by gravity in surface irrigation or draining trenches.

Washing solutions injected from the main injection network are composed of nontoxic, biodegradable surfactant compounds. After reacting with these compounds, recuperated washing solutions form emulsions that are processed through a complete on-site wastewater treatment system.

This in situ technology adapts to any contamination distribution up to a depth of 10 m. This technology is designed to remove the four phases of a contamination enclave, i.e., the free (supernatant phase), residual, dissolved, and gaseous phases. The gaseous phase comprises volatile compounds and is directed to a biofilter. This technique has already been demonstrated during the operation of previous soil decontamination projects.

CASE STUDY — IN SITU REMEDIATION UNDER A BUILDING

Prior to fieldwork, parameters were evaluated to assess whether the in situ technology was applicable, including hydrogeologic properties (permeability, particle size distribution, soil heterogeneity); hydraulic properties (effective porosity, depth and thickness of the water table, hydraulic conductivity); contaminant properties (type of contaminant, concentration of contaminant, contamination heterogeneity, contaminant biodegradability); laboratory studies (surfactant selection, contaminant biodegradability, wastewater treatment, computer modelization); and microbiological properties (presence of active bacterial population, growth and nutrient conditions, presence of inhibitory factors such as heavy metals).

Level of Contamination and Distribution

This site remediation was performed inside a building where steel parts-manufacturing activities took place. Supply and recovery networks of the cutting oil had leaked and the storage area of oily parts was also a source of contamination. Site characterization revealed the presence of 1,800 m³ of soil heavily contaminated with cutting oil, as well as a free organic phase reaching up to 1 m in thickness. The contamination can be summarized as follows:

- Accumulation of contaminants underneath the concrete floor
- Contaminants present in both the vadose and saturated zones
- Volume contaminated estimated at 1,800 m³
- Average concentration 57,000 mg/kg, maximum measured concentration of 110,000 mg/kg, and maximum calculated concentration of 200,000 mg/kg.

Contaminated Soil Characteristics

The soil was composed of fine sand with 10 to 12% silt. The water table level was at −3.5 m with groundwater flow from east to west. Hydraulic conductivity measured on site was in the vicinity of 10^{-4} cm/s.

Remediation Technology

The chosen technological approach consisted of isolating the area of treatment from the surrounding zones and performing in situ treatment with successive hydraulic operations. Washing solutions that were injected and recuperated through various distribution networks had been enriched with nontoxic surfactants. After having reacted with these compounds, the spent washing solutions formed emulsions that were processed through a complete on-site wastewater system.

We installed a network of 400 injection/recuperation points divided into three distinct areas (in three different recuperation/injection systems). The first one, the peripheral network, was installed to isolate the treatment area and control the water-table level. The secondary network is used to recover the washing solution. The main network has the dual function of injecting and recovering the washing solution in the soil.

The on-site conditions of application and operation procedures were first defined during feasibility trials performed in the laboratory. Four aspects were covered during these trials:

1. Surfactants were selected for use during in situ treatment operations.
2. Washing experiments of contaminated soil taken from the site with the help of selected surfactants were performed.
3. The biodegradability and toxicity of the washing solution and of the contaminant were evaluated in the laboratory.
4. Hydraulic activities were planned with the help of the SEEP/W application program (injection output, pumping flow, theoretical levels, and reaction times).

A computerized system for data acquisition was installed to monitor groundwater movement.

The saturation method selected consisted of first injecting enough washing solution, using the injection/recovery points, to raise the water table 2 m (from 4.5 m to 2.5 m depth) inside the treatment area.

Implementing the Procedure

The different treatment sequences were followed and controlled using 12 caps for automatic water level monitoring installed on different piezometers to observe the water table level during operations. These caps were located in such a way as to characterize the hydraulic plotting in each work zone. A data acquisition system was used to perform real-time analysis of the data.

The technique of hydraulic movement consists of creating a hydraulic barrier at the exterior of the enclave of contaminated soils to contain the treatment solutions injected from the secondary and main networks. This hydraulic action is achieved by using a peripheral network to isolate the plume of contaminated soils from the regional flow of groundwater. Injection of water in the peripheral network creates the hydraulic barrier required to contain and increase ground-water flow (or washing solution flow) through a steep artificial gradient toward the main network (in pumping mode). The secondary network, installed within the immediate perimeter of the plume of contaminated soils, enhances the hydraulic action achieved with the addition of treatment solutions. Finally, the main network complements the hydraulic action of the secondary network. Spent treatment solution is recovered only through the main network.

Technological Performance

The in situ program for the follow-up/control of decontamination operations at the site includes activities such as analytical follow-up of treatment solutions (injection, recovery, and treatment), monitoring of groundwater, control of hydraulic action, and validation of remediation work with soil sample analyses.

We began recovery of the free-hydrocarbon phase during 20 days in the fall of 1993 and another 30 days during the winter of 1994. A total of 37,600 L of free oil was recovered, and the sludges produced in the water treatment system trapped the equivalent of 9,500 L of oil. The second step consisted of applying eight cycles of washing operations underneath the building using biodegradable, nontoxic surfactant solutions. These operations extended over 60 days.

The results (Table 1) show that a total of 160,000 kg of hydrocarbon was extracted from the soil to decontaminate the site to a regulatory-approved level. Daily recovery rates varied between 400 and 2,500 kg/d.

At the end of the washing operations, microbial analyses showed high levels of specific hydrocarbon-degraders, with average counts of 10^6 colony-forming units/g in the soils. These results corroborate other findings from laboratory studies on the biodegradation of both the contaminant and the surfactant blend and suggest that a biological step could possibly be induced after a soil-washing sequence. Indeed, the same injection networks used during washing operations can distribute nutrient solutions to stimulate degradation. The hardware can also be used for air sparging or bioventing.

CONCLUSION

This new process provides efficient recovery and control of the hydraulic operations (hydraulic and mass balances) and achieves high performance beneath infrastructure without excavation, with minimal effect of the surfactants used in the process on the soil microflora. Finally, this process can be extended to biodegradation and offers enough flexibility to perform bioventing as well as sparging in the sequential restoration of a site.

TABLE 1. Loads (kg) of mineral oils and greases recovered during restoration below an industrial building.

Phase	Seq.	H$_2$O Pumped (m^3)	Free Oil Recovered (m^3)	Equivalent Load (kg) H$_2$O	Equivalent Load (kg) Oil	Total Load (kg)	Cumulative MOG Load (kg)	Cumulative MOG Load (L)
I	—	2,563	15.00	2,500	12,825	15,325	15,325	17,027
II	—	4,643	22.60	6,964	19,323	26,287	41,612	46,236
	1	194	0.00	347	0	347	41,959	46,621
	2	4,160	14.50	6,363	12,398	18,761	60,720	67,467
	3	1,815	4.20	4,745	3,591	8,336	69,056	76,729
III	4	1,600	0.00	4,988	0	4,988	74,044	82,271
	5	2,910	0.60	2,680	513	3,193	77,237	85,819
	6	4,020	13.20	16,052	11,286	27,388	104,575	116,194
	7	18,968	11.17	45,774	9,784	55,558	160,133	177,926
	8	2,680	0.95	2,092	684	2,776	162,909	181,010

REFERENCES

MEF (formerly MENVIQ). 1988. "Politique de réhabiliation des terrains contaminés." Direction des substances dangereuses, February.

Preslo, L., M. Miller, W. Suyana, M. McLearn, P. Kostecki, and E. Fleischer. 1989. "Viable remedial technologies for petroleum contamination in soils." *National Conference on the Environmental and Public Health Effects on Soils Contaminated with Petroleum Products*, Amherst, MA, September 28-30. Lewis Publishers, Chelsea, MI. pp. 115-125.

U.S. Environmental Protection Agency (U.S. EPA). 1985. *Handbook: Remedial Action at Waste Disposal Sites* (revised). U.S. Department of Commerce, NTIS, Report no. EPA/625/6-85/006, p. 681.

Bioremediation of a PAH-Contaminated Gasworks Site with the Ebiox Vacuum Heap System

Daniel R. Eiermann and Reinhard Bolliger

ABSTRACT

A former gasworks site in the industrial city of Winterthur, Switzerland, was extremely contaminated with polycyclic aromatic hydrocarbons (PAHs); benzene, toluene, ethylbenzene, and xylenes (BTEX); phenols; ammonia; and mineral oils. Three vacuum heaps, with a total volume of 10,500 m^3 of contaminated soil, were bioremediated during 1993/94. Separating excavated soil material into different soil qualities was of particular importance because of the pathway definition of the specific soil material (recycling, bioremediation, backfill, etc.). Excavation of contamination took longer than 10 months, delivering continuously different contaminated soil-type material for bioremediation. Conditioning and subsequent biostimulation of the large soil volumes were the prerequisites for most advanced milieu optimization. The degradation results demonstrated the potential for successful application of bioremediation on former industrial sites. PAH-concentration reductions ranged from 75 to 83% for the soil values and from 87 to 98% for the elution values. Soil and elution target qualities were met within 6 to 12 months, depending on initial PAH-concentration and soil structure. The achieved target quality for the bioremediated soil allowed subsequent reuse as high-value backfill material for the ongoing building project.

THE WINTERTHUR GASWORKS SITE

Multicomponent contamination on the Winterthur gasworks site revealed a "cocktail" of gasworks-specific contaminants, such as mineral oils, PAHs, BTEX, phenols, and ammonia. Therefore, a microbiological treatability study according to general guidelines (Dott 1992) was carried out to check the microbiological pollutant degradation potential. The soil contained 25 to 35% silt and clay. The results and conclusions drawn from the lab study (data not shown) led to the gasworks site-specific bioremediation concept.

TECHNOLOGICAL ASPECTS

Ebiox bioremediation represents enhanced natural decontamination processes by means of biostimulation focused on natural contaminant-adapted microorganisms. The soil structure remains unchanged during bioremediation and represents intact soil quality. This allows high-value reuse of the bioremediated soil in the civil engineering industry.

A rubble recycling plant and a crusher equipped with the required safety measures for contaminated soil conditioning (best possible mechanical homogenization) were installed. No additives such as wood chips, compost, sewage sludge, or microorganisms from external sources were introduced. After conditioning, the contaminated soil was piled up to 4.5 m in several layers on a sealed biobed to provide high remediation throughput on the smallest bioremediation sites. Between the layers, perforated plastic piping was installed, which was connected with manifolds to a vacuum blower system (see also Figure 1). By pulling a vacuum through the perforated pipes, outside air can be uniformly drawn through the soil by bioventing in order to provide sufficient oxygen supply for the aerobic microorganisms. Permanent low-pressure conditions preclude air emissions to the atmosphere. All volatile compounds are, therefore, sucked out through the vacuum system and purified by a biofilter. Seepage waters are captured by the base drainage layer in a sump and pumped into the bioplant system. The dissolved contaminants are then degraded to water and carbon dioxide. After treatment in the bioplant system, the purified, oxygen-saturated, water-laden nutrients (macronutrients) and trace elements (micronutrients) are resprayed by a sector-controlled irrigation system on top and alongside the vacuum heap, which guarantees optimal moisture content. All heavier petroleum fractions undergo a double effect bioremediation: in situ biodegradation within the vacuum heap and dissolved biodegradation in the bioplant system. The entire heap is covered with a black plastic liner to prevent moisture evaporation and loss of passive solar heat.

SAFETY AND CONTROL STANDARDS

The most important parameters to be controlled are toxicity, mobility, and persistence. Figure 2 shows the principal mechanisms of biotic and abiotic metabolic processes in the soil and their impact on the environment (Bolliger 1993). An organic pollutant is generally mineralized by biological catalysts (microorganisms and enzymes), a cascade mechanism intermittently releasing "free" (soluble and volatile) by-products and microbial biomass of the organisms involved in the degradation process. Available data from sophisticated monitoring concepts indicate, however, that no significant pools of intermediates accumulate during the clean-up of PAH-contaminated sites. Ideally, the oxidative pollutant degradation, its metabolites and its biomass result in carbon dioxide and water. On an actual remediation site, however, microbial competition and interference of different abiotic physical-chemical reactions may occur. The mineralization of

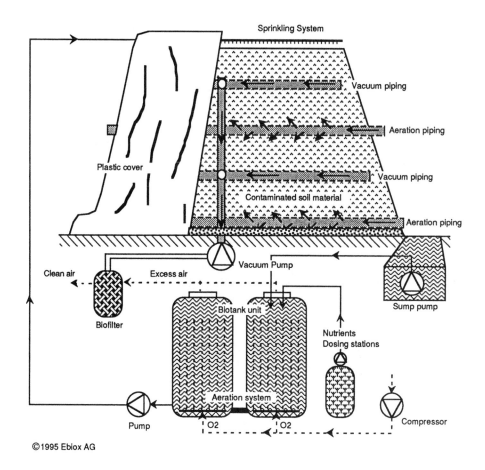

FIGURE 1. System flow chart of Ebiox Vacuum Heap™ systems: air circulation and water circulation.

PAHs can be influenced by humification, whereas mineral oil compounds always yield complete mineralization without toxic by-products. The direct correlation between the total organic carbon content (TOC) and the PAH-degradation potential is used as a tool to assess bioremediation feasibility (Weissenfels et al. 1992).

PROJECT MONITORING

The cleanup process is controlled by a sophisticated analytical monitoring program. To meet high quality standards, it must cover the whole range of possible pathways for breakdown of organic matter, as well as the potential human health hazards (Bolliger & Eiermann 1994). This is feasible only with a balanced combination of scientific know-how and fundamental experience. The applied

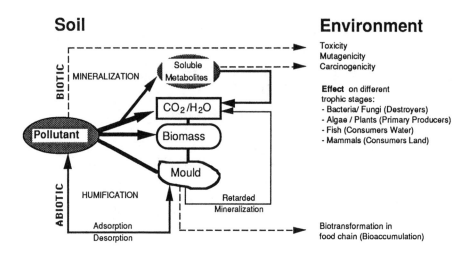

FIGURE 2. Principal mechanisms of biotic and abiotic metabolic processes in the soil and their impact on the environment.

quality standards are highly progressive and set the trend for future regulations. A thorough sampling for extended chemical and microbiological analyses is carried out on monthly intervals. Weekly controls of the biosystem including reduced site monitoring with field test kits are conducted by a briefed specialist.

RESULTS

The PAH soil and elution concentrations were the priority decision-making bioremediation targets. (See also the bioremediation plot for vacuum heap 2 in Figure 3 and the bioremediation soil and elution plots for vacuum heap 3 in Figures 4 and 5.) Unfortunately, large-scale projects carried out under commercial conditions do not allow adequate scientific monitoring to perform detailed mass balances (volatilization, solubilization vs. degradation). The results are listed below:

Vacuum Heap 1: Volume: 3,897 m³
- Startup soil concentration for PAHs (16 of EPA): 1,316 mg/kg
- Soil concentration after 12 months of bioremediation: 218 mg/kg
- Startup elution concentration for PAHs (16 of EPA): 4,447 µg/L
- Elution concentration after 269 days of bioremediation: 90 µg/L
- Degradation rates of 83% for soil and 98% for elution

Vacuum Heap 2: Volume: 4,606 m³
- Startup concentration for PAHs (16 of EPA): 500 mg/kg
- Soil concentration after 270 days of bioremediation: 83.2 mg/kg

- Startup elution concentration for PAHs (16 of EPA): 3,908 µg/L
- Elution concentration after 269 days of bioremediation: 284 µg/L
- Degradation rates of 83% for soil and 93% for elution

Vacuum Heap 3: Volume: 2,061 m³
- Startup concentration for PAHs (16 of EPA): 167 mg/kg
- Soil concentration after 207 days of bioremediation: 42 mg/kg
- Startup elution concentration for PAHs (16 of EPA): 263 µg/L
- Elution concentration after 207 days of bioremediation: 34 µg/L
- Degradation rates of 75% for soil and 87% for elution

The other important project monitoring parameters (mineral oil, BTEX, phenols, and ammonia) showed even more convincing bioremediation results. Not only in the soil values, but in the elution data as well, bioremediation targets were achieved within 3 months for vacuum heap 1 and within 2 months for vacuum heaps 2 and 3. No intermediates accumulated, indicating that the contaminants were, in fact, eliminated or incorporated into the stable organic fraction of the soil ecosystem. In all heaps, the enhanced toxicity of the contaminated material could be reduced to the background levels of uncontaminated reference soils from the surrounding area. (See also toxicity pattern of vacuum heap 2 in Figure 6.)

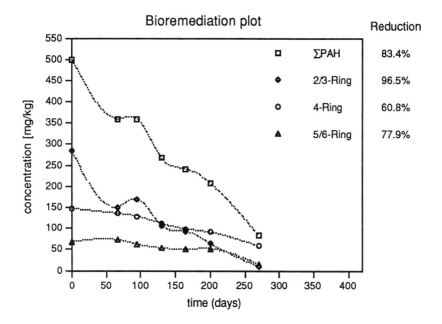

FIGURE 3. PAH-concentration reduction during bioremediation of contaminated industrial soil (sampling series A-H). The bioremediation plot data represent average values from 3 boreholes and 3 layers (n = 9).

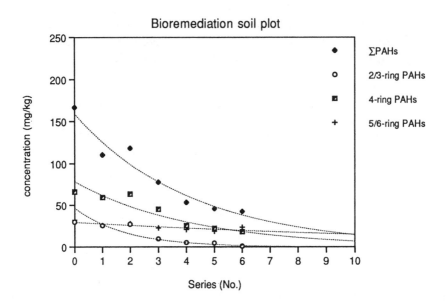

FIGURE 4. Bioremediation pattern of the PAH soil values (averages from all 5 sampling locations and from 3 layers, 90 samples in total). ΣPAH: sum of 16 U.S. EPA PAHs. 2/3-ring, 4-ring, 5/6-ring: substance classes with different degradation potentials.

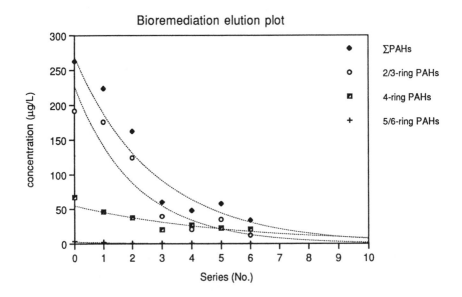

FIGURE 5. Bioremediation pattern of the PAH elution values (averages from all 5 sampling locations and from 3 layers, 90 samples in total). ΣPAH: sum of 16 U.S. EPA PAHs. 2/3-ring, 4-ring, 5/6-ring: substance classes with different degradation potentials.

CONCLUSIONS

Bioremediation of three vacuum heaps, with a total volume of 10,500 m³ of contaminated soil, was successfully executed on a former gasworks site in Winterthur, Switzerland, during 1993/94, which demonstrated the application potential on former industrial sites. PAH degradation ranged from 75 to 83% for soil values and from 87 to 98% for elution values. Soil and elution target qualities were met within 6 to 12 months depending on initial PAH concentration and soil structure. The Microtox® toxicity test was chosen to follow the toxicity of the contaminated soil material. One of the key features documented was the massive reduction of the toxicity value fluctuation range during the bioremediation process. Compared to the uncontaminated reference soil, no elevated hazardous health risk for humans, or the environment is expected for the soil material after bioremediation. Close investigation of the opportunistic pathogen, *Pseudomonas aeruginosa* revealed no elevated risk at any time. This organism was

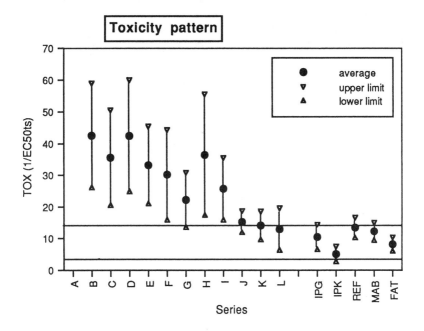

FIGURE 6. Toxicity reduction during bioremediation of contaminated industrial soil (sampling series A-L). The toxicity data represent average values from 7 boreholes and 3 layers (n = 21). Reference samples: IPG (n = 11), IPK (n = 5), REF (n = 3), MAB (n = 3), FAT (n = 3). Analytical methodology: Microtox® bacteria test, solid phase protocol (TOX = toxicity index = 1/EC50ts, average values and standard deviation [upper limit, lower limit with 95% confidence interval], the dotted lines mark the fluctuation range of the average of all 5 reference samples).

not enriched during the bioremediation. Complimentary data from different monitoring parameters indicated that no significant pools of intermediates accumulated during the cleanup (PAH reduction, TPH reduction, and toxicity reduction in line). Redox and pH-conditions remained in an aerobic milieu. The consequent analytical monitoring of the nutrients showed normal nutrient uptake and consumption (no accumulation of ammonia and nitrate). The vacuum heap biostimulation system (Eiermann & Menke 1993) is well suited for large-scale treatment of excavated soil (thousands of cubic meters at a time) and best applied for bioremediation projects requiring short completion deadlines, confined working space, and tough air emission restrictions.

REFERENCES

Bolliger, R. 1993. "Sicherheitsaspekte bei der Überwachung von biologischen Bodensanierungen." *TerraTech* 4: 54-57.
Bolliger, R. and D. R. Eiermann. 1994. "Bioremediation of PAH-contaminated soils: A Swiss Case Study." *OECD Workshop on Industrial Products of Modern Biotechnology Intended for Release to the Environment*, Fribourg, Switzerland, May 17-20, 1994.
Dott, W. 1992. "Labormethoden zur Beurteilung der biologischen Bodensanierung." In J. Klein (Ed.), *DECHEMA-Arbeitskreis Umweltbiotechnologie — Boden*. DECHEMA, Chemische Technik und Biotechnologie e.V., Frankfurt am Main, Germany.
Eiermann, D. R. and R. Menke. 1993. "No-bug biostimulation new remediation standard." *Technology News International* 10: 19-20.
Weissenfels, W. D., H. J. Klewer, and J. Langhoff. 1992. *Applied Microbiol. Biotechnology* 36: 689-696.

Biopile Treatability, Bioavailability, and Toxicity Evaluation of a Hydrocarbon-Impacted Soil

Kelly W. Hayes, Jeffrey D. Meyers, and Robert L. Huddleston

ABSTRACT

A parametric study was conducted to evaluate use and enhancement of engineered biopiles to remediate weathered, hydrocarbon-impacted soil. The study used fifteen 1.2-yd^3 (0.9-m^3) biopiles under continuous vacuum aeration for 45 wk. Various amendments, evaluated for their effectiveness to enhance remediation, included bulking materials, inorganic fertilizer, waste activated sludge, and a surfactant. The average total petroleum hydrocarbon (TPH) concentration was reduced approximately 55%, with no significant difference between any of the treatment amendments or controls. Posttreatment soil samples were subjected to 6-wk slurry reactor tests, achieving an additional 15% TPH reduction, for a total of 70%. Because these reductions fell short of treatment goals, toxicity tests were conducted to determine if an acceptable, risk-based, treatment endpoint had been reached. Despite TPH residuals, neither treated nor untreated soils were found to be toxic. The low toxicity of this soil was attributed to sorption mechanisms that left residuals sequestered, but slowly available for biodegradation, greatly reducing or eliminating toxicity and bioavailability. This work was conducted by Conoco as a portion of Petroleum Environmental Research Forum (PERF) Project No. 93-02 and was partially funded by the DuPont Bioremediation Team.

INTRODUCTION

Degradability of petroleum hydrocarbons by soil microflora is well established and has been used advantageously to develop low-cost bioremediation treatment methods. By early 1992, vendors were advocating use of biopiles for remediating hydrocarbon-impacted soils as an environmentally acceptable and cost-effective treatment method. As practiced, biopile treatment is an ex situ process whereby soils can be mixed with amendments, then ventilated to promote biological oxidation of hydrocarbon contaminants. The biopile process has been considered ideal for treating soils with volatile constituents because of optional use of a vacuum aeration system that allows such compounds to be collected and treated, if necessary. Similarly, controlled moisture conditions prevent soluble constituents from leaching. In the continuing quest for more cost-effective soil treatment methods, Conoco undertook this study to evaluate the use and optimization of biopiles.

MATERIALS AND METHODS

Biocell Test System and Experimental Design

The treatment system consisted of 15 biocells, each 4 ft (1.2 m) square and 3 ft (0.9 m) deep, with a soil depth of 2.5 ft (0.76 m). An airflow of 1 ft³/min (CFM) (0.03 m³/min) at 0.5 in (1.3 cm) of water was maintained in each biocell via a common vacuum system. A schematic of a biocell is shown in Figure 1. Test cells were housed in a heated building; however, no cooling was available. Table 1 summarizes the parameters, treatment amendments, and addition levels evaluated.

Since stockpiled soil was excavated from refinery construction project sites and beneath dismantled aboveground storage tanks, soil was impacted by a weathered mixture of refined products and some crude oil dating to the early 1920s. After removal from the stockpile, soil was homogenized, sieved, amended, and loaded into the biocells. Where used, inorganic nutrient additions of NH_4NO_3 and K_3PO_4 were based on a carbon:nitrogen:phosphorus (C:N:P) ratio of 100:10:1, yielding NO_3-N and total-P concentrations of 240 and 25 mg/kg, respectively. Throughout the test period, soil temperature and moisture were monitored and controlled, averaging 23°C and 23 wt%, respectively.

Sampling Procedures

A representative sample consisting of a composite of eight soil cores per biocell was collected weekly. Exhaust air from each cell was monitored routinely during the first 5 wk for volatile organic carbon (VOC) content, and initially for BTEX (benzene, toluene, ethylbenzene, and xylenes).

Analytical Methods

Because of regulatory acceptance and cost, the primary analysis used to monitor for hydrocarbon loss was TPH by EPA Method 418.1, where $MgSO_4$ and Freon-113® were used as the drying agent and extraction fluid, respectively. All TPH samples were run in duplicate after removal of bulking agents. Other analyses periodically performed by SW-846 protocol were BTEX, 8020; total VOC, 8015; polycyclic aromatic hydrocarbons (PAH), 8270; gas chromatography/mass spectroscopy (GC/MS) fingerprinting, 8270; oil and grease (O&G), 9070; total metals, 6010; and hydrocarbon fractions by thin-layer chromatography (TLC). Samples were also sent to a soils testing laboratory where nutrient analyses (total N, P, K, and NO_3-N), soil classification, pH, water-holding capacity (WHC), total organic carbon (TOC), cation-exchange capacity (CEC), and sodium-adsorption ratio (SAR)

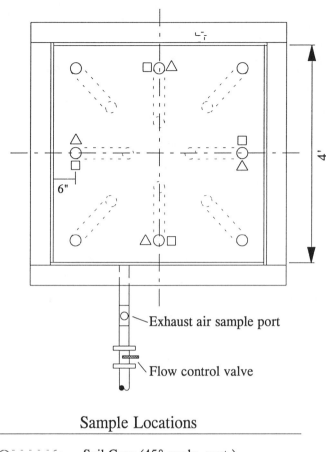

Sample Locations

○ ⁻ ⁻ ⁻ ⁻ ◌ - Soil Core (45° angle, vert.)

□ - Moisture Probe Measurement

△ - Temperature Probe Measurement

FIGURE 1. Biocell schematic and sampling diagram.

were determined with standard protocols. Leachate was analyzed for O&G, and the oxygen (O_2) content of the soil pore space and exhaust air of selected cells was monitored using a Fyrite® O_2 analyzer. Off-gas samples were analyzed for BTEX and total VOCs using EPA Methods 8020 and TO-3 (Winberry), respectively.

Slurry Reactor Test

To establish an ultimate treatability endpoint, a slurry reactor test was conducted on soil from an aerated control cell (5,200 mg/kg TPH) at the conclusion

TABLE 1. Biocell treatment summary.

Biocell Number	Treatment Scheme
BIOCELL 1	Soil Only ($\approx$ 1.2 tons), No Aeration
BIOCELL 2	Aeration Only ($\approx$ 1 cfm)
BIOCELL 3	Bulking Agent 1A[a] + Aeration
BIOCELL 4	Bulk. 1B[b] + No Aeration
BIOCELL 5	Bulk. 1B + Aeration
BIOCELL 6	Bulk. 1A + Aeration + Nutrients (C:N:P of 100:10:1)
BIOCELL 7	Bulk. 1B + Aeration + Nutrients
BIOCELL 8	Bulk. 2A[c] + Aeration + Nutrients
BIOCELL 9	Bulk. 2B[d] + Aeration + Nutrients
BIOCELL 10	Bulk. 1A + Aeration + Nutrients + ASU Sludge 1[e]
BIOCELL 11	Bulk. 1A + Aeration + Nutrients + ASU Sludge 2[f]
BIOCELL 12	Bulk. 1A + Aeration + Nutrients + Peat Moss[g]
BIOCELL 13	Bulk. 1A + Aeration + Nutrients + Weekly Mixing
BIOCELL 14	Bulk. 1A + Aeration + Nutrients + 3.5 ft Soil Depth
BIOCELL 15	Bulk. 1A + Aeration + Nutrients + Surfactant[h]

(a) 2.5 wt% shredded tree waste
(b) 10.0 wt% shredded tree waste
(c) 2.5 vol% (0.23 wt%) wheat straw
(d) 10.0 vol% (0.89 wt%) wheat straw
(e) 0.006 wt% refinery ASU sludge
(f) 0.06 wt% refinery ASU sludge
(g) 1.0 wt% Sphag Sorb® peat moss
(h) 10.0 mg/kg soil conc. of VISTA ALFONIC® 810-60 ETHOXYLATE
All additions made and concentrations expressed on a dry-weight basis.

of the 45-wk test. Soil was prepared and slurried at a 1:3 soil-to-water ratio using a buffered nutrient solution formulated to achieve a 100:10:1 C:N:P ratio. All flasks were placed on a rotary shaker to provide aeration and thorough mixing. The system was run for 6 wk with individual reactors sacrificed weekly for soil TPH analysis and O&G measurements on several water samples.

RESULTS

Soil Composition

Native soil was a silty clay containing 42% and 44% clay and silt, respectively, and had a CEC of 14.2 meq/100 g, TOC (Walkley Black) of 1 wt%, and pH of 6.3. Soil characteristics are summarized in Table 2.

Hydrocarbon Degradation — Biocell and Slurry Reactor Tests

Soil TPH and BTEX concentrations immediately after removal from the stockpile were 13,000 mg/kg and 74 µg/kg (BTEX = 4, 3, 18, 49 µg/kg), respectively. After removal, mixing, amendment addition, and biocell loading operations, a process which required 10 days, TPH and BTEX concentrations had declined to an average of 9,500 ± 960 mg/kg (1 standard deviation) and 22 µg/kg, respectively, for all 15 biocells. At startup, analysis indicated 6 mg/kg of PAH compounds. This value was the sum of 16 PAHs, the highest of which were phenanthrene at 3.5 mg/kg; and acenaphthene, anthracene, fluorene, and pyrene, each present at approximately 0.5 mg/kg. Analyses for BTEX and PAHs were discontinued based on these low concentrations. By week 18 average TPH had declined from 9,500 mg/kg to 6,800 ± 520 mg/kg and, at shutdown, after 45 wk, to 4,200 ± 290 mg/kg, a 55% reduction. Because of statistically insignificant differences between degradation rates for all treatments (95% confidence level, t-test), TPH data from all cells were averaged and plotted as shown in Figure 2.

During the course of study there was concern about the unexpectedly slow rate of TPH loss. To address this perceived problem, numerous tests were conducted to ensure (1) aerobic conditions — 20% soil pore O_2 concentration; (2) no

TABLE 2. Summary of background soil analyses and constituents[a].

Constituent/Parameter	Level/Units
Soil Type	Silty Clay
Sand	14%
Silt	44%
Clay	42%
Cation Exchange Capacity (CEC)	14.2 meq/100 g
pH	6.3
Electrical Conductivity	1.3 mmhos/cm
Total Organic Carbon (TOC)	1 wt%
Water-Holding Capacity (WHC)	34%
Wilting Point (WP)	14%
Sodium Adsorption Ratio (SAR)	6.5
Total Nitrogen-N	600 mg/kg
NO_3-N	10 mg/kg
Total Phosphorus-P	20 mg/kg
Total Potassium-K	260 mg/kg

(a) All concentrations are expressed on a dry-weight basis.

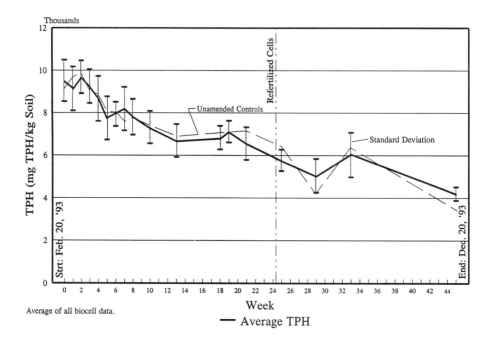

FIGURE 2. Average TPH data (corrected for moisture).

short-circuiting — smoke tests; (3) presence of a viable microbial population — average fungal and bacterial populations by plate count, 10^6 and 10^8 colony-forming units (CFU)/g, respectively; (4) nontoxic metal levels — 13 and 15 mg/kg Pb and Cr, respectively, all others at background; (5) ample moisture — 23 wt% or 68% of WHC; (6) degradable hydrocarbons — 48% saturates, 30% aromatics, 22% asphaltics, with approximately 30% of saturates being branched and little change in class composition or C_{17}:pristane and C_{18}:phytane ratios between weeks 0 and 45; and (7) acceptable pH — generally 6 to 7. In summary, no controllable inhibitory conditions were found that could explain the slow TPH degradation.

The objective of the slurry reactor test was to determine if the extent of TPH degradation could be improved by increasing the bioavailability of hydrocarbons through enhanced microbial contact. This test showed that an additional 15% reduction in TPH was possible, but that a relatively high treatment residual (3,000 mg/kg TPH) still remained.

Air Emissions

Other than the initial drop of TPH during soil preparation, little volatilization occurred. At startup average BTEX concentration was only 16 ppb in the exhaust air. Average VOC concentrations during the first days after startup were 10 ppm, declining to 5 ppm by day 8; 2 ppm by day 28; and below detection (<1 ppm) by day 35. Due to the virtual absence of VOCs and BTEX, air sampling was discontinued after 5 wk.

Leachability and Toxicity

Although evaluation of leachability was not one of the original objectives, valuable data were collected during slurry reactor tests and when leachate was inadvertently generated by overwatering. Water samples were tested for O&G and found to be below detection (<10 mg/L) in all cases.

As a part of PERF 93-02, Shell evaluated soil samples for toxicity using an earthworm survival bioassay; the University of Texas (UT) conducted Microtox® and rat liver-cell assays. The earthworm bioassay indicated no toxicity in either background or untreated soils. This lack of toxicity was verified in tests at UT, which evaluated 3 initial and 2 treated soil samples. Microtox® data showed only one initial sample to be slightly toxic, whereas data from rat liver-cell tests indicated no toxicity in any samples.

Material Balance

Combining air emission, leaching, and TPH loss data shows that ≪1% of the TPH was lost to volatilization and/or leaching. Consequently, >99% of the TPH removal was due to biological degradation.

DISCUSSION

Bioremediation of petroleum hydrocarbon-impacted soils usually is the lowest cost treatment method and can be managed in a sound and environmentally acceptable manner (Pope and Matthews 1993). Unfortunately, its use often is precluded because of regulatory treatment endpoints set at arbitrary TPH concentrations or by using technology-based standards, e.g., incineration. A growing body of data, mostly unpublished, shows that posttreatment residuals have lost their toxicity and have little hydrocarbon leachability. For example, Wang and Bartha (1990) treated jet fuel, heating oil, and diesel oil in soil lysimeters starting at initial concentrations of approximately 7,000 mg/kg. Using Microtox®, microbial activity, seed germination, and plant growth assays as indicators, soil recovery was complete within 20 wk, in spite of treatment residuals containing several thousand mg/kg. Similar results were demonstrated with Microtox® for laboratory land treatment of oily refinery wastes (Symons and Sims 1988). In our study, treated soil, and even untreated initial soil containing 1 wt% TPH, showed no toxicity in either earthworm or rat liver-cell tests. Only the Microtox® assay showed slight toxicity for one untreated soil, but no toxicity for treated soil.

While decline in TPH was observed in all biocell soils, column chromatography and GC/FID data provided by Exxon showed little change in either class composition or C_{17}:pristane and C_{18}:phytane ratios. One explanation for these data and the overall lack of toxicity is that residual hydrocarbons were sequestered by complex mechanisms (Alexander 1994) that include sorption onto clay/silt surfaces, dissolution into and complexation with humic materials, and physical entrapment in micropore spaces. These mechanisms have been studied, validated, and published extensively by the Agricultural Chemicals Industry for many herbicides, insecticides, and fungicides. Combined, these data and information seem to indicate that TPH constituents become less extractable and, hence, less available with time.

The issue of environmentally acceptable treatment endpoints for hydrocarbon-impacted soils has national implications because of the huge sums of money being spent with little apparent reduction in risk to human health and the environment. Organizations currently addressing this issue are a Gas Research Institute-led coalition, the U.S. Air Force-led TPH Criteria Working Group, and the PERF Bioremediation Discussion Group, all of which will publish extensively in the near future.

REFERENCES

Alexander, M. 1994. *Biodegradation and Bioremediation.* Academic Press.

Pope, D. F. and J. E. Matthews. 1993. "Bioremediation Using the Land Treatment Concept." EPA/600/P-93/164. U.S. Environmental Protection Agency.

Symons, B. D. and R. C. Sims. 1988. "Assessing Detoxification of a Complex Hazardous Waste, Using the Microtox® Bioassay." *Arch. Environ. Contam. Toxicol.* 17:497-505.

Wang, X. and R. Bartha. 1990. "Effects of Bioremediation on Residues, Activity and Toxicity in Soil Contaminated by Fuel Spills." *Soil Biol. Biochem.* 22(4):501-505.

BTX Degradation and Dynamic Parameters Interaction in a 50-L Biofilter

Karim Tahraoui, Réjean Samson, and Denis Rho

ABSTRACT

A composted peat moss and chicken manure blend was used to degrade benzene, toluene, and xylenes (BTX) in a 50-L laboratory-scale biofilter. Temperature, moisture content, and oxygen consumption rate of the filter material were examined for 2 weeks. The biofilter was operated with two superficial gas velocities (9.6 and 24.1 $m^3 \, m^{-2} \, h^{-1}$) and an inlet BTX concentration ranging between 1,974 and 3,611 $mg \, m^{-3}$. The elimination capacity (EC) for the whole bed reached a maximum value of 82.0 $g \, m^{-3} \, h^{-1}$, with a BTX load of 91.8 $g \, m^{-3} \, h^{-1}$. The moisture content of the filter material varied from 53.6 to 31.5 wt% and 62.5 to 65.0 wt% at a height of 15 and 86 cm, respectively. The EC of each section of the biofilter was affected by the moisture content through the bed.

INTRODUCTION

Biological processes have long been used in industry to reduce concentration of organic compounds in wastewater effluents (Van Groenestijn & Hesselink 1993). The application to the treatment of waste gases has been shown to be most successful with low-molecular-weight compounds that are readily biodegradable (Leson et al. 1991). Biofiltration is based on aerobic degradation of air pollutants in a solid-phase reactor. The target pollutants diffuse into the biofilm surrounding the filter material particles, where aerobic degradation by microorganisms occurs. End products from the complete biodegradation of pollutants are carbon dioxide, water, and microbial biomass. The elimination rate for a particular contaminant depends primarily on its water solubility, biodegradability, and its concentration in off-gas (Flederbach et al. 1993).

The objectives of our research were to study the removal of benzene, toluene, and xylenes (BTX) which are the most frequently identified aromatic substances of gasoline-contaminated soil (Miller & Canter 1991) and to examine parameters that influence the aerobic degradation of BTX, such as temperature and moisture content of the filter material, the inlet BTX concentration, superficial gas velocity and axial gas dispersion (gas distribution through the filter bed). This paper presents research that focuses on the biofilter's dynamic behavior during a period of 15 days, where inlet concentration, temperature, oxygen rate consumption, water content, and superficial gas velocity were followed to determine the attributes of biofiltration.

MATERIAL AND METHODS

The biofilter reactor was made of two 45-cm (height) glass columns with an inner diameter of 25.2 cm. Top, bottom, and flanges of the biofilter were made of nylon material. Each column was provided with a stainless steel grid (MESH 4) at its bottom. Throughout this study, the biofilter was operated with downflow gas stream. The experiment was carried out at room temperature (21 to 24°C). Gas sampling ports and temperature probes were located at seven different levels along the biofilter (0, 15, 34, 48, 67, 86, and 98 cm). BTX gas samples were collected into a glass sampling tube and immediately injected in a gas chromatograph (flame ionization detector) using a gas syringe. The reactor was filled with a commercial composted peat moss and chicken manure blend. Air supplied to water and solvent columns (benzene, toluene, and xylenes) was independently controlled by four mass-flow controllers (0 to 200 L min^{-1} for the humidification system, and 0 to 2 L min^{-1} for the three solvent columns). Four filter material sampling ports located along the side of the biofilter (15, 34, 67, and 86 cm from the bottom) were used to follow the microbial oxygen consumption rate of the filter bed, using a barometric respirometer. Further details about the biofilter setup, filter media, analytical methods, and respirometry are described by Tahraoui et al. (1994).

RESULTS AND DISCUSSION

The biofilter system was operated for 106 days at three superficial gas velocities (9.6, 24.1, and 36.1 m^3 m^{-2} h^{-1}). Throughout the experimental period, the inlet BTX concentration ranged from 216 to 5,721 mg m^{-3}, and two actions were taken to examine the biofilter behavior on BTX removal efficiency: watering the biofilter, and testing the gas flow direction (up- and downflow [Tahraoui et al. 1994]). Here we examine the dynamic profile of the biofiltration system for a 15-day period within 106 days (day 20 to day 34).

For 15 days, the inlet BTX concentrations were maintained at 1,974 mg m^{-3} (day 1 to day 8), and at 3,344 ± 267 (n = 2) mg m^{-3} (day 8 to day 15), with a superficial gas velocity of 9.6 m^3 m^{-2} h^{-1}. Figure 1 shows the dynamic temperature, oxygen consumption rate, and moisture content profiles along the biofilter for 15 days. At day 1, the inlet BTX concentration was 1,974 mg m^{-3}; temperatures were 23.5, 28.4, 26.1, 26, and 24.7°C; oxygen consumption rates were 43.2, 110.6, 127.7, and 79.1 mg kg^{-1} dry wt h^{-1}; moisture contents were 53.6, 53.8, 59.6,

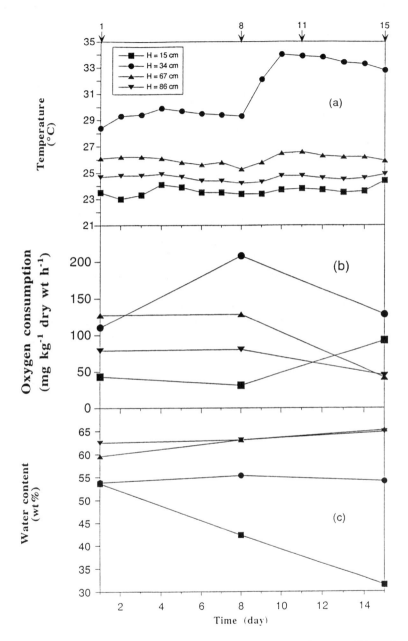

FIGURE 1. Profiles of temperature (a), oxygen consumption rate (b), and water content (c) of the filter bed throughout 15 days.

and 62.5 wt% at 15, 34, 67, and 84 cm, respectively. During a period of 8 days, temperature at each port of the biofilter varied slightly: 23.5 ± 0.3, 29.4 ± 0.4, 25.9 ± 0.3, and 24.6 ± 0.2 ($n = 8$) °C, at a height of 15, 34, 67, and 86 cm, respectively. At day 8, the inlet BTX concentration was increased from 1,974 to 3,344

± 267 (n = 2) mg m^{-3}. During 2 days, temperature at each port increased to reach an average value of 23.8 $\pm$ 0.3, 33.5 $\pm$ 0.4, 26.3 $\pm$ 0.2, and 24.7 $\pm$ 0.1 (n = 6) °C, at 15, 34, 67, and 86 cm, respectively.

The elimination capacity (defined as the concentration gradient between two sections of the filter bed, multiplied by the superficial gas velocity and divided by the height of the section) for each section of the filter bed is shown in Table 1. The second section of the filter bed (height 15 to 34 cm) reached maximum ECs (3.4 to 107.6 and 109.1 g m^{-3} h^{-1}) at day 11 and 15, respectively. This EC increase was accompanied by an increase of temperature at the second level (+4.7°C) due to the BTX biodegradation activity, which is an exothermic reaction and depends on oxygen consumption. The maximum value of the oxygen consumption rate at this level (207.9 mg kg^{-1} dry wt h^{-1}) was obtained 4 h after the inlet BTX was changed.

Moisture content in the filter bed at different levels varied over time (profiles shown in Figure 1). At day 8, the moisture content decreased at 15 cm (54 to 42 wt%) although it was almost constant at 34 cm (53.8 to 55.3 wt%), 67, and 86 cm (59.6 to 63.1 and 62.5 to 63.1, respectively). Although 400 mL of fresh water were added from the top to compensate for evaporation, the moisture content continued to decrease at 15 cm to reach a value of 31.5 wt% at day 15, while at the other heights of the filter bed it was constant. Maintaining the moisture content constant through the filter bed was difficult; the water was accumulated at the bottom part of the biofilter due to maldistribution of water through the filter bed. The consequence of this water accumulation at height 67 and 86 cm resulted in a decrease of oxygen consumption rate at these levels (127.7 to 41.6 and 128.6 to 44.6 mg kg^{-1} dry wt h^{-1}, respectively), according to the time. At day 15, the inlet BTX concentration decrease was accompanied by an oxygen consumption rate decrease at a height of 34 cm (Table 1). As shown in Figure 1, the oxygen consumption rate at 15 cm increased (31.2 to 92.7 mg kg^{-1} dry wt h^{-1}), even when the EC was 75.2 g m^{-3} h^{-1} and 18.2 g m^{-3} h^{-1} at days 11 and 15, respectively. If the respirometry measure had been possible at day 11, it would have been certainly high at 15 cm (high EC); Rho et al. (1995) have found a linear correlation between EC and oxygen consumption rate for their biofilter (toluene degradation). The variation of the moisture content into the filter bed seems to affect the biological activity from the top (height of 15 cm) and at the bottom (height of 67 and 86 cm). Van Lith et al. (1989) described the role of the moisture content of the filter bed, which appeared to be a critical operating parameter that can seriously affect the biofilter effectiveness.

Figure 2 shows the BTX degradation profiles along the 98 cm of the filter bed height. Three inlet BTX concentrations were represented (1,974, 3,078, and 3,611 mg m^{-3}) at a superficial gas velocity of 9.6 m^3 m^{-2} h^{-1}. The inlet BTX concentration decreased to reach zero at 67 cm at day 1, 11, and 15. At high BTX inlet concentration (day 11 and 15), the BTX concentration profile shows an important decrease, from 0 to 34 cm (Table 1), and the energy generated by the exothermic biological reaction led to an increase of temperature at 34 cm (Figure 1). The concentration of 3,433 mg m^{-3} corresponded to a relatively short time of the experiment (2 hours) at day 8. The superficial gas velocity varied from 9.6 to 24.1 m^3 m^{-2} h^{-1}, reducing the empty residence time from 366 to 146 s.

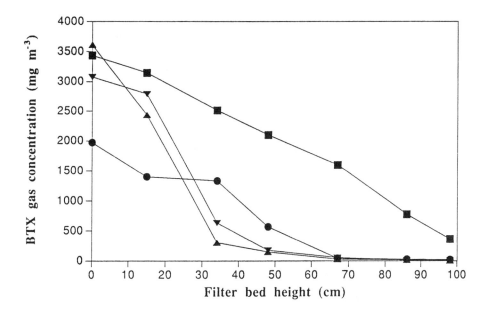

FIGURE 2. BTX concentration profiles as function of the filter bed height at two superficial gas velocities: $v = 9.6 \text{ m}^3 \text{ m}^{-2} \text{ h}^{-1}$ and $v = 24.1 \text{ m}^3 \text{ m}^{-2} \text{ h}^{-1}$, on days 1, 11, and 15.

The biofilter immediately responded to the velocity step change by stimulating all the biofilter microflora in order to degrade BTX at the same rate (BTX profile almost linear) with an average elimination capacity of 71.2 ± 19.7 (n = 6) g m^{-3} h^{-1} of each section of the filter bed. The biofilter rapidly responded to an organic

TABLE 1. BTX elimination capacity within the 50-L biofilter (height = 98 cm).

Section of Filter Bed (cm)	Day 1		Day 11		Day 15	
	Load[a]	EC[b]	Load	EC	Load	EC
0 - 15	126.3	36.8	231.1	75.2	197.0	18.2
15 - 34	70.7	3.4	123.1	107.6	141.1	109.1
34 - 48	91.3	52.3	21.0	10.9	43.5	31.3
48 - 67	28.7	26.6	7.5	6.1	9.0	6.1
67 - 86	2.1	0.7	1.4	0.7	2.9	2.1
86 - 98	1.7	0.6	0.9	0.6	0.9	0.1

(a) Load is given in g m^{-3} h^{-1}.
(b) EC is given in g m^{-3} h^{-1}.

load shock (32.8 to 91.8 g m^{-3} h^{-1}) in contrast to Peters et al. (1993), who observed that their biofilter took 1 week to adapt to load-shock variation (2.4 to 6.0 g C m^{-3} h^{-1}).

In conclusion, high performance has been reached in a biofilter that used a composted peat moss and chicken manure blend as a filter material to remove benzene, toluene, and xylenes in contaminated airstreams. The biofilter responded rapidly to a BTX load variation, and showed its dynamic behavior to be tied to physical parameters such as moisture content, oxygen consumption, and temperature, all of which can seriously affect the aerobic degradation of BTX and the biofilter performance.

REFERENCES

Flederbach, Jr., W., E., M. Traister, and J. Rinko, Jr. 1993. "Choosing the Proper Pollution Control System for VOC Emissions." *Proceedings of 86th Annual Meeting & Exhibition of the Air, and Waste Management.* Denver, CO.

Leson, G., A. M. Winer, and D. S. Hodge. 1991. "Application of Biofiltration to the Control of Air Toxics, and Other VOC Emissions." *Proceedings of 84th Annual Meeting of the Air & Waste Management.* Vancouver, BC.

Miller, D. E., and L. W. Canter. 1991. "Control of Aromatic Waste Air Stream by Soil Bioreactor." *Environmental Progress* 4(10): 300-306.

Peters, D. A., G. T. Hickman., J. G. Stefanoff., and M. B. Garcia, Jr. 1993. "Laboratory Assessment of Biofiltration for Fuel Derived Emissions Control." *Proceedings of 86th Annual Meeting & Exhibition of the Air, and Waste Management.* Denver, CO.

Tahraoui, K., R. Samson, and D. Rho. 1994. "Biodegradation of BTX from Waste Gases in a Biofilter Reactor." *Proceedings of 87th Annual Meeting & Exhibition of the Air, and Waste Management.* Cincinnati, OH.

Rho, R., P. Mercier, J. F. Jetté, R. Samson, J. Lei, and B. Cyr. 1995. "Respirometric Oxygen Demand Determinations of Laboratory- and Field-Scale Biofilters." In R. E. Hinchee, G. D. Sayles, and R. S. Skeen (Eds.), *Biological Unit Processes for Hazardous Waste Treatment,* pp. 211-218. Battelle Press, Columbus, OH.

Van Groenestijn, J. W., and P.G.M. Hesselink. 1993. "Biotechniques for Air Pollution Control." *Biodegradation* 4: 283-301.

Van Lith, C., S. L. David, and R. Marsh. 1989. "Design Criteria for Biofilters." *Proceedings of 82nd Annual Meeting & Exhibition of the Air, and Waste Management.* Anaheim, CA. pp. 127-138.

In Situ Demonstration of Anaerobic BTEX Biodegradation Through Controlled-Release Experiments

Martin Reinhard, Gary D. Hopkins, Eva Orwin,
Shubo Shang, and Carmen A. Lebron

ABSTRACT

Anaerobic biodegradation of the aromatic hydrocarbons benzene, toluene, ethylbenzene, *m*-xylene and *o*-xylene (BTEX) was studied in situ within the anaerobic zone of a weathered gasoline spill site. Slug tests were conducted in which approximately 1,000 L of treated anaerobic groundwater was injected into a test zone through a multiport injection well. The injectate contained bromide as the conservative tracer, nitrate or sulfate as the electron acceptor, and trace concentrations of BTEX compounds. Following injection, water was withdrawn and analyzed for bromide, nitrate, sulfate, and BTEX. Under denitrification conditions, transformation was complete within 8 days for toluene, ethylbenzene, and *m*-xylene and within 75 days for *o*-xylene. Benzene removal was not observed within the time span and the conditions of the experiment. With sulfate as the predominant electron acceptor under sulfidogenic conditions, toluene, and *m*- and *o*-xylene were transformed and completely removed over a period of 40 to 50 days. Ethylbenzene removal began to accelerate after 30 days. Benzene removal was slow (approximately 0.01 mg/m^3-h) but appeared to be significant.

INTRODUCTION

Both active and passive (intrinsic) bioremediation of gasoline sites using anaerobic processes is receiving increasing attention. Anaerobic biotransformation of hydrocarbons is still poorly understood, and rates are difficult to predict. Therefore, such processes are not usually considered as a treatment option. Several microcosm studies have reported aromatic hydrocarbon degradation under denitrifying (e.g., Zeyer et al. 1986, Hutchins et al. 1991, Barbaro et al. 1992) and sulfate-reducing (e.g., Beller et al. 1992, Edwards et al. 1992, Edwards and Grbic-Galic, 1992), as well as iron(III)-reducing conditions (Lovley and Lonergan 1990) and methanogenic conditions (Grbic-Galic and Vogel 1987). The reported studies indicate that when present as a mixture, the degradation rates of the BTEX compounds tend to be sequential, with toluene most readily degraded under both denitrifying and sulfidogenic conditions. Benzene was often found to be resistant except in a study by Edwards and Grbic-Galic (1992) under presumed sulfidogenic conditions.

The paucity of data demonstrating that results of small laboratory studies can be extrapolated to the field makes it difficult to take advantage of anaerobic processes for site cleanup. This is unfortunate since the potential payoff could be very significant. So far, few attempts have been made to demonstrate intrinsic anaerobic bioremediation at the field scale under controlled conditions and then only under denitrifying conditions (Patrick et al. 1985 and 1986, Barbaro et al. 1992, Hutchins et al. 1991). This paper summarizes the results of two controlled-release experiments designed to evaluate anaerobic BTEX biotransformation in situ under nitrate- and sulfate-reducing conditions. Previous to the experiments discussed here, three preliminary slug tests (EO1 through EO3) were conducted. In one (EO3) excess nitrate was added as the electron acceptor and BTEX compounds were essentially removed from the test zone (Reinhard et al. 1995).

CONTROLLED-RELEASE EXPERIMENTS

Controlled-release experiments were conducted within the anaerobic plume of a weathered gasoline plume site. The controlled-release experiments consisted of slug tests in which approximately 1,000 L of pretreated groundwater was slowly injected into the anaerobic test zone. The slug was augmented with bromide salt as the tracer, salts to readjust the ionic strength, electron acceptors such as nitrate and sulfate as needed, and trace quantities of BTEX compounds. Contaminant behavior was studied by comparing the concentration vs. time profile of the reactant with that of the conservative tracer and with model predictions. The inner test zone (the slug) was surrounded by a concentric buffer of medium with the same composition (but without the organics and the tracer) as the reaction zone. Thus, constant reaction conditions were maintained even during the period of decreasing tracer and organics concentration.

The site hydrogeology is characterized by a small hydraulic gradient, and the plume appears to spread radially. The aquifer consists of sandy/silty alluvial and coastal deposits with some clay lenses (Schroeder 1991). Inside the plume, sulfidogenic and methanogenic conditions existed in wells as evidenced by the occurrence of black iron sulfide precipitate and methane gas in the headspace of the wells. Outside the gasoline plume, the groundwater was aerobic and the background sulfate, nitrate, and bromide concentrations were approximately 85 mg/L, 5 mg/L, and 0.6 mg/L, respectively.

The wells were screened over 5 ft (1.5 m) depth starting from 1 ft (0.3 m) below the water table. They were instrumented with multilevel samplers consisting of a central ¼-in. (0.6-cm) stainless steel tube capped at the lower end and six individual tubes reaching to different depths. Samples collected from these multi-level samplers were numbered 1 through 6, with 1 representing the uppermost point and 6 representing the deepest point. Samples collected through the central ¼-in. (0.6-cm) tube were considered a composite sample. Here, only data of sampler tube 3 are discussed.

Water used for the designed injection experiments was extracted from a well designated as EO and treated by activated carbon adsorption (GAC) for organics removal and ion exchange columns. Residual dissolved oxygen in the injection water was removed by passing the water through a helium-purged gas stripping tower. Chloride salts of calcium, magnesium, and sodium were added back to the injection water to readjust the ionic strength to values similar to the average value measured in the native groundwater. The concentrations of the injection water for the nitrate- and sulfate-reducing experiments (designated as EO4 and EO6) are indicated in Table 1. For injection, the bromide-spiked water was metered into the well at an average flow rate of 1.5 L/min to minimize pressure mounding during the injection. Sampling was the main driving force for the reversed flow during the "pullback" phase, which thus was discontinuous. At weekly or biweekly intervals, 60 L of water was extracted from the composite and each multilevel sampling tube and sent to Stanford University for analysis of bromide, sulfate, nitrate, and BTEX compounds. Approximately 8 h after the injection, a set of samples was taken without purging to determine the concentration in the injection water. These water samples were taken from within the well casing but without contacting the aquifer. Thereafter, the samples were collected at regular intervals with sufficient flushing of the well borehole to produce water from outside the well casing.

TABLE 1. Experimental conditions for the nitrate- (EO4) and sulfate-reducing (EO6) experiments.

	Experiment	
	Nitrate Reducing, EO4	Sulfate Reducing, EO6
Test Volume (L)	900	750
NO_3-Buffer Vol. (L)	948	1,530 (35.5 mg/L)[a]
SO_4-Buffer Vol. (L)	0	735
Bromide (mg/L)	58	56
Nitrate (mg/L)	230	0
Sulfate (mg/L)	2	45
Benzene (µg/L)	241	204
Toluene (µg/L)	286	259
Ethylbenzene	286	296
m-Xylene	211	227
o-Xylene	250	277

(a) Nitrate buffer around sulfate buffer.

RESULTS AND DISCUSSION

A model was developed that considered advective-dispersive flow coupled with a zero-order reaction term (Reinhard et al. 1995). Radial advective flow in the direction of the extraction wells was assumed to occur only during sampling. The dispersivity and the regional groundwater flow velocity were obtained by fitting the tracer response curve to the bromide data. The tracer response curves were reproducible in successive tracer tests, indicating that the hydraulic conditions were stable. The longitudinal dispersivity and the regional groundwater velocity were estimated as 5 cm and 0.7 cm/day, respectively (Reinhard et al. 1995).

Figure 1 shows the predicted responses of transforming solutes along with the measured concentration vs. time profile for the normalized conservative tracer (Br/Br_o). The Br/Br_o data were taken from the nitrate experiment and are included to indicate breakthrough of the buffer. For the first 30 days, the tracer concentration remained constant, indicating that undiluted slug water was withdrawn. Then, the Br/Br_o ratio gradually decreased as the buffer began breaking

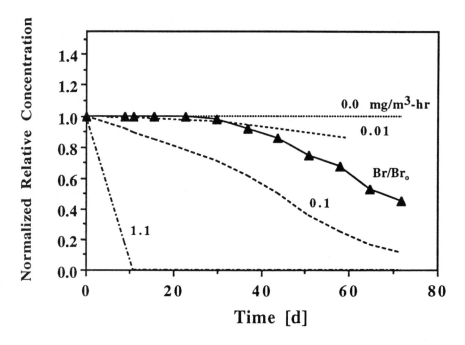

FIGURE 1. Normalized relative concentration of reactive solutes with different zero-order reaction rates (in mg/m^3-h) and tracer concentration normalized to the initial concentration (Br/Br_o). Conditions were selected to approximately match results observed in the nitrate- (EO4) and sulfate-reducing experiments (EO6). The Br/Br_o data was developed in EO4, the nitrate-reducing experiment.

through and the slug water was diluted. The nitrate experiment was terminated when Br/Br_o was below 0.5. In calculating the concentration responses for reactive solutes, zero-order kinetics was assumed. The experimental conditions and zero-order rates (K_b) used (0, 0.01, 0.1, and 1.1 mg/m^3-h) were selected to approximately match the observed BTEX responses in the nitrate and sulfate experiments discussed below. The concentrations indicated are normalized to the initial concentrations of the respective solute (C/C_o) and relative to the normalized tracer concentration (Br/Br_o). Thus, the concentrations shown represent the normalized relative concentrations given by ratio $C_r = (C/C_o)/(Br/Br_o)$. Dividing C/C_o by Br/Br_o accounts for the effects of dispersion.

The model predicts a linear decrease of C_r for compounds that are completely transformed during the undiluted period (the first 30 days). For compounds that degrade more slowly, the C_r decreases linearly during extraction of the undiluted slug. Then, as the dilution becomes more and more significant, C_r decreases faster. For compounds that transform very slowly, the effect of breakthrough on C_r is less pronounced: the slope of C_r for the compound which transforms at 0.01 mg/m^3-h remains relatively small even when the slug is diluted by more than 50%. For nontransforming solutes such as bromide ($K_b = 0.0$ mg/m^3-h), C_r remains constant at 1. This applies both to the tracer [($C_r = (Br/Br_o)/(Br/Br_o)$)] and to solutes that sorb but do not transform. Thus, the shape of the curve is not influenced by sorption as long as it does not influence the rate of transformation.

Figure 2 shows an analogous plot for the aromatics tested in the nitrate experiment. The data from sampler tube 3 are shown. These data were representative for the contaminant behavior observed at other levels and in the composite sampler

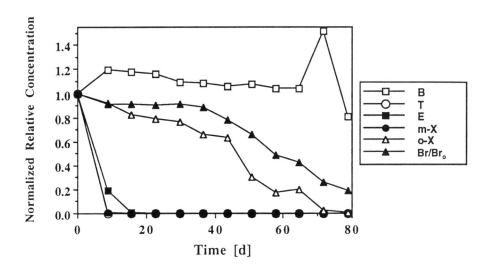

FIGURE 2. Denitrification conditions: normalized concentrations (C/C_o) of benzene, toluene, ethylbenzene, and *m*- and *o*-xylene relative to Br/Br_o.

tube, although some variation between the various sampling points were observed. The initial nitrate concentration was 230 mg/L, in excess of the theoretical demand, and remained constant (data not shown). The bromide-to-nitrate concentration ratio remained constant for the first 38 days when undiluted injection water was withdrawn. Then, after approximately 38 days (or extraction of 0.36 relative pore volume), the nitrate buffer around the test slug began to break through and, consequently, the relative bromide concentration started to decrease. Note that the nitrate concentrations in the slug and the buffer were equal.

The organics showed a distinct behavior. Toluene, m-xylene, and ethyl-benzene decreased rapidly and were completely removed by day 16; o-xylene decreased only slowly for the first 40 days and but more rapidly thereafter. By day 72, o-xylene had disappeared. Benzene increased initially from 241 to 260 µg/L, probably due to desorption from the aquifer material. After the first sampling event, the relative concentration remained constant for the first 60 days, indicating no significant removal. After day 60, the benzene data were more variable. Rapid removal of toluene, ethylbenzene, and m-xylene and slow removal of o-xylene also were observed in laboratory experiments. The persistence of benzene was consistent with results from laboratory experiments, which used Seal Beach solids (Ball et al. 1993).

Figure 3 shows the results of the controlled-release experiment under sulfate-reducing conditions. This experiment lasted for 60 days. The aromatics' removal was also sequential as in the nitrate-reducing experiment with toluene, o-xylene, and m-xylene being removed first and relatively rapidly. Ethylbenzene and benzene were more resistant to degradation. The removal patterns of toluene and the xylenes were more complex, however, and did not fit the simple kinetic rate

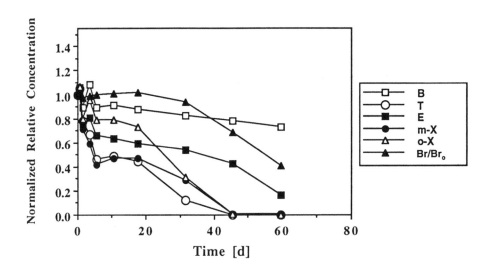

FIGURE 3. Sulfate-reducing conditions: normalized concentrations (C/C$_o$) of benzene, toluene, ethylbenzene, and m- and o-xylene relative to Br/Br$_o$.

laws. Removal for toluene and *o*- and *m*-xylene was rapid during the first 4 days when they reached a plateau that lasted for at least 10 days. Thereafter, their concentrations decreased and reached zero by day 47. In contrast, ethylbenzene remained stable for the first 30 days when removal began to accelerate. Benzene removal was slow but appears significant when compared with the model predictions. The slope fits approximately the 0.01 mg/m^3-h-curve in Figure 1. The observed slow removal is consistent with results obtained in the laboratory (Edwards and Grbic-Galic, 1992) but should be confirmed in longer-term experiments.

The fact that toluene was degraded in the test zone without a lag time, under presumed sulfidogenic conditions, immediately after the denitrifying experiment indicates that sulfidogenic bacteria remain active even when high concentrations of nitrate (230 mg/L) are present. The removal of toluene was observed in laboratory microcosms with Seal Beach sediments and groundwater (Edwards et al. 1992, Ball et al. 1993). However, in these cultures, toluene appeared to inhibit the degradation of *m+p*-xylene, which commenced only after toluene was completely removed. Interestingly, when sulfate-reducing media were used, the onset of toluene degradation was delayed by a lag of 25 days; thereafter, *m+p*-xylene degradation and toluene degradation were concurrent.

In summary, the controlled release experiments demonstrated rapid toluene, ethylbenzene, *o*- and *m*-xylene transformation in situ under nitrate- and sulfate-reducing conditions. Benzene removal appeared slow but significant and needs to be further investigated in longer-term experiments; *p*-xylene was not tested. The observed field data are in general agreement with laboratory results and lend credence to bioremediation schemes that consider intrinsic anaerobic removal processes.

ACKNOWLEDGMENTS

Funding for this project was provided by the U.S. Department of Navy, Naval Facilities Engineering Service Center, Port Hueneme, California, under a grant No. R-815738-01 through the U.S. Environmental Protection Agency supported Western Region Hazardous Substance Research Center. Additional support was provided by the Chevron Research and Technology Company. The content of this study does not necessarily represent the views of these organizations. We thank Lew Semprini, Oregon State University, for suggesting the slug test methodology and Dale Lorenzano for technical assistance.

REFERENCES

Ball, H. A., M. Reinhard, E. Orwin, H. F. Ridgway, and D. Phipps. 1993. *Factors Influencing the Anaerobic Biodegradation of Gasoline Hydrocarbons by Groundwater Bacteria at Seal Beach, CA.* Orange County Water District, Fountain Valley, CA.

Barbaro, J. R., J. F. Barker, L. A. Lemon, and C. I. Mayfield. 1992. "Biotransformation of BTEX Under Anaerobic, Denitrifying Conditions: Field and Laboratory Observations." *Journal of Contaminant Hydrology* 11: 245-272.

Beller, H. R., D. Grbic-Galic, and M. Reinhard. 1992. "Microbial Degradation of Toluene under Sulfate-Reducing Conditions and the Influence of Iron on the Process." *Applied and Environmental Microbiology* 58(3): 786-793.

Edwards, E. A., L. E. Wills, M. Reinhard and D. Grbic-Galic. 1992. "Anaerobic Degradation of Toluene and Xylene by Aquifer Microorganisms under Sulfate-Reducing Conditions." *Applied and Environmental Microbiology* 58(3): 794-800.

Edwards, E. A., and D. Grbic-Galic. 1992. "Complete Mineralization of Benzene by Aquifer Microorganisms under Strictly Anaerobic Conditions." *Applied and Environmental Microbiology* 58(8): 2663-2666.

Grbic-Galic, D., and T. M. Vogel. 1987. "Transformation of Toluene and Benzene by Mixed Methanogenic Cultures." *Applied and Environmental Microbiology* 53(2): 254-260.

Hutchins, S. R., G. W. Sewell, D. A. Kovacs, and G. A. Smith. 1991. "Biodegradation of Aromatic Hydrocarbons by Aquifer Microorganisms Under Denitrifying Conditions." *Environmental Science and Technology* 25(1): 68-76.

Lovley, D. R., and D. J. Lonergan. 1990. "Anaerobic Oxidation of Toluene, Phenol, and *p*-cresol by the Dissimilatory Iron-Reducing Organism, GS-15." *Applied and Environmental Microbiology* 56(6): 1858-1864.

Patrick, G. C., C. J. Ptacek, R. W. Gillham, J. F. Barker, J. A. Cherry, D. W. Major, C. I. Mayfield, and R. D. Dickhout. 1985. *The Behavior of Soluble Petroleum Product Derived Hydrocarbons in Groundwater*. Pet. Assoc. Conserv. Can. Environ., Ottawa, Ont., PACE Phase I, Rep. No. 85-3, 70pp.

Patrick, G. C., J. F. Barker, R. W. Gillham, C. I. Mayfield, and D. Major. 1986. *The Behavior of Soluble Petroleum Product Derived Hydrocarbons in Groundwater*. Pet. Assoc. Conserv. Can. Environ., Ottawa, Ont., PACE Phase II, Rep. No. 86-1, 59 pp.

Reinhard, M., S. Shang, P. K. Kitanidis, E. Orwin, G. Hopkins, and C. A. LeBron. 1995. *Measurement of In Situ BTEX Biotransformation Rates in an Anaerobic Gasoline Plume under Different Electron-Accepting Conditions*. Technical Report WRC-6; Western Region Hazardous Substance Research Center; Stanford, CA, 1995.

Schroeder, R. A. 1991. *Delineation of a Hydrocarbon (Weathered Gasoline) Plume in Shallow Deposits at the U.S. Naval Weapons Station, Seal Beach, California*. U.S. Geological Survey.

Zeyer, J., E. P. Kuhn, and R. P. Schwarzenbach. 1986. "Rapid Microbial Mineralization of Toluene and 1,3-Dimethylbenzene in the Absence of Molecular Oxygen." *Applied and Environmental Microbiology* 52(4): 944-947.

Anaerobic In Situ Bioremediation: Injected Nutrient and Substrate Fate and Transport

John T. Leethem, Ralph E. Beeman, Michael D. Lee,
Alfred A. Biehle, David E. Ellis, and Steve H. Shoemaker

ABSTRACT

An anaerobic in situ bioremediation field pilot test was operated at a Gulf Coast chemical manufacturing site. The primary objective of the test was to gain a better understanding of mechanisms affecting the movement and distribution of nutrients and substrate through the aquifer. Another objective was to investigate whether delivery of high concentrations of substrate would inhibit microbial growth at the delivery well and control plugging in the aquifer. Concentrated solutions of nutrients (ammonia and phosphate) and substrate (acetate and benzoate), with a bromide tracer, were injected alternately. Groundwater concentrations of the nutrients and substrate were determined at 26 locations, 140 days after delivery started, using cone penetrometer technology. Little lateral dispersion was observed. Cone penetrometer sampling confirmed that nutrient and substrate delivery was accomplished, and that the delivery of high concentrations of substrate-controlled plugging.

INTRODUCTION

Beeman et al. (1994) demonstrated that 10 µM tetrachloroethylene (1.7 mg/L) could be completely reductively dechlorinated to ethene. Higher concentrations of substrate and nutrients may be required to effectively treat greater contaminant concentrations. This technology has been demonstrated; however, the limiting factor of anaerobic in situ bioremediation may be the distribution of nutrients and substrate through the aquifer.

An anaerobic in situ test was operated at a chemical manufacturing site on the Texas Gulf Coast. Objectives of this test were to (1) better understand the mechanisms affecting movement of nutrients and substrate through the aquifer, (2) investigate whether delivery of high concentrations of substrate could inhibit microbial growth and plugging at the delivery well, and (3) aid the effective dispersal of nutrients and substrate through the aquifer.

The site geology consists of fluvial sand, silt, and interbedded clay. The lithology of the study area, in order of increasing depth, was interpreted from cone penetrometer tests (CPTs) and boring logs. The upper lithologic unit is a clay (sandy to silty) about 2 m thick; under that is a 9-m-thick water-bearing sand consisting of a fining-upward sequence (fine-grained above coarse-grained particles); and beneath the sand lies a confining clay unit.

The sand contains one aquifer, but there are two distinct flow regimes. Groundwater in the lower section of the aquifer moves faster (0.09 m/day) than in the upper section (0.06 m/day) by virtue of the fining-upward sequence. The groundwater gradient in the area is controlled by an existing recovery well field located downgradient of the test site.

METHODS AND MATERIALS

The pilot system shown in Figure 1 consisted of three delivery wells (IW-1, IW-2, and IW-3), four monitoring wells (MW-1, MW-2, MW-3, and MW-4), and

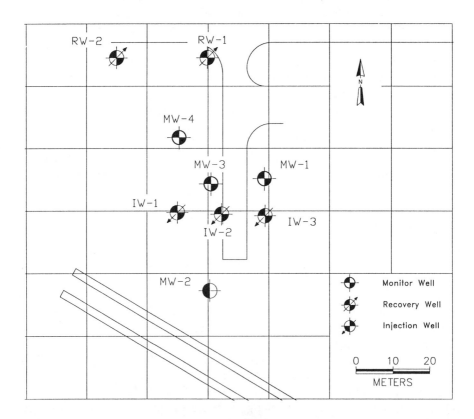

FIGURE 1. Bioremediation system well location map.

two recovery wells (RW-1 and RW-2) pumping a total of 53 L/min. All wells are screened across the entire aquifer except MW-1 and MW-2, which are screened only in the upper flow regime.

MW-3 and MW-4 are located downgradient (8.2 and 22.6 m) from IW-2. MW-3 and MW-4 are in the injectate flow path. MW-2 is upgradient of the test site and MW-1 is outside the influence of the injectate plume. RW-1 and RW-2 are approximately 39 m and 47 m, respectively, from the delivery wells.

From May to October 1993 (131 days), 120,000 L of nutrients and 99,000 L of substrate were delivered by gravity feed through the three delivery wells. Concentrated solutions of nutrients (ammonium and phosphate) and substrate (acetate and benzoate) were delivered alternately. Movement of nutrients, substrate, and bromide tracer was monitored to determine their fate and transport.

Nutrient and substrate mixtures used in this test are presented in Table 1. The acetate/benzoate mixture was selected as substrate based on the individual reported success of these compounds in previous reductive dehalogenation field experiments (Semprini et al. 1992; Beeman et al. 1994). The concentrations were set to be inhibiting to microbial growth near the point of injection. According to Miller and Litsky (1976), benzoic acid was used as a preservative at 0.05 to 0.1%, and acetic acid at 0.005 to 1.0%. Therefore, the injected concentrations of both sodium acetate and sodium benzoate were maintained at or above 1.0% by weight in water. In turn, nutrient concentrations were an approximate 100:10:1 ratio of carbon:nitrogen:phosphorus. Sodium bromide (NaBr) was added at a concentration of 1,000 mg/L to the substrate and nutrient solution to serve as a conservative tracer. Groundwater samples were collected from the monitoring and recovery wells over a period of 400 days.

TABLE 1. Injectate composition.

Chemical Components	Weeks 0 to 6, %[a]	Weeks 7 to 20, %[a]
Substrate Mix		
Sodium Benzoate	2.5	1.0
Sodium Acetate	2.5	1.0
Sodium Bromide	0.1	0.1
Nutrient mix		
Ammonium Chloride	2.0	2.0
Sodium Dibasic Phosphate	0.1	0.1
Potassium Monobasic Phosphate	0.1	0.1
Sodium Bromide	0.1	0.1

(a) Percentages listed are percent of water by weight, not total solution percentages.

Weekly sampling results indicated two distinct flow regimes in the aquifer. Groundwater samples were collected from MW-3 and MW-4 near the top of the aquifer's upper flow regime (UFR) at a depth of approximately 5 m and at a lower level in the aquifer's lower flow regime (LFR) at a depth of approximately 9 m. Samples were collected from the UFR of wells MW-1, MW-2, RW-1, and RW-2, which were screened only across the UFR. Groundwater samples were analyzed by SW-846 methods for total organic carbon (TOC), chemical oxygen demand (COD), acetate, benzoate, ammonia-nitrogen, bromide, sulfate, and total phosphate.

In order to most effectively sample discrete intervals from wells, the following groundwater sampling procedures were used. First, water levels were measured and three well volumes were removed using a Grundfos® Redi-Flo 2 pump placed in the middle of the screened interval. Next, the pump was placed at a depth of 9 m and the lower sample was obtained at a low flowrate (approximately 100 mL/min). Then the upper samples were taken using a bailer, from a depth of approximately 5 m.

RESULTS

Arrival times for bromide, ammonia-nitrogen, TOC, and COD at monitoring wells MW-3 and MW-4 are shown in Table 2. Separate travel times have been determined for the UFR and LFR in each well. Monitoring wells were used to track the injectate plumes to determine when the injectate would reach the recovery wells. A CPT groundwater survey was performed to determine the location and shape of the injectate plume.

TABLE 2. Injectate arrival times at wells.

Constituents	MW-3 UFR (Day)	MW-3 LFR (Day)	MW-4 UFR (Day)	MW-4 LFR (Day)
Bromide	73	77	281	294
TOC	180	112	358	196
COD	170	112	393	270
Acetate	164	170	156	200
Benzoate	164	170	266	266
Ammonia-Nitrogen	170	165	165	170
Phosphate	266	408	Not Sampled	Not Sampled
Sulfate	Variable	Variable	Variable	Variable

UFR is the upper flow regime; LFR is the lower flow regime.

The injectate plume was defined by collecting groundwater samples from both flow regimes at 26 locations using CPT technology. Samples were collected from two depths at each location (5 m and 9 m). Samples were collected 147 to 169 days after delivery started, before injectate mass was removed by recovery wells. Logical constraints (e.g., buildings and other structures) limited the number of CPT samples that could be collected from the plume originating from IW-1.

Bromide distribution in the UFR is shown in Figure 2. Plumes emanating from the injection wells are almost completely separated. The plume shape was somewhat variable in orientation with the western-most plume oriented almost northwest and the eastern plume almost north. The maximum bromide concentration observed from CPT samples in the UFR was 70 mg/L.

Bromide concentration in the LFR is shown in Figure 3. The highest bromide concentration observed in the LFR was 250 mg/L. Three plumes originating at the injection wells were evident. The bromide plume associated with IW-2 was 6.7 m by 23.0 m at the 100 mg/L contour line. The plume associated with IW-1 was 4.6 m by 21.3 m, and the plume associated with IW-3 was 7.6 m by 22.9 m. The entire plume was 29 m long and 33.5 m wide.

There was a relatively slow rate of dispersion and diffusion compared to advection. Bromide concentrations were approximately one order of magnitude higher in the LFR than in the UFR. The greater areal extent of the lower bromide plume was due to higher permeability at the base of the aquifer and density effects of the concentrated substrate and nutrient solutions. Arrival times indicate the average flowrate was 0.09 m/day in the LFR.

Figure 4 shows the TOC distribution (used to monitor benzoate and acetate) in the upper flow regime. TOC concentrations ranged from a high of 578 mg/L to a low of between 1 to 47 mg/L on the plume edges. Elevated acetate concentrations were generally associated with elevated TOC levels, and the distribution of acetate was similar to the TOC distribution. However, benzoate was detected only around the center plume associated with well IW-2.

TOC in the lower flow regime (Figure 5) is distributed similarly to the bromide, except the plumes are separated, more distinct, and the highest concentrations of TOC extend only approximately half as far as the highest concentration of bromide. The highest concentration of TOC was 2,126 mg/L. The upgradient and downgradient edges of the plume have only between 3 to 5 mg/L of TOC. The substrates moved further in the LFR than in the UFR and were more evenly distributed.

Distribution of ammonia-nitrogen in the UFR is shown in Figure 6. Three small plumes of ammonia-nitrogen extend from each injection well. Three other areas of higher concentrations appear to be separated from the injection wells, probably due to the alternating delivery of substrate and nutrients. Phosphate did not move readily through the upper flow regime. Only one location contained a detectable concentration of phosphate (2 mg/L). Sulfate concentrations in the upper flow regime ranged from 13 to 300 mg/L, with 15 of 25 CPT samples containing more than 100 mg/L sulfate. At the lower concentrations, the availability of sulfate could limit the activity of sulfate-reducing bacteria. Figure 7

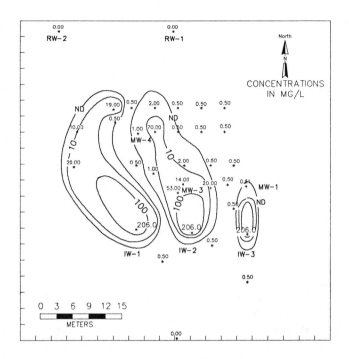

FIGURE 2. Bromide isoconcentration map for top of aquifer.

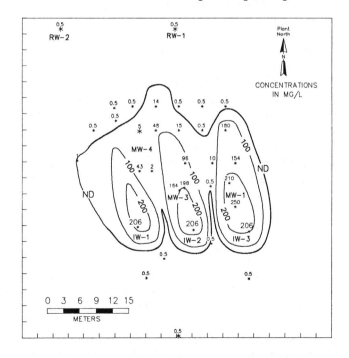

FIGURE 3. Bromide isoconcentration map for base of aquifer.

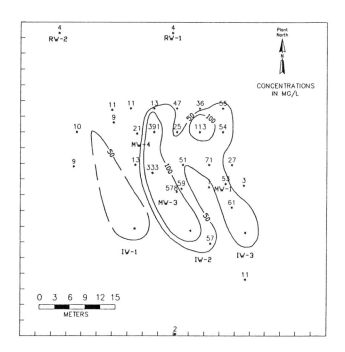

FIGURE 4. TOC isoconcentration map for top of aquifer.

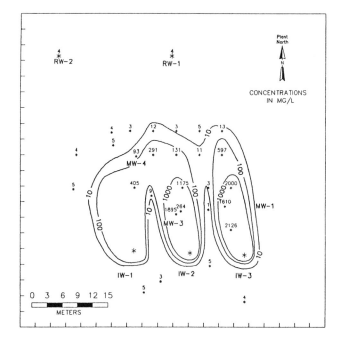

FIGURE 5. TOC isoconcentration map for base of aquifer.

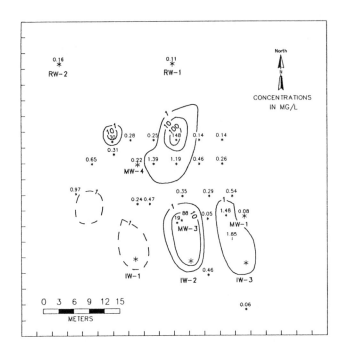

FIGURE 6. Ammonia/nitrogen isoconcentration map for top of aquifer.

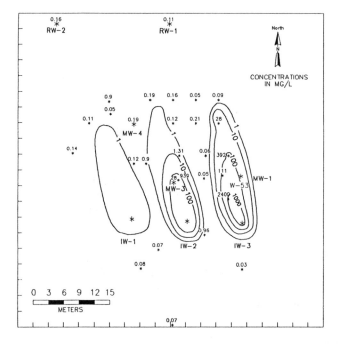

FIGURE 7. Ammonia/nitrogen isoconcentration map for base of aquifer.

presents the distribution of ammonia-nitrogen in the lower flow regime. Three ammonia-nitrogen plumes were identified. The parallel plumes trend north-northwest toward the recovery wells. The maximum concentration of ammonia-nitrogen was 2,400 mg/L. Ammonia-nitrogen concentrations less than 1 mg/L define the boundaries of each plume. Phosphate was detected in only three CPT samples (from the western plume). No evidence for the transport of phosphate was found for the other injection wells. Sulfate concentrations in the lower flow regime ranged from 16 mg/L, but only four of the 26 samples had more than 50 mg/L sulfate. The low sulfate concentrations in the lower flow regime could limit the activity of sulfate-reducing bacteria.

DISCUSSION

The strategy of injection at inhibitory levels was successful. Substrate was transported through the aquifer with little evidence of plugging in the injection wells or aquifer. Ammonia-nitrogen and phosphate transport was limited. The aquifer was heterogeneous, which impacted movement of injectate. The conservative tracer allowed for a mass balance to substantiate the injectate location. Mass balance calculations indicated that approximately 90% of the nutrients and 69% of the substrate were removed by biological activity or sorption (see Table 3).

Results indicate that difficulty in delivering ammonia-nitrogen and phosphate to the aquifer could limit microbial growth. However, the loss of substrate suggests microbial utilization of benzoate and acetate. Addition of nitrogen and phosphate may not be necessary to enhance microbial activity, but may be necessary for microbial growth in situ. It is speculated that clay in the aquifer rapidly sorbed and retarded the movement of ammonia-nitrogen and phosphate through the aquifer.

TABLE 3. Mass balance analysis of injectate plume.

Constituents	Upper Flow System (kg)	Lower Flow System (kg)	Injected Mass (kg)	Percent Change (%)
Bromide	73	77	151	0.0
Acetate	597	285	1,860	−52.6
Benzoate	23	280	2,163	−86.0
Ammonia-Nitrogen	3	75	549	−85.9
Phosphate	0	5	115	−95.6

Aquifer thickness is calibrated such that bromide was conserved.

REFERENCES

Beeman, R. E., J. E. Howell, S. H. Shoemaker, E. A. Salazar, and J. R. Buttram. 1994, "A Field Evaluation of In Situ Microbial Dehalogenation by the Biotransformation of Chlorinated Ethanes." In Hinchee, R. E., A. Leeson, S. Semprini, and S. K. Ong (Eds.), *Bioremediation of Chlorinated and Polycyclic Aromatic Hydrocarbon Compounds*, pp. 14-27. Lewis Publishers, Boca Raton, FL.

Miller, B. M. and W. Litsky. 1976. *Industrial Microbiology*. McGraw-Hill Book Company, New York, NY, p. 278.

Semprini, L., G. D. Hopkins, P. V. Roberts, and P. L. McCarty. 1992. "Enhanced Reductive Dechlorination: In-Situ Carbon Tetrachloride Transformation Under Anoxic Conditions." *Subsurface Restoration Conference Proceedings*, pp. 80-82. National Center for Ground Water Research, Houston, TX.

Aromatic Solvent Bioreclamation in a Highly Anaerobic Aquifer

Ralph E. Moon and Nicholas Albergo

ABSTRACT

Historical losses of aromatic solvents at a manufacturing facility resulted in groundwater contamination, severe odor problems, metal corrosion, and health concerns. Solvent releases were attributed to system failures, accidental losses, and poor housekeeping practices. A bioreclamation system consisting of both soil venting and a bioaeration unit was used to reduce the groundwater contamination and to eliminate odor and potential health concerns. System performance was monitored every 6 months. Benzene, toluene, diethyl ether, and hydrogen sulfide concentrations decreased in all monitoring wells, and dissolved oxygen increased from zero to several mg/L. The remediation schedule was threatened when an accidental acetone spill contaminated groundwater; however, within 9 months of the release, acetone concentrations were reported below the detection limit. A single air sparging well was installed to complement the in situ bioremediation system and to enhance the removal of a remaining hot spot via stripping and biodegradation. In situ bioremediation was remarkably effective. The estimated duration of treatment was 8 years; now it appears likely that groundwater restoration will be achieved within 6 years.

INTRODUCTION

The manufacturing facility was built in the late 1960's. Groundwater contaminants were attributed to leaking underground pipes, concrete sumps, a solvent storage area and a solvent recovery area. Poor petroleum handling practices may have also contributed to the groundwater contamination.

Groundwater contaminants were distributed nonuniformly; however, an acetone release of several thousand gallons was distributed throughout the site with the aid of the groundwater recovery system. The highest constituent concentrations coincided with areas of solvent use and reclamation. Groundwater chemicals of concern included benzene, toluene, ethylbenzene, xylenes, diethyl ether, and hydrogen sulfide. Benzene and toluene concentrations exceeded 20,000 µg/L in selected monitoring well samples. Hydrogen sulfide was detected in all monitoring wells; some samples exceeded 50,000 µg/L.

One of the unusual features about this case history was our finding that the endemic microbial population had degraded the leading edge of the contaminant plume years before our investigation was initiated. The plume had not appreciably degraded beneath several production facilities because solvent releases had overwhelmed the endemic aerobic microbes. As conditions became less favorable for aerobic respiration, opportunistic facultative anaerobic microbes that were better adapted to oxidize aromatic compounds where sulfur was the predominant electron acceptor.

Our strategy was to re-establish the aerobic microbial population with supplemental oxygen and nutrients. Because the groundwater plume was nearly devoid of oxygen, ambient air was introduced into the subsurface to inhibit hydrogen sulfide production and control odor.

SITE SETTING

The manufacturing facility is located on an island underlain by limestone. Soil borings consisted of consolidated limestone from land surface to approximately 20 ft (6.1 m) below land surface (bls). Karst features, as evidenced by increasing porosity in core samples were noted below 20 feet. The top of the water table was encountered at 20 to 24 ft (6.1 to 7.3 m) (bls). The tide influenced water table elevations profoundly; fluctuations of 1.5 to 2.0 ft (0.46 to 0.61 m) were recorded uniformly in each monitoring well. The site was underlain by a thin freshwater lens (7 to 15 ft [2.1 to 4.6 m] thick) above the saltwater. This finding prompted the remedial design to prevent the distribution of saltwater into the bioaeration unit and to protect the freshwater lens from saltwater mixing induced by pumping.

Before remediation, the dissolved oxygen (DO) content in groundwater was below the detection limit (0.1 mg/L). Outside the plume, nonimpacted groundwaters contained 1.8 to 2.4 mg/L DO. Chemical oxygen demand (COD) measurements within the contaminant plume ranged from 100 to 255 mg/L. Measurements obtained outside the plume ranged from below the detection limit to 47 mg/L. Measurements for pH ranged between 6.5 and 7.4 throughout the remediation process. Temperature measurements ranged from 28.0°C to 32.9°C. The highest temperatures were recorded within the contaminant plume and are symptomatic of microbial activity.

METHODS

Bacteriological Characterization

The bacterial evaluation tests were conducted prior to remediation to support the in situ bioremediation strategy. The subsurface region between 20 and 24 ft

(6.1 and 7.3 m) below land surface (bls) was selected for bacterial sampling. This coincided with the top of the fresh water table, where the vadose zone was exposed to tidal fluctuations. Six locations were selected to represent the impacted and background conditions. Core samples were prepared by crushing the core with a hammer within a sterile plastic wrap.

Heterotrophic Bacterial Counts. Heterotrophic aerobic bacteria were prepared for counting by placing a 3-g portion of the crushed core sample in a 40-mL vial. A basal sterile mineral buffer was aseptically dispensed into the vial and extracted for 10 to 15 min. Following extraction, serial dilutions (10^{-1} to 10^{-8}) were removed and plated on standard plate-count agar. The plated samples were incubated at 28°C for 7 days, and results reported as colony forming units (CFUs).

Bacterial Metabolism. Two isolation methods (i.e., direct plating method and disk diffusion) were used to determine the presence of heterotrophic aerobic bacteria capable of using specific carbon sources. These techniques are described elsewhere (Moon et al. 1992). A nutrient adsorption evaluation also was conducted to determine whether nutrients would adsorb to the limestone.

Groundwater Modeling

Endemic aerobic bacteria were essential to the remediation program. Groundwater modeling was conducted to determine the appropriate pumping rates and recovery well locations to sustain the freshwater lens and the bacteria.

Groundwater Remedial Design and Construction

The in situ bioremediation system was designed to fulfill three tasks: (1) recover groundwater; (2) remove volatile organic constituents; and (3) introduce oxygen, nutrients, and bacteria into the aquifer. The primary operational unit for the treatment system was a groundwater aeration unit, and a design based on trickling filter technology. Plastic media provided surface area for the aerobic bacteria to attach to and grow, and for oxygen to transfer into the water. The entire treatment system consisted of 13 groundwater-recovery wells, the aeration unit, and 10 injection wells. An air sparging well was constructed specifically to decrease benzene concentrations near the solvent recovery area, a residual contaminant source. The 1-inch (2.5-cm)-diameter steel pipe delivered 1.5 ft³ (0.05 m^3)/min. of air at 75 psi.

RESULTS

The highest bacterial counts (1.7×10^7 to 2.1×10^7 CFU/g) were obtained in areas with the least H_2S odor; the lowest counts (2.2×10^4 to 7.8×10^5 CFU/g) were reported in areas with the highest H_2S odor. No additional bacterial counts

were obtained after remediation began; however, observable microbial populations were observed attached to all recovery and injection wells after 6 to
12 months of operation.

The direct plating method degrader plate counts ranged from no growth
to 2.4×10^3 CFU/g. In contrast, the disk diffusion method showed bacterial
growth and carbon source metabolism in all sample areas.

The results showed that ammonia and orthophosphate ion solution at pH 7.6
had no affinity for limestone, indicating that the addition of nutrients could
migrate throughout the aquifer without significant adsorption to the aquifer
substrate. There was no analytical evidence that ammonia and orthophosphate
were released from the limestone; pH analyses were stable.

The modeling results indicated that at least 10 recovery wells, pumping at
10 gpm, would be required to provide an appropriate capture zone for the contaminant plume. This recovery scheme would also prevent saltwater intrusion
into the aquifer. A detailed explanation of the modeling assumptions, computer
methods and results is presented elsewhere (Moon et al. 1992).

The in situ bioremediation unit removed the majority of volatile organic
and sulfur constituents within 4 years of operation, from 1990 to 1994 (Figure 1).
After the August 1993 acetone release, acetone concentrations returned to below
the detection limit in March 1994 (Figure 2). The rapid recovery was attributed
primarily to in situ microbial degradation. DO measurements obtained from the

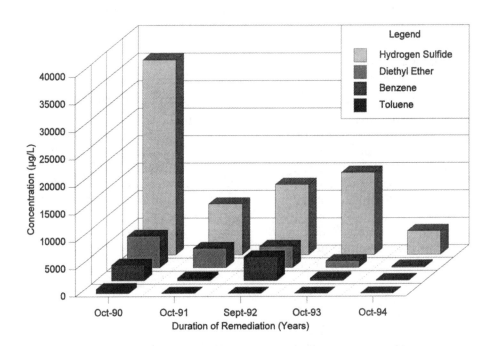

FIGURE 1. Average chemical concentrations in groundwater (1990-94).

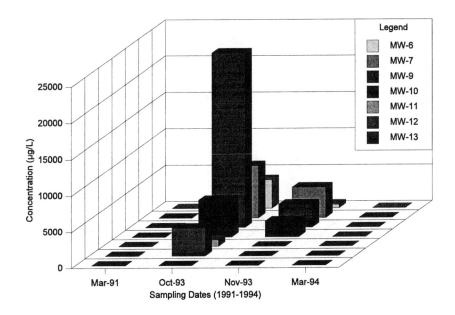

FIGURE 2. Acetone concentrations in groundwater before and after accidental release.

aeration unit (influent and effluent) and the recovery wells showed an overall increase during site remediation (Figure 3). Low DO concentrations reported in February 1992 were attributed to the other solvent releases from production and higher COD.

In March 1992, benzene concentrations near one monitoring well appeared to increase. After operating the air sparging well (October 1993), benzene concentrations in the nearest monitoring well (MW-17) dropped rapidly. The decline was attributed to air stripping and bioremediation. The success of the air sparging well has shortened the proposed duration of treatment by 2 years. The remediation phase will end once the groundwater can sustain a DO of 0.5 mg/L without operation of the aeration unit.

CONCLUSIONS

In situ biological treatment in combination with vapor extraction and air sparging successfully treated the groundwater contamination plume beneath an active manufacturing facility. Karst features enhanced the movement of nutrients and oxygen through the groundwater and the capture of groundwater contaminants. Improved groundwater quality was evident by decreased solvent concentrations, higher dissolved oxygen, and greatly reduced hydrogen sulfide odors.

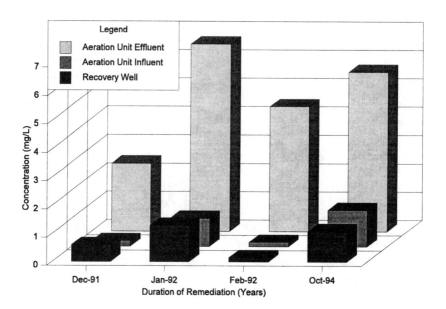

FIGURE 3. Average dissolved oxygen concentrations in recovery wells and aeration unit.

ACKNOWLEDGMENTS

The authors would like to acknowledge the assistance of Lloyd Cheong, Gary Boettcher, Chris Amstutz, Evan Nyer, Greg Rorech, Greg Ruskauff, and James Rumbaugh, who comprised the project team.

REFERENCE

Moon, R. E., E. Nyer, and P. Gurney-Read. 1992. "In Situ Groundwater Bioremediation in a Karst Aquifer." *HMC/Superfund '92 Proceedings*. Hazardous Materials Control Resources Institute, Greenbelt, MD. pp. 653-660.

In Situ Electrobioreclamation in Low-Permeability Soils

Reinout Lageman, Wieberen Pool,
Marcel van Vulpen, and Robert D. Norris

ABSTRACT

In situ bioreclamation has been widely practiced for the remediation of soils and groundwater contaminated with petroleum hydrocarbons and other compounds easily biodegraded under aerobic conditions. Success is dependent upon a number of conditions including biodegradability of the organic compounds, availability of nutrients and/or electron acceptors, pH, soil temperature, and permeability. Recent laboratory tests based on geokinetics field and laboratory experience have demonstrated that the application of an electric field in low-permeability soils provides important benefits in addition to electrokinetic transport of ionic species. Additional tests have shown that at a constant temperature and a current density of 20 amps/m^2, microbial growth is enhanced with no observable deleterious effects, nitrate transport can be predicted, and beneficial temperature increases can be achieved.

INTRODUCTION

The hydraulic permeability (k) of clay soils is generally less than 10^{-8} m/s (Freeze and Cherry 1979). This means that one of the basic conditions for successful bioreclamation, i.e., efficient delivery of nutrients, molecular oxygen, and/or other electron acceptors to the contaminated soil zone, is difficult to meet in clayey soils (Brown et al. 1984, Norris et al. 1994, Rittman et al. 1992). Extensive experience with and successful implementation of electrokinetic transport for the remediation of low-permeability soils contaminated with (heavy) metals (Lageman 1989, 1993; Cabrera-Guzman et al. 1990) has provided the technical basis for transport of nutrients and/or electron acceptors in low-permeability and heterogeneous formations to be remediated through in situ bioremediation.

ELECTRORECLAMATION

With the presently known aquifer remediation technologies, heavy metals can be removed only with great difficulty, especially in low-permeability soils.

The hydraulic permeability of these soils ranges from almost zero (clay) to moderate (clayey sand) which makes it difficult, if not impossible to "flush" the soil with aqueous solutions in order to remove the pollution. One technology that can overcome these limitations, electrokinetic reclamation, is based on electrokinetic phenomena that occur when the soil matrix is charged with electrical current induced into the soil material by means of alternating anode and cathode arrays. The electrokinetic processes cause ionic pollutants to collect around the electrodes where they are captured and removed. All pollutants that are ionic or can be brought into ionic form participate in the process.

As a consequence of the applied potential, the following processes can be observed. The positively charged particles move in the direction of the negatively charged cathode. As a result, the concentration of the metal ions in the liquid phase (soil moisture or groundwater) will decrease. The decrease in concentration of the displaced ions in the groundwater will be restored by exchange with the solid phase (mineral phase). This ion displacement and ion exchange will continue as long as the electrical field is maintained. The final concentration of any heavy metal thus depends on the initial concentrations in the liquid and solid phase, the electrokinetic mobility of the metal, and the mutual exchange capacity with the other metal ions.

At the anode, moreover, H^+ ions are formed through electrolysis of water. These positively charged ions move via soil moisture or groundwater in the direction of the cathode. As the H^+ ions exchange rather easily with the (heavy) metal ions of the mineral phase and lower pH of the groundwater, the concentrations of (heavy) metals will increase, thus accelerating the processes of exchange and displacement.

At a certain point near the cathode, the metal ions move toward the cathode, but the total concentration of the metal ions will stay the same, because an equal amount of ions is being supplied from the point situated on the anode side. The total concentration of metals will decrease when the supply from the anode side is less than the transport to the cathode side.

Apart from electrokinetic processes, inducement of electricity into the soil generates heat. The increase of temperature results in an increase in hydraulic permeability and, as discussed later, an increase in the solubility of organic constituents.

Also during electroreclamation, an electroosmotic water flow is generated. The electroosmotic flow velocity is a function of the applied potential. For example, when applying a potential of 100 V/m, the average electroosmotic water transport amounts to 5×10^{-7} m/s. The amount of water transport per m² depends, moreover, on the porosity and the water content of the clay. Typically, the rate of transport of ions by electroosmotic effects is 20% of the rate resulting from electrokinetic effects.

Description of a Typical Installation

The core of an electrokinetic installation consists of the electrodes and their housing as shown in Figure 1, a schematic drawing of the laboratory-scale system.

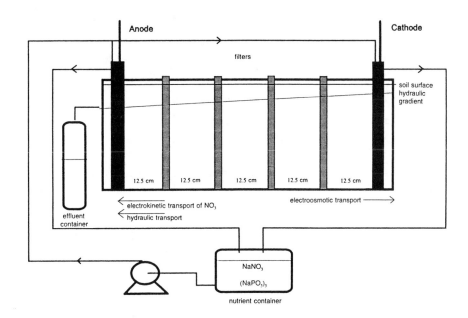

FIGURE 1. Laboratory reactor for electrobioreclamation experiments.

For in situ electroreclamation, the electrodes can in principle be installed at any depth. The same holds for on- or off-site electroreclamation, when the soil is excavated and dumped in a temporary remediation deposit. A third possibility is electroreclamation batch reactors, where the excavated and pretreated soil is remediated in specially constructed electrically isolated containers fixed with permanent electrode compartments.

In all cases, anodes and cathodes are integrated in circulation systems, wherein water circulates with some chemical additives, e.g., HCl, NaOH, or complexing agents. Apart from capturing the pollutants, the circulation systems are used to control the pH and the redox potential conditions around the electrodes. Such control is a major prerequisite for the process to continue successfully. Uncontrolled electroreclamation will result in acidification of the soil material around the anodes and precipitation of metal hydroxides around the cathodes.

The electrode solutions with the captured contaminants are periodically brought to an aboveground treatment system where the solutions are run through an electrolytic device that removes heavy metals. Following metal removal, the two solutions are mixed to achieve a nominally neutral pH without addition of HCl or NaOH.

Electrokinetic Transport for Bioremediation

Unlike hydraulic transport, electrokinetic transport is independent of soil permeability and thus lends itself as a means to distribute ionic forms of electron acceptors, electron donors, and nutrients in low-permeability and heterogeneous aquifers. Thus, microbial processes that benefit from nitrate or sulfate as electron acceptors or nitrate, ammonium, or various forms of phosphate as nutrients can potentially benefit from use of electrokinetic techniques.

EXPERIMENTS WITH ELECTROKINETIC TRANSPORT FOR BIOREMEDIATION

Initial screening tests were conducted to test electrokinetic transport of nitrate and several phosphate salts. An important consideration in the selection of a phosphate source is the ability to form soluble, rather than insoluble, complexes with calcium and other metals. On this basis and on the results of screening tests, orthophosphate salts were eliminated from consideration and sodium nitrate ($NaNO_3$) and sodium metaphosphate ($(NaPO_3)_3 \cdot XH_2O$) were selected for further testing.

To approximate anaerobic in situ electrobioreclamation as much as possible under laboratory conditions, three laboratory reactors were used. The reactors, as shown in Figure 1, consist of containers with these dimensions: length, 70 cm; width, 50 cm; and height, 35 cm. Electrodes are located at the outer ends. Monitoring filters are located at regular intervals (= 12.5 cm) between the electrodes. Each container is divided lengthwise to allow for duplicate experiments. The containers are then filled with (saturated) soil material from the contaminated site. Three reactors were used for the following experiments: (1) measurement of hydraulic and electrokinetic transport with addition of nutrients ($(NaPO_3)_3 \cdot XH_2O$ and $NaNO_3$); (2) measurement of only hydraulic transport of nutrients; and (3) a control without nutrients.

The soil tested consists of poorly sorted fine clayey sand contaminated with diesel oil with concentrations up to 10,000 mg/kg. Further important parameters are as follows:

- Porosity — 24%
- k-value (measured) — 3.9×10^{-7} m/s
- Hydraulic transport — 200 cm^3/day
- Cross-sectional area — 200 cm^2
- Hydraulic velocity — 1 cm/day
- Electrokinetic velocity (bulk NO_3) – 6 cm/day
- Electrokinetic mobility (bulk NO_3) – 2.5×10^{-8} m^2/Vs
- Electroosmotic mobility – 5×10^{-9} m^2/Vs
- Electroosmotic velocity — 1.5 cm/day
- Electroosmotic transport — 260 cm^3/day
- Specific resistivity of the soil — 80 Ωm
- Specific conductivity of the soil — 12.5 mS/m
- Mean potential drop — 40 V/m
- Mean current density — 0.5 A/m^2

PRELIMINARY RESULTS

At the time of publication, it was premature to report the extent of bio-degradation. However, some interesting results can be reported. As measured by increased adsorption of light, the application of successively higher voltage resulted in increased microbial populations. At an applied potential of 22.5 V/m, a 50% increase was observed. A shift in the relative population of microbial species was observed following application of an electrical potential. The initial predominance of *Aerominas hydrophila* was replaced with a dominance of various *Pseudomonas* sp. Additional tests showed that, under neutral pH conditions, bacteria behave as anions, migrating toward the anode.

The transport of nitrate was observed by sampling each of the 10 monitoring filters. In Figure 2, comparison of the back row (predicted transport based on the current in the test cell) with the row immediately in front of the back row (total nitrate calculated from concentrations in the monitoring filters) shows that 85% of the nitrate is accounted for. The data suggest that 15% of the nitrate was consumed as electron acceptors and/or nutrients with, possibly, some adsorption to the soil. The front three rows show the concentration of nutrients in the first three monitoring filters. By contrast, phosphate had not been detected at a travel distance of 12.5 cm after 10 days. The short duration of these tests at the time of publication was not sufficient to see a decrease in hydrocarbon levels.

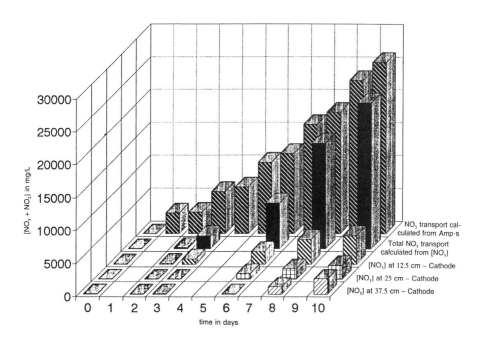

FIGURE 2. Transport of nitrate in the laboratory reactor during the initial test.

SUMMARY

Preliminary test results have shown that transport of nitrate, which can serve as both an electron acceptor and nutrient, can be accelerated predictably through the use of electrokinetic transport. Test results indicate other potential benefits of increased microbial growth and elevated temperatures. Changes in relative populations of microbial species were observed; however, it has not been determined if this is beneficial. The tests described herein are continuing and will be reported in later publications.

REFERENCES

Brown, R. A., R. D. Norris, and R. L. Raymond. 1984. "Oxygen Transport in Contaminated Aquifers." Paper presented in Proceedings of Petroleum Hydrocarbons and Organic Chemicals in Groundwater: Prevention, Detection, and Restoration. November 5-7, Houston, TX. Water Well Publishing Company, Dublin, OH.

Cabrera-Guzman, J. T. Swartzbaugh, and A. W. Weisman. 1990. "The Use of Electrokinetics for Hazardous Waste Site Remediation." *J. Air Waste Management Association 40*: 1670-1676.

Freeze, R. A. and J. A. Cherry (Eds.). 1979. *Groundwater*, pp. 26-30. Prentice Hall, Englewood Cliffs, NJ.

Lageman, R. 1989. "NATO/CCMS Pilot Study: Demonstration of Remedial Action Technologies for Contaminated Land and Groundwater." In *Theory and Practice of Electro-Remediation*. Copenhagen, Denmark.

Lageman, R. 1993. "Electroreclamation: Applications in the Netherlands." *Environmental Science & Technology 27*: 2648-2654.

Norris, R. D., R. E. Hinchee, R. Brown, P. L. McCarty, L. Semprini, J. T. Wilson, D. H. Kampbell, M. Reinhard, E. J. Bouwer, R. C. Borden, T. M. Vogel, J. M. Thomas, and C. H. Ward. 1994. *In-Situ Bioremediation of Groundwater and Geological Material: A Review of Technologies*. Office of Research and Development, U.S. Environmental Protection Agency, Ada, OK.

Rittmann, B. E., A. J. Valocchi, E. Seagren, C. Ray, and B. Wrenn. 1992. *A Critical Review of In Situ Bioremediation*. EPA/600/R-93/124. Gas Research Institute, Chicago, IL.

Land Treatment of Produced Oily Sand

Charles A. Bleckmann, Ernest J. Wilson,
Kelly W. Hayes, and Neta L. Hercyk

ABSTRACT

Land treatment successfully treated oily waste generated during the production of crude oil. More than 13 years of safe operations demonstrated the environmental acceptability of the method. Nearly 80% of the applied waste oil was removed by natural biodegradation processes. The oily fraction of the waste was found to have an average half-life in the soil of approximately 3 years, with significant variability between years. There was a slight increase in the proportion of heavy hydrocarbons (resins and asphaltenes) in the soil, suggesting the preferential degradation of the lighter constituents.

INTRODUCTION

Land treatment or landfarming has been used successfully as a treatment and disposal technique in the petroleum industry for decades (Raymond et al. 1976; Martin et al. 1986; Loehr et al. 1993). A significant body of both laboratory and field experimental work has demonstrated biodegradability of oily wastes and the environmental safety of the process (Schwendinger 1968; Dibble and Bartha 1979; Bossert et al. 1984). However, relatively few data from full-scale, operational units have been published. This paper describes the results of 13 years of field experience at a controlled site receiving and treating oily waste generated during the production of crude oil.

Biodegradation and natural attenuation of oily wastes in soils are well documented in field and laboratory studies and in operations. However, reported rates of degradation are variable and often difficult to define (Martin et al. 1986). Factors influencing bioremediation were described in a recent review of the topic (Pollard et al. 1994). The replicate sampling and analyses of this controlled site provide data on total degradation in a natural environment over many years. This demonstrates the variability found in an operational unit, subject to weather changes and loading rate differences.

MATERIALS AND METHODS

The land treatment facility, located in rural, south-central Oklahoma, was established in 1978. Waste was first applied in late 1978 and early 1979. Plow-zone and subplowzone soil samples were collected and analyzed at least annually. The 0.93-ha. site was subdivided into five equal plots (each approximately 25 × 73 m) for waste application and sampling. At each sampling, 20 to 30 plowzone soil cores were composited from each plot for analysis. Analyses included oil and grease or extractable hydrocarbon, metals, and several inorganic constituents. Data presented here represent the average results of analyses from the five plots.

The soil extractable hydrocarbon concentrations were determined by Soxhlet extraction using a solution of 2:1 toluene and isopropanol, a rigorous extraction method used for determination of oil in oil-bearing rock. This extract, diluted in tetrahydrofuran, was characterized by thin layer chromatography (TLC) as aromatics, paraffins, and resins and asphaltenes (R&A).

The compositions (oil, water, and solids) of several waste samples collected occasionally during waste application are shown in Table 1. The oil fraction

TABLE 1. The oily waste composition was measured several times during the operation of the land treatment site (upper values). The oily fraction of the waste was further characterized by TLC on two occasions (lower values).

Year	Weight % Solids	Weight % Water	Weight % Oil
1977	67.0	10.0	23.0
1982	65.2	24.6	6.5
1986	63.0	16.4	20.6
1987	70.9	13.8	15.2
1987	74.5	11.1	14.4
1987	78.0	7.4	14.6
1988	54.7	23.6	21.7
1989	58.8	21.3	19.9
1989	73.9	6.1	20.0
Average	67	15	18

	Thin Layer Chromatography % Composition		
	Paraffins	Aromatics	Resins and Asphaltenes
1974	20	26	54
1977	20	22	58
Average	20	24	56

was further characterized by TLC and separated into paraffins, aromatics, and R&A (Table 1). The crude oil had an API gravity of approximately 14, indicating a relatively heavy oil. Oil distillation recovered approximately 1% of the material at 134°C (274°F), demonstrating the very small volatile component of the waste.

The oily wastes were transported directly from the nearby crude oil production units to the treatment site. The site was tilled regularly during the typical agricultural growing season for the area (March-April to October), which ensured aeration of the plowzone and even distribution of the waste. The plowzone was held to a depth of approximately 20 cm. This relatively shallow depth made mixing simple and enhanced the availability of oxygen to the microorganisms performing the biodegradation. Agricultural-grade fertilizer was applied routinely to ensure that microbial activity was not nutrient limited. The fertilization program goal was to maintain approximately 25 mg/kg nitrogen, as either ammonia or nitrate, and 10 mg/kg orthophosphate in the plowzone or treatment zone of the site.

RESULTS

Oil removal rates and half-life calculations are shown in Table 2. Over the course of 13 years of operation, approximately 304,000 kg of waste oil was applied to the site. Of this amount, approximately 238,000 kg, or 78% of the organic fraction of the waste was removed (Figure 1 and Table 2). Because of limited data, and to simplify the half-life calculation, we used the conservative assumption that oily waste for 1 year was applied immediately after sampling for the previous year. An approximate reaction rate, K, was calculated as follows:

$$\frac{[\ln (\text{Oil measured in previous year} + \text{Oil added in current year})] - [\ln (\text{Oil measured in current year})]}{\text{Days between samplings}}$$

This reaction rate was then used in the first order, half-life equation ($t_{1/2} = \ln 2/K$) (Sawyer et al., 1994). Variations in annual application volumes, timing of applications, and normal seasonal variations of microbial activity caused wide fluctuations in the short-term biodegradation rates. Nevertheless, the data from the 13 years of operation demonstrated clearly that land treatment is an active and effective means of oily waste treatment.

The data for 2 years, 1982 and 1986, are clearly anomalous. The half-life calculations suggest that oil was created in the plowzone (Table 2) and, in 1982 the waste applied equaled that detected in the plowzone (Figure 1). This was likely due to inaccurate application records from early in the project, or perhaps nonrepresentative samples for hydrocarbon analyses. In several years, multiple plowzone samplings were conducted and all data are shown in Figure 2. Only the end-of-year samples were used for half-life calculations (Table 2). Even with these minor inconsistencies, over the course of the project the land treatment process was demonstrated to be effective.

TABLE 2. Annual oily waste application data and plowzone residual were used to calculate the half-life of the organic fraction.[a]

Year	Elapsed Time (Days)	Plowzone Hydrocarbon (wt %)	Plowzone Hydrocarbon (kg)	Annual Oil Added (wt %)	Cumulative Oil Added (wt %)	Cumulative Oil Added (kg)	Cumulative % Oil Degraded	Reaction Rate K[b]	Half-Life, Years[c]
1978	0	0.28							
1979	274	1.70	45,786	2.38	2.38	64,008	28.5	0.0016	1.17
1980	705	2.87	77,297	1.78	4.16	112,014	31.0	0.0004	4.23
1981	866	2.93	78,967	0.85	5.01	134,874	41.5	0.0015	1.29
1982	1,407	5.21	140,320	0.30	5.30	142,829	1.8	−0.0009	(−2.14)
1983	1,624	4.39	118,289	0.42	5.73	154,259	23.3	0.0011	1.65
1984	2,040	3.19	85,969	0.25	5.98	161,117	46.6	0.0009	2.10
1985	2,426	3.08	83,061	1.48	7.46	200,894	58.7	0.0011	1.77
1986	2,880	3.95	106,384	0.62	8.08	217,581	51.1	−0.0001	(−13.38)
1987	3,246	3.75	101,052	0.32	8.40	226,268	55.3	0.0004	5.35
1988	3,589	4.63	124,753	1.71	10.11	272,354	54.2	0.0005	3.95
1989	4,017	2.28	61,407	0.56	10.67	287,304	78.6	0.0019	0.99
1990				0.60	11.27	303,535			
1991	4,653	2.41	64,908		11.27	303,535	78.6	0.0003	6.74
							Average (excludes negative years)	0.0003	2.92

(a) Soil density assumed to be 1,441 kg/m³ (90 lb/ft³). Waste density assumed to be 1.67 (67% sand @ 2, 18% oil @ 0.97, 15% water @ 1). Application area = 73 m × 128 m × 0.2 m (240' × 420' × 8") = 1,869 m³. Plowzone weight = 1,869 m³ × 1,441 kg/m³ (67,234 ft³ × 90 lb/ft³ = 2,693,277 kg (6,051,000 lb).

(b) K = [1n (Measured previous year + Added current year)] − [1n (Measured current year)]/(Days between samplings).

(c) Half-life (years) = (0.693/K)/365.

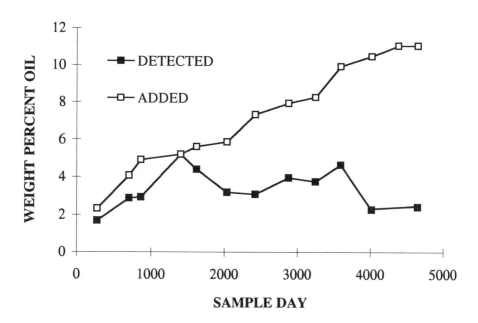

FIGURE 1. Cumulative oil added and detected. The fourth data set is clearly anomalous because applied and detected oil should not be equal.

In addition to measuring concentration, the plowzone oily wastes or extractable hydrocarbons were characterized for broad molecular composition by TLC. Figure 2 shows the concentrations of paraffins, aromatics, and R&A in the plowzone soil. The extractable hydrocarbon analysis detected low levels of naturally occurring constituents in soil. The background extractable hydrocarbon concentration (1978A), measured before the application of any waste, was 0.28 weight percent (wt %) and was composed largely of R&A (Figure 2). Upon application of the first waste, the recoverable extractable material took on the approximate characteristics of the waste.

DISCUSSION

The practices of an operational treatment facility complicated the calculation of degradation rates and half-lives of the oily waste. Waste applications occurred sporadically throughout the year, in response to the demands of field maintenance operations. Site sampling events provide single data points for several months' or the year's activity. Because of the magnitude and duration of the project, samples were not always collected at ideal times. Sampling events present an accurate description of conditions at a single time, but do not reflect variations over the course of the year. Application data provide a measure of material applied over a year, but may not reflect conditions at a single time.

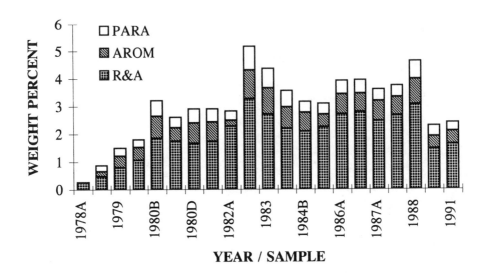

FIGURE 2. Soil extractable hydrocarbon composition. The resins and asphaltenes fraction showed a slight proportional increase with time.

Given the relatively high viscosity and low volatility of the crude oil, clearly evaporation played a very minor role (<1%) in loss during application or treatment of the waste. The subplowzone monitoring demonstrated that losses due to leaching of hydrocarbon from the plowzone were minimal. Instances of deeper waste deposition, due to tilling and contouring operations, amounted to very small relative volumes of waste removal from the plowzone. This leaves biodegradation as the most prominent route of removal of the organic fraction of the oily waste.

Bossert et al. (1984) demonstrated the microbial conversion of oily waste into solvent insoluble fractions, a process they called humification. It has been speculated that the R&A fraction of oily waste would increase as microorganisms degraded the lower-molecular-weight materials and converted some of the carbon into cell mass. A small but consistent upward trend was seen in the R&A fraction of the oily waste residue, from 54 to 67%, over the life of the land treatment site (Figure 2). Regression analysis of the plowzone samples (time vs. R&A concentration) gives an R^2 value of 0.59, indicating a low correlation.

CONCLUSIONS

Results from this site demonstrate that, when properly managed, land treatment is an appropriate means of oily waste treatment and disposal. Hydrocarbon-containing wastes were immobilized and the organic fractions were degraded in the plowzone soils.

Using a very conservative method of calculation, the half-life of the organic fraction of the oily waste averaged about 3 years over the course of the study. The calculation assumed that all oily waste applied during a year was added immediately after sampling for the previous year. This method of calculation gives a worst-case result. Although not directly comparable because of differences in the organic composition, the half-lives of the oily portion of refinery wastes and sludges in other industrial land treatment units have been reported to range from 50 to 150 days (API 1987).

As others have reported (Bossert et al. 1984), there was an indication of a shift in the composition of the plowzone extractable oil. The heavy R&A fraction of the oily waste, expected to be more resistant to degradation, showed a slight relative increase, and the lighter fractions, i.e., the paraffins and aromatics, showed a corresponding decrease in relative concentration.

REFERENCES

American Petroleum Institute (API). 1987. *The Land Treatability of Appendix VIII Constituents Present in Petroleum Refinery Wastes: Laboratory and Modeling Studies.* Washington, DC.

Bossert, I., W. M. Kachel, and R. Bartha. 1984. "Fate of Hydrocarbons During Oily Sludge Disposal in Soil." *Applied and Environmental Microbiology* 47: 763-767.

Dibble, J. T. and R. Bartha. 1979. "Effect of Environmental Parameters on the Biodegradation of Oil Sludge." *Applied and Environmental Microbiology* 37: 729-739.

Loehr, R. C., D. C. Erickson, and L. A. Kelmar. 1993. "Characteristics of Residues at Hazardous Waste Land Treatment Units." *Water Research* 27: 1127-1138.

Martin, J. P., R. C. Sims, and J. Matthews. 1986. "Review and Evaluation of Current Design and Management Practices for Land Treatment Units Receiving Petroleum Wastes." *Hazardous Waste & Hazardous Materials* 3: 261-280.

Pollard, S.J.T., S. E. Hrudey, and P. M. Fedorak. 1994. "Bioremediation of Petroleum- and Creosote-Contaminated Soils: A Review of Constraints." *Waste Management & Research* 12: 173-194.

Raymond, R. L., J. O. Hudson, and V. W. Jamison. 1976. "Oil Degradation in Soil." *Applied and Environmental Microbiology* 31: 522-535.

Sawyer, C. N., P. L. McCarty, and G. F. Parkin. 1994. *Chemistry for Environmental Engineering*, 4th ed. McGraw-Hill, Inc., New York, NY.

Schwendinger, R. B. 1968. "Reclamation of Soil Contaminated with Oil." *Journal of the Institute of Petroleum* 54: 182-197.

Application of Hexametaphosphate as a Nutrient for In Situ Bioreclamation

Martin Steiof and Wolfgang Dott

ABSTRACT

Our investigation concerns bioremediation of an old fuel oil-contaminated site where the amount of leaked fuel oil was approximately 15,000 to 17,000 L. The larger portion of the oil floating on the groundwater was removed at the end of the 1970s. The highest concentrations of total petroleum hydrocarbons (TPH) in the soil are about 16,000 mg/kg dry weight. The pollution is distributed to 4 to 9 m below ground level, thus lying in the aquifer. The in situ remediation design includes two infiltration wells, two production wells, and an on-site groundwater processing plant. To cover the electron acceptor demand of the metabolizing microorganisms, hydrogen peroxide and nitrate, as well as phosphate, were added to the reinfiltrated water to cover the nutrient demand. Using disodium dihydrogen diphosphate as a phosphorus source resulted in the precipitation of insoluble phosphates, which plugged the infiltration wells and the surrounding aquifer. Alternatively, sodium hexametaphosphate was used as a phosphorus source. Using polyphosphate as a phosphorus source eliminated precipitation and plugging in the infiltration wells and, for the first time, a phosphorus supply for the whole contaminated area was observed.

INTRODUCTION

Although groundwater is the major source of drinking water, it often is found to be contaminated with a wide variety of organic chemicals. In contaminated soils and groundwaters, these organics act as the most important energy source, whereby heterotrophic bacteria dominate. As well as being the required electron acceptor, phosphate is an essential nutrient and one of the most limiting factors of hydrocarbon degradation during in situ bioremediation.

Nearly all in situ bioreclamation projects use ortho- or diphosphate as an added phosphorus source in the reinfiltrated process water, which often leads to problems with precipitation because of the insoluble phosphates (besides the precipitation problems of iron and manganese oxides and hydroxides) (Lee et al. 1988). Microorganisms can use only orthophosphate for biochemical processes. Therefore, the bioavailability of phosphorus in the course of a bioremediation process depends on the presence of orthophosphate. All polyphosphates have to be first hydrolyzed. The two primary influencing factors for the biological availability of inorganic phosphates are their interaction with soil (sorption and desorption) and their stability in water (precipitation with cations such as iron, magnesium, and calcium). Sorption of orthophosphate to soil is very strong, in addition to its ready precipitation with iron and calcium. No mobilization or solubilization of these retarded orthophosphates was observed in normal groundwater with a pH of 6 to 9 (Robertson & Alexander 1992).

Most observations concerning the hydrolysis of polyphosphates have dealt with di-, tripoly-, and trimetaphosphates (Dick & Tabatabai 1978; Tabatabai & Dick 1979; Stott et al. 1985), because these are the main phosphorus sources in agricultural fertilizers. The hydrolysis of polyphosphates can be described as a function of pH, biological activity, and temperature (Hossner & Melton 1970; Blanchar and Riego 1976; Dick & Tabatabai 1986; Hons et al. 1986). Alkaline pH activates enzymatic hydrolysis whereas acidic pH enhances chemical hydrolysis (Busman & Tabatabai 1985). However, even in acidic soils (pH of 4.8), chemical hydrolysis of polyphosphate is only 25% of total hydrolysis, whereas the remaining percent is due to biological hydrolysis (Gilliam & Sample 1968). The temperature optimum for the complete hydrolysis is 30 to 35°C and, at lower temperatures, biological hydrolysis increases and chemical hydrolysis decreases. With increasing chain length (> 5 P-atoms) of polyphosphates, the intensity of their interaction with soil decreases. However, it is very difficult to separate the two influencing factors: physical adsorption and chemical precipitation. Nevertheless, the shorter polyphosphates such as diphosphate and tripolyphosphate also exhibit interaction with the soil matrices, but their retardation is more reversible than the retardation of orthophosphate (Blanchar & Hossner 1969).

MATERIALS AND METHODS

Laboratory Investigations with Different Phosphates

The bioavailability of different inorganic phosphates was studied in the laboratory. These phosphates were: orthophosphate (NaH_2PO_4; Merck, Darmstadt, Germany), diphosphate ($Na_2H_2P_2O_7$; Fluka, Buchs, Switzerland), tripolyphosphate ($Na_5P_3O_{10}$; Merck, Darmstadt, Germany), trimetaphosphate ($Na_3P_3O_9$; Benckiser-Knapsack, Ladenburg, Germany), hexametaphosphate ($[NaPO_3]_n$, n = 5 – 7; Albafoss 187 L; Benckiser-Knapsack, Ladenburg, Germany), and a water-soluble polyphosphate ($Na_{15}P_{13}O_{40}$ – $Na_{20}P_{18}O_{55}$; Calgon; Sigma Chemicals, St. Louis, Missouri). To obtain a simultaneous method for determining the P-concentration of a solution and the bioavailability of the phosphorus source, we developed a miniaturized *Pseudomonas putida* growth inhibition test (a variation of that in the German Standard Methods 1991) in standard microtitration plates (Greiner, Nürtingen, Germany), thus creating a phosphorus-limited cryo-conserve of *P. putida*.

The microtitration plates were incubated for 30 h at 21°C. Growth curves were recorded by measuring the optical density every 20 minutes at 405 nm. Immediately before each measurement, the plates were shaken for 1 minute. The relative growth stimulation of *P. putida* was calculated as the area under the growth curves, in relation to the growth in a parallel, phosphorus-free, experiment. More details have been described elsewhere (Reinke et al. 1995).

Description of the Contaminated Site

The contamination caused by a leaking pipeline 45 to 50 years ago is assumed to be associated with fuel oil. The estimated amount of leaked fuel oil is 15,000 to 17,000 L and most of the oil floating on the groundwater was removed at the end of the 1970s. The subsoil of the contaminated area is characterized as a Pleistocene aquifer with fine and medium sands. The average permeability (kf) is 10^{-4} to 5×10^{-4} m/s. The highest concentration of TPH is about 16,000 mg/kg dry weight (Figure 1, ram boring S1 at a depth of 5 to 6 m and ram boring S3 at a depth of 6 to 7 m). The pollution is distributed to a depth of 4 to 9 m below ground level, thus lying in the aquifer (the groundwater level is approximately 4.5 m below ground level).

Gas chromatographic profiles of water and soil extracts showed no typical n-alkanes, thus indicating that these compounds already have been degraded. No polychlorinated biphenyls or other chlorinated organic compounds could be detected. Microbiological investigations included estimations of total cell counts; viable cell counts on different media (R2A-agar, according to Reasoner & Geldreich 1985; DEV-agar, according to German Standards Methods 1971); and number of methylotrophic, denitrifying, sulfate-reducing, anaerobic (with the exception of methanogenic organisms), and hydrocarbon-degrading bacteria. Viable and hydrocarbon-degrading bacteria were detected in all water and soil samples. Further details concerning the microbiological diversity and activity at this site have been described previously (Kämpfer et al. 1991). A plan of the contaminated area, illustrating the position of the production and infiltration wells, all sampling wells, and the distribution of the hydrocarbons, is given in Figure 1.

Remediation Design

The in situ remediation design includes two infiltration wells, two production wells, and an on-site groundwater processing plant. This groundwater processing plant consists of an iron-removal filter, an oxygenator (using technical oxygen), a manganese-removal filter, and an air-stripping column. Before the reinfiltration of the treated groundwater, it is possible to add electron acceptors and nutrients. To meet the electron acceptor demand, hydrogen peroxide and nitrate are added to the reinfiltrated water, as well as phosphate to meet the nutrient demand. The average groundwater flow time from the infiltration wells to the production wells is about 20 days, whereas the fastest flow time is only 4 days.

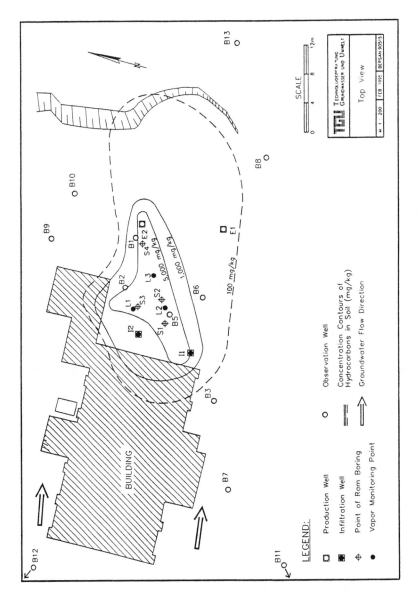

FIGURE 1. Plan of the contaminated area with TPH concentration (inner circle: >5,000 mg/kg dry weight, next circle: >1,000 mg/kg dry weight), infiltration wells (I1 and I2), production wells (E1 and E2), observation wells (B1 to B13), points of ram boring with open-sided tube (S1b to S4b), and sampling points of vapor.

The reinfiltration rate of the treated groundwater is 10% less (about 9 m³/h) than the production rate (about 10 m³/h). Because of this, the recirculating groundwater is clearly limited within an area of 600 to 700 m².

For the first 2 months of remediation, 1.5 mg PO_4-P/L as disodium dihydrogen diphosphate ($Na_2H_2P_2O_7$; Benckiser-Knapsack, Ladenburg, Germany) was added to the infiltration water, after which dosage of phosphate was stopped; 6 weeks later, about 1.5 mg PO_4-P/L was added in the form of sodium hexametaphosphate (straight-chain polyphosphate with 5 to 7 P-atoms).

RESULTS

Laboratory Investigations

In laboratory experiments, the microbiological availability of hexametaphosphate as a phosphorus source was compared with five other inorganic phosphates. *P. putida* showed a phosphorus-dependent growth of between 1 and 10 mg/L phosphorus (see Figure 2). Therefore, it was shown that these different phosphates, especially hexametaphosphate, are highly available for biochemical processes.

P. putida was chosen, because it is a typical heterotrophic strain, possessing hydrocarbon-degradation abilities. Moreover, *P. putida* strains were also found in the contaminated aquifer (Kämpfer et al. 1991). The availability of the examined phosphates for *P. putida* in the laboratory is not a proof of the availability for the microorganisms in the contaminated aquifer, but it can be seen as a clear indication.

Field Testing Program

As illustrated in Figure 3, the oxygen concentrations in all wells in the restoration field increased following addition of hydrogen peroxide (initial concentration: 50 mg/L on 2nd of November 1991; later concentration: 100 mg/L on 20th of July 1992), due to oxygen migration through the whole aquifer. After adding disodium dihydrogen diphosphate as a phosphorus source (starting concentration: 1.5 mg/L PO_4-P on 12th of February 1992), the oxygen concentration dropped in each well, except for well B2, which is the shortest distance from the infiltration well and has the least contamination in the surrounding aquifer. This observation suggests that phosphorus was the limiting factor for heterotrophic bacterial activity. It is probable that the addition of phosphate stopped the limitation, and oxygen was utilized in, and immediately around, the injection wells. On the other hand, during the use of diphosphate, problems occurred with the precipitation of insoluble phosphate salts, and, as a consequence, plugging of the infiltration wells resulted. This plugging led to a decrease in the injection rate, and the infiltration wells overflowed. Moreover, no phosphate was transported into the whole aquifer and, as a consequence of biological utilization and chemical precipitation in and immediately around the infiltration wells, no phosphate could be detected in the groundwater wells of the contaminated area (Figure 4).

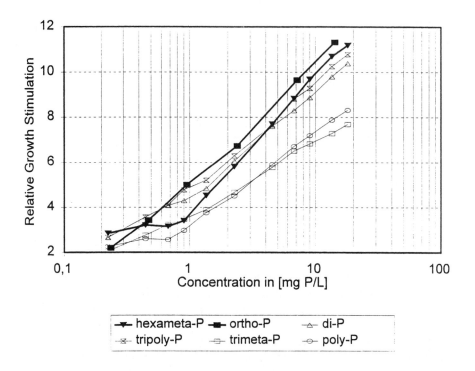

FIGURE 2. Relative growth stimulation of *Pseudomonas putida* by various phosphates at different concentrations (laboratory investigations in standard microtitration plates); hexameta-P = $(NaPO_3)_n$, $n = 5-7$; ortho-P = NaH_2PO_4; di-P = $Na_2H_2P_2O_7$; tripoly-P = $Na_5P_3O_{10}$; trimeta-P = $Na_3P_3O_9$; poly-P = $Na_{15}P_{13}O_{40} - Na_{20}P_{18}O_{55}$.

After 2 months, addition of this phosphorus source was stopped, and the infiltration wells were regenerated with H_2O_2 and acid; 6 weeks later, dosage of an alternative phosphorus source, sodium hexametaphosphate, was started. The use of polyphosphate as a phosphorus source in the field eliminated problems with precipitation and plugging in the infiltration wells and the surrounding aquifer. More than 95% of the analyzed phosphates in the observation wells of the contaminated area consisted of orthophosphate and not of polyphosphate. Accordingly, polyphosphate has been hydrolyzed during its migration through the aquifer. For the first time since restoration was initiated, the phosphorus supply of the whole contaminated aquifer for biochemical degradation processes was observed.

The effect of nutrient addition could not be observed by direct measurement of the hydrocarbons in the groundwater. The highest TPH concentration was only 1,600 µg/L (in the most observation wells < 1,000 µg/L) and there was no significant decrease during 1992. A decrease was not expected because there existed a permanent solubilization of compounds from the hydrophobic fuel oil on the soil matrix into the water matrix.

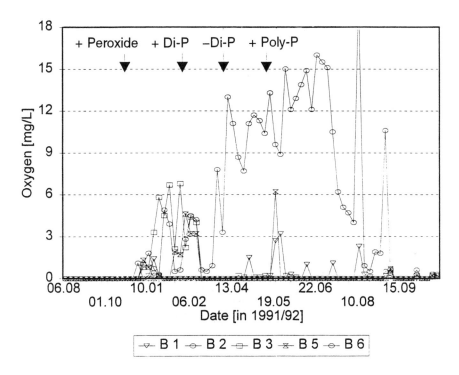

FIGURE 3. Oxygen concentrations in the five sampling wells of the contaminated area after infiltration of hydrogen peroxide (02.11.1991: 50 mg/L; from 20.07.1992: 100 mg/L); [+ Peroxide = start addition of H_2O_2; + Di-P = start addition of diphosphate; − Di-P = stop addition of diphosphate; + Poly-P = start addition of hexametaphosphate].

Nevertheless, as a clear indicator of stimulation, the numbers of hydrocarbon-degrading bacteria in the groundwater of the field rose slightly from about 10^3 to 5×10^3 colony forming units (CFU)/mL in the beginning of 1992 to about 10^4 CFU/mL at the end of the same year on vacuum-gas oil-agar, and from 3×10^3 to 8×10^3 CFU/mL to 5×10^3 to 3×10^4 CFU/mL on fuel oil-agar (Steiof 1993). The amount of produced inorganic carbon, measured as acid- and base-capacity, also increased. The acid-capacity went up from 4 to 5 mmol/L to nearly 7 mmol/L, and the base capacity from about 0.5 mmol/L to 1 to 1.5 mmol/L during the same time (Steiof 1993). The bioremediation is still under way and an end is expected in 1996.

DISCUSSION

The current literature covering use of polyphosphates in bioremediation has focused exclusively on tripolyphosphates. Glaser (1991) reported the application

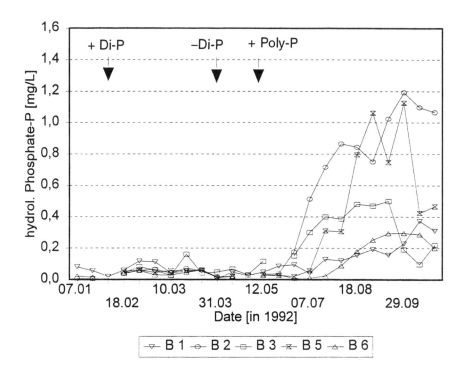

FIGURE 4. Concentration of phosphate-P in the five sampling wells of the contaminated area after infiltration of 1.5 mg/L diphosphate (+ Di-P = start addition, – Di-P = stop addition) and hexametaphosphate (+ Poly-P = start addition).

of tripolyphosphate as a phosphorus source to fertilize the contaminated beaches after the *Exxon Valdez* spill in 1989. Hinchee et al. (1991) also used tripolyphosphate, but only in addition to orthophosphate, during the in situ bioremediation of a jet fuel-contaminated site. In laboratory investigations with the same jet fuel-contaminated soil, Aggarwal et al. (1991) demonstrated the superiority of trimetaphosphate over ortho-, di-, and tripolyphosphate. Morgan & Watkinson (1992) reported the use of tripolyphosphate, but only in laboratory investigations. Our investigations demonstrated the superiority of polyphosphate (hexametaphosphate with a chain-length of 7 to 8 P-atoms) over orthophosphate on a field scale.

Both molecules, the trimetaphosphate as well as the examined hexametaphosphate, have complexing qualities for cations such as Ca^{2+} and Mg^{2+}. Therefore, they do not precipitate with these cations as easily as do orthophosphate or diphosphate. Poly- and metaphosphates also interact with soil, but their sorption is not as strong. As a consequence, the mobilization of these polyphosphates is much better and their transport over long distances in the aquifer is more probable (chromatographic effect). Nevertheless, all polyphosphates have to be hydrolyzed before they can be used for biochemical purposes. However, our laboratory investigations showed that hydrolysis of the tested polyphosphates is not the rate-limiting step when using them as a phosphorus source for biochemical purposes. From this point of view, sodium hexametaphosphate has a greater advantage for transporting phosphorus over longer aquifer distances than does orthophosphate or the other commonly used phosphates.

ACKNOWLEDGMENTS

We thank Irena Savric and Robin Gerlach for performing the laboratory investigations with *P. putida*.

REFERENCES

Aggarwal, P. K., J. L. Means, and R. E. Hinchee. 1991. "Formulation of Nutrient Solutions for In Situ Bioremediation." In R. E. Hinchee and R. F. Olfenbuttel (Eds.), *In Situ Bioreclamation: Applications and Investigations for Hydrocarbon and Contaminated Site Remediation.* Butterworth-Heinemann, Stoneham, MA. pp. 51-60.

Blanchar, R. W., and L. R. Hossner. 1969. "Hydrolysis and Sorption of Ortho-, Pyro-, Tripoly and Trimetaphosphate in 32 Midwestern Soils." *Soil Science Society of America — Proceedings* 33: 622-625.

Blanchar, R. W., and D. C. Riego. 1976. "Tripolyphosphate and Pyrophosphate Hydrolysis in Sediments." *Soil Science Society of America — Journal 40:* 225-229.

Busman, L. M., and M. A. Tabatabai. 1985. "Hydrolysis of Trimetaphosphates in Soils." *Soil Science Society of America — Journal 49:* 630-636.

Dick, W. A., and M. A. Tabatabai. 1978. "Inorganic Pyrophosphatase Activity of Soils." *Soil Biology and Biochemistry 10:* 59-65.

Dick, R. P., and M. A. Tabatabai. 1986. "Hydrolysis of Polyphosphates in Soils." *Soil Science 142:* 132-140.

German Standard Methods. 1971. "Mikrobiologische Verfahren." *Deutsche Einheitsverfahren zur Wasser-, Abwasser- und Schlammuntersuchung* DIN 38411 Teil 8, K5.

German Standard Methods. 1991. "Testverfahren mit Wasserorganismen, Bestimmung der Hemmwirkung von Wasserinhaltsstoffen auf Bakterien — Pseudomonas-Zellvermehrungs-Hemmtest." *Deutsche Einheitsverfahren zur Wasser-, Abwasser- und Schlammuntersuchung* DIN 38412 Teil 8, L8.

Gilliam, J. W., and E. C. Sample. 1968. "Hydrolysis of Pyrophosphate in Soils: pH and Biological Effects." *Soil Science 106(5):* 352-357.

Glaser, J. A. 1991. "Nutrient-Enhanced Bioremediation of Oil-Contaminated Shoreline: The *Valdez* Experience." In R. E. Hinchee and R. F. Olfenbuttel (Eds.), *On Site Bioreclamation: Processes for Xenobiotics and Hydrocarbon Treatment.* Butterworth-Heinemann, Stoneham, MA. pp. 366-384.

Hinchee, R. E., D. C. Downey, and P. K. Aggarwal. 1991. "Use of Hydrogen Peroxide as an Oxygen Source for In Situ Biodegradation Part I. Field Studies." *Journal of Hazardous Material 27(3):* 287-299.

Hons, F. M., W. M. Stewart, and L. R. Hossner. 1986. "Factor Interactions and their Influence on Hydrolysis of Condensed Phosphates in Soils." *Soil Science 141(6):* 408-416.

Hossner, L. R., and J. R. Melton. 1970. "Pyrophosphate Hydrolysis of Ammonium, Calcium, and Calcium Ammonium Pyrophosphates in Selected Texas Soils." *Soil Science Society of America — Proceedings 34:* 801-805.

Kämpfer, P., M. Steiof, and W. Dott. 1991. "Microbiological Characterization of a Fuel-Oil Contaminated Site Including Numerical Identification of Heterotrophic Water and Soil Bacteria." *Microbial Ecology* 21: 227-251.

Lee, M. D., J. M. Thomas, B. C. Borden, P. B. Bedient, C. H. Ward, and J. T. Wilson. 1988. "Biorestoration of Aquifers Contaminated with Organic Compounds." *CRC Critical Reviews in Environmental Control* 18: 29-89.

Morgan, P., and R. J. Watkinson. 1992. "Factors Limiting the Supply and Efficiency of Nutrient and Oxygen Supplements for the In Situ Biotreatment of Contaminated Soil and Groundwater." *Water Research* 26(1): 72-78.

Reasoner, D. J., and E. E. Geldreich. 1985. "A New Medium for the Enumeration and Subculture of Bacteria from Potable Water." *Applied and Environmental Microbiology 49*: 1-7.

Reinke, M., G. Kalnowski, and W. Dott. 1995. "Evaluation of an Automated, Miniaturized *Pseudomonas putida* Growth Inhibition Assay using Kinetic Measurement." *Applied and Environmental Microbiology,* submitted.

Robertson, B. K., and M. Alexander. 1992. "Influence of Calcium, Iron, and pH on Phosphate Availability for Microbial Mineralization of Organic Chemicals." *Applied and Environmental Microbiology 58*(1): 38-41.

Steiof, M. 1993. "Biologische in situ Sanierung eines mit Dieselöl kontaminierten Aquifers." Ph. D. Thesis and Publication from the Department of Hygiene, Technical University of Berlin, Germany.

Stott, D. E., W. A. Dick, and M. A. Tabatabai. 1985. "Inhibition of Pyrophosphatase Activity in Soils by Trace Elements." *Soil Science 139*(2): 112-117.

Tabatabai, M. A., and W. A. Dick. 1979. "Distribution and Stability of Pyrophosphatase in Soils." *Soil Biology and Biochemistry 11*: 655-659.

Hydrodynamics of Foam Flows for In Situ Bioremediation of DNAPL-Contaminated Subsurface

Jacques X. Bouillard, Michael Enzien, Robert W. Peters, James Frank, Robert E. Botto, and George Cody

ABSTRACT

In situ remediation technologies such as (1) pump-and-treat, (2) soil vacuum extraction, (3) soil flushing/washing, and (4) bioremediation are being promoted for cleanup of contaminated sites. However, these technologies are limited by flow channeling of chemical treatment agents (e.g., surfactant, solvent, or microbial stimulant), which renders bioremediation of dense nonaqueous-phase liquid (DNAPL) pools or ganglia ineffective. Argonne National Laboratory (ANL), the Gas Research Institute, and the Institute of Gas Technology are collaboratively investigating a new bioremediation technology using foams. The ability of a foam to block pores and limit flow bypassing makes it ideal for DNAPL remediation. The hydrodynamics of gas/liquid foam flows differ significantly from the hydrodynamics of single and multiphase nonfoaming flows. This is illustrated using a multiphase flow hydrodynamic computer model and a two-dimensional flow visualization cell. Predicted foam and pressure-front propagation in the two-dimensional visualization cell containing sandy soils compared well to experimental data. Pressure drops recorded were found to be much greater than those observed using surfactant soil flushing or air sparging technologies. A state-of-the-art, nonintrusive, three-dimensional magnetic resonance imaging technique was developed to visualize DNAPL mobilization in three dimensions. Mechanisms to be investigated are in situ DNAPL interactions with the foam, DNAPL emulsification, DNAPL scouring by the foam, and subsequent DNAPL mobilization/redeposition in the porous media.

INTRODUCTION

Foams have been extensively used in enhanced oil recovery as blocking agents of high-permeability subsurface regions to limit fingering/channeling effects and to improve oil recovery efficiencies (Kovscek & Radke 1993, Kovscek et al. 1993). Similarly, foams could be used as blocking agents for in situ remediation of contaminated subsurfaces, to improve NAPL mobilization, and to deliver bionutrients. The use of foams is expected to yield higher remediation efficiencies than those encountered in surfactant flushing because the foams can force the delivery of surfactants and bionutrients in areas of difficult access such as in tight clay lenses. ANL has already established that the efficiency of foam flushing is about 10 times greater than that of surfactant flushing alone (Enzien et al. 1994). However, foam flushing introduces in situ hydraulic behaviors that need further understanding if this technology is to be deployed on a large scale.

To this goal, we address the mathematical and physical coupling between the multiphase (liquid/gas/solid) flow model and foam rheology/stability submodels. In future studies, we will explore the transport of contaminants, with adsorption/desorption, volatilization, and ion exchange/precipitation phenomena. These latter phenomena have already been modeled in the past and reported in the literature for nonfoam flows.

Background

When gas and dilute surfactant solution (present in a foam) flow simultaneously through a porous medium, measured pressure drops can be orders of magnitude larger than those exhibited in sparging flows (Kovscek & Radke 1993, Kovscek et al. 1993). The high flow-resistance of a foam in porous media makes it a desirable mobility-control agent for improving mobilization of DNAPL in contaminated subsurfaces.

Foam in a porous medium exists as a gas phase dispersed in a continuous liquid phase. Foams can be generated either in situ or ex situ. Foams generated ex situ are sometimes termed colloidal gas aphrons (CGAs). A typical foam generated by a disk foam generator using NaDBS (sodium dodecyl benzosulfonate) diluted in tap water is shown in Figure 1. The mean gas (air) bubble diameter is about 60 μm and the gas volume fraction of these foams is about 65%. When flowing into the porous medium, the wetting surfactant solution of the foam fills the smallest pore channels and generates thin liquid lamellae (soap films) that stretch across pore spaces in the subsurface matrix. The lamellae divide the gas phase into bubbles that are on the order of the size of the pores in the subsurface matrix. The pressure drop of flowing foams is determined primarily by large viscous stresses in the liquid phase that separate percolating bubbles (Edwards et al. 1991). It is this discontinuous nature of the gas phase that causes foam to exhibit low flow mobility in porous media. If the foam is unstable (that is, if the lamellae break or rupture), the foam is destroyed and is no longer an effective mobility-control agent. The capillary pressure in the porous medium can be expressed in terms of the surface tension, the permeability, and the void fraction through the Leverett function (Bear 1972). This function shows a strong dependency with respect to the water saturation.

Low-permeability media (i.e., clay lenses) at low liquid saturations display high capillary pressures that can significantly affect the stability of the foam and

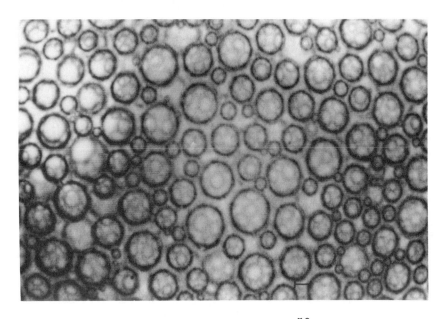

50 μm

FIGURE 1. Typical photomicrographs of foam bubbles (or colloidal gas aphrons) at 64% foam quality.

hence its in situ flow characteristics. The detailed description and derivation of this model can be found in Enzien et al. (1994). This model is based on phase-continuity principles, species conservation, and momentum balance for each phase. Standard Corey exponent models are adopted for relative permeability functions. The foam viscosity was measured with a Brookfield viscometer and was found to be non-Newtonian and to display Krieger rheological behavior (Krieger 1972). The treatment of the viscous stresses follows the discussion presented by Bouillard (1994).

Computer Model Predictions

One of the first problems to study is the flow of foam in a homogeneous permeable sandy porous medium. A sandy porous medium was chosen to elimi-nate the effects of surfactant adsorption and desorption on the soil surfaces. The foam is assumed to be stable throughout the porous medium, which is the case at high surfactant concentrations, i.e., above the critical micelle concentration (CMC). The computer model was tested against experimental foam-flow data obtained in a two-dimensional visualization cell constructed by Longe at the Virginia Polytechnic Institute (Longe 1989). This cell was constructed to study the penetration and dispersion of CGAs through well-characterized soil/ground-water systems. The frontal advancement of the gas and liquid phases of CGAs

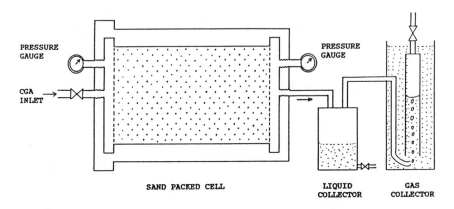

FIGURE 2. **Schematic of the two-dimensional foam flow visualization cell apparatus.**

and pressure drop across the cell were monitored as functions of CGA properties and flow variables.

The visualization cell consists of two rectangular Plexiglas™ plates and is shown schematically in Figure 2. This cell housed a porous medium region that was 25.5 cm wide, 0.8 cm deep, and 38.1 cm long. Three different Ottawa testing sands of mean particle size 0.718 mm, 0.343 mm, and 0.254 mm were used in the study. The variables studied during foam displacement through the sandy material were the gas- and liquid-front advancements and the pressure differential across the cell. A blue dye, made with 0.025 g/L of bromophenol blue, was added to the surfactant solution to improve the visualization of the liquid-front advancement for CGA flow in porous medium. A detailed description of the apparatus can be found in Longe (1989).

Model predictions of foam- and pressure-front propagation in the two-dimensional cell compared favorably with experimental data as shown in Figures 3 and 4. As can be seen, the liquid phase of the foam advances much more rapidly (about twice as fast) than the gas phase. This is indicative of a lag-behind phenomenon of the gas phase with respect to the liquid phase. It is precisely this phenomenon that contributes to the buildup of pressure in the porous medium and the increase in the local gas volume fraction. This hydraulic characteristic of foam flows sharply contrasts with gas sparging where gas bubbles progress faster than the liquid phase. The increase in pressure drop is relatively insensitive to the viscosity increase produced by the increase of surfactant concentration in the aqueous phase, but is a strong function of the inlet foam quality. The effect of surfactant types (cationic, anionic, and nonionic) on the foam- and pressure-front propagations was not significant. The pressure drops measured and calculated for different soil permeabilities showed inverse variations with the square of the mean particle diameter of the porous medium. This follows the well-known Carman-Kozeny permeability dependency with respect to the mean particle diameter of the medium (Bear 1972).

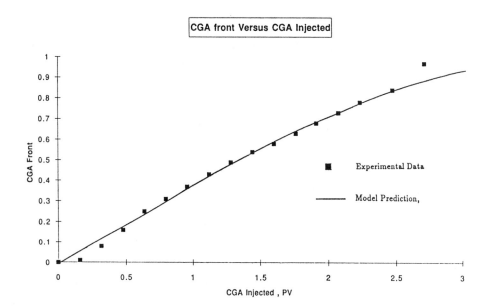

FIGURE 3. Foam-front propagation in sandy porous medium: soil permeability, 366 darcies; soil mean particle size, 720 microns; inlet foam quality, 65%; foam flowrate, 0.75 cm³/s; and surfactant concentration, 500 ppm. Surfactant: NaDBS.

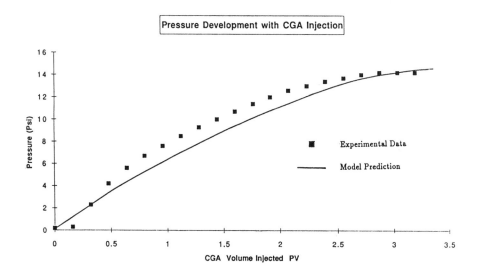

FIGURE 4. Pressure-front propagation and buildup in sandy porous medium: soil permeability, 366 darcies; soil mean particle size, 720 microns; inlet foam quality, 65%; foam flowrate, 0.75 cm³/s; and surfactant concentration, 500 ppm. Surfactant: NaDBS.

To further understand DNAPL mobilization in porous media, state-of-the-art, nonintrusive, three-dimensional magnetic resonance imaging (MRI) techniques are being developed to visualize DNAPL mobilization. Mechanisms being investigated are in situ DNAPL interactions with the foam, DNAPL emulsification, DNAPL scouring by the foam, and subsequent DNAPL mobilization/redeposition in the porous medium.

The application of MRI to nonintrusive visualization of NAPL is relatively new, and the preliminary experiments carried out during this project are illustrative of the potential capabilities of the ANL MRI facility. Because no NAPL imaging in porous media was done in the past, coil frequency tuning and pulsing-sequence testing were performed. In a sandy soil sample, a typical visualization of a NAPL ganglion made of a vegetable oil has been successfully imaged using the ANL MRI 2.3 Tesla machine, as shown in Figure 5. MRI visualization provides the three-dimensional rendition of proton densities of the NAPL. Brighter spots indicate higher NAPL concentrations. As can be seen, the ganglion is not uniformly distributed in the pore space. With such MRI tools, local emulsifications and transport mechanisms can be elucidated at a small pore-space scale.

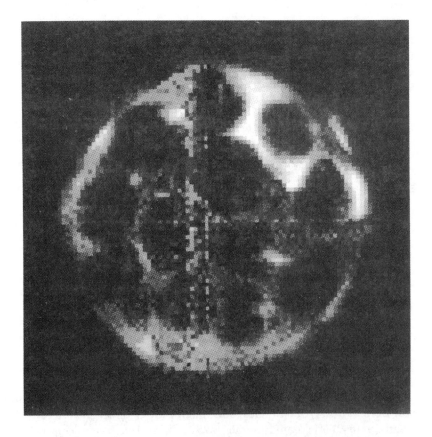

FIGURE 5. Proton MRI slice of typical NAPL ganglion in aqueous solution.

CONCLUSIONS

Three major conclusions were obtained in this study:

1. The hydrodynamic model provides insight as to how and why large pressure drops develop for foam flowing in porous media.
2. The predicted pressure profiles and foam-front propagation were in good agreement with those observed in the two-dimensional visualization cell experiment. These pressure drops are, however, much greater than those encountered in air sparging and surfactant flushing technologies. Such high pressures could present potential dangers of soil heaving, fracturing, and even lifting if not carefully controlled.
3. MRI visualization of foam remediation permits direct imaging of DNAPL ganglia and globule dynamic behavior during flushing operations.

REFERENCES

Bear, J. 1972. *Dynamics of Fluids in Porous Media*. Dover Publications, Inc., New York, NY.

Bouillard, J. X. 1994. "NMR imaging and hydrodynamic analysis of neutrally buoyant non-Newtonian slurry flows." *Powder Technology, 78*: 99-103.

Edwards, D. A., H. Brenner, and D. T. Wasan. 1991. *Interfacial Transport Processes and Theology.* Butterworth-Heinemann Series in Chemical Engineering.

Enzien, M. J., J. X. Bouillard, D. L. Michelsen, R. W. Peters, J. Frank, R. E. Botto, and G. Cody. 1994. *NAPL-Contaminated Soil/Groundwater Remediation Using Foams.* Technical Report, Argonne National Laboratory.

Kovscek, A. R., T. W. Patzek, and C. J. Radke. 1993. "Simulation of foam transport in porous media." *SPE, 26402*: 309-322.

Kovscek, A. R. and C. J. Radke. 1993. *Fundamentals of Foam Transport in Porous Media, Chapter 3. Foams: Fundamental Applications in the Petroleum Industry.* American Chemical Society.

Krieger, I. M. 1972. *Adv. Colloid Interface Sci., 3*: 111.

Longe, T. A. 1989. "Colloidal gas aphrons: generation, flow characterization and application in soil and groundwater decontamination." PhD thesis, Virginia Polytechnic Institute and State University, Blacksburg, VA.

Use of Oily Waste Organics as Amendment to Soils

Rodolfo E. Mendoza, Miguel A. Taboada,
Daniel Rodriguez, Osvaldo Caso, and René Portal

ABSTRACT

The effect of oily waste organics (OWO) from petroleum wells used as amendment in soils of Tierra del Fuego (Argentina) was studied. The soil in Tierra del Fuego is dominated by a xeric heath community of very little forage value for sheep. In a pot experiment, applying OWO as a band 2 cm below the soil surface decreased water evaporation, increased the soil temperature by 15%, and decreased the growth of orchard grass (*Dactylis glomerata*) by 29% with respect to the control. In another pot experiment, OWO was mixed with soil (0, 10, and 20% w/w), fertilized with N and P, and incubated for 0, 18, 39, and 75 days at 4 and 30°C. Incubation increased the population of nitrifier bacteria in soil only when OWO was applied at 0 or 10%; at 20% nitrifier bacteria were depressed. Fertilization increased the growth of orchard grass and overcame any depressive effect of OWO on shoot yield. In a third experiment, the percentage of germination of orchard seeds was not affected by adding up to 40% of OWO, although the addition of OWO depressed root elongation rate. In a field experiment, adding OWO (1 kg/m^2) between rows of potato plants increased soil water content (P = 0.05), and total potato yield (P = 0.20).

INTRODUCTION

Tierra del Fuego is one of the most productive areas in Argentina of both petroleum and wool. Thus, the petroleum industry and wool production must be compatible. Many areas near petroleum wells have been contaminated during the last 20 years. Exploring techniques for petroleum in this area include soil excavation near the pumping site to form a lagoon into which liquid residues are pumped. Basically, the contaminant material consists of crude petroleum free-floating on runoff rain water. Remedial action has consisted of pumping and recycling the petroleum. Nevertheless, after that remedial action, a considerable amount of contaminant remains in the surface. This material was used for the current study. The area is characterized by low temperatures and low rainfall during the year. Due to the winds, soil erosion prevails in the area. The experiments were carried out on low-productivity grasslands with the main objective of studying the feasibility of using landfarming as a tool to increase the productivity of sheep farms taking into account the risk for contamination of the environment. Landfarming is a cost-effective and simple technique that not only is used to increase the productivity of the land but also is a good alternative to eliminate OWO residues. This latest is because of the capacity of the soil to decompose the applied waste (Lynch & Genes 1989).

EXPERIMENTAL PROCEDURES AND MATERIALS

Site, OWO, and Soil Description

The soil used (pH 4.9) was an acid Crioumbrept, dominated by a xeric heath community cover (77%) of a postrate evergreen shrub (*Empetrum rubrum*) with very little forage value for sheep. The OWO utilized in the experiments was a mixture of crude petroleum, rocks, and soil (19.1% organic C). The material was sieved to 2 mm for the experiments. The climate of the region is cold, windy, and generally cloudy. Annual rainfall ranges from 250 to 350 mm, with a small peak in December. Frequent and strong winds from the west contribute to the dryness of the ecosystem.

First Pot Experiment

OWO was applied in 3.5-L pots, in 2-cm-thick layers, 2 cm below the soil surface. The soil was moistened to field capacity and transferred to a glasshouse. The soil water content and soil temperature were measured over a period of 9 days at a point 4 cm below the soil surface. Then 20 plants of orchard grass (*Dactylis glomerata*) were grown and evaluated by the dry matter production of tops in two harvests, at 45 and 65 days after sowing (Figure 1).

Second Pot Experiment

OWO (0, 10, or 20% w/w) was mixed homogeneously with moistened soil (15% w/w) and fertilized with N and P (100 µg/g), and incubated for 0, 18, 39, and 75 days at 4 and 30°C. For each temperature and period of incubation, the amount of nitrifier bacteria was measured. The incubated samples were transferred to 700-mL pots, replicated twice. Three plants of orchard grass per pot were cultivated in glasshouse conditions 45 days after sowing, and the dry matter production of the tops was measured (Figure 2).

Germination Experiment

OWO (0, 1, 5, 10, 20, and 40% w/w) was mixed with the soil and an appropriate amount of sample was transferred to a Petri dish, forming a band of 1.0 cm. The percentage of germination (50 seeds per dish) after 21 days, and the root elongation over a period of 14 days, were measured in a humid and dark environment at 25°C (Figure 3).

Effect of OWO on the Yield of Potato

OWO at a rate of 1 kg/m² was added between the rows of potato plants (*Solanum tuberosum*), 1 month after planting, in a field experiment. The rows of potato plants were separated by 0.70 m, the OWO was added between rows, in a central band 0.50 m wide. The plots of 2.8 × 5 m, with and without OWO,

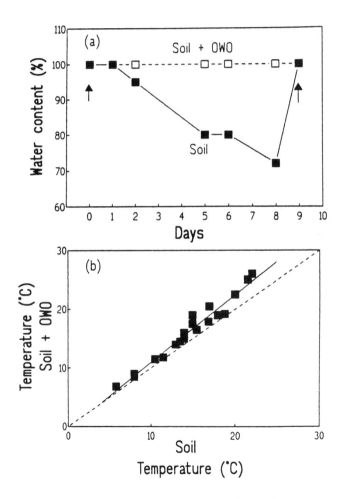

FIGURE 1. Effect of adding OWO as a layer 2 cm from the soil surface on the water content (a) and the temperature (b) of the soil. Arrows in Figure 1a indicate irrigation time. Dashed line in Figure 1b represents the relationship 1:1, and the solid line represents the linear regression, y = −0.67 + 1.15 x; R2 = 0.97.

322 Applied Bioremediation of Petroleum Hydrocarbons

were replicated three times. After harvesting, the skin and flesh of potato tubers were analyzed for total and polycyclic aromatic hydrocarbons (PAHs), by gas chromatography-mass spectrometry (GC-MS).

RESULTS

First Pot Experiment

After 8 days without irrigation, the water content of the soil without OWO decreased near the 70% w/w, whereas the amended soil did not show a change in the water content (Figure 1a). Adding OWO to the soil, as a layer 2 cm below the soil surface, prevented water evaporation, and maintained the soil at a higher temperature than the control treatment (Figure 1b).

The soil temperature was always higher for the soil amended with OWO, and the differences between samples increased by increasing soil temperature (Figure 1b). OWO also affected plant growth. For the first harvest the yield of tops of orchard grass was depressed by adding OWO, but the regrowth was not affected (Table 1).

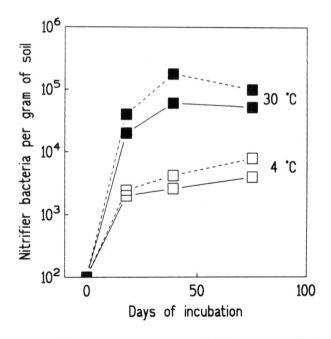

FIGURE 2. Effect of adding OWO (solid lines) at a rate of 20% (w/w) on the population of nitrifier bacteria in soil after the indicated periods and temperatures of incubation. Soils without OWO are represented by dashed lines.

TABLE 1. Dry matter yield of tops (g/pot) of *D. glomerata* from two harvests 45 and 65 days after sowing.

Treatment	45 Days	65 Days
Control	4.56	1.04
OWO	3.24	1.00

Second Pot Experiment

The amount of nitrifier bacteria in soil was affected by fertilization, addition of OWO, and by the period and temperature of incubation (Figure 2). The number of bacteria per gram of soil increased markedly during the first 18 days of incubation. After this first period, the rate of increase slowed down. For all the periods of incubation there was a consistent and negative effect of adding OWO on the number of bacteria per gram of soil (Figure 2).

In all cases, OWO mixed homogeneously with the soil (up to 20%) did not show any depressive effect on the yield of the orchard grass (Figure 3). The most important effect on the yield was the addition of N and P, which markedly

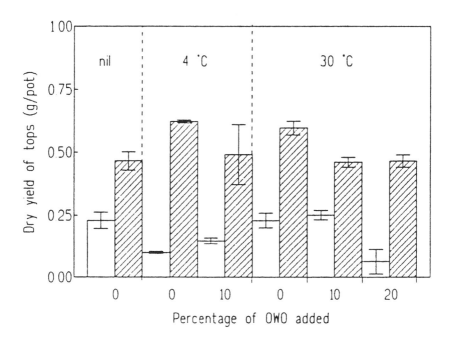

FIGURE 3. Effect of fertilization with N and P (filled-in bars), OWO added, and temperature of incubation after a period of 75 days, on dry yield of tops (and standard error) of *D. glomerata* in pots in the second experiment. No fertilized pots are represented by empty bars.

increased the growth of the grass and overcame any possible depressive effect of OWO (Figure 3).

Germination Experiment

Mixing OWO with the soil (up to 40%) did not affect the percentage of germination of seeds of orchard grass (Table 2), but markedly affected root elongation (Figure 4).

Effect of OWO on the Yield of Potato

Adding OWO to the soil surface increased the water content of the soil at a depth of 0 to 3 cm, but it did not affect soil water content below that depth (Figure 5a). Even if the total potato yield increased by adding OWO (Figure 5b), those differences were not significant (P = 0.05). Figure 6 shows that neither the OWO nor the potato flesh chromatograms had PAH peaks as shown by the standards (Figure 6a).

DISCUSSION

Adding OWO to an acid soil of Tierra del Fuego increased water conservation and soil temperature. These factors are very important for increasing the productivity of the forage ecosystems, specially because of the cold and dry climate of Tierra del Fuego.

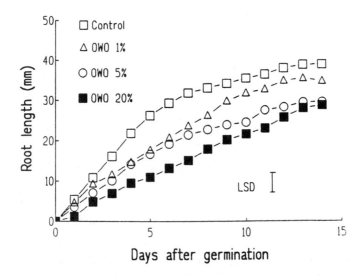

FIGURE 4. Root elongation at the indicated level of OWO added 15 days after sowing. Least significant differences (LSD) at a level of 5% is presented.

TABLE 2. Effect on the percentage of seed germination (PG) of adding OWO up to 40% over a period of 21 days.

OWO Added	PG	sd[a]
Control	63.4	4.2
OWO 10%	68.0	3.4
OWO 20%	68.6	12.8
OWO 40%	61.4	9.4

(a) sd is standard deviation.

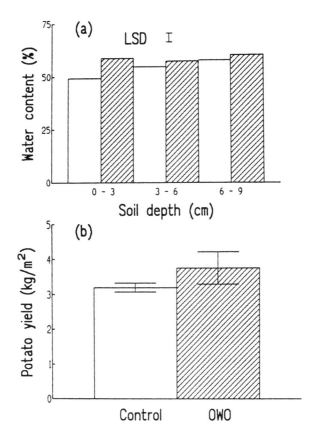

FIGURE 5. (a) Effect of OWO added (1 kg/m²) between rows of potato plants in the field experiment on water content of the soil at the indicated soil depth. Fill-in bars represent OWO added. Least significant differences (LSD) at a level of 5% is presented. (b) Effect of OWO added as indicated in Figure 5a on potato yield. Standard error of mean is presented. Least significant differences (LSD) at a level of 5% is presented.

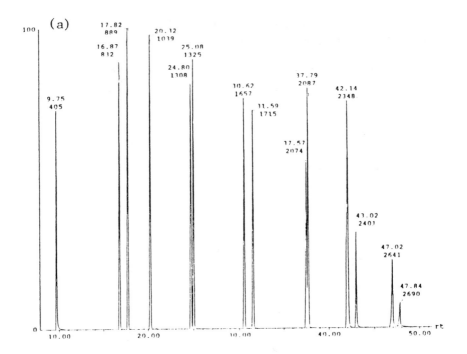

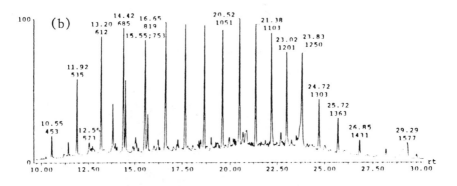

FIGURE 6. (a) Chromatograms of standard samples of PAHs identified by: 9.75:naphthalene; 16.87:acenaphthene; 17.82:acenaphthylene; 20.32:fluorene; 24.80:phenanthrene; 25.08:anthracene; 30.62:fluoranthene; 31.59:pyrene; 37.79:chrysene; 37.57:benz(a)anthracene; 43.02:benz(a)pyrene, benz(e)pyrene, and benz(k)fluoranthene; 47.84:benz(ghi)perylene. (b) Chromatograms of the OWO used in the field experiment for potato yield.

Adding OWO homogeneously mixed with the soil seems more appropriate than adding OWO as a concentrated layer in terms of the effect on plant yield. In addition, it is known that mixing the OWO with the soil increased the carbon mineralization rate of the OWO (Rasiah et al. 1991a).

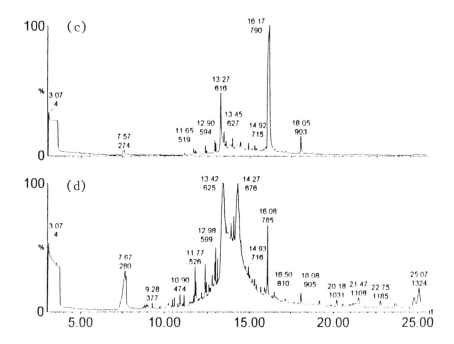

FIGURE 6 (continued). (c) Chromatograms of the flesh of potatoes in soil without OWO. (d) Chromatograms of the flesh of potatoes in soil amended with OWO.

Applying OWO depressed the population of nitrifier bacteria in soil. Adding N and P, and increasing the period and the temperature of incubation, always promoted bacteria population. Adding OWO consistently depressed it. The main factor that affected plant growth were the deficiencies of N and P. Thus, adding these nutrients overcame any possible depressive effect of OWO on plant growth. In addition, it was reported that N increased the carbon mineralization rate of OWO (Rasiah et al. 1991b).

Seed germination was not affected by applying OWO. Seed germination depends mostly on imbibition, temperature, and oxygen availability. These factors appear not to have been affected by adding OWO up to 40%. Nevertheless, the root elongation rate was depressed.

Potato production was not significantly affected by applying OWO, but it showed a tendency to increase when OWO was applied. This effect could be related to the ability of OWO to increase water retention. The analysis of the skin and flesh of potato tubers indicated that PAHs were not present above the guide values for the assessment and remediation criteria established for PAHs by Dutch and Canadian standards (Wilson & Jones 1993), and this is an important and positive aspect to study the feasibility of practicing landfarming.

We concluded that, although amending the soil with OWO may increase soil water retention and soil temperature, we cannot assure that OWO will promote or depress plant yield.

REFERENCES

Lynch, J., and R. Genes. 1989. "Land Treatment of Hydrocarbon Contaminated Soils." In P. Kostecki and E. Calabrese (Eds.), *Petroleum Contaminated Soils.* Lewis Publishers, Chelsea, MI. pp. 163-174.

Rasiah, V., R. Voroney, and G. Kachanoski. 1991a. "Bioavailability of Stabilized Oily Waste Organics in Ultrasonified Soil Aggregates." *Water, Air, and Soil Pollution* 63: 179-186.

Rasiah, V., R. Voroney, and G. Kachanoski. 1991b. "Effect of N Amendment on C Mineralization of an Oily Waste." *Water, Air, and Soil Pollution* 59: 249-259.

Wilson, S., and K. Jones. 1993. "Bioremediation of Soil Contaminated with Polynuclear Aromatic Hydrocarbons (PAHs): A Review." *Environmental Pollution* 81: 229-249.

Bioslurping State of the Art

Ben A. Keet

ABSTRACT ━━━━━━━━━━━━━━━━━━━━━━━━━━━━━━━━━━━━━━

Bioslurping combines in situ biodegradation of low-volatility hydrocarbons with vapor extraction of more volatile fractions and vacuum-enhanced recovery of free product. In its simplest form, a bioslurping installation consists of wells screened at least over the capillary fringe zone, a "slurper spear" positioned near the hydrostatic groundwater level, and a vacuum system capable of removing air and liquids from the wells. Bioslurping has been a recognized technique for more than 2 years and has been applied on a number of sites in the United States, Europe, and Australia. Application has been mainly in fine to medium-fine sediments; however, successful operation has also been achieved in medium-coarse sands and fractured rock. A number of these applications were described during presentations at the Third International Symposium for In Situ and On-Site Bioreclamation, as well as at presentations on multiphase flow mechanics and their beneficial and adverse affects.

INTRODUCTION

Bioslurping effectively combines soil vapor extraction with removal of liquid hydrocarbons from the surface of the groundwater table. In principle, bioslurping is a low-cost and relatively simple technique. However, in practice, successful execution of a bioslurping project relies on creative designs to overcome site-specific difficulties such as low- and dual-porosity formations, soil and rock heterogeneities, limited surface access, and technical difficulties, including liquid separation and treatment of vapors, emulsions, and wastewater.

In its simplest form, a bioslurping installation consists of one or a number of wells screened at least over the capillary fringe zone, a "slurper spear" positioned near the hydrostatic groundwater level, a vacuum pump system capable of removing air and liquids, a separation/treatment system, and a collection/metering system to handle the hydrocarbons, water, and vapors produced. Individual design variations are made to optimize system performance: for example, the seals between "slurper spear" and well can be at the top or by packer lower down in the well to reduce the risk of casing leaks (Connolly et al. 1995); or pre-pump fluid/vapor separation may be added to the treatment system.

The main objective of bioslurping is to activate in situ biodegradation of hydrocarbons. This is more effective for the medium- to low-boiling point distillates because the lighter fractions will be evacuated from the soil by evaporation. The extraction of air from the soil creates a vacuum, which induces a flow of fresh air toward the contaminated zones. The transport of oxygen by this method is efficient and rapid, even when soils have low permeability or when a high percentage of capillaries are filled with water. Most systems to date rely on natural infiltration of air through the topsoil to replace the air removed by the "slurper" system.

The secondary objective of bioslurping is to remove hydrocarbons from the groundwater table. As a result of the induced vacuum, the recovery is not limited to the hydrocarbons that flow freely into the wells. A significant portion of capillary-bound hydrocarbons will also migrate toward the wellbore (Baker 1995) as a result of the vacuum. Although the introduction of a vacuum would raise the water table, as is observed in projects aimed at extracting soil vapors, using bioslurping counteracts this by removing excess fluids through the "slurper spear." The resulting stable water table ensures an undisturbed movement of hydrocarbons horizontally through the zone of high hydrocarbon saturation (Barnes and McWhorter 1995). The relative permeability to hydrocarbons in this zone, in and above the (water) capillary fringe, therefore will remain high. This is in contrast to techniques that rely on significant changes of the groundwater table and resulting movement of the capillary fringe. The movement of hydrocarbons toward the well is enhanced by the vacuum-induced pressure gradient as well as by the friction of the air moving rapidly through the partly hydrocarbon-filled soil pores toward the well.

HISTORIC USE OF VACUUM-ENHANCED
LIQUID EXTRACTION SYSTEMS

Vacuum-enhanced liquid extraction systems have been used for several decades in the building and excavation industry. Rows of spear points are commonly used for dewatering or to form cutoff "trenches" by creating an elongated depression in the water table.

"Slurping" hydrocarbon recovery systems have been applied ever since environmental problems related to this highly concentrated form of soil contamination were first recognized. The early systems merely had a hose draining a well to a certain level. The level was "regulated" by varying the length of the hose, usually connected to a diaphragm pump. The air/water/hydrocarbon mixture often was separated by gravity in a tank. Occasionally, the well would be sealed in an attempt to increase the fluid flow toward the well (Keet 1988).

The added objective of increasing the oxygen concentration in the contaminated soil zone was first applied at the Naval Air Station (NAS), Fallon, Nevada (Hoeppel et al. 1995). The term bioslurping was coined by R. N. Miller on this site. Despite the emphasis on the "bio" (i.e., biodegradation) in most projects to date, the "slurping" of the free product is the most visible result of the technique.

FREE HYDROCARBON REMOVAL

Removal of free hydrocarbons is often part of the first phase of a remediation project. The classic dual-pump systems and other techniques that rely on the drawdown of the water table may give an initial high recovery rate if sufficient hydrocarbon quantities are present or if the formation is relatively permeable. However, the environmental damage done due to the migration of the hydrocarbons deep into the previously uncontaminated saturated zone (or saturated zone without any adsorbed-phase hydrocarbons) can be very serious. Techniques that minimize vertical movement, and therefore smearing, of the hydrocarbon layer are preferred for several reasons:

1. Further vertical contamination of aquifer material is minimized.
2. Relative permeability to oil is minimally reduced.
3. Horizontal migration of contaminants through deeper, more permeable layers (as can occur in systems that depress the water table) is prevented.

Bioslurping is one of a number of techniques that minimize movement of the groundwater table. However, bioslurping has the added advantage of enhancing the recovery of hydrocarbons held in small pores by negative pore pressure. Bioslurping does this by inducing a partial vacuum in the well, which reverses this negative pore pressure.

IN SITU STIMULATION OF BIOACTIVITY

In situ aerobic biodegradation of hydrocarbons is possible when:

1. Hydrocarbon (energy source) is available to the microorganisms.
2. Sufficient oxygen is present.
3. Secondary cell-building materials such as nitrate and phosphorous are present.
4. The environment favors growth of microorganisms (moist, nontoxic, acceptable temperature and pH range, etc).

In natural soils, items 3 and 4 are not commonly the limiting factors. It is widely recognized that oxygen is practically always in short supply. Techniques such as bioventing (air injection), soil vapor extraction (air removal), and air/biosparging (air injection in saturated zone) all aim to increase oxygen levels. Most microorganisms live in the water phase. As a result, the existence of saturated hydrocarbon conditions near the capillary fringe, when free hydrocarbons are present, is a limiting factor to the bioavailability of hydrocarbons. Even after removal of all mobile hydrocarbons, full colonization of the upper capillary fringe zone by microorganisms will be a slow process.

MONITORING BIOSLURPING

Important factors in monitoring the performance of a bioslurping system are:

- Volume and composition of fluids, vapors, and air recovered
- Composition of air, vapors, and fluids remaining in the soil at different levels
- Vacuum levels in the "slurper" wells and in the soil surrounding the wells
- Water level in and around the area of active slurping.

Bioslurping is the amalgamation of several remediation techniques. Consequently, monitoring involves a larger number of parameters. First, it is necessary to keep track of the volume and composition of the fluids and gases removed. Not only is a gradual change to recovery of lower-boiling-point hydrocarbons (and thus fewer vapors) expected, but also the O_2 and CO_2 concentrations are likely to change as biodegradation becomes more important.

Second, it is important to know the changes in the distribution and composition of gases, vapors, and liquids in the formation to allow quantification of in situ processes. It is often this time-related quantification process that is difficult to "sell." In commercial remediation projects, the client may want to limit monitoring to recording the volume of product recovered. It is often difficult to obtain approval for detailed monitoring and time-related quantification.

Third, vacuum distribution in the soil is an indirect measure of the air replacement process as well as an indication of elevation of the water table. Too high a vacuum may lead to undue water table rises around the "slurper" wells, forming circular "dikes" in the groundwater table. The circular "dikes" will reduce the hydrocarbon flow through the capillary zone as the increased water saturation lowers the relative permeability to hydrocarbons.

Other factors to consider in monitoring bioslurping system performance are possible nutrient deficiencies, the discharge and commission limits of the water and air treatment systems, and the silting up of wells, oil/water separators, and any filters in the lines or elsewhere in the system.

ADVANTAGES, DISADVANTAGES, AND TYPICAL AREAS OF APPLICATION

Several advantages of bioslurping have been observed in case studies to date:

1. Free product recovery is increased, especially in medium- to fine-grained sediments, but also in coarser sediments and fractured rock.
2. The groundwater table is practically undisturbed, resulting in little or no change to the relative permeability distribution in the capillary fringe zone.

3. Hydrocarbons are extracted from the formation at pressures below atmospheric, allowing pores with otherwise negative pore pressure to contribute to the production of hydrocarbons from the wells.
4. Oxygen concentration is increased and carbon dioxide concentration is reduced due to the refreshing of soil air as a result of the soil vapor/air extraction.

Several disadvantages of bioslurping and possible solutions have been suggested:

1. High-velocity pump systems (such as liquid ring vacuum pumps) tend to form emulsions, especially when diesel is part of the recovered fluids. Pre-pump separation or a de-emulsification unit is required to solve this problem.
2. The removal of free product will form the major contaminant reduction mechanism during the early stages of the project as biodegradation of the hydrocarbons is retarded due to the low concentration of water in the zone of highest hydrocarbon saturation. It is likely that after recovery of the mobile hydrocarbons other techniques may need to be used concurrently to remedy this. Biosparging may be promising when combined with some (intermittent) flushing to increase horizontal mixing of dissolved oxygen and nutrients.
3. Bioslurping will create emissions to air and water and in most cases both will require treatment that adds to the complexity of the system.

Bioslurping may be applied in the following typical areas:

- Recovery of free product from the groundwater table in fine- to medium-fine sediments and fractured rocks.
- Increased recovery from formations where the hydrocarbons are held under a negative pore pressure (i.e., hydrocarbons are present in the formation but do not flow freely into the wells).
- Biodegradation of hydrocarbons in the unsaturated and capillary zones above the free product layer.
- During the early phases of a remediation project, augmented by other techniques as the project matures.

REFERENCES

Baker, R. S. 1995. "One-, Two-, and Three-Phase Flow During Free-Product Recovery." In R. E. Hinchee, J. A. Kittel, and H. J. Reisinger (Eds.), *Applied Bioremediation of Petroleum Hydrocarbons*, pp. 349-359. Battelle Press, Columbus, OH.

Connolly, M., B. Gibbs, and B. Keet. 1995. "Bioslurping Applied to a Gasoline and Diesel Spill in Fractured Rock." In R. E. Hinchee, J. A. Kittel, and H. J. Reisinger (Eds.), *Applied Bioremediation of Petroleum Hydrocarbons*, pp. 371-377. Battelle Press, Columbus, OH.

Hoeppel, R., J. Kittel, R. Hinchee, and F. Goetz. 1995. "Bioslurping Technology Applications at Naval Middle Distillate Fuel Remediation Sites." In R. E. Hinchee, J. A. Kittel, and H. J. Reisinger (Eds.), *Applied Bioremediation of Petroleum Hydrocarbons*, pp. 389-400. Battelle Press, Columbus, OH.

Keet, B. 1988. "Vacuum Enhanced Viscosified Water Drive Project, Waiwhetu Terminal," Wellington, New Zealand. *Internal report, Oil Recovery Services Ltd.* PO Box 43232, Wainuiomata, Wellington, New Zealand.

Barnes, D. L., and D. B. McWhorter. 1995. "Mechanics of Vacuum-Enhanced Recovery of Hydrocarbons." In R. E. Hinchee, J. A. Kittel, and H. J. Reisinger (Eds.), *Applied Bioremediation of Petroleum Hydrocarbons*, pp. 361-370. Battelle Press, Columbus, OH.

Test Plan and Technical Protocol for Bioslurping

Andrea Leeson, Jeffrey A. Kittel, Robert E. Hinchee,
Ross N. Miller, Patrick E. Haas, and Ronald E. Hoeppel

ABSTRACT

Bioslurping is a new dynamic technology designed to efficiently recover free-floating petroleum hydrocarbons (free product) from the subsurface while simultaneously enhancing natural biodegradation of petroleum hydrocarbons in the vadose zone. Bioslurping is a vacuum-enhanced fluids-pumping technology that simultaneously extracts groundwater, free product, and soil gas in the same process stream. The U.S. Air Force has initiated a multisite program to evaluate the widespread application of bioslurping at free-product-contaminated Air Force sites. The Air Force Bioslurper Initiative is designed to assess the field application of the bioslurping technology at 23 Air Force sites. The field studies are designed to evaluate the efficacy of bioslurping for the recovery of free-floating fuel (free product) and to evaluate the potential for bioventing to enhance natural biodegradation of petroleum contaminants. The technical approach for conducting the bioslurper pilot tests includes assessing the geologic and hydrologic characteristics of each site, free-product baildown testing in site monitoring wells, soil gas analysis, and a bioslurper pump test. The efficiency of bioslurping is compared to that of conventional skimming and dual-pump free-product recovery technologies. Bioventing potential is assessed via in situ respiration testing. The Air Force field program was initiated in July 1994. Preliminary results to date demonstrate that bioslurping shows higher free-product recovery rates than conventional technologies.

INTRODUCTION

The Bioslurper Initiative is funded and managed by the U.S. Air Force Center for Environmental Excellence (AFCEE) Technology Transfer Division. The AFCEE Bioslurper Initiative is a multisite program designed to evaluate the efficacy of bioslurping technology for (1) recovery of light, nonaqueous-phase liquid (LNAPL) from groundwater and the capillary fringe, and (2) enhancement of natural in situ biodegradation of petroleum contaminants in the vadose zone via bioventing.

The *Test Plan and Technical Protocol for Bioslurping* (Battelle 1995) was developed as overall guidance to support preparation of site-specific Test Plans for each of the more than 35 sites where short-term field tests will be conducted (Figure 1). The overall protocol contains details on the general materials and methods for the bioslurper testing. Describing the aspects of testing applicable to all sites in one protocol will increase the consistency and efficiency of the overall effort. The bioslurper protocol was developed from a similar protocol for bioventing (Hinchee et al. 1992).

Objectives

The main objective of the Bioslurper Initiative is to develop procedures for evaluating the potential for recovering free-phase LNAPL present at petroleum-contaminated sites. The overall study is designed to evaluate bioslurping and to identify site parameters that are reliable predictors of bioslurping performance. To measure LNAPL recovery in a wide variety of in situ conditions, tests are being performed at many sites.

The purpose of the field testing is to collect data to support determination of the predictability of LNAPL recovery and to evaluate the applicability, cost, and performance of the bioslurping technology for removal of free product and remediation of the contaminated area. The on-site testing was structured to allow direct comparison of LNAPL recovery achieved by bioslurping with the performance of more conventional LNAPL recovery technologies. The test method included an initial evaluation of site variables followed by LNAPL recovery testing. The three technologies used to recover free LNAPL floating on the water table are skimmer pumping, bioslurping, and drawdown pumping.

Testing Approach

Initial site characterization activities are conducted to evaluate site variables that may affect LNAPL recovery efficiency, and to determine the bioventing potential of the sites. These activities include estimating the persistence of LNAPL in site monitoring wells through baildown tests, soil sampling to determine physical/chemical site characteristics, determining soil gas permeability to estimate the well's radius of influence, and in situ respiration testing to evaluate microbial activity. The site characterization approach is aimed at providing the environmental manager with a stepwise procedure for determining the feasibility of product recovery as well as aid in the design of the pilot- or full-scale system.

Following the site characterization activities, a short-term bioslurper pilot test is conducted. A bioslurper system is installed on a single selected well and typically is operated as follows: 2 days in the skimmer mode (no vacuum); 4 days in the bioslurper mode (vacuum-mediated); 1 day in the skimmer mode (follow-up repeatability test); and 2 days in the groundwater depression mode. Measurements of the extracted soil gas composition, free-product thickness, and

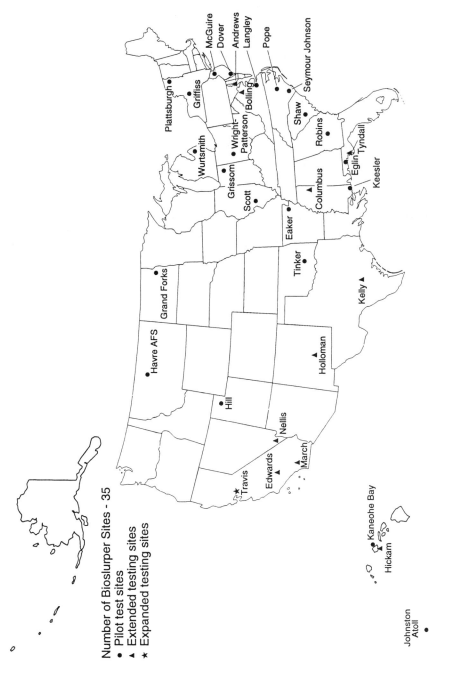

FIGURE 1. AFCEE Bioslurper Initiative sites (phases 1 and 2).

groundwater level are made during the test. The mass of extracted free product, groundwater, and soil gas is quantified over time. These measurements are used to evaluate the long-term effectiveness of bioslurping.

The U.S. Air Force has already installed monitoring points or other wells at many sites that are suitable for use in this study. In keeping with the objective of developing a cost-effective program for site remediation, every effort is made to use existing wells and to minimize drilling costs.

INTRODUCTION TO LNAPL RECOVERY AND BIOSLURPING

Historic handling practices and past spills and leaks have caused petroleum releases to the environment to occur at most industrial and government fuel-handling facilities. When a fuel release occurs, the contaminants may be present in any or all of three phases in the geologic media:

- Sorbed to the soils in the vadose zone,
- In free-phase form floating on the water table, and/or
- In solution phase dissolved in the groundwater.

Of the three phases, dissolved petroleum contaminants in the groundwater are considered to be of greatest concern because of the risk of humans being exposed to the contaminants through drinking water. However, the liquid- and sorbed-phase hydrocarbons act as feedstocks for groundwater contamination, so any remedial technology aimed at reducing groundwater contamination must address these sources of contamination.

At many contaminated sites, petroleum contamination is present as free product in both the vadose zone and the capillary fringe. Regulatory guidelines generally require that free-product recovery take precedence over other remediation technologies. One significant point is that product often is not recoverable, especially when conventional gravity-driven recovery technologies are used. Also, the conventional wisdom has been to complete free-product removal activities prior to initiating vadose zone remediation. This "phased" approach to site remediation is costly and slow because conventional free-product recovery technologies have little or no effect on soil contamination; when LNAPL recovery is complete, a second remediation system must be installed, operated, and maintained to treat residual soil contamination.

Skimmer Technologies

Skimmer LNAPL recovery systems are designed to remove LNAPL from the groundwater surface in a recovery well or trench collection system. These systems can consist of a variety of pump types and configurations, but the basic operation is the same. Skimmer recovery systems rely on the passive movement of LNAPL into the product recovery system. These systems are designed to remove LNAPL only and pump very little groundwater, reducing operation and maintenance costs.

Skimmer systems are very popular because of ease of use. The main limitation to skimmer systems is that they have a very small radius of influence. Because skimmer pumps cause little or no drawdown of the water table, they do little to cause preferential migration of LNAPL to the recovery well. Except in instances when the LNAPL mass is very large and very mobile, and the subsurface permeability is high, skimmer systems tend to have very low LNAPL recovery rates.

Pump Drawdown Technologies

Pump drawdown LNAPL recovery systems are designed to pump LNAPL and groundwater from an LNAPL recovery well or trench. Groundwater is extracted to lower the water table around the LNAPL collection system (cone of depression), inducing a gravity gradient for LNAPL to flow into the collection system. Each foot of groundwater-level depression provides a driving pressure of about 0.45 psi. In most instances, the cone of depression will increase LNAPL recovery rates.

The two types of drawdown recovery systems are single-pump, total-fluids recovery systems and dual-pump recovery systems. Both systems work under the same principle, i.e., the fluid flow gradient into the recovery system is increased by lowering the liquid level in the recovery well to induce gravity flow of LNAPL to the extraction pump. These systems work well when aquifer hydraulic conductivities and saturated thicknesses are large. High aquifer conductivity reduces the resistance to LNAPL flow to the extraction point. A large saturated thickness allows recovery of a higher ratio of LNAPL to water and/or less complex pumping controls.

There are several drawbacks to drawdown LNAPL recovery systems. It may be necessary to extract large volumes of groundwater to maintain the cone of depression, greatly increasing treatment and disposal costs for extracted groundwater. The cone of depression creates a contamination smear zone below the original water table level, which will be difficult to remediate. Permeability usually is higher in the horizontal direction, parallel to geologic stratification, which can inhibit flow down along the cone of groundwater depression. Complex water/LNAPL-level detection and pump-control systems may be needed to maintain desired fluid levels and/or improve LNAPL recovery. Pumps must be in the well or trench, requiring placement of complex equipment in a remote location and possibly corrosive environment. For pumping systems in wells, the diameter of the well must be large enough to accommodate the pumping equipment. Typical monitoring wells, therefore, cannot be used.

Bioslurper Technology

Bioslurping is a new dynamic technology that teams vacuum-assisted free-product recovery with bioventing to simultaneously recover free product and remediate the vadose zone. Unlike other LNAPL recovery technologies, bioslurping systems treat two separate geologic media simultaneously. Bioslurping pumps are designed to extract free-phase fuel from the water table and to aerate vadose zone soils through soil gas vapor extraction. The systems also can be designed to achieve hydraulic control as is done with conventional pump-and-treat technology. The bioslurper system withdraws groundwater, free product, and soil gas in the same process stream using a single pump. Groundwater is separated from the free product and is treated (when required) and discharged. Free product is recovered and can be recycled. Soil gas vapor is treated (when required) and discharged.

Bioslurping may improve free-product recovery efficiency without requiring the extraction of large quantities of groundwater. The bioslurper system pulls a vacuum of up to 20 inches of mercury on the recovery well to create a pressure gradient to force movement of fuel into the well. The system is operated to cause very little drawdown in the aquifer, thus reducing the problem of free-product entrapment.

Bioventing of the vadose zone soils is achieved by withdrawing soil gas from the recovery well. The slurping action of the bioslurper system cycles between recovering liquid (free product and/or groundwater) and soil gas. The rate of soil gas extraction is dependent on the recovery rate of liquid into the well. When free-product removal activities are complete, the bioslurper system is easily converted to a conventional bioventing system to complete remediation of the vadose zone soils.

Bioslurper systems are designed to minimize environmental discharges of groundwater and soil gas. As done in bioventing, bioslurper systems extract soil gas at a low rate to reduce volatilization of contaminants. In some instances volatile discharges can be kept below treatment action levels. The slurping action of a bioslurping system greatly reduces the volume of groundwater that must be extracted compared to conventional LNAPL recovery systems, thus greatly reducing groundwater treatment costs. Figure 2 illustrates the differences between conventional dual-pump LNAPL recovery and bioslurping.

A significant feature of the bioslurping process is the induced airflow, which in turn induces LNAPL flow toward the well. The pressure gradient created in the air phase results in a driving force on the LNAPL that is significantly greater than that which can be induced by pumping the LNAPL with no airflow. Also of importance is the fact that the airflow created by the vacuum actually enhances the LNAPL content around the well. That is, the LNAPL tends to accumulate or pile up around the well. The accumulation around the well ensures that the permeability controlling the conductivity to LNAPL is maximum. For these reasons, bioslurping has the potential for removing more LNAPL and at greater rates than do other pumping mechanisms.

SITE CHARACTERIZATION

Site characterization activities generally consist of standard techniques which are well documented. Therefore, a summary of the activities conducted is provided below:

- LNAPL analysis for benzene, toluene, ethylbenzene, and xylenes (BTEX) and boiling-point distribution of the hydrocarbons.
- Soil analyses of particle-size distribution, bulk density, porosity, moisture content, BTEX, and total petroleum hydrocarbons (TPH).
- Baildown tests to determine the rate of LNAPL recovery.
- Soil gas permeability test to determine the radius of influence of the extraction well (conducted during the bioslurping test).
- In situ respiration test to determine biodegradation rates.

Additional details on these techniques may be found in Hinchee et al. (1992) and Battelle (1995).

BIOSLURPER SYSTEM CONSTRUCTION AND OPERATION

Bioslurper Extraction Well Selection

For most of the tests, an existing well with a history of free-product contamination is selected for installation of the bioslurper. Selection of the bioslurper

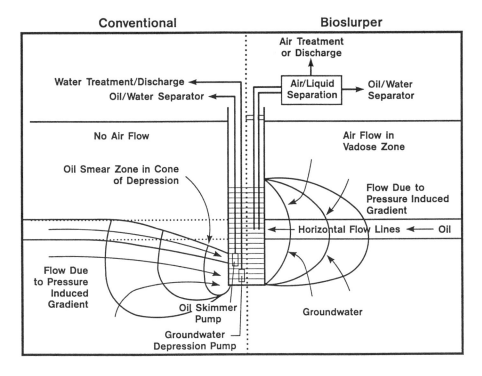

FIGURE 2. Comparison of conventional LNAPL recovery and bioslurping.

extraction well is based on the data collected during the site characterization phase. The following factors are evaluated: historical data on the persistence and recoverability of LNAPL from each well; results of the LNAPL baildown tests; and wells with a proper surface seal and optimum screened interval in the vadose zone. If no suitable existing well is identified, a new well is drilled to accept the bioslurping suction tube. Installed bioslurper wells are placed with the screened section in contaminated soil and groundwater and are located near the center of the contaminated area.

System Components

Each trailer-mounted unit includes a bioslurper liquid ring pump, a gasoline- or diesel-powered electrical generator capable of supplying all power requirements for the pilot testing, an oil/water separator with 10-gpm flow capacity, a transfer tank and pump for directing extracted groundwater to the base-supplied effluent disposition system, and vapor treatment equipment (Figure 3). Liquid ring pumps are used for all pilot testing because they have efficient pump curves and are inherently explosion-proof total fluid pumps.

Aqueous/Vapor Discharge

The bioslurper system generates a point source vapor emission and has an aqueous discharge as well. In many cases the discharge rate of petroleum contaminants in the vapor stream is below local regulatory treatment levels and is discharged directly to the atmosphere with regulatory approval. If treatment is necessary, the following options are considered: reinjection for in situ biodegradation; carbon treatment; or destruction in an internal combustion engine. The mass of hydrocarbons dissolved in the aqueous phase will be much lower than the mass dissolved in the vapor discharge. In most cases, bioslurper aqueous effluent will be discharged to the sanitary sewer for treatment.

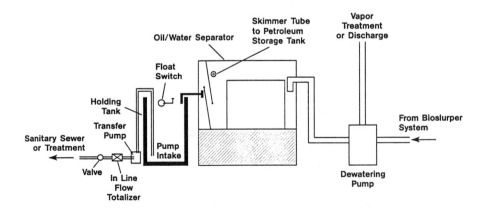

FIGURE 3. Schematic diagram of mobile bioslurper pilot test system.

In some instances, the vapor and/or the aqueous effluent will require treatment before discharge. Generally, the contaminant of concern will be benzene, which is present in relatively high concentrations in JP-4 jet fuel and in gasoline. Local regulatory requirements vary, and at each site it is necessary to determine discharge treatment requirements prior to mobilization to the field site.

All discharges from the bioslurper system are quantified and contaminant concentration is determined. The groundwater extraction volume is quantified using an in-line flow-totalizer meter calibrated in gallons, and effluent samples are collected from the bioslurper oil/water separator discharge for analysis of BTEX and TPH. The volume of vapor discharge is quantified using a pitot tube (Annubar Flow Characteristics Model #HCR-15) flow indicator, and discharge samples are collected from the bioslurper vapor discharge stack for analyses of BTEX and TPH. The LNAPL recovery volume is quantified using an in-line flow-totalizer meter calibrated in gallons.

BIOSLURPER SYSTEM STARTUP

Initial Skimmer Simulation Test

In this test the slurper tube is set at the LNAPL/groundwater interface with the wellhead ball valve open to the atmosphere (Figure 4). The skimmer test is operated continuously for 48 h, with free-product and groundwater extraction

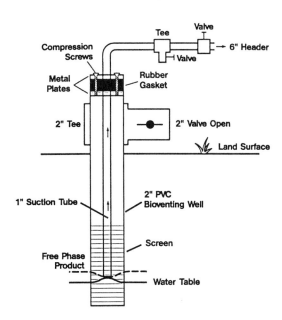

FIGURE 4. Well construction detail and slurper tube placement for the skimmer test configuration.

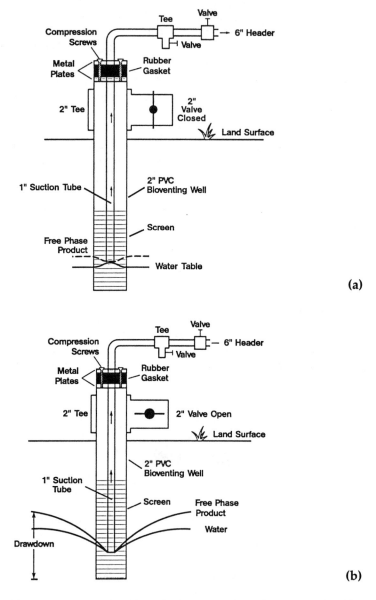

FIGURE 5. Well construction detail and slurper tube placement for the bioslurper (a) and drawdown (b) test configurations.

rates being monitored on an as-needed basis throughout the test. LNAPL/ groundwater levels are monitored periodically in the site monitoring wells (every 0.5 h for 2 h, then as needed thereafter). After 48 h have elapsed, final readings are taken for LNAPL and groundwater extraction rates. Final LNAPL and groundwater levels in the site monitoring wells are recorded at that time.

Bioslurper Vacuum-Enhanced Extraction Test

When the skimmer test is complete, the ball valve at the extraction wellhead is closed to begin bioslurping (Figure 5a). The bioslurper test begins immediately after the skimmer test is completed and continues for 96 h. Before closing the extraction wellhead ball valve, initial soil gas pressures are taken at all soil gas monitoring points and from any site monitoring wells fitted with the vacuum-tight oil/water interface probe. The bioslurper test continues for 96 h. During the bioslurping test, a soil gas permeability test is conducted to determine the radius of influence.

Skimmer Simulation Test Repetition

Following the 96-h bioslurper test, the skimmer simulation test is repeated. The wellhead valve is reopened to simulate skimmer operation. The postbioslurp-ing skimmer simulation test is run for 24 h. Repeating the skimmer simulation test provides a more accurate basis for comparing sustainable LNAPL recovery rates with conventional technology and bioslurping.

Dual-Pump/Drawdown Simulation Test

A drawdown simulation test is conducted for 48 hours after completion of the 96-hour bioslurper test and the second skimmer simulation test. The extraction wellhead ball valve is opened to the atmosphere and the slurper tube is lowered further into the well, to a level below the static groundwater level measured during baseline measurements (Figure 5b).

To allow direct comparison between the bioslurper test and the drawdown simulation test, the drop tube is placed at a depth equal to the wellhead vacuum observed during the bioslurper test. For example, if the wellhead vacuum during bioslurping is approximately 18 in. (46 cm) H_2O, the drop tube would be placed 18 in. (46 cm) below the original elevation of the water table. In cases of extremely high vacuum or very low vacuum, default values of maximum 3 ft (0.9 m) and minimum 1 ft (0.3 m) are used. Some sites will have extremely permeable aqui-fers, for which drawdown tests are not feasible.

LNAPL and groundwater are extracted for 24 h in the dual-pump/drawdown simulation mode. Data collection and process monitoring continues as with the skimmer and bioslurper recovery tests.

PRELIMINARY COMPARISON OF FREE-PRODUCT RECOVERY TECHNOLOGIES

A summary of data from four Bioslurper Initiative sites is presented in Table 1. The amount of fuel recovered is shown in terms of gallons per day (liters per day) for each of the technologies tested. At all sites, the bioslurping

TABLE 1. Fuel recovery during testing of skimmer, bioslurping, and drawdown technologies at Bioslurper Initiative sites.

| Site | Fuel Recovered (gallons [liters]/day) by Technology | | | |
	Skimmer (Test 1)	Bioslurping	Skimmer (Test 2)	Drawdown
Andrews	7.8 (29.5 L)	79 (299 L)	0.73 (2.76 L)	NA (NA)
Bolling	17 (64 L)	60 (227 L)	8.2 (31 L)	31 (117 L)
Kaneohe	0 (0 L)	2.4 (9 L)	0.055 (0.2 L)	0 (0 L)
Wright Patterson	4.0 (15 L)	4.6 (17 L)	NA (NA)	2.5 (9.5 L)

NA = Not applicable.

configuration recovered more field than either the skimmer or drawdown configurations; in some cases, nearly an order of magnitude increase was observed in fuel recovery rates.

Of particular interest is the site at Kaneohe AFB. At this site, free product could not be recovered during either the skimmer or drawdown configuration. However, in the bioslurping configuration, a small but significant rate of fuel recovery was observed (Figure 6). These results emphasize the efficacy of bioslurping for free-product recovery.

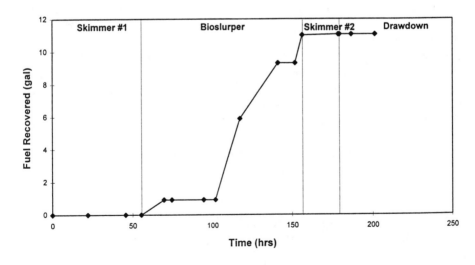

FIGURE 6. Fuel recovery during three test configurations at Kaneohe AFB, Hawaii.

SUMMARY

The Air Force Bioslurper Initiative is designed to assess the field application of the bioslurping technology at 23 Air Force sites. Data from the Bioslurper Initiative will be used to evaluate the feasibility of bioslurping in comparison to conventional technologies. In addition, site characterization data will be evaluated to determine which site parameters aid in determining the potential feasibility of bioslurping at a specific site.

The technical approach for conducting the bioslurper pilot tests includes assessing the geologic and hydrologic characteristics of each site, free-product baildown testing in site monitoring wells, soil gas analysis, and a bioslurper pump test. Bioslurping free-product recovery efficiency is compared to conventional skimming and dual-pump free-product recovery technologies. Bioventing potential is assessed via in situ respiration testing. Preliminary results to date demonstrate that bioslurping shows higher free-product recovery rates than conventional technologies. In some instances, recovery rates during bioslurping are an order of magnitude higher than with conventional technologies. These results indicate the potential feasibility of bioslurping as an alternative fuel recovery technology.

REFERENCES

Battelle. 1995. *Test Plan and Technical Protocol for Bioslurping.* Report prepared by Battelle Columbus Operations for the U.S. Air Force Center for Environmental Excellence, Brooks Air Force Base, TX.

Hinchee, R. E., S. K. Ong, R. N. Miller, D. C. Downey, and R. Frandt. 1992. *Test Plan and Technical Protocol for a Field Treatability Test for Bioventing* (Rev. 2). Report prepared by Battelle Columbus Operations, U.S. Air Force Center for Environmental Excellence, and Engineering Sciences, Inc. for the U.S. Air Force Center for Environmental Excellence, Brooks Air Force Base, TX.

One-, Two-, and Three-Phase Flow During Free-Product Recovery

Ralph S. Baker

ABSTRACT

An increasing variety of options is becoming available for recovering organic liquids from the subsurface following releases from leaking underground storage tanks, buried pipelines, and surface spills. Multiphase fluid flow in porous media during product recovery must be considered to optimize desired effects and minimize unintended consequences. Free-product recovery commonly focuses first on soils that are saturated with respect to nonaqueous-phase liquid (NAPL), especially when a substantial thickness of floating product is apparent in monitoring wells. This paper also addresses product recovery from soils that are unsaturated with respect to NAPL, such as in the transition zone between the water table and the capillary fringe. Considering both saturated and unsaturated soils, the available product recovery methods can generally be classified as those that aim to recover NAPL only; NAPL and water; and NAPL, water, and vapor. The corresponding flow processes, respectively, involve one, two, and three phases. Examples of these distinctly different approaches are presented, along with their applicability, advantages, and disadvantages.

INTRODUCTION

In situ remediation systems treating mixtures of contaminants increasingly combine technologies such as groundwater extraction, soil vapor extraction (SVE), bioventing, and NAPL recovery, applying them together at a single well or adjacent wells (NRC 1994). Such technology integration is inherently efficient because it reduces unnecessary redundancy in collection, treatment, and control components, and it allows practitioners the flexibility to focus the applied mechanical energy on one or more target phases simultaneously. In doing so, however, unanticipated physical effects can result, as when applying a force to one phase induces multiphase flow. If we hope to properly design, operate, and evaluate the performance of integrated technologies, the multiphase effects must be recognized, anticipated, modeled, and monitored. As a preliminary step, this paper attempts to identify some of the known or envisioned effects and the circumstances that give rise to them.

METHODS OF FREE-PRODUCT RECOVERY

Where NAPL is present in soil as a result of a substantial spill or leak, free-product recovery to remove the bulk of the floating product is generally considered a necessary precursor to the application of in situ remedial technologies, such as bioventing, that require a well-aerated soil for spatially distributed microbial growth and hydrocarbon degradation. The successful removal of NAPL depends greatly on the method of free-product recovery that is selected.

Let us consider a soil having pore volume V_{pores}. Saturation, S, is the fraction of that pore volume occupied by a given fluid; i.e., $S = V_{fluid}/V_{pores}$. In a multiphase system, all the pores will be occupied by one or another of the phases present, such that $S_w + S_o + S_a = 1$, with S_w, water saturation; S_o, NAPL saturation; and S_a, air saturation. Residual NAPL saturation, S_{ro}, may be defined as the NAPL saturation that remains in a soil that, having contained NAPL, is subjected to drainage until the NAPL becomes immobile and its saturation cannot be further reduced (Wilson et al. 1989).

Free-product recovery commonly focuses first on soil zones that are saturated with respect to NAPL ($S_o \approx 1$), especially those zones in which a substantial thickness of floating product is apparent in monitoring wells, in which case the gauge pressure of the NAPL must be positive (i.e., greater than atmospheric pressure). Attention is also directed here to removal of product from soils, such as in the transition zone between the water table and the capillary fringe, which are unsaturated with respect to NAPL ($S_{ro} < S_o < 1$). In either case, free-product recovery methods can be generally classified as those that aim to recover (1) free product only; (2) free product and water; and (3) free product, water, and vapor. These types of systems constitute one-, two-, and three-phase flow processes, respectively. The following paragraphs offer examples of these distinctly different approaches and discuss when they are applicable, their compatibility with bioventing, and their advantages and disadvantages.

NAPL-Saturated Soils

Where floating product forms a lens on the water table, and especially in coarse-textured soils (e.g., sands and gravels) that are saturated with respect to NAPL, conventional modes of free-product recovery using submersible and skimmer pumps in wells/trenches are generally effective (API 1989). Submersible pumps generally extract NAPL and water, whereas skimmer pumps may extract NAPL only.

Recovery of NAPL and Water. A submersible single- or double-pump system (Figure 1) creates a cone of depression in the water table. The resulting drawdown increases the well's capture zone and the hydraulic gradient, causing

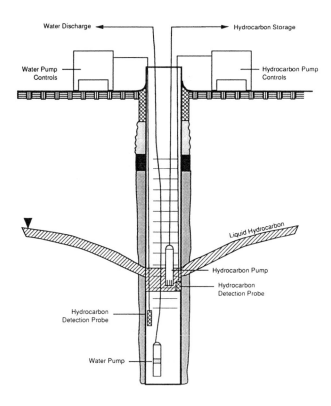

FIGURE 1. Free-product recovery system schematic diagram: two-pump system (after API 1989).

floating product to flow into the well. Because water is also recovered, however, it must be treated prior to discharge. Initially, high NAPL recovery rates can sometimes not be sustained because of clogging of wells. Also, in the process of drawing down the water table to create a cone of depression, a substantial mass of NAPL can become smeared below the former water table position. More significantly, when pumping produces diminishing returns and drawdown is therefore suspended, some of the NAPL tends to become entrapped and immobilized in the soil rather than being carried back upward as floating product with the rebounding water table. Consequently, although the initial rates of recovery with such systems can be relatively high, the total mass that remains after further free-product recovery has become infeasible may be considerable.

Recovery of NAPL Only. Skimmer systems (Figure 2) recover floating product only and thus have neither the advantages nor disadvantages associated with drawdown and subsequent treatment of water. Floating filter scavenger systems, for example, can remove product down to thin layers as they track fluctuations in the water table. Such systems tend to be most suitable for moderately permeable formations, or where recovery rates would not be sufficient to justify

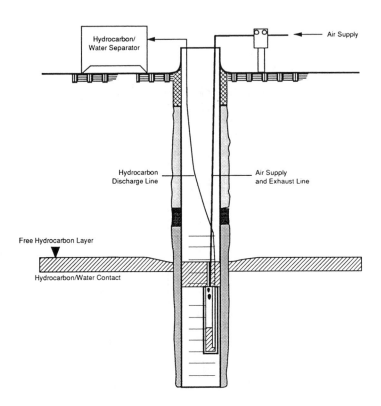

FIGURE 2. Free-product recovery system schematic diagram: pneumatic skim-
    ming pump (after API 1989).

operation of more costly combined water and product recovery systems. Absorbent bailers and belt skimmers also fall within this category, but are suitable only
when very low product recovery rates are acceptable.

    In both the pump and the skimmer systems, the pressure that is maintained
in the extraction well is equal to atmospheric pressure. Thus, only water or
NAPL residing at pore pressures greater than atmospheric pressure (i.e., at
positive gauge pressures) can overcome capillary forces and drain from the
formation into the recovery well. Therefore, as soon as the formation is no longer
saturated with respect to NAPL, recovery by those methods ceases.

NAPL-Unsaturated Soils

    Once floating product has been removed, soils in the transition zone between
the water table and the capillary fringe will be unsaturated with respect to NAPL,
with the actual saturation value, S_o, being dependent on the air and water saturations, such that $S_o = 1 - (S_w + S_a)$ and $S_{ro} < S_o < 1$. A substantial quantity of
organic liquid may be present within this wide range, however. As an example,
Wilson and coworkers (1989) measured a mean unsaturated zone residual NAPL

saturation (S_{ro}) of 0.091 for Sevilleta sand and found that the maximum NAPL saturation in their vadose column experiments averaged 0.66. Between these bounds, the equivalent volumetric retention would range from approximately 30 to 220 L NAPL/m^3 soil. This potentially considerable volume of NAPL resides at negative gauge pressures, but is not necessarily unrecoverable. The capillary forces that cause this NAPL to be retained in soils under atmospheric pressure can be overcome by applying sufficient subatmospheric pressures, as described in the following paragraphs.

Recovery of Product, Water, and Vapor. Vacuum-enhanced free-product recovery (Blake and Gates 1986; Hayes et al. 1989; API 1989) is one method that can mobilize a portion of such NAPL through the exertion of a subatmospheric gas-phase pressure for some radius around the extraction well while water and NAPL are also extracted. If the vacuum being exerted on the formation adjacent to the well is greater than its air entry suction, capillary forces preventing water and NAPL from draining into the well can be overcome (Baker and Bierschenk 1995), and water and NAPL extraction can be enhanced. Application of a vacuum also augments the liquid-phase pressure drop between the formation and the well, increasing the hydraulic gradient that is the driving force for flow of NAPL and water toward the well. It should be noted that vacuum enhancement is also employed to increase recovery rates of product from NAPL-saturated soils (Blake and Gates 1986). This integrated technology is especially applicable to medium-textured soils, where the applied vacuum does not suffer excessive head losses and where the radii of influence of the vacuum wells are thus acceptable. Because three phases are extracted, however, this method has the disadvantages that oil-water and air-water separations are required. Water treatment is usually necessary, and vapor treatment may be also.

Recovery of Product, Water, and Vapor with Bioslurping. A variation of a vacuum-enhanced free-product recovery system that has been developed to be compatible with bioventing has been termed the "bioslurper" (AFCEE 1994). In this approach, a tube connected to a vacuum pump is lowered within a recovery well to no deeper than the free-product/water-table interface (Figure 3). As a vacuum is exerted on the tube, product, along with some water, is extracted, until at some point the flowrate of liquids toward the well is not sufficient to deliver product or water to the tube. Vapor is then drawn into the tube, inducing airflow from the unsaturated zone toward the well, until water and/or product reenter the well and are again extracted. Liquids and vapor are thus alternately extracted, with the volume of water being minimized by adjusting the depth of the intake.

The degree to which the bioslurper system aerates the soil can be monitored and controlled to minimize unnecessary overaeration. The bioslurper well thus recovers product plus some water and vapor that require aboveground separation and treatment, while aerating the soil to stimulate biodegradation of fuel hydrocarbons in the capillary fringe zone. Although, as described here, the bioslurper

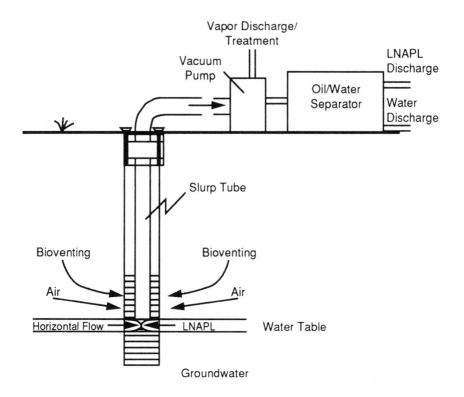

FIGURE 3. Free-product recovery system schematic diagram: bioslurper system (AFCEE 1994).

well does not rely on drawing down a cone of depression in the water table, it can be expected to cause some degree of inwelling of transition zone water and NAPL toward the tube if the applied vacuum is large. At lower applied vacuums, inwelling will not be a concern, but neither will it be possible to extract product residing in NAPL-unsaturated soil unless the applied vacuum in the well is greater than the air entry suction of the formation (Baker and Bierschenk 1995). A further disadvantage of actively aerating the well while collecting product would be biofouling of well screens. Thus, it may be better to complete product recovery prior to the initiation of bioventing.

PILOT TEST OF VACUUM-ENHANCED PRODUCT RECOVERY

To illustrate some of the advantages and disadvantages associated with three-phase flow, the results of a pilot vacuum-enhanced free-product recovery test are briefly reviewed. The pilot test was performed at an industrial facility in the southeastern United States, where diesel fuel was discovered to have leaked into the subsurface from underground piping. The test was designed to evaluate the effectiveness of recovery of NAPL and water vs. vacuum-enhanced recovery of NAPL, water, and vapor. A more detailed account of the pilot test is presented elsewhere (Baker and Bierschenk 1995).

Materials and Methods

Stratigraphy in the contaminated area consists of between 0.3 and 0.9 m of gravelly fill, 3.0 to 4.5 m of silty clay, and 3.0 to 4.5 m of a very compact silty sand saprolite, underlain by fractured bedrock. The air-NAPL interface was observed in monitoring wells at 3.9 to 4.5 m below ground surface (bgs), with as much as a meter of floating product accumulating in some wells. Figure 4 illustrates the relative locations of monitoring wells, pumping wells, the vapor extraction well, air piezometers, and neutron access tubes at the test location. The relative elevations of various subsurface components of the pilot test are shown in cross section in Figure 5.

The 10.2 cm ID vapor/liquid extraction well (VE-1) was screened from approximately 0.9 to 8.5 m bgs. Monitoring points included 1.0 cm ID air piezometer

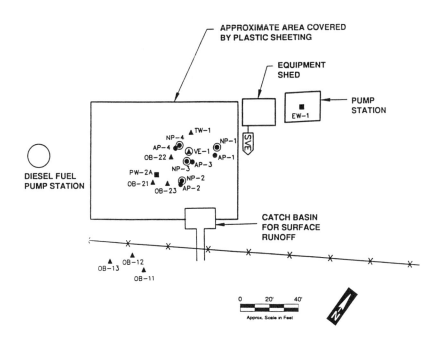

FIGURE 4. Site plan of vacuum-enhanced product recovery pilot test. VE = extraction well; AP = air piezometer; NP = neutron probe access tube; OB, PW, and TW = monitoring wells; EW = groundwater pumping well; and SVE = soil vapor extraction blower. (Baker and Bierschenk 1995. Reprinted by permission of Lewis Publishers, an imprint of CRC Press, Boca Raton, Florida.)

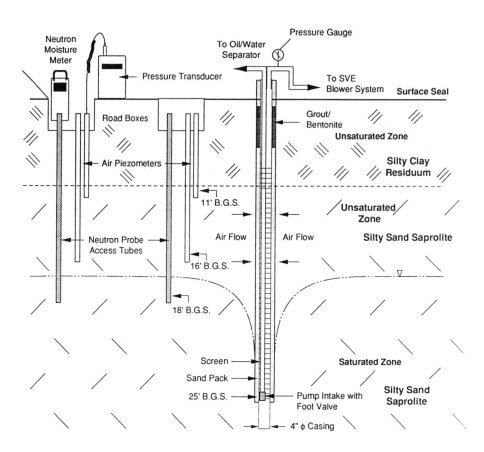

FIGURE 5. Cross section of vacuum-enhanced product recovery pilot test along
plane of VE-1, AP-3, and AP-2, showing approximate stratigraphy; relative
positions and depths of extraction well screen, water table, and monitoring
points. (Baker and Bierschenk 1995. Reprinted by permission of Lewis
Publishers, an imprint of CRC Press, Boca Raton, Florida.)

(AP) tubes set within 0.3 m thick sand packs at depths of 3.4 and 4.9 m bgs;
and adjacent 3.8 cm ID neutron probe (NP) access tubes placed to depths of at
least 5.4 m bgs. Each AP tube was located 0.7 to 0.9 m from an NP access tube.
To prevent short-circuiting of air during vapor extraction, a minimum of 0.3 m
of bentonite was placed around the upper portion of each NP and AP tube, and a
temporary surface seal consisting of polyethylene sheeting was installed over
a 23-m by 30-m area around VE-1 (Figure 4).

A double-diaphragm pump was employed to extract NAPL and groundwater
from VE-1 in a single conduit, followed by separation of the two phases in an
aboveground oil/water separator (Figure 5). During the 4 d of Phase 1, NAPL
and water were extracted while VE-1 was maintained at atmospheric pressure.
During the subsequent 21 d of Phase 2, when vacuum-enhanced recovery of

NAPL, water, and vapor was carried out, a blower was used to exert a vacuum at VE-1 of 240 to 280 cm H_2O. Because of the low permeability of the subsurface, the mean airflow rate from the well during Phase 2 was 0.10 standard m^3/min. To assess the volume of liquid and fuel oil recovered, two totalizing flow meters were monitored daily during Phases 1 and 2, as was the volume of NAPL that accumulated in the oil/water separator. The SVE system lost power on two occasions, day 2 and days 9 to 10 of Phase 2, presumably allowing temporary resaturation of the soil within the cone of depression surrounding VE-1.

Undisturbed soil (saprolite) cores were collected from depths of 3.4 and 4.9 m bgs at AP-3 and AP-4 and submitted to a laboratory for measurement of soil hydraulic properties. Mean saturated hydraulic conductivity was 2×10^{-4} cm s^{-1} for the shallower cores and 3×10^{-4} cm s^{-1} for the deeper cores. The soils were compact, silty sands (USCS classification), with a predominance of fine pores that would be expected to restrict the movement of fluids. None of the cores appeared to intersect a major saprolite fracture zone, although such fractures were suspected over a larger scale.

RESULTS AND DISCUSSION

Over the 4 d of Phase 1, recovery of NAPL was less than could be measured (<0.1 L), while an average of about 190 L/d of water were extracted (Figure 6). By contrast, over the 21 d of Phase 2, averages of 6.6 L/d of NAPL and 760 L/d of water were recovered, a significant increase for both liquids (Figure 6). The measured vacuums during Phase 2 generally diminished with distance from VE-1, but fluctuated substantially with time, probably a result of two major rainstorms, 76 mm on day 4, and 51 mm on day 8. The strongest consistent vacuum (22 cm H_2O) was detected at AP-3S; the other APs exhibited considerably smaller vacuums, and showed positive pressures for approximately half of Phase 2, indicating that the influence of SVE was not uniformly distributed in space or time.

Repeated in situ measurements were made via the neutron access tubes of the degree of liquid saturation in the formation. Neutron depth gauges precisely quantify the relative degree of saturation of soil by hydrocarbon-rich materials (i.e., water and hydrocarbons), but cannot distinguish between them (Kramer et al. 1992). For the nearly saturated soils for which data are presented in Figure 7, the soil volume monitored around each neutron probe measurement point was estimated to have a radius of 15 to 30 cm (Gardner 1986).

Figure 7 reveals that between days 1 and 3 of Phase 2, the two shallow locations 1.5 m to either side of VE-1 became significantly more saturated, while the two shallow locations 4.5 m to either side of VE-1 became concomitantly less saturated. After day 3 the readings remained quite steady. Similar observations were noted within the saprolite at the other depths monitored that are not presented in Figure 7. The data reflect a redistribution ("piling up") of transition-zone liquid toward the extraction well, evidence of inwelling anticipated by McWhorter (1990) and predicted by the conceptual model of Baker and McWhorter (1992).

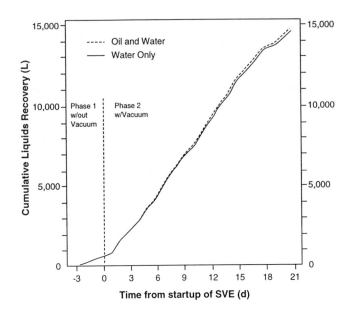

FIGURE 6. Cumulative liquids recovery in liters during Phases 1 and 2. NAPL recovery is indicated by the difference between the two curves. (Baker and Bierschenk 1995. Reprinted by permission of Lewis Publishers, an imprint of CRC Press, Boca Raton, Florida.)

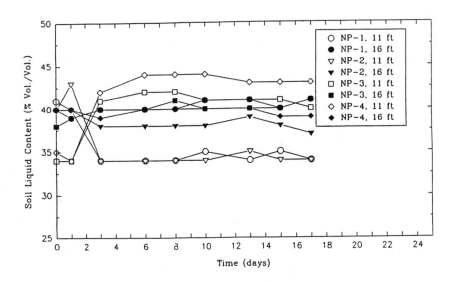

FIGURE 7. Relative soil liquid content defined as: (volume of water + volume of NAPL)/bulk soil volume, over time during Phase 2. (Baker and Bierschenk 1995. Reprinted by permission of Lewis Publishers, an imprint of CRC Press, Boca Raton, Florida.)

Implications of the Pilot Study

Vacuum-enhanced NAPL recovery also produces enhanced water recovery and in medium-textured soils, where enhancement of NAPL recovery is most likely to be effective, enhancement of water recovery will far exceed that of NAPL, as has been observed previously (Blake and Gates 1986). A disadvantage of increased water recovery is the increased cost of water treatment. Moreover, the redistribution of water and NAPL toward the vacuum well and associated increases in liquid saturation near the well screen can be expected to result in markedly reduced air permeability manifested as well losses (McWhorter 1990), and impeded aeration near the well screen.

The results of the pilot test exemplify the fact that multiphase recovery technologies can have both beneficial and potentially adverse effects. The significance of these effects on the design and effectiveness of innovative integrated remediation technologies is only beginning to be recognized.

REFERENCES

Air Force Center for Environmental Excellence (AFCEE). 1994. *Technology Profile: Vacuum-Mediated LNAPL Free Product Recovery/Bioremediation (Bioslurper)*. AFCEE Fact Sheet., Issue 1, March 1994. Brooks Air Force Base, San Antonio, TX.

American Petroleum Institute (API). 1989. *Guide to the Assessment and Remediation of Underground Petroleum Releases*, 2nd ed. API Publication 1628. API, Washington, DC.

Baker, R. S., and J. Bierschenk. 1995. "Vacuum-Enhanced Recovery of Water and NAPL: Concept and Field Test." *J. Soil Contamination* 4(1):57-76.

Baker, R. S., and D. B. McWhorter. 1992. "Vacuum-Enhanced Recovery of Water and NAPL: Model and Proposed Field Test." In *Agronomy Abstracts*, Annual Meetings, Soil Science Society of America, (Nov. 1-6, 1992, Minneapolis, MN). p. 210.

Blake, S. B., and M. M. Gates. 1986. "Vacuum Enhanced Hydrocarbon Recovery: A Case Study." In *Proc. NWWA/API Conf. Petrol. Hydrocarbons and Org. Chem. in Ground Water: Prev., Detect. and Restor.* (Nov. 12-14, 1986, Houston, TX). pp. 709-721.

Gardner, W. H. 1986. "Water Content." In A. Klute (Ed.), *Methods of Soil Analysis, Part 1. Physical and Mineralogical Methods*, pp. 493-544. Agronomy Monograph No. 9 (2nd ed.), Amer. Soc. Agron.-Soil Sci. Soc. Amer., Madison, WI.

Hayes, D., E. C. Henry, and S. M. Testa. 1989. "A Practical Approach to Shallow Hydrocarbon Recovery." *Ground Water Monitoring Review*, (Winter): 180-185.

Kramer, J. H., S. J. Cullen, and L. G. Everett. 1992. "Vadose Zone Monitoring with the Neutron Moisture Probe." *Ground Water Monitoring Review*, (Summer): 177-187.

McWhorter, D. B. 1990. "Unsteady Radial Flow of Gas in the Vadose Zone." *J. Contaminant Hydrology*, 5: 297-314.

National Research Council (NRC). 1994. *Alternatives for Ground Water Cleanup*. National Academy of Sciences, Washington, DC.

Wilson, J. L., S. H. Conrad, W. R. Mason, W. Peplinski, and E. Hagan. 1989. *Laboratory Investigation of Residual Liquid Organics from Spills, Leaks, and the Disposal of Hazardous Wastes in Groundwater*. U.S. Environmental Protection Agency Technical Report, EPA/600/6-90/004. USEPA-RSKERL, Ada, OK.

Mechanics of Vacuum-Enhanced Recovery of Hydrocarbons

David L. Barnes and David B. McWhorter

ABSTRACT ━━

A growing body of field data demonstrates the enhancement of product recovery that can be achieved by applying a partial vacuum to recovery wells. Typical explanations for the observed improvement in performance invoke an increased slope of the cone of depression created in the water-table surface. Explanations related to water-table slope do not consider the gradient induced in the hydrocarbon by virtue of the airflow. Also, the airflow may induce a gradient in the aqueous phase that is not reflected in a water-table drawdown. The equations for steady-state flow of three immiscible fluids elucidate the fundamental mechanics of vacuum-enhanced recovery or bioslurping. Airflow to the recovery well causes hydrocarbon to migrate toward the well, independent of any gravity effects that may be created. Also, the relative permeability to hydrocarbon is affected by both water and airflow in the vicinity of the recovery well. Two critical airflow rates delineate the conditions for which only air is recovered, air and hydrocarbon are recovered, and all three phases are recovered.

INTRODUCTION

In the past few years, vacuum recovery systems have been popular for removing volatile organic compounds from the vadose zone. These systems are commonly called soil vapor extraction (SVE) systems. The use of SVE systems in the vadose zone results in a redistribution of the water (and any other liquids) contained in the soil to the extraction point. This movement of the water in the soil is due to the vacuum created in the extraction well and the resulting decrease in capillary pressure in the zone around the well (Barnes et al. 1994). The same principles that govern the flow of soil gas and water to an extraction well can be used to induce a flow of hydrocarbons to an extraction well. This process of free product removal is commonly called vacuum-enhanced liquid recovery (VELR).

As in soil vapor extraction, VELR uses extraction wells to induce an airflow through the unsaturated soil. In addition to the screen and casing of the extraction well, an inner pipe is added to remove the hydrocarbons by suction (Kittel et al. 1994). Within the literature, several case studies discuss the method of inducing a vacuum in the subsurface with extraction wells and describe removal rates achieved with this process (Baker & McWhorter 1992, Blake & Gates 1986, Blake et al. 1990, Kittel et al. 1994).

THEORY OF THREE-PHASE FLOW

Several researchers have updated the conceptual picture of a hydrocarbon pool floating on top of the groundwater table as a free product under static conditions (Farr et al. 1990, Lenhard & Parker 1990). The more accurate conceptual picture is shown in the cross section in Figure 1. Thus, instead of a pool of hydrocarbon residing on top of the water table, there is a zone that contains both hydrocarbon and water. This zone can be subdivided into a portion that contains both phases under positive pressures, and a portion in which the water is under a negative pressure and the hydrocarbon is under a positive pressure. Above this zone is a region in which air, hydrocarbon, and water exist simultaneously. Finally there is the region where only air and water are present.

In a porous medium containing three fluids, the order of wettability is water > hydrocarbon > air. Leverett (1941) proposed that the water saturation and the hydrocarbon saturation can be considered a total liquid saturation. The degree of total liquid saturation is dependent upon the capillary pressure on air-hydrocarbon interfaces, and the degree of water saturation is dependent upon the capillary pressure on water-hydrocarbon interfaces. With this assumption, the equations for the capillary pressure in a three-phase system can be written as follows:

$$h_c^{ao} = h_a - h_o , \qquad h_c^{ow} = h_o - h_w \qquad \text{(1), (2)}$$

where h_c^{ao} is the air-hydrocarbon (the superscript "o" is used to symbolize an organic liquid or hydrocarbon) capillary pressure, h_c^{ow} is the hydrocarbon-water capillary pressure, h_a is the air pressure, h_o is the hydrocarbon pressure, and h_w is the water pressure. The pressures in the above equations are expressed as equivalent heights of a vertical water column and are often referred to as pressure heads.

Currently, a common method of free product removal is to create a drawdown of water in a recovery well, causing the free product to follow the gradient created and flow into the extraction well. The fact that the hydrocarbon exists under negative pressure in the zone containing three phases restricts this volume of hydrocarbon from being removed by this technique. VELR, on the other hand, removes free product under conditions in which the wellbore pressure is less than atmospheric, thus allowing the hydrocarbon in this zone to flow into an extraction well. Focus will be given to this area of the porous media.

With the creation of a vacuum at a VELR extraction well, h_c^{ao} in a radial zone around the extraction well is decreased from the static capillary pressure that exists initially. Similarly, h_c^{ow} in this zone is reduced from the static value. We treat the vacuum pressure created by the extraction well as a drawdown of air

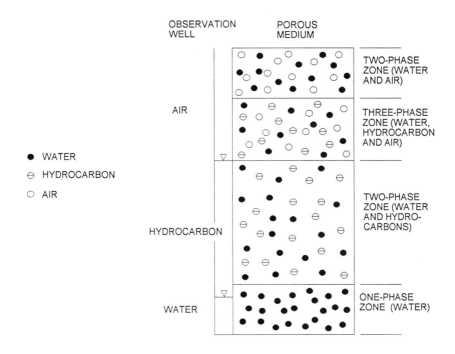

FIGURE 1. Distribution of air, hydrocarbon, and water in a porous medium and an observation well (Farr et al. 1990).

pressure. As the air-pressure drawdown is further increased at the well, a value will be reached in which h_c^{ao} will equal zero, but h_c^{ow} will still be greater than zero. At this value of air-pressure drawdown, hydrocarbon will begin to flow into the extraction well, but because h_c^{ow} is still greater than zero, water will not flow into the well. As the air-pressure drawdown at the well is further increased, a pressure will be reached in which h_c^{ow} is equal to zero. At this point both h_c^{ao} and h_c^{ow} are zero, and all three phases will flow into the well.

A horizontal layer situated in the three-phase zone is shown in Figure 2. The region outside the assumed range of effect of the extraction well is defined as the far field. We can determine the phase pressures at the boundaries by using the equations for the capillary pressure presented above and making the following assumptions: the flow is horizontal, the soil is homogeneous, a representative h_c^{ao} and h_c^{ow} in the far field for the layer under static conditions can be determined, the air drawdown is such that the soil water does not flow into the well, and the flow of the air and the hydrocarbon is steady state.

The assumption of steady-state flow requires boundary conditions that are not strictly achieved by a single, isolated well pumping from a zone of infinite extent. Nevertheless, we make this assumption under the expectation that a pseudo steady state develops, as is known to occur for isolated groundwater wells in an infinite aquifer. This assumption allows us to define a far-field condition in

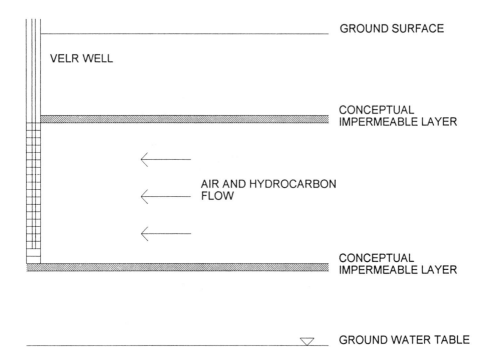

FIGURE 2. Cross section of a layered soil with a VELR extraction well.

which all three phases are in static equilibrium. If the effects of hysteresis are not considered, the far-field phase pressures can be determined by using the principles of static equilibrium, together with a known thickness of hydrocarbon in a far-field observation well.

With reference to Figure 1, the following equations can be derived for both the air-hydrocarbon and hydrocarbon-water capillary pressure heads under static conditions:

$$h_c^{ao} = \frac{\rho_o}{\rho_w} (z - T), \qquad z \geq T \qquad (3)$$

$$h_c^{ow} = z\left(1 - \frac{\rho_o}{\rho_w}\right), \qquad z \geq 0 \qquad (4)$$

where ρ_o is the density of hydrocarbon, ρ_w is the density of water, z is the elevation from the hydrocarbon-water interface in the observation well, and T is the thickness of hydrocarbon in the observation well.

If a direct connection exists between the atmosphere and the porous medium, we can assume that h_a at the far field is atmospheric pressure and is equal to zero gauge pressure. Knowledge of the air pressure, coupled with Equations 3 and 4, permits calculations of the individual phase pressures. The equations for the phase pressures at far field are shown below:

$$h_a = 0 \tag{5}$$

$$h_o = \frac{\rho_o}{\rho_w}(z - T), \qquad z \geq T \tag{6}$$

$$h_w = \frac{\rho_o}{\rho_w}T - z, \qquad z \geq T \tag{7}$$

It is emphasized that our analysis is for a layer in which the hydrocarbon is at less than atmospheric pressure. Hydrocarbon will flow to the well when the air-hydrocarbon capillary pressure at the well is zero. This condition occurs when

$$h_c^{ao}(r = \infty) \leq \Delta h_a(r_w) \tag{8}$$

where $h_c^{ao}(r = \infty)$ is the air-hydrocarbon capillary pressure in the far field and $\Delta h_a(r_w)$ is the air-pressure drawdown at the well. Thus, Equation 8 represents a condition that must be satisfied if hydrocarbon is to be pumped from the zone in question. Of course, the left side of Equation 8 is determined through use of Equation 3, with z being taken as a representative elevation for the layer in question.

While any air-pressure drawdown that satisfies the above inequality will ensure a pressure gradient in the hydrocarbon, it is desirable to create a maximum gradient in the hydrocarbon without incurring simultaneous water flow. Thus, the range of air-pressure drawdowns that will result in hydrocarbon flow, but no water flow, from the layer in question is given by:

$$h_c^{ao}(r = \infty) < \Delta h_a(r_w) \leq \frac{\rho_o}{\rho_w}T - z \tag{9}$$

where z is, as before, a representative elevation for the layer in question.

If the air-pressure drawdown at the well is such that h_c^{ow} is zero, but the flowrate of water is still zero, then this is the point of incipient flow of water into the well. At this point, the air pressure at the well is the minimum (maximum drawdown) that can be obtained and have only air and hydrocarbon flowing into the well. The air pressure at this point is equal to the water pressure in the system. The maximum air pressure (minimum drawdown) at the well that is required to obtain flow of air and hydrocarbon is the point in which h_c^{ow} at the well is equal to h_c^{ow} in the far field. The air pressure at the well required to obtain hydrocarbon flow into the well is the sum of h_c^{ow} in the far field and the water pressure. These maximum and minimum air pressures at the well show that there is an operating air pressure at the well in which the range between the maximum and minimum values is equal to the far-field h_c^{ow}.

Beginning with Darcy's law and using the assumptions outlined above, the flow equations can be derived. The resulting flow equations are as follows:

$$Q_t = \frac{2\pi r b k \rho_w g}{\mu_a} \frac{k_{ra} f}{f - F} \frac{dh_c^{ao}}{dr} \tag{10}$$

$$Q_t = \frac{2\pi r b k \rho_w g}{\mu_o F} k_{ro} \frac{dh_c^{ow}}{dr} \tag{11}$$

where Q_t is the total flowrate (flowrate of air and hydrocarbon), b is the thickness of the horizontal layer, k is the intrinsic permeability, ρ_w is the density of water, g is the gravity, μ is the viscosity of air (a) or hydrocarbon (o), k_r is the relative permeability of either air or hydrocarbon, and r is the radius from the well. In the above equations, F is the fractional flow function, which is the ratio of the hydrocarbon flowrate to the total flowrate as is indicated in Equation 12. The expression for f is given by Equation 13.

$$F = \frac{Q_o}{Q_t}, \qquad f = \left(1 + \frac{k_{ra}\mu_o}{k_{ro}\mu_a}\right)^{-1} \tag{12, 13}$$

In Equations 10 and 11, k_{ra}, k_{ro} and f depend upon both h_c^{ao} and h_c^{ow}. Thus, the solution of these equations requires that the relationship between h_c^{ao} and h_c^{ow} be known in the region of flow. By equating Equations 10 and 11 this relationship can be determined and is as follows:

$$\frac{dh_c^{ow}}{dh_c^{ao}} = \frac{\mu_o k_{ra}}{\mu_a k_{ro}} \frac{f F}{(f - F)} \tag{14}$$

Note that Equation 14 predicts that the relationship between h_c^{ow} and h_c^{ao} does not explicitly depend upon radius, r. We can now rewrite Equations 10 and 11 as follows:

$$Q_t = \frac{2\pi b k \rho_w g}{\ln(r_e/r_w)\mu_a} \int_{h_c^{ao}(r_w)}^{h_c^{ao}(r_e)} \frac{k_{ra} f}{f - F} dh_c^{ao} \tag{15}$$

$$Q_t = \frac{2\pi b k \rho_w g}{\ln(r_e/r_w)\mu_o F} \int_{h_c^{ow}(r_w)}^{h_c^{ow}(r_e)} k_{ro} dh_c^{ow} \tag{16}$$

where r_e is the radius to the far field and r_w is the radius of the well.

Applications of the flow equations presented above require a functional relationship between capillary pressure and saturation for the three phases. The two most common relationships of this type are the Brooks-Corey equations (Brooks & Corey 1964) and the van Genuchten equations (van Genuchten 1980).

Because the three-phase relative permeability relationships are all available in the literature, we chose to use the van Genuchten equations in this paper. Parker et al. (1987) extended the use of the van Genuchten equations to cases in which three phases are present. The equations use the assumption that Leverett (1941) hypothesized, which was presented above.

By dividing Equations 15 and 16 through by the respective constants h_α^{ao} and h_α^{ow}, which are the van Genuchten curve fitting parameters for the saturation equations, we can now normalize the flow equations as follows:

$$\hat{Q}_t = \frac{Q_t \mu_a}{bk\rho_w gh_\alpha^{ao}} = \frac{2\pi}{\ln(r_e/r_w)} \int_{\hat{h}_c^{ao}(r_w)}^{\hat{h}_c^{ao}(r_e)} \frac{k_{ra} f}{f - F} d\hat{h}_c^{ao} \tag{17}$$

$$\hat{Q}_t^* = \frac{Q_t \mu_o}{bk\rho_w gh_\alpha^{ow}} = \frac{2\pi}{\ln(r_e/r_w)} \int_{\hat{h}_c^{ow}(r_w)}^{\hat{h}_c^{ow}(r_e)} k_{ro} d\hat{h}_c^{ow} \tag{18}$$

$$\frac{d\hat{h}_c^{ow}}{d\hat{h}_c^{ao}} = \frac{h_\alpha^{ao}\mu_o k_{ra}}{h_\alpha^{ow}\mu_a k_{ro}} \frac{f F}{(f - F)} \tag{19}$$

where $\hat{h}_c^{ao}$ and $\hat{h}_c^{ow}$ are now the normalized air-hydrocarbon and hydrocarbon-water capillary pressures, respectively. In Equation 18, $\hat{Q}_t^*$ is not equal to $\hat{Q}_t$ in Equation 17. This inequality is due to the normalization process for each individual equation. The air drawdown can be normalized by dividing it by the water pressure in the system. Because the water pressure is constant and the maximum air drawdown at the well is the water pressure, the normalized air-pressure drawdown will range from zero to unity. We will denote the normalized air-pressure drawdown by $\hat{s}_a$.

Upon the selection of F, Equation 19 is solved numerically, beginning at the known conditions in the far field. With the tabulated values of capillary pressures obtained from solving Equation 19, Equation 17 or 18 can now be solved for $\hat{Q}_t$ or for $\hat{Q}_t^*$, respectively. Knowing $\hat{h}_c^{ow}$ at the extraction well, the air pressure at the extraction well required to achieve the total flowrate can be calculated.

APPLICATION

The data required to apply the flow equation presented above are (1) the thickness of hydrocarbon in a far-field observation well (refer to Figure 1), (2) the properties of the soil and the location of the lower and upper boundaries of the horizontal layer, and (3) a representative far-field air-hydrocarbon capillary pressure and the corresponding hydrocarbon-water capillary pressure.

The use of these equations on two different systems that have horizontal layers, each containing a different volume of hydrocarbon, is illustrated below.

For both layers, the van Genuchten constant, m, is equal to 0.45, and the thickness of hydrocarbon measured from the datum in a far-field observation well is 40 cm. For the first layer (condition A) the lower boundary is at the top of the hydrocarbon body in the observation well and the upper boundary is located at 45 cm. The lower boundary of the second horizontal layer (condition B) is located at 45 cm and the upper boundary is located at 55 cm.

The determination of the representative far-field capillary pressures for each layer is done by a weighted average, with the weighting factor being the hydrocarbon effective saturation. For these systems, the representative values for $\hat{h}_c^{ao}(\infty)$ and $\hat{h}_c^{ow}(\infty)$ for condition A are 0.341 and 2.544 and for condition B are 1.297 and 2.943, respectively.

For each layer, the hydrocarbon flowrates can be determined for different air drawdowns at the well by choosing different values of F and calculating the resulting hydrocarbon flowrate. The results are shown in Figures 3 and 4.

Several observations can be made from these curves. When a large volume of hydrocarbon is contained in the system, such as in condition A, a lower value of air-pressure drawdown is required to create a hydrocarbon flow into the extraction well. We can also conclude from Figures 3 and 4 that an asymptotic value of hydrocarbon flow is reached as the normalized air-pressure drawdown approaches unity. This maximum value of hydrocarbon flow is reached at lower values of air-pressure drawdown under conditions where larger volumes of hydrocarbon exist in the porous medium, such as condition A. The fact that the hydrocarbon flowrates become asymptotic indicates that the maximum air-pressure drawdown is not required to create the maximum hydrocarbon flowrate.

In Figures 3 and 4 the curves for the airflow rates are also shown. The notable observation from these airflow curves is that in systems containing small

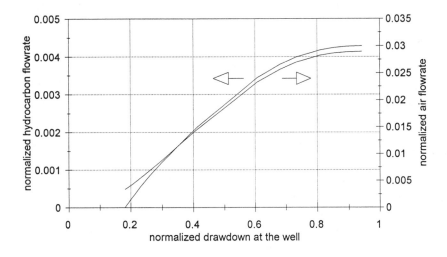

FIGURE 3. Normalized flowrates of hydrocarbon and air as a function of air drawdown for soil layer A, with a far-field $\hat{h}_c^{ao} = 0.341$ and $\hat{h}_c^{ow} = 2.544$.

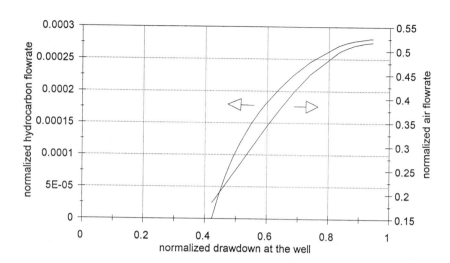

FIGURE 4. Normalized flowrates of hydrocarbon and air as a function of air drawdown for soil layer B, with a far-field $\hat{h}_c^{ao} = 1.297$ and $\hat{h}_c^{ow} = 2.943$.

amounts of hydrocarbon (condition B), the majority of the total flow (airflow plus hydrocarbon flow) is the airflow.

CONCLUSIONS

The mathematical model presented above is a first step toward determining the hydrocarbon removal rates from the portion of the porous medium in which all three phases are present (air, hydrocarbon, and water). VELR is also able to remove hydrocarbon in the region containing only hydrocarbon and water. In this region a two-phase flow model can be used to determine the hydrocarbon and water flowrates into an extraction well. Limits on the length of this manuscript prevent us from extending the analysis to this important zone.

Using the three-phase model presented above and an appropriate two-phase model, the process of obtaining the overall free product removal rates would involve determining the contributions to hydrocarbon flow from individual soil layers assigned to the profile. The results from each layer would then be combined to obtain the overall removal rate from the system.

REFERENCES

Baker, R. S., and D. B. McWhorter. 1992. "Vacuum Enhanced Free Product Recovery: Model and Field Test." Presented at the Symposium on Multiphase Fluid Flow and Chemical Transport, Soil Science Society of America Annual Meeting, Minneapolis, MN.

Barnes, D. L., D. B. McWhorter, and R. C. Ward. 1994. "Optimum Conditions for Utilizing Soil Vapor Extraction." Presented at the University Council on Water Resources Annual Meeting and Environmental Restoration Conference, Big Sky, MT.

Blake, S. B., and M. M. Gates. 1986. "Vacuum Enhanced Hydrocarbon Recovery: A Case Study." *Proceedings of Petroleum Hydrocarbons and Organic Chemicals in Groundwater: Prevention, Detection and Restoration*, pp. 709-721. Water Well Journal Publishing Company, Dublin, OH.

Blake, S., B. Hockman, and M. Martin. 1990. "Applications of Vacuum Dewatering Techniques to Hydrocarbon Remediation." *Proceedings of Petroleum Hydrocarbons and Organic Chemicals in Groundwater: Prevention, Detection and Restoration*, pp. 211-225. Water Well Journal Publishing Company, Dublin, OH.

Brooks, R. H., and A. T. Corey. 1964. *Hydraulic Properties of Porous Media*. Colorado State University Hydrology Paper No. 3. Colorado State University, Fort Collins, CO.

Farr, A. M., R. J. Houghtalen, and D. B. McWhorter. 1990. "Volume Estimation of Light Nonaqueous Phase Liquids in Porous Media." *Ground Water* 28(1): 48-56.

Kittel, J. A., R. E. Hinchee, R. Hoeppel, and R. Miller. 1994. "Bioslurping — Vacuum-Enhanced Free-Product Recovery Coupled with Bioventing: A Case Study." *Petroleum Hydrocarbons and Organic Chemicals in Groundwater: Prevention, Detection and Restoration*, pp.225-269. Houston, TX.

Lenhard, R. J., and J. C. Parker. 1990. "Estimation of Free Hydrocarbon Volume from Fluid Levels in Monitoring Wells." *Ground Water* 28(1): 57-67.

Leverett, M. C. 1941. "Capillary Behavior in Porous Solids." *Transactions AIME, Petroleum Engineering Division* 142: 152-169.

Parker, J. C., R. J. Lenhard, and T. Kuppusamy. 1987. "A Parametric Model for Constitutive Properties Governing Multiphase Flow in Porous Media." *Water Resources Research* 23(4): 618-624.

van Genuchten, M. T. 1980. "A Closed-Form Equation for Predicting the Hydraulic Conductivity of Unsaturated Soils." *Soil Science Society of America Journal* 44: 892-898.

Bioslurping Applied to a Gasoline and Diesel Spill in Fractured Rock

Mark Connolly, Bruce Gibbs, and Ben Keet

ABSTRACT ━━━━━━━━━━━━━━━━━━━━━━━━━━━━━

Leaks from two adjoining underground storage tanks released product into fractured basalt rock, beneath an urban industrial site upgradient from a major stream. Preliminary investigations indicated a free product plume of approximate dimensions 80 m by 35 m. A bioslurping system was designed and installed for economical and effective recovery of free product and removal of the associated subsurface vapor. The successfully operating system uses a liquid ring vacuum pump (LRVP) to extract vapor, product, and water in the form of an emulsion from 11 recovery wells and pumps the mixture directly from the LRVP to a liquid/air separator cyclone. The vapor-laden air extracted is passed to a biofilter for treatment. The liquid phase passes through a coalescing-plate oil/water separator where the bulk of product is removed. Outlet water from the oil/water separator still contains product in emulsion, which is removed by passing the outlet water through a custom-designed coalescing filter. Product collected here is pumped back to the oil/water separator and from there to storage tanks. Water is recirculated to cool and lubricate the LRVP, and excess water is passed through the biofilter before discharge to the sewer. Bioslurping has been an effective and economical technology for recovery of product and vapors. On this site, the entire recovery network is below ground level to allow total site access to heavy construction vehicles.

INTRODUCTION

Leaks from two adjoining underground storage tanks (one gasoline, one diesel) released an estimated 15,000 to 25,000 L of product into fractured basalt rock with an uneven water table at approximately 5 m depth. The leak occurred at an urban industrial site, 100 m upgradient from a major stream. Preliminary investigations indicated a free product plume of approximate dimensions 80 m by 35 m, but no leakage of contamination to the stream.

Floating product was present in nine wells, and laboratory analyses of groundwater samples from other wells showed high levels of benzene, toluene, ethylbenzene, and xylenes (BTEX). Individual BTEX compound concentrations varied from well to well, and spanned the range from <5 µg/L to >7,000 µg/L. The apparent thickness of floating product in the wells varied from <1 cm to >100 cm. The product thickness varied from well to well across the plume. Although a part of this variation can be explained by well location relative to the spill source, it is likely that product migration pathways are largely determined by the uneven distribution of cracks and fissures in the fractured basalt bedrock present across the site.

To meet the requirements for the economical and effective recovery of free product and removal of vapor, and the removal/remediation of contaminated groundwater, a bioslurping system was designed and installed. This paper describes the design, installation, and operation of that system.

OPERATING PRINCIPLES AND SYSTEM DESIGN

The bioslurping system installed at the site has three main sets of components: recovery wells; liquid/vapor and oil/water separation components; and the water and vapor treatment biofilter.

The bioslurping system operates under the principle that each well is pumped by means of an adjustable-length spear, sealed against the upper well casing by O-ring seals. Liquid and vapor removed from recovery wells are separated in a liquid/air separator. The vapor then passes through a biofilter prior to discharge to the atmosphere. The liquid is further treated to separate product from water, and the water is reused to cool and lubricate the recovery pump. Excess water passes through a biofilter system prior to discharge to the sewer. The system setup is illustrated in Figure 1.

Recovery Wells

The 11 recovery wells are constructed of 50-mm polyvinyl chloride (PVC) casing, slotted above and below the water table. The spacing of recovery wells was determined on the basis of air permeability testing on the well network installed during the site investigation. The location of individual wells was a compromise between the optimum well network and site access limitations resulting from building and machinery locations.

Each recovery well is pumped by means of an adjustable-length spear, sealed against the upper well casing by a brass piston with O-ring seals. The depth to which each spear penetrates its well is adjustable by manually sliding the spear within the well casing. The well design is shown in Figure 2.

In operation, the groundwater/product level in the well is rapidly pumped down to the level of the spear inlet. Once this condition is reached, the spear sucks ("slurps") air and vapor, thereby placing the well under a partial vacuum.

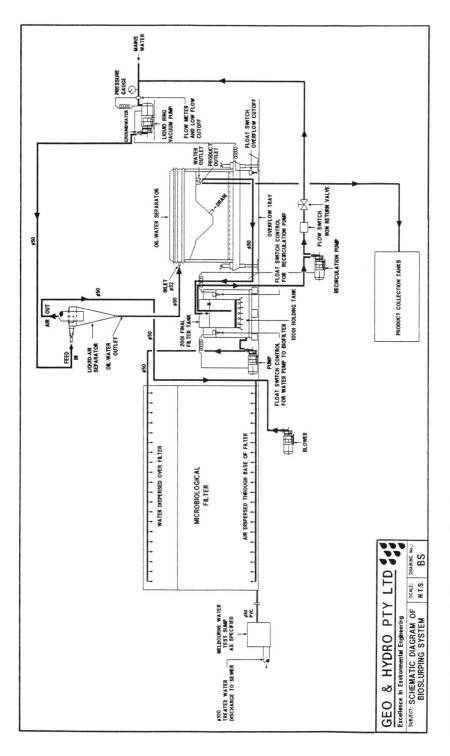

FIGURE 1. Schematic layout and main components of the bioslurping system.

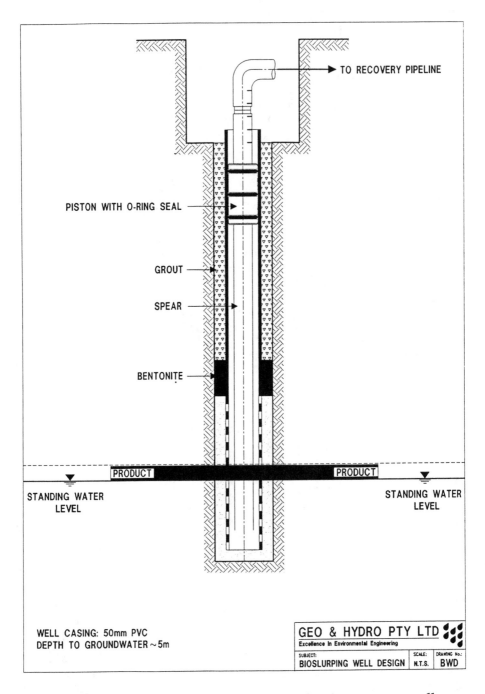

FIGURE 2. Design and components of the bioslurping recovery well.

This partial vacuum enhances the movement of contaminated groundwater and free product into the well. It also promotes air movement through the subsurface. On this site, because of the concrete cover over much of the site, the hard-packed gravel elsewhere, and the restricted permeability of the fractured basalt substrate, conditions for oxygen replenishment and hence biodegradation are not optimal. For budget reasons, there has been no in-ground monitoring of O_2/CO_2 levels. However CO_2 concentrations at the vapor outlet of the liquid/vapor separator were measured to be >10,000 ppm, indicating the possible presence of increased biological activity.

Liquid/Vapor and Oil/Water Separation

The wells are pumped using the LRVP, which ensures each well is maintained under negative pressure. The recovery pipe network, the LRVP, and the other system components were designed to handle a recovered liquid flow of up to approximately 12 L/min. This figure was based on pump testing of investigation wells and air permeability testing. In operation the recovery rate is 4 to 5 L/min.

The LRVP requires a constant water supply of approximately 15 L/min for cooling and lubrication. This water combines in the LRVP with output from the wells to yield approximately 20 L/min of well-mixed water, product, and vapor. This output is pumped directly from the LRVP to a centrifugal liquid/vapor separator. The resulting vapor passes through a biofilter before being released to the atmosphere.

The liquid output from the liquid/air separator comprises an emulsion of product and water. This emulsion flows under gravity to a conventional design coalescing-plate oil/water separator, which coalesces product droplets of about 20 µ size or greater. This product feeds under gravity to storage tanks to await collection and re-refining.

Water output from the oil/water separator (still containing oil in <20 µ droplets) then passes under gravity through a coalescing filter system of three layers, each comprising one layer of medium-grade chopped fiberglass matting (0.2 cm thick), medium-grade steel wool (2 cm thick), and surgical cotton wool (0.2 cm thick). The filter system design was selected after bench trials of numerous combinations of materials and thicknesses. The system trades off flowrate against filtering efficiency, with cotton wool providing high coalescing efficiency but rapidly decreasing the flowrate as the cotton layer thickness increases.

The coalescing filter demulsification system is constructed in a 200-L tank (a modified fuel drum) suspended within a 1,000-L holding tank. After passing through the filter, water flows through outlets in the base of the filter tank to the holding tank. This water is then recirculated using a simple solenoid and flowswitch-controlled system to supply the 15 L/min required for lubrication and cooling of the LRVP. Excess water is limited to about 4.5 L/min recovered from wells, and is pumped, under float-switch control, from the holding tank to the top of the biofilter. On exiting the biofilter this water passes through a sand filter of approximately 40 L sand volume before discharge to the sewer. Product that accumulates in the filter tank and holding tank is pumped back to the oil/water separator and from there to the product storage tanks.

Water and Vapor Treatment Biofilter

Water and vapor are treated in a single biofilter of approximately 17 m^3 capacity prior to discharge to the sewer and atmosphere, respectively. The biofilter consists of layers of peat moss and mulched timber suspended on steel mesh racks and separated by layers of volcanic scoria. The top layer of the biofilter is graded mineral sand (monitoring well packing sand). A blower continuously supplies fresh air to the base of the biofilter.

Vapor from the liquid/air separator is injected to the base of the biofilter, where it is dispersed through five rows of slotted PVC pipe running along the length of the biofilter base. This vapor passes through 1.75 m vertical thickness of biofilter material before release to the atmosphere. Air monitoring immediately above the biofilter has detected no emission of volatiles.

Water treated in the biofilter consists of water in excess of the 15 L/min required for cooling and lubrication of the LRVP. This water is dispersed over the sand surface of the biofilter through four rows of slotted PVC pipe running the length of the biofilter and supported above it. The flowrate of water to the biofilter averages approximately 4.5 L/min. This water, containing remnant hydrocarbons, filters under gravity through the 1.75-m thickness of the biofilter before draining to the sewer. The water resides in the biofilter about 60 min. Regular sampling and analysis of output water gives nondetect results for total petroleum hydrocarbons (TPH) and BTEX, and compliance results for dissolved solids, pH, and other parameters for which monitoring is required by the discharge authority.

SYSTEM PERFORMANCE

From system startup in January 1994 to November 1994, 3,900 L of product have been recovered. Although the system is designed to run continuously, there have been numerous shutdown periods to enable modifications to the system. These modifications have included installation of a 1,000-L demulsification tank; system changes to enable reuse of LRVP cooling water; installation of larger product collection tanks; changeover of the liquid/vapor separator from a cylindrical model to a conical model; installation of a sand filter for final filtration of water before discharge to the sewer.

The average product recovery rate during operation is 1.4 L/h. This rate has varied from 0.78 L/h to 3.51 L/h. The highest recovery is obtained immediately after system startup, and during periods of low water table (that is, during dry weather conditions).

The above product volumes relate only to liquid-phase recovered product. They do not include vapor-phase product separated in the liquid/air separator and directed to the biofilter system. Nor do these volumes take into account any petroleum hydrocarbons that may be degraded in situ as a result of the vacuum enhancement of subsurface aeration.

CONCLUSION

Work to date on this project has concentrated on the practical aspects of system design, installation, trouble shooting, and product recovery. With the system now in continuous operation, the next phase (subject to client approval and budget availability) will involve investigation of the environment created by the bioslurping process: specifically, the contribution of vapor recovery to total product recovery to enable mass balance calculation; ongoing monitoring of operating vacuum pressures; and assessment of the contribution of bioslurping-enhanced biodegradation to product removal. System design and installation costs were approximately U.S. $80,000, and operating expenses have totalled about U.S. $40,000 per year, including the system modifications discussed above.

Vacuum-Enhanced Pumping to Improve DNAPL Recovery in a Confined Aquifer

H. James Reisinger, Stewart A. Mountain,
Perry Hubbard, Jr., Paul Montney, and Keith Carlson

ABSTRACT

Dense, nonaqueous-phase liquids (DNAPLs) in the form of chlorinated solvents have been used in various phases of U.S. industry for many years. As a result of their use prior to the advent of standardized handling and disposal regulations, they have found their way into the environment at many active and inactive industrial sites. Because of their unique physiochemical characteristics, DNAPLs present unique challenges in the site remediation process. At one such site in the northeast United States, dichloromethane, or methylene chloride, entered a confined aquifer from underground storage tanks (USTs) and became subject to environmental remediation. The initial remediation approach was conventional groundwater extraction and treatment via physical separation and diffused aeration. The expansion of the dichloromethane plume resulted in the need for improved DNAPL recovery and dissolved-phase hydraulic control. Through conceptual analysis and pilot testing, vacuum-enhanced dual-phase recovery was determined to be a feasible remedial alternative. Vacuum-enhanced recovery, using a custom-designed pump, was implemented in this confined aquifer, increasing the volume of methylene chloride impacted groundwater recovered by a factor of nearly three, and hydraulic control of the plume was realized.

INTRODUCTION

At a northeastern U.S. site active since 1890, solvents used in an industrial process, including DNAPLs, were stored in steel USTs (Figure 1). These solvents included acetone and dichloromethane (a.k.a. methylene chloride [MECL]), a volatile DNAPL with a specific gravity of 1.33. Solvent releases from these tanks have impacted the upper (unconfined) and lower (confined) aquifers at the site (Figure 2). After more than two years of remediation, it became necessary to

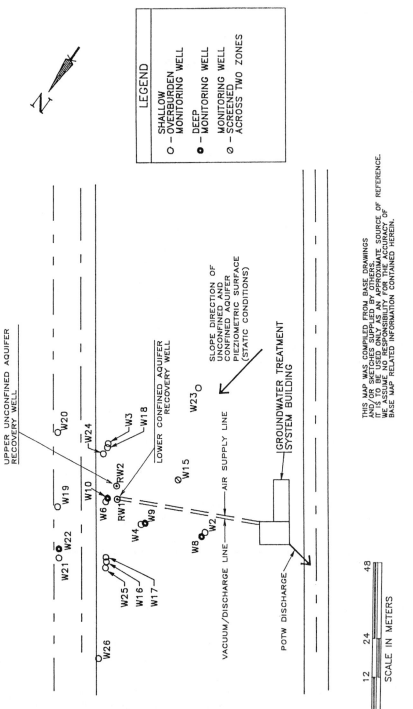

FIGURE 1. Site configuration with monitoring well locations.

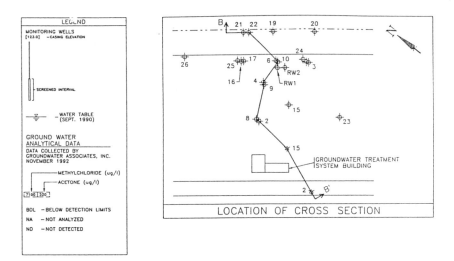

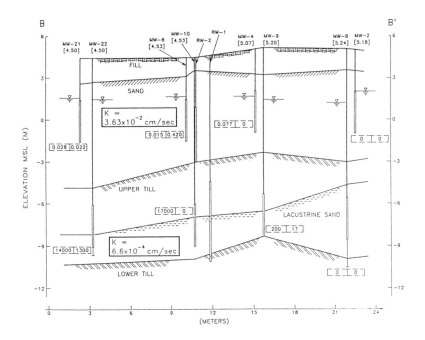

FIGURE 2. Downgradient cross section.

improve dissolved-phase MECL recovery, to achieve hydraulic control of the lower confined aquifer, and to implement improvements to the existing ground-water extraction and treatment system.

The site's Pleistocene unconsolidated sediments consist of five distinct hydro-geologic units: an upper fill layer, an upper glacial outwash sand aquifer, an upper confining bed of glacial till, a lower lacustrine fine sand aquifer with interfingering till, and a silt and clay lower confining unit (GWA 1992). Reported stratigraphic unit thicknesses, hydraulic conductivities, well construction and piezometric elevations, and dissolved-phase MECL concentrations are displayed on Figure 2. Dissolved-phase MECL was detected at a concentration near or exceeding the compound's aqueous solubility of 20,000 mg/L at 20°C (Verschueren 1983) in the confined aquifer near source well MW-10 and downgradient at well MW-22 (Figures 1 and 2). Acetone was detected at much lower concentrations than MECL.

Aquifer testing performed in 1990 showed that hydraulic control and concurrent dissolved-phase plume capture could be maintained in the unconfined and confined aquifers if withdrawal rates of 19 to 23 LPM and 1.9 to 3.8 LPM, respectively, could be maintained. The recovery system, consisting of an electric submersible pump in well RW-2 (unconfined aquifer) and a bottom-filling pneumatic pump in well RW-1 (confined aquifer), was activated in May 1991. The treatment system consisted of a DNAPL phase separator for RW-1 and the treatment of dissolved-phase MECL and acetone by diffused aeration. Volatilized solvent from RW-1's influent tank was processed through a halocarbon refrigeration vapor recovery unit; treated effluent was discharged to local publicly owned treatment works (POTW) under permit.

At system startup (May 1991), MECL concentrations in samples from the unconfined and confined aquifers were 6 mg/L and 13,000 mg/L, respectively; withdrawal rates were 11.3 and 1.9 LPM from the unconfined and confined aquifers, respectively. These pumping rates, however, could not be maintained because precipitated iron and iron bacteria slime had encrusted the well screens. RW-2 was pumping at 5.7 LPM and RW-1 was pumping at 1.1 LPM in August 1992 (GWA 1992). Equilibrium pumping rates of less than 1.1 LPM for the confined aquifer had been regularly observed. The initial groundwater recovery operation was somewhat successful in maintaining hydraulic control in the unconfined aquifer, but dissolved-phase MECL in the confined aquifer continued to migrate northeast toward MW-22 (Figure 1).

DESIGN APPROACH

Vacuum-enhanced recovery was considered the most feasible and cost-effective approach to improve hydraulic containment and remediation of the dissolved-phase MECL plume. The application of moderate vacuum (34 to 51 kPa) at a low permeability site in Georgia has improved groundwater recovery by 300% above that predicted from aquifer testing information (Reisinger et al. 1993). In a groundwater system, total head (h_t) is generally considered as the elevation head (z) plus the pressure head h_p. During groundwater recovery, the total head is reduced as water is withdrawn and the water level in the well decreases. The decline in water level steepens the hydraulic gradient between the well and the surrounding aquifer and increases flow in accordance with Darcy's law, where Q = KIA. Applying vacuum to the well also reduces the pressure head component and further steepens the hydraulic gradient between the aquifer and the well, which results in enhanced well recharge. Therefore, a vacuum-enhanced system reduces the number of extraction points necessary for hydraulic control and remediation of an impacted aquifer.

A vacuum-enhanced pumping regime was envisioned for this site; a high vacuum would be applied to the well head; and a downhole pump, powered by either compressed air or electricity, would lift the impacted water from the well to the treatment system. A downhole pump, rather than direct vacuum lift, would be required because the total discharge head would exceed 13.7 m; also, the formation was confined, thereby precluding vapor withdrawal and air entrainment, which lowers the fluid specific gravity. Furthermore, the well headspace would be sealed under high vacuum, and atmospheric pressure would not assist groundwater discharge from the well, unlike typical shallow groundwater (i.e., <8 m) bioslurper applications open to the vadose atmosphere. Optimization modeling, using increased transmissivity values, simulated a vacuum-enhanced recovery system's operation over 6 years; it predicted substantially improved hydraulic containment and dissolved-phase plume remediation over conventional pumping.

A pilot test was performed to determine the degree to which vacuum application at RW-1 would improve groundwater recovery. The pilot also tested the existing pneumatic pump and a submersible pump under the high vacuum and under the chemically aggressive environment in RW-1. A high vacuum (34 to 68 kPa) was applied through a sealed wellhead in RW-1 using a liquid ring pump. The submersible pump could not achieve complete drawdown in RW-1 because the net positive suction head available at the pump intake was insufficient due to the vacuum applied to the well. The renovated pneumatic pump obtained a similar result. An alternative pumping concept was explored to enable complete drawdown and to alleviate the frequent and troublesome fouling inherent in the existing pneumatic pump and discharge piping.

The pilot test measured atmospheric (nonenhanced) recharge to RW-1 to be 1.13 LPM and vacuum-enhanced recharge at 68 kPa vacuum to be 3.13 LPM, a 276% increase. A prototype airlift pump system with high scouring and low fouling potential that could operate under high vacuum with drawdown within 0.3 m of the pump intake was then successfully tested. A full-scale vacuum-environment airlift pump (VEAP) was then custom-designed and built. The design focused on achieving an airtight seal with the wellhead, filling to near the pump intake under high vacuum, discharging up to 4 LPM from a well depth of 12 m, resisting clogging and corrosion, and being capable of in situ steaming or acid wash. Figure 3 provides a schematic diagram of the VEAP developed for RW-1.

RESULTS OF VACUUM ENHANCEMENT

The VEAP was installed to a depth of 13 m in RW-1 in February 1993. The integrated liquid ring pump was rated for 98 kPa vacuum and a 125 actual m^3

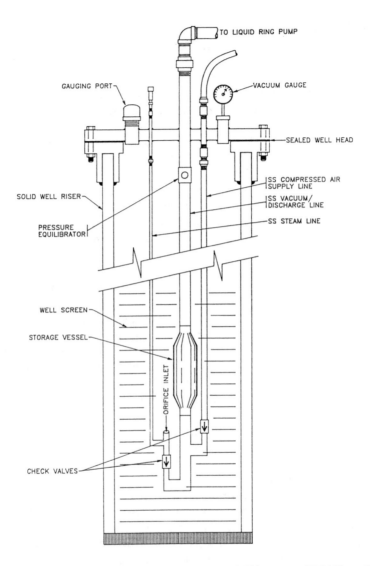

FIGURE 3. Schematic of vacuum environment airlift pump (VEAP) and recovery well configuration (not to scale).

per hour maximum airflow and drew its seal water from the RW-1 treatment tank. A nonsubmerged pressure equilibrator, plumbed in the 2.5-cm discharge/vacuum line, achieved pressure equalization (Figure 3). Maximum well recharge was achieved by maintaining the highest average vacuum within the well. Maximum pumping rate was achieved, in part, by maintaining high average vacuum within the vacuum extraction/water discharge pipe. The initial pumping strategy called for long refill (air evacuation) and long discharge (airlift) cycles. This created large negative pressure fluctuations in the discharge line and in the well headspace. Short cycling provided the best combination of well draw-down, well recharge, pumping rate, and pump efficiency (the lowest ratio of air consumption to pumping rate).

The vacuum-enhanced recovery system now continuously provides 68 to 71 kPa vacuum at RW-1. The VEAP system has resulted in a recharge/pumping rate of 2.4 to 6.8 LPM, a two to sixfold increase over the 0.94 to 1.13 LPM achieved using nonvacuum-enhanced recovery (Figure 4). The VEAP operates to create an equilibrium drawdown of 7 to 8 m below static water level, corre-sponding to a depth of 10.5 to 11 m below the top of the well casing. Com-pressed air delivery at 275 kPa and air consumption are similar to those in the former pump system, averaging 8.5 to 10 standard m³ per hour. Lift from the dewatered depth is being achieved through a combination of (1) high vacuum in the discharge pipe that reduces the lift head required; (2) a flow-inducing pressure differential to the pump; (3) air entrainment during groundwater dis-charge that effectively lowers the specific gravity of the fluid, reducing discharge head requirements; and (4) the compressed air acting as a pneumatic piston to deliver the groundwater up the discharge piping to the treatment system.

Implementation of the vacuum and VEAP at RW-1 has vastly improved hydraulic control and concurrent capture of any remaining DNAPL and the dissolved-phase MECL plume. Average drawdown in a nearby monitoring well, MW-10, has increased 1 m (> 100%), and the average drawdown in downgradient well MW-22 has increased by more than 0.3 m (> 100%). The improved draw-down in MW-22 indicates that downgradient hydraulic control of the plume has improved. Figure 5 illustrates this by comparing the confined aquifer's poten-tiometric levels among three conditions: static (no pumping), nonenhanced pump-ing, and vacuum-enhanced pumping. Figure 4 illustrates that two to threefold increases in dissolved-phase MECL recovery have occurred since vacuum-enhanced recovery was implemented in March 1994, despite substantial improve-ments in well RW-1 water quality.

CONCLUSIONS

Vacuum-enhanced groundwater recovery applied to a single recovery well has improved dissolved-phase MECL capture and has significantly improved hydraulic control within a confined aquifer. Continuously applying a high vacuum (68 to 71 kPa) at a sealed wellhead has improved average groundwater recharge and withdrawal. A special pumping strategy, which used vacuum equilibration and short, compressed air pulses, was required to dewater the confined aquifer. The VEAP has operated without substantial fouling, has been steam-cleaned in situ, and has improved drawdown near the source and in a heavily impacted downgradient well. Continued operation and optimization of the vacuum-enhanced recovery system has led to improved hydraulic control and a large increase in mass removal of DNAPL through accelerated capture of the dissolved-phase MECL plume.

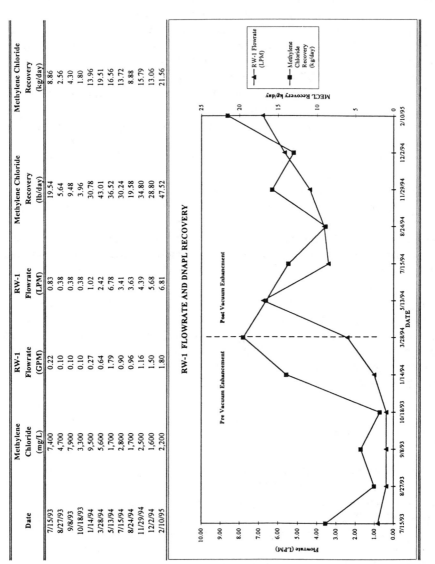

Date	Methylene Chloride (mg/L)	RW-1 Flowrate (GPM)	RW-1 Flowrate (LPM)	Methylene Chloride Recovery (lb/day)	Methylene Chloride Recovery (kg/day)
7/15/93	7,400	0.22	0.83	19.54	8.86
8/27/93	4,700	0.10	0.38	5.64	2.56
9/8/93	7,900	0.10	0.38	9.48	4.30
10/18/93	3,300	0.10	0.38	3.96	1.80
1/14/94	9,500	0.27	1.02	30.78	13.96
3/28/94	5,600	0.64	2.42	43.01	19.51
5/13/94	1,700	1.79	6.78	36.52	16.56
7/15/94	2,800	0.90	3.41	30.24	13.72
8/24/94	1,700	0.96	3.63	19.58	8.88
11/29/94	2,500	1.16	4.39	34.80	15.79
12/2/94	1,600	1.50	5.68	28.80	13.06
2/10/95	2,200	1.80	6.81	47.52	21.56

FIGURE 4.   Well RW-1 DNAPL recovery data.

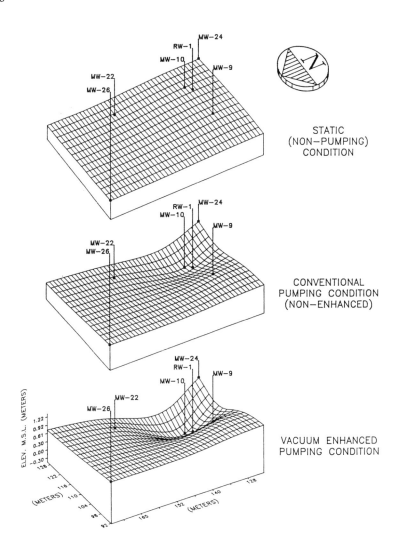

FIGURE 5. Three-dimensional plot of potentiometric surface, among static, conventional pumping, and vacuum-enhanced pumping conditions.

REFERENCES

Ground Water Associates, Inc. (GWA). 1992. *Ground Water Modeling of a Glacial Sediment Aquifer System, Georgia-Pacific Corporation, Newark, New Jersey.* Bridgewater, NJ.

Reisinger, H. J., P. Hubbard, Jr., S. A. Mountain, and C. W. Brigham. 1993. "Integrated Site Remediation Using High Vacuum Application to Address Ground-Water Extraction, Soil Venting, and In Situ Biodegradation." In U.S. Environmental Protection Agency, Region IV, *Groundwater Remediation Stabilization Conference Manual.* U.S. EPA, Atlanta, GA.

Verschueren, K. 1983. *Handbook of Environmental Data or Organic Chemicals*, 2nd ed. Van Nostrand Reinhold Company, New York, NY.

Bioslurping Technology Applications at Naval Middle Distillate Fuel Remediation Sites

Ronald E. Hoeppel, Jeffrey A. Kittel, Frederick E. Goetz, Robert E. Hinchee, and James E. Abbott

ABSTRACT

Bioslurping technology, a combination of bioventing and vacuum-enhanced free-product recovery of light, nonaqueous-phase liquid (LNAPL), has been employed at Fallon Naval Air Station (NAS), Nevada, for over 2 years and was initiated at Marine Corps Base Hawaii (MCBH) and a radar station near Hofn, Iceland. These sites have low-volatility fuels on the groundwater table in low- to medium-permeability soils. LNAPL recovery rates from 48 wells in silty fine sand to clay loam profiles at Fallon have ranged from 57 to 227 L/day (15 to 60 gal/day), with an average of 170 L/day (45 gal/day), at 10 to 30 cm of mercury (0.13 to 0.40 atmosphere) vacuum. Mass discharge from the bioslurper system for LNAPL and vapor averaged 97% and 2.7%, respectively, with an average soil gas extraction rate of 0.024 m^3/min (50 cfm). Based on periodic soil gas analyses from 90 isolated soil gas sampling points in the vadose zone of the treatment plot, bioslurping appeared to satisfy O_2 limitations in the contaminated soil profile. Despite no apparent O_2 limitation for fuel biodegradation, low oxygen utilization rates were observed while performing in situ respiration tests following system shutdown. Preliminary in situ respirometry, soil gas, laboratory microcosm, stable carbon isotope, and soil characterization data indicate that both a low fuel surface area to volume ratio and bacterial cell damage may be involved in the observed low LNAPL bioemulsification and biodegradation rates.

INTRODUCTION

The primary purpose of bioventing is to promote in situ aerobic biodegradation of organic contaminants, especially low volatility fuels, rather than to vent organic vapors to ground surface collection or treatment systems. Oxygen is transported rapidly through water-unsaturated soils, including many with low water permeability, when low positive or negative pressures are exerted on subsurface soil pores as a result of low-volume soil gas extraction or air injection (Hoeppel et al., 1991; Hinchee, 1993). However, factors other than oxygen limitation can impede biodegradation of petroleum hydrocarbon compounds in the vadose zone at specific sites. Excessive LNAPL concentrations in soils can greatly limit biodegradation rates, despite the presence of significant bioactive aerobic microorganisms (Kittel et al. 1994a; *Biotreatment News* 1994). Bury and Miller (1993) summarized the interactions between LNAPL and commercial surfactants or biosurfactants. The general consensus is that excessive immiscible hydrocarbons can limit the emulsifying and solubilizing action of hydrocarbon-degrading microorganisms, resulting in greatly reduced degradation rates.

Many field sites with fuel contamination have mobile LNAPL residing on the water table and immobile LNAPL in the capillary fringe. In such cases bioremediation of fuel can be a slow process, not only because LNAPL dispersion, bioemulsification, and solubilization are impeded, but also because oxygen diffusion rates through capillary fringe soils are limited by water and fuel liquid ganglia. This is especially true in fine-grained soils. Bioslurping is a new in situ technology that teams bioventing with vacuum-assisted free-phase fuel recovery to promote biodegradation in the vadose zone while simultaneously recovering free product from the water table and capillary fringe soil pores. This dual treatment is promoted by pulling a low to medium vacuum (0.2 to 0.7 atmospheres) on recovery wells, through an unslotted open-ended "slurper tube" that is positioned near the fuel-groundwater interface. This vacuum pulls atmospheric oxygen into the unsaturated soil profile, thus promoting aerobic biodegradation, while also creating a pressure gradient in the saturated soils. The negative pressure developed near the slurping well pulls fuel and fuel-water mixtures into the well, probably from both the free-fuel zone and capillary fringe.

Unlike conventional dual pumping, which relies primarily on a vertical hydraulic gradient (cone of depression in the groundwater table) to draw fuel to the well, bioslurping appears to create primarily a horizontal force, operating in the soil plane having the highest permeability and hydraulic conductivity (Rodeck et al. 1994). Bioslurper systems are designed to minimize discharges of groundwater and soil gas. Additional information on bioslurping is given in Kittel et al. (1994a,b).

Bioslurping technology is being applied at several Naval sites that have free fuel on the groundwater table: Naval Air Station (NAS) Fallon, Nevada (JP-5 jet fuel); MCBH (JP-5 jet fuel); and Hofn, Iceland (diesel fuel). The NAS Fallon bioslurping system has been in operation since January 1993; this paper discusses data from this site.

SITE AND SYSTEM DESCRIPTION

The NAS Fallon field site is located in the high desert of western Nevada. The saturated soil profile is lacustrine clay overlain by a 1-m-thick fine sandy horizon terminating at the groundwater table, at depths ranging from 2.5 to 3.5 m; the contaminated vadose zone is composed primarily of soils classified as clay loam. Seasonal groundwater temperature varies between 12 and 18°C and is of brackish salinity (averaging 23 mmho/cm conductivity; 38,000 mg/L total dissolved solids). The major salts are almost evenly distributed between sodium sulfate and sodium chloride. Soil pH is high (9.1 to 9.3) but groundwater pH fluctuates seasonally from 9.0 during low precipitation periods to 7.75 during high precipitation periods. Nitrogen concentrations in the groundwater appear to be adequate for biodegradation, with nitrate, ammonia, and total kjeldahl nitrogen averaging 4.0, 1.4, and 2.15 mg/L, respectively. Groundwater phosphate concentrations are high, with average values of 17.6 and 9.8 for total phosphorus and orthophosphate phosphorus, respectively. Soil nutrient concentrations are given in Table 1. Arsenic is a natural soil constituent.

The 1-acre (0.4 ha) bioslurper system consists of 48 wells placed on a 9.2-m by 9.2-m grid, with all slurper wells interconnected to a 10-hp liquid ring vacuum pump with soil surface airtight polyvinyl chloride (PVC) piping. Each bentonite-sealed well has a 5-cm PVC casing, slotted from 1.5- to 3.7-m depth, into which a 2.5 cm PVC slurper tube is inserted to the groundwater-free fuel interface and sealed airtight at the top of the outer well casing (Figure 1). Five groundwater

TABLE 1. Physical and chemical parameters for fuel-contaminated subsoil from within and 30 m outside the bioslurper plot.

Parameter	Subsoil Inside Plot (mg/kg)	Subsoil at SGP-7c (mg/kg)	Subsoil Background (mg/kg)
pH	9.29 (9.19–9.39)[a]	9.11 (9.07–9.14)	9.20 (9.03–9.37)
Alkalinity, mg/kg	3560 (1840–6100)	4155 (1470–6840)	4005 (1670–6340)
Nitrate-N, mg/kg	1.5 (<1.2–1.8)	2.1	<1.3
Total Kjeldahl-N, mg/kg	156 (49–280)	99 (87–110)	160 (70–250)
Total Phosphorus, mg/kg	919	1140	720
Total Iron, mg/kg	14,300	25,000	14,600
Total Arsenic, mg/kg	17.8 (9.9–23.7)	14.2 (11.0–17.4)	43.1 (22.0–64.2)
Total Lead, mg/kg	7.9 (7.7–8.1)	7.9	12.2

(a) Ranges for 3 values inside plot and 2 values at SGP-7c and background, for most parameters.

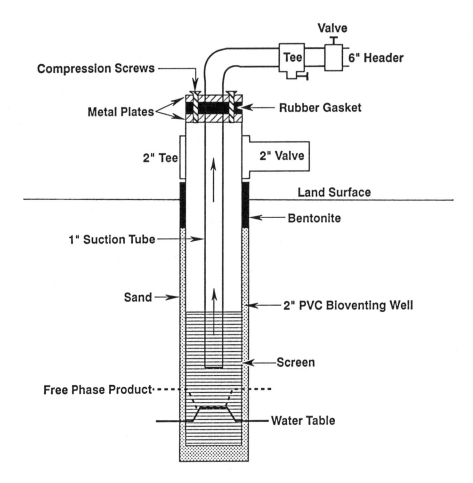

FIGURE 1. Diagram of a bioslurper well.

monitoring wells also were installed. The surface treatment system consists of a 90-L/min oil-water separator (OWS), storage tanks, and a metered fuel transfer pump. Treated groundwater is discharged to the base sanitary sewer, and vapor is discharged to the atmosphere from the vacuum pump. Additional information and figures depicting the bioslurper system are given in Kittel et al. (1994a,b). Monthly water samples collected from the OWS effluent and periodic vapor discharge samples are analyzed to estimate fuel mass discharge from the system.

SOIL GAS ANALYSIS AND IN SITU RESPIROMETRY METHODS

A total of 30 permanent soil gas and temperature monitoring points were installed in vadose zone soils within and surrounding the bioslurping treatment plot. Each monitoring point location consisted of three sampling probes established at three depth intervals per point (0.8 m, 2.1 m, and just above the water table or free-fuel layer) as described elsewhere (Ong et al. 1991; Hinchee and Ong 1992). Each sampling probe was sealed with hydrated bentonite to include a vertical interval of 0.4 to 0.5 m. Soil gas analyses were conducted using the procedures outlined in Hinchee et al. (1992). Samples were analyzed for CO_2; O_2; benzene, toluene, ethyl benzene, and total xylenes (BTEX); and total petroleum hydrocarbon (TPH) concentrations using field instrumentation (GasTech Model 32520X CO_2/O_2 analyzer and GasTech Trace-Techtor hydrocarbon analyzer). Methods employed for determining $^{13}C/^{12}C$ ratios for CO_2 in soil gas are provided in Aggarwal and Hinchee (1991).

RESULTS AND DISCUSSION

Bioslurper System Operation

The bioslurper system at NAS Fallon has been in operation about 75% of the time over the past 2 years. As shown in Figure 2, the fuel recovery rate has remained fairly constant over the operational period, perhaps partly because of the use of a more efficient vacuum pump in the second year and a slight increase

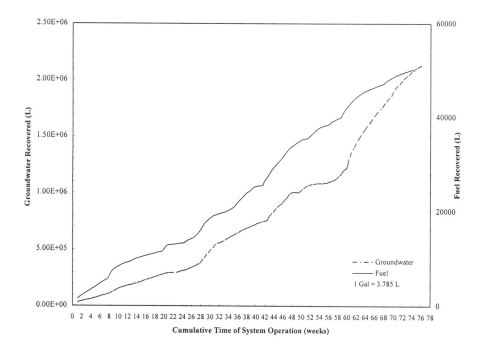

FIGURE 2. Cumulative free-product and groundwater extraction volumes for the NAS Fallon bioslurper system.

in groundwater extraction rate (Figure 2). LNAPL removal in the first year averaged 24 gal/day (91 L/day) with an average groundwater extraction rate of
0.46 gal/min (1.75 L/min), using a conventional 10-hp dewatering pump. Second
year LNAPL recovery rates, using a more efficient liquid ring vacuum pump,
increased up to 60 gal/day (227 L/day). The most recent data available (October
1994) show a fuel removal rate of 45 gal/day (170 L/day), which is the average
for the 2-year period. However, groundwater discharge from the system has
increased from 0.3 gal/min (1.1 L/min) initially to 2.5 gal/min (9.5 L/min)
recently. Total fuel recovered by the end of January 1995 was 12,900 gal (48,800 L),
and groundwater recovery was approximately 530,000 gal (2.01 × 10⁶ L). Figure 3
indicates that a positive correlation exists between fuel recovery rates and the
vacuum placed on the system, based on vacuum fluctuations between 12.5 and
30.5 cm of mercury.

The estimated total mass of hydrocarbons removed by the bioslurper system
during the first year of operation was 21,450 kg (assuming a specific gravity of
0.85 for JP-5 fuel). Of this amount, 97% (20,800 kg) was removed as free liquid,
whereas only 0.3% was released with the aqueous discharge, most being associated

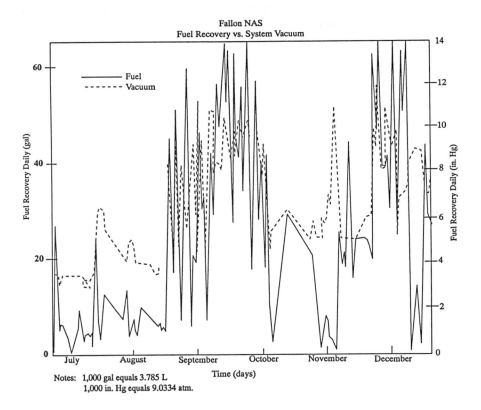

FIGURE 3. Graph of bioslurper system daily free-product recovery volumes
and vacuum.

with particulate matter. Vapor discharge to the atmosphere from the pump accounted for 2.7% (580 kg) of the total fuel mass removed by the bioslurper system.

Soil Gas Analysis and In Situ Respirometry

Soil gas data collected following bioslurper system shutdown have indicated that most of the field plot is not oxygen limited. The presence of nitrate in the contaminated soil (Table 1) and groundwater also indicates that the soil profile is not O_2 deficient. Furthermore, soil gas data from most soil gas monitoring probes indicated initial O_2 levels in excess of 18%, with an insignificant decline over a period of up to 2 weeks following system shutdown. Oxygen levels above about 4% in vadose zone soil gas have previously been shown not to limit aerobic biodegradation appreciably (Miller et al. 1991).

In situ respirometry tests were conducted at sites showing possible O_2 limitation or decline in soil gas after the bioslurper system was shut off. One monitored site (SGP-10c) was located near the edge of the treatment plot and another (SGP-7c) was located 30 m outside the plot in the same vicinity, closer to the fuel farm. SGP-10c and SGP-7c displayed initial O_2 levels immediately above the free-fuel layer of 8% and 1%, respectively. Figure 4 shows O_2 depletion rates observed during 90-h in situ respiration tests initiated after temporary shutdown of the system. Soil O_2 utilization rates observed near the plot edge (SGP-10c) and 30 m outside the plot (SGP-7c) were 2.3% and 11.1%/day, respectively. An uncontaminated background station, which gave a similar rate curve for tracer helium gas decline over the monitoring period, showed an insignificant O_2 decline (0.1%/day). Based on O_2 utilization rates (%/day), biodegradation rates (mg hydrocarbon/kg soil/day) were computed according to the methods of Hinchee and Ong (1992) for SGP-10c and SGP-7c as 1.85 and 8.9 mg/kg/day, respectively.

Figure 4 shows insignificant increases in CO_2 during the in situ respiration tests. This is probably due to the high pH values of the soils (pH 9.1 to 9.3), which promote CO_2 fixation as carbonates. However, stable carbon isotope analyses ($^{13}C/^{12}C$ ratios) were performed on CO_2 samples collected from soil gas monitoring probes showing high O_2 utilization rates after system shutdown (SGP-10c, SGP-7c), probes showing low O_2 utilization rates after system shutdown (SGP-4c, SGP-11c, SGP-17c), and an uncontaminated background station probe (BKGD-c). Prior research has indicated that atmospheric CO_2 is isotopically heavy (higher in ^{13}C) compared to CO_2 from the degradation of fossil fuels (Galimov 1976). Biodegradation of recent organic matter tends to produce intermediate values of ^{13}C enrichment, but the types of compounds being degraded and metabolic pathways involved (e.g., aerobic vs. anaerobic) tend to broaden isotopic fractionation values so that there is some overlap (Games and Hayes 1976). However data from various fuel-contaminated sites have indicated that stable carbon isotope ratios are useful for confirming in situ biodegradation of fuel hydrocarbons (Aggarwal and Hinchee 1991).

As depicted in Figure 5, there was close correlation between sampling locations having the highest oxygen depletion rates and those with CO_2 $^{13}C/^{12}C$

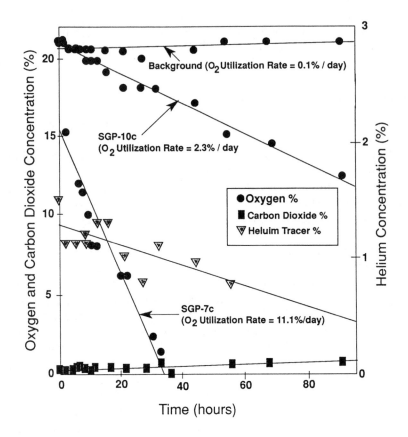

FIGURE 4. In situ respiration data for SGP-10c (in treatment plot) and SGP-7 (30 m outside of treatment plot) at NAS Fallon.

isotope ratios showing the greatest depletion of ^{13}C (more negative values compared to the standard). The CO_2 C^{13}/C^{12} isotope ratios observed from locations with minor O_2 depletion indicated that the CO_2 source was primarily from the degradation of recent organic matter or dissolution of carbonates in the soil.

Soil Nutrient and Hydrocarbon Analyses

Soil analytical data from select locations within the bioslurping treatment plot indicate that the fuel contaminant is primarily unweathered JP-5 jet fuel. For example, no benzene and only sporadic low levels of toluene (1.8 mg/kg in one sample) were detected during two soil sampling events. In contrast, soil samples from boreholes surrounding SGP-7c, 30 m outside the treatment plot, showed benzene levels up to 0.87 mg/kg and toluene in all samples collected, ranging from 1.0 to 1.9 mg/kg. Toluene and benzene are major, moderately soluble constituents of gasoline and are usually not present in JP-5. Thus, the high respiration rates observed outside the treatment plot (near SGP-7c) may be due to

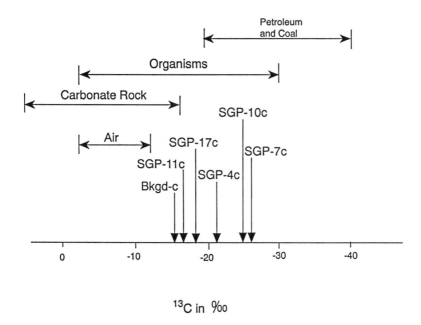

FIGURE 5. Ratio curve for $^{13}C/^{12}C$ measured in soil gas CO_2 from locations near the NAS Fallon bioslurper system.

biodegradation of soluble-phase fuel hydrocarbons, primarily the monoaromatics found in gasoline contamination coming from another source area.

Nutrient and major inorganic compounds were analyzed in soil samples collected from the fuel-contaminated zone within the bioslurper field plot and 30 m outside the field plot, near SGP-7c (Table 1). These data indicate that the soils from both areas, including the background area, are highly variable but similar for most parameters, including nutrients and pH. Arsenic is a natural soil constituent at the Fallon site and the data in Table 1 indicate that lead levels are also not of anthropogenic origin. Average arsenic and lead concentrations did not vary appreciably in soils collected within and 30 m outside the field plot. Exchangeable ammonium and iron were below detection. Soil moisture was 23% and 24% within and 30 m outside the field plot, respectively.

Laboratory Microcosms

Total aerobic heterotrophic and hydrocarbon-degrading bacteria were enumerated using the 15-tube most probable number (MPN) technique. When a basal salts medium was adjusted in specific ion concentrations to simulate soils from the Fallon site (Fallon BSM) and supplemented with yeast extract and casamino acids as food sources (supplemented Fallon BSM), heterotrophic bacterial counts were ~10^7/g soil (wet wt); this was one to four orders of magnitude higher than the MPN counts in nutrient broth, plate-count broth, and Bushnell-Haas or minimal medium A supplemented with yeast extract and casamino acids. Furthermore, numbers of heterotrophs in supplemented Fallon BSM adjusted to pH 9 were an order of magnitude greater than when grown at pH 7. Many of the soil heterotrophic bacteria preferred sodium ion concentrations and pH similar to those found in the field, and supplementation with potassium ions at equimolar concentration reduced cell numbers four orders of magnitude. However, no aerobic heterotrophs were isolated from fuel-saturated soil from Fallon with any MPN medium tested.

The number of hydrocarbon-degrading bacteria isolated on Fallon BSM medium supplemented with fresh JP-5, weathered JP-5 recovered from the field site, or mineral oil as the only food source was ~10^4/g soil (wet wt). However, growth in the MPN tubes was evident only after at least 3 weeks of incubation and only when less heavily contaminated soils were sampled. Only Fallon BSM or supplemented Fallon BSM supported the growth of hydrocarbon degraders and this growth was augmented when the medium was supplemented with sodium at concentrations present in Fallon soils.

The long lag time required for growth in the MPN tubes and the ability of some organisms to grow in Fallon BSM supplemented with JP-5 following a loop transfer of bacteria grown on Fallon BSM with glucose as the sole carbon source, suggest that the hydrocarbon-degrading bacteria have been stressed in soil heavily contaminated with JP-5. Alternatively, lack of active bioemulsifying bacteria or bioemulsifying activity promoted by natural soil factors may account for the slow growth on the low-solubility hydrocarbons found in JP-5. The fuel itself does not appear to be toxic to the heterotrophs. The MPNs of heterotrophs in supplemented Fallon BSM and Fallon BSM supplemented with JP-5 were similar. However, the recovered fuel was not extensively degraded by the heterotrophic bacterial isolates. This suggests that selection for and outgrowth of an active population of hydrocarbon degraders may be occurring slowly. Growth on an easily degradable, soluble carbon source helps the hydrocarbon degraders to overcome their poor ability to grow on low-solubility hydrocarbons found in JP-5 and mineral oil. Retardation of biosurfactant production appears to be involved and growth on easily degradable, water-soluble food sources may help to resuscitate damaged bacterial cells or to overcome other conditions that limit biosurfactant production. The specific mechanisms involved have not yet been determined. This interpretation could account for the limited in situ respirometric activity in soils contaminated only with JP-5 and the significantly higher O_2 utilization rates at sites showing cross-contamination with more soluble gasoline hydrocarbons.

CONCLUSIONS

Bioslurping at NAS Fallon has shown that vacuum-enhanced pumping of LNAPL from soils having low or mixed permeabilities can result in long-term recovery of significant quantities of liquid fuel. Data collected over the past 2 years have shown average daily LNAPL removal of 170 L (45 gal), with recovery rates appearing to correlate directly with vacuum placed on the system. With low volatility fuels, such as JP-5 jet fuel, vapor discharge of about 2.3 kg (5 lb) per day can be expected using a liquid ring pump, although the discharge quantity is probably dependent on depth to the water table and degree of fuel weathering.

Despite the presence of a moist clay loam soil cap, oxygen was generally not found to be limiting during bioslurping activities, which indicates that this technique has the dual capability to draw atmospheric oxygen into low permeability unsaturated soil profiles. However, biodegradation of the fuel appears to be minimal at the site, based on in situ respirometry. Comparative data for CO_2 stable carbon isotope ratios and in situ O_2 utilization rates were collected from both field locations contaminated solely with JP-5, and locations cross-contaminated with gasoline. These data strongly indicate that microbial accessibility to the very low-solubility hydrocarbon compounds found in JP-5 may be the major inhibitory problem. Excessive free product on the groundwater table and fuel dispersion inhibition caused by moist, low-permeability soils immediately above the aquifer zone may suppress bioemulsification and solubilization of the LNAPL. Laboratory studies involving growth on different liquid media, with and without JP-5 supplementation, also indicate that hydrocarbon-degrading bacteria in Fallon soils may have a diminished ability to bioemulsify LNAPL hydrocarbons after exposure to high concentrations of JP-5 jet fuel. Whether this is caused by physical damage to the bacteria, which inhibits their ability to produce biosurfactants, is yet to be determined. Further studies at NAS Fallon and bioslurping studies at other sites are in progress to obtain better answers to the observed problems.

REFERENCES

Aggarwal, P. K., and R. E. Hinchee. 1991. "Monitoring In Situ Biodegradation of Hydrocarbons by Using Stable Carbon Isotopes." *Environ. Sci. Technol.* 25(6): 1178-1180.

Biotreatment News. 1994. "Number of Bacterial Cells and Diesel Degradation." 4(9): 11.

Bury, S. J., and C. A. Miller. 1993. "Effect of Micellar Solubilization on Biodegradation Rates of Hydrocarbons." *Environ. Sci. Technol.* 27(1): 104-110.

Galimov, E. M. 1976. "Variations of the Carbon Cycle at Present and in the Geological Past." In J. R. Nriagu, *Environmental Biogeochemistry, Volume 1*, pp. 3-11. Ann Arbor Science, Ann Arbor, MI.

Games, L. M., and J. M. Hayes. 1976. "On the Mechanisms of CO_2 and CH_4 Production in Natural Anaerobic Environments." In J. R. Nriagu, *Environmental Biogeochemistry*, Vol. 1, pp. 51-73. Ann Arbor Science, Ann Arbor, MI.

Hinchee, R. E. 1993. "Bioventing of Petroleum Hydrocarbons." In *Handbook of Bioremediation*, pp. 39-59. Lewis Publishers, Boca Raton, FL.

Hinchee, R. E., and S. K. Ong. 1992. "A Rapid In Situ Respiration Test for Measuring Aerobic Biodegradation Rates of Hydrocarbons in Soil." *J. Air and Waste Manage. Assoc.* 42(10): 1305-1312.

Hinchee, R. E., S. K. Ong, R. N. Miller, D. C. Downey, and R. Frandt. 1992. *Test Plan and Technical Protocol for a Field Treatability Test for Bioventing*. Report to U.S. Air Force Center for Environmental Excellence, Brooks AFB, TX.

Hoeppel, R. E., R. E. Hinchee, and M. F. Arthur. 1991. "Bioventing Soils Contaminated with Petroleum Hydrocarbons." *J. Ind. Microbiol.* 8: 141-146.

Kittel, J. A., R. E. Hoeppel, R. E. Hinchee, T. C. Zwick, and R. J. Watts. 1994a. "In Situ Remediation of Low-Volatility Fuels Using Bioventing Technology." In E. J. Calabrese, P. T. Kostecki and M. (Eds.), *Hydrocarbon Contaminated Soils*, Vol. IV, pp. 43-68. ASP, Amherst, MA.

Kittel, J. A., R. E. Hinchee, R. E. Hoeppel, and R. Miller. 1994b. "Bioslurping — Vacuum-Enhanced Free-Product Recovery Coupled with Bioventing: A Case Study." In *Petroleum Hydrocarbons and Organic Chemicals in Groundwater: Prevention, Detection and Remediation*, pp. 255-270. National Groundwater Association, Dublin, OH.

Miller, R. N., C. C. Vogel, and R. E. Hinchee. 1991. "A Field-Scale Investigation of Petroleum Hydrocarbon Biodegradation in the Vadose Zone Enhanced by Soil Venting at Tyndall AFB, Florida." In R. E. Hinchee and R. F. Olfenbuttel (Eds.), *In Situ Bioreclamation: Applications and Investigations for Hydrocarbon and Contaminated Site Remediation*, pp. 283-302. Butterworth-Heinemann, Stoneham, MA.

Ong, S. K., R. E. Hinchee, R. E. Hoeppel, and R. Scholze. 1991. "In-situ Respirometry for Determining Aerobic Degradation Rates." In R. E. Hinchee and R. F. Olfenbuttel (Eds.), *In Situ Bioreclamation: Applications and Investigations for Hydrocarbon and Contaminated Site Remediation*, pp. 541-545. Butterworth-Heinemann, Stoneham, MA.

Rodeck, S. A., B. A. DeVantier, and B. M. Das. 1994. "Air Permeability Measurement for Soil at Low and High Pressure." *J. Environ. Eng. (ASCE)* 120(5): 1337-1343.

Double-Phase Vacuum Extraction System: A Treatment for Variable Water Levels

Pascal Roudier and Renaud Chapuis

ABSTRACT

Gas and liquid extraction techniques are applied simultaneously in an alluvial site with strong to medium permeability. Usually, the water level variations are negligible and the design of the treatment system does not take into account these piezometric variations. In this example, the refinery site is located near the Seine, in an estuary zone. The river level varies by more than 6 m. The purpose of the treatment was twofold: (1) to contain the hydrocarbon infiltrations from soil to free water at a site with high hydraulic-gradient conditions (low tide); and (2) to optimize the free and volatile hydrocarbon recovery ratios. The process finds its support in two new concepts: the double-phase vacuum extraction system and lowering by "needles," or lances. All the geologic and hydrodynamic conditions were taken into account for the choice of on-site and in situ equipment. The variability of the conditions applied to the system limits over time had conditioned both the equipment and the choice of the process automatization. The first results obtained with this new approach of a mixed confinement/extraction problem, in a specific locale, are explained herein.

INTRODUCTION

The treatment of polluted sites in the estuarine zone by double-phase extraction makes the decontamination process adaptation dependent on thorough knowledge of the system characteristics in question (saturated zone, unsaturated zone) as well as the condition limits applied. Soil characteristics unfavorable to the large-scale contaminant remobilization as well as the significant time variability of hydrogeologic conditions in place require an important adaptation and a new management strategy for the double-phase extraction process on the site of a refinery in the North of France. The main objectives of the treatment were to eliminate all seepage possibilities in a neighboring river and to optimize the recovery rate of nonaqueous-phase liquid (NAPL) and dissolved hydrocarbons.

GEOLOGIC AND HYDROGEOLOGIC CONTEXT

The treated site is located on the bank of a river (15 m) under the influence of the tide. The studied system is geometrically defined by the lining up of 30 7-m-deep extraction wells, at intervals of 1 m (Figure 1). On average, the static level of the groundwater was 5 m deep. The soil volume involved in the treatment was estimated to be about 1,000 m^3.

From a geologic point of view, the subsoil is characterized by alternating layers of silt without extended lateral continuity and by very fine-grained sand on a calcareous limestone substratum. The different on-site and laboratory tests carried out revealed water permeability values of about 5×10^{-7} m/s and air permeabilities of about 2×10^{-6} m/s (Figure 1). Due to the proximity of the river receiving the full weight effects of the tide, there was a significant time variability of the hydrodynamic conditions that applied to the limits of the system. In fact, the tide amplitude of the watercourse — sometimes as high as 6 m — causes a gradient inversion on the groundwater every 12 h (Figure 2).

Hydrogeologic recordings made on-the-spot for all of the 30 needles revealed the spatial variability of the water levels and emphasized the heterogeneity of the subsoil, which was subject to mechanical waves varying over time (Figure 2). Therefore, hydrocarbon pollutant transfer present under free phase and dissolved form is influenced by this particular hydrodynamic context. Prior to the treatment, the river border zone showed significant heights of floating phase at low tide. By contrast, high tide was characterized by the total absence of free hydrocarbons on the groundwater surface.

ADAPTATION OF THE PROCESS

The major arguments that swayed the balance in favor of the double-phase extraction process that was finally used was the need for several tapping points and for more flexible and centralized management. The treatment priority objectives were to prevent any possible seepage of the pollutant into the river and to extract it in liquid form. Therefore, extraction wells were made to comply with the conditions of a depression hydraulic barrier establishment.

Earlier work performed on the site with the pump-and-treat method had revealed a problem in the transport of fine soil particles. Because of this problem, and regardless of the type of pipe and filtering medium used, wells were used so that each radius of influence would intersect for a few hundred liters per hour (critical flows = 5 m^3/h) unit water flowrates. All the needles within an interval of 1 m were connected to extraction, separation, and treatment units through an upgrade section collector.

The product pumping in the works and its circulation in the system was induced by creating a depression gradient. A vacuum pump capable of extracting up to 1,060 m^3/h of air under a depression of 750 mbars was necessary to generate a sufficient vacuum. The specific type of needles makes it possible to use

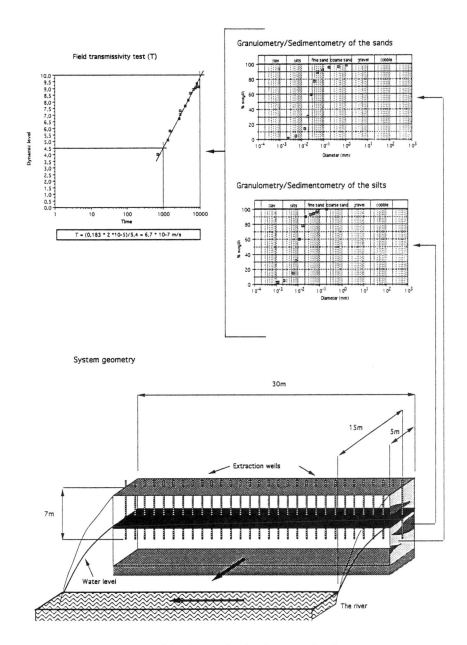

FIGURE 1. Geologic and hydrogeologic characterization.

different modes of transport: volumetric (capillary transport of a mixed liquid phase (water + pollutant)) and pneumatic (water and contaminant transfer in spray form) (see Figure 3). These two modes of transport require different adapted treatments; in this case, by mechanical separation.

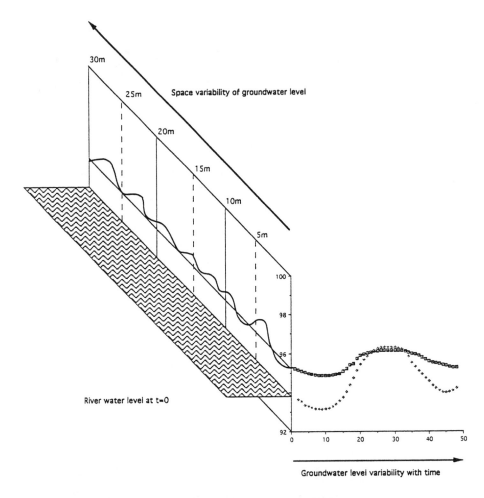

FIGURE 2. **Variability of the hydrodynamic conditions.**

A test phase enabled us to validate the adequacy of the design retained for this particular project and to characterize in situ the intrinsic parameters of the system. For a unit water flowrate of 0.2 m³/h, in aerosol form, the sum of all the radii of influence was enough to intercept all hydrocarbon flows toward the river. Under these conditions, the influence front of the hydraulic barrier was located 4 m within the site. Similarly, for a unit air flowrate of 35 to 50 m³/h (the rate varies with the distance of the needle from the machine), the influence revealed by the measurement of induced depressions was 7 m in the axis of the extraction plant. Strictly speaking, it should be borne in mind that the term "double-phase extraction" begins to apply only when the bases of the internal rods are completely dewatered. Hydrocarbons in gaseous and free form are then simultaneously extracted.

MANAGEMENT PROCESS

Because each needle device (the heights of strainers) is determined by the groundwater tide magnitude, an oversizing process (air flowrate of the vacuum

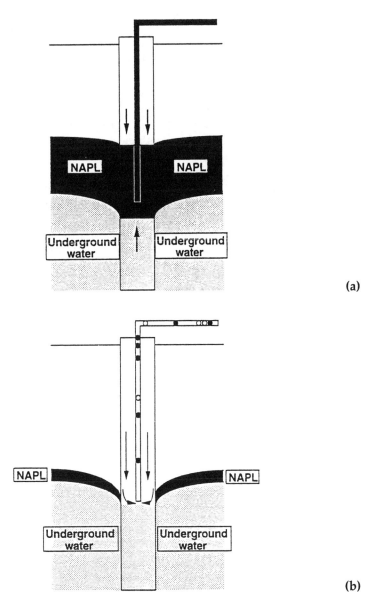

(a)

(b)

FIGURE 3. Specific equipment of the needles and working modes. (a) Volumetric transport (liquid phase — water and NAPL). (b) Pneumatic transport (liquid phase — water and NAPL; gaseous phase — air and VOC).

pump) was calculated to increase the number of treatment possibilities by adopting a management strategy that will remain in place over time. In fact, in absolute terms, the specific recovery of the floating phase would have required only one series of short-lasting pumpings determined by each hydrologic cycle. Because each pumping lasted until all the needles were empty, the pollutant transfer would have been performed exclusively by capillary transport.

Within this scenario, the extraction begins according to computations of tide coefficient published annually and the wave transfer in the ready subsoil. In addition, these clock-programmed starts are subject to a groundwater-level control system. The average pumping cycle lasts 10 minutes, beginning with the start of the machine and ending whenever the pollutant extraction is completed. The time necessary for the water level to rise up to the initial static level is the time lapse separating two pumping cycles — a lapse of about 2 hours. Therefore, three 10-minute pumpings at low tide are sufficient to extract all the free hydrocarbons.

As the implemented system induces compulsory airflow in the unsaturated zone, we computed the necessary gas extraction time for removal of the air in the soil. By maintaining the extraction another hour after the end of the pumping cycle, we were able to establish good aeration in the unsaturated zone. It was thus possible, without any additional overhead, to optimize the treatment by associating extraction with sustained biodegradation. Results of respirometric tests confirmed the natural bacterial biodegradation activity.

ASSESSMENT AND PERSPECTIVES

Since initiation of the treatment, no new seepage has been detected in the river surroundings. A follow-up of the hydrocarbon quantities extracted in dissolved and free form was carried out throughout system use. The curve of the accumulated quantities (see Figure 4) is indicative of recovery dynamics of hydrocarbons floating on the groundwater surface. Recovery rates vary from 5,000 L/day at the early stages of the treatment to 100 L/day after 3 months of treatment. At the time of writing, despite the low recovery, the treatment remained in operation because it still met the objective of confining flow around the river. Due probably to the ever-increasing distance, the system's low recovery yield should continue.

Respirometric measurements have been taken on control piezometers located outside the treatment point. The results are only qualitative because the piezometers used were not designed for such usage. However, there is an increase in the oxygen content of the gas measured in a piezometer located 3 m away from the treatment point. In a first step, the oxygen content increases before the rapid and definitive stabilization at concentration levels higher than those obtainable prior to the treatment. Therefore, the renewal of the air in the soil, at least partially, is effective a few meters away from the extraction point. Similarly, the stabilization of oxygen content suggests the existence of biodegrading biological activity.

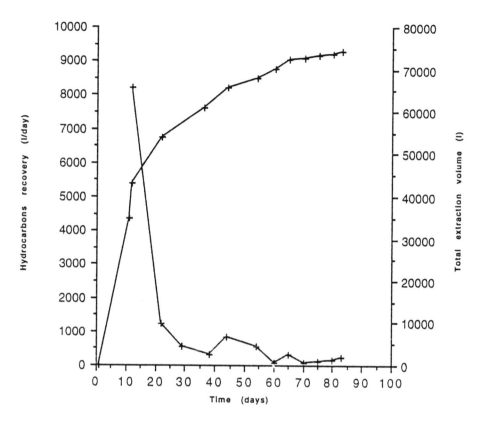

FIGURE 4. Hydrocarbon recovery ratios.

CONCLUSION

This experiment shows that a double-phase extraction system is well suited to the decontamination of a low-permeability soil in a complex hydrodynamic context. The system makes it possible to maintain an efficient hydraulic barrier by associating it with the recovery of NAPL and dissolved hydrocarbons. As the induction of airflow in the soil is conducive to biodegradation, it is, in this case, a side effect that needs to be quantified with some precision. We are currently working on this characterization phase.

Oil-Water Separator for Pretreating Petroleum-Contaminated Water

Yuan-Yang Zheng and Lian-Kui Wen

ABSTRACT

An oil-water separator with inclined corrugated-plate packing was developed. Because of the special passageway formed by the corrugated plates, more opportunities are provided for collisions and coagulation among the oil droplets and for adhesion and coalescence between the oil droplets and the corrugated plates. This separator has, therefore, greatly increased the efficiency of oil removal. Based on the results of the experiments, a mathematical model has been developed for predicting the oil removal efficiency.

INTRODUCTION

A new high-efficiency oil-water separator was developed by the authors and their coworkers (Figure 1). The device is a horizontal container. Except for the water intake and outlet ports and the oil-collecting chambers, the main part of this device is the separation chamber, in which the inclined corrugated plates are used as the separation medium. This oil-water separator has the following advantages:

1. As the inclined corrugate plates are placed one over the other, alternately angled and placed front to back, this oil-water separator not only can increase the oil removal efficiency with the narrowest possible gap between plates, but is also easy to install and repair.
2. The special passageway formed by the corrugated plates provides more opportunities for collisions and coagulation among the oil droplets and for adhesion and coalescence between the oil droplets and the corrugated plates. This separator has, therefore, effectively increased the efficiency of oil removal.
3. Because the corrugated plates have a low corrugation height, the equivalent diameter is small, and the state of laminar flow can be maintained while treating a larger flow. Also, because of the relatively even distribution of liquid flow in the plate packing, the typical problems of short-circuiting and stagnant-zone inducement can be avoided.

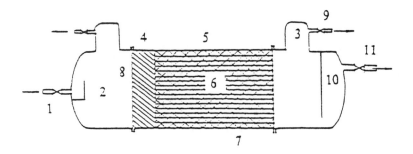

FIGURE 1. An illustration of the oil-water separator. (1) intake pipe; (2) intake
chamber; (3) oil-collecting chamber; (4) vertical plates section; (5) horizontal
plates section; (6) corrugated plates; (7) case body; (8) grid; (9) oil outlet
pipe; (10) water outlet chamber; (11) water outlet pipe.

4. The installation of a section of vertically placed corrugated plates at the
   intake end, not only maintains an even distribution of liquid flow but also
   is useful in removing suspended solids.
5. The corrugated plates can be made of metal, plastic, or fiberglass-reinforced
   plastic, especially the kind of plastic or fiberglass plates whose surface is
   hydrophobic and conducive to the adhesion and coalescence of oil droplets
   onto the surface of the corrugated plates.

Laboratory and commercial data show that the device can attain greater
than 90% of oil-separating efficiency within 30 minutes, so that oil droplets of
20 μm upwards can be separated in the main separation chamber.

To establish a method of design, a mathematical model has been developed.
This study presents the mathematical model.

MATHEMATICAL MODEL

In the packing, the liquid flow direction continuously makes three dimen-
sional changes. The actual flow path is longer than the packing section's total
length L. The cross section of flow changes. The velocity also undergoes changes.
As the oil droplets move with the water flow in the corrugated-plate packing,
the larger oil droplets come up to the surface of the corrugated plates and some
of the smaller oil droplets can also, as a result of collision, form into droplets
that are large enough to be separated after being attached to the surface of the
corrugated plates. Therefore, the liquid flow and the distribution of the oil droplet sizes in the packing also change continuously.

It would be difficult to reflect accurately the above situation in a mathematical model. For the sake of treatment, some simplified assumptions are made
as follows:

1. The liquid flow in the packing is represented equivalently such that the shape of the flow cross section is a rectangle, its height is equal to the corrugation height, h, of the corrugated plates, and its length equals to the total length, L, of the corrugated plates packing as shown in Figure 2. The velocity distribution of the liquid is even.
2. Saouter's mean diameter D_{32} is used to represent the oil droplets.
3. As a result of adopting equivalent flow and mean grain size, a situation different from the actual conditions will necessarily arise. This difference should be expressed by bringing in a rectifying factor. Because the changes of the liquid and the distribution of the oil droplet sizes are related to the state of liquid flow in the corrugated-plate packing, the introduced factor should be related to the state of the liquid flow, i.e., the liquid Re.

As shown in Figure 2, adopting a microelement length dz in the liquid flow direction z, the oil droplets of size D_{32} move forward with the velocity u of liquid flow and float upward at the terminal velocity, v_t. Because the height of the liquid layer is h, and the distribution of the oil droplets at the inlet of the microelement length dz is even, then, in the microelement length dz, the separation rate of oil droplets should be $v_t dz/uh$. The concentration of oil droplets in water is represented by C and the rectifying factor k is introduced; then, within the microelement length dz, changes in the concentration of oil droplets in water are as follows:

$$-dC = kC \frac{v_t}{uh} dz \tag{1}$$

The length L of the entire packing is integrated and the concentrations of oil droplets in the water at the intake and outlet are C_0 and C_e, respectively. Thus,

$$\frac{C_0}{C_e} = exp \left[k \frac{v_t}{uh} L \right] \tag{2}$$

The terminal velocity can be expressed by the Stokes' equation, and the oil separation efficiency η is

$$\eta = 1 - exp[-k(\rho - \rho_0)g D_{32}^2 L / 18\mu\, uh] \tag{3}$$

where ρ = density of water (kg/m³)
ρ_0 = density of oil (kg/m³)
μ = viscosity of water (Pa·s)

This is the mathematical expression of the oil-water separator.

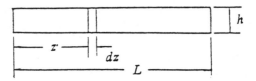

FIGURE 2. The equivalent liquid flow.

EXPERIMENT

The experimental device is a horizontal container, inside which there is the corrugated-plate packing of a specified length. The oil-water mixture containing dispersed oil droplets is prepared in an agitating tank, where crude oil and tap water are mixed. Spectrophotometry with a Shimadzu 120-02 (UV/VIS) spectrometer is used to analyze the oil concentration in water (Forum 1984). To determine the distribution of the oil droplets, the flotation method is adopted and checked by using microphotographic counting.

Table 1 shows the structural parameters of the relevant experimental device. The oil concentration in water prepared for the experiment is in the range of 50 to 2,600 mg/L, the particle size of the oil droplets is within ≤ 150 μm, oil density at temperature 20°C is 810 to 860 kg/m^3, and the water temperature for the experiment is maintained at 10 to 20°C.

RESULTS OF EXPERIMENT

Distribution of Oil Droplet Diameters

By omitting the truncation factor, the distribution of oil droplet size can be expressed as

$$f(x_i) = \frac{1}{\sqrt{2\pi}\, x_i ln\sigma_g}\, exp\left[-\left(\frac{ln\frac{x_i}{x_g}}{\sqrt{2}\, ln\sigma_g}\right)\right] \tag{4}$$

where x_i = diameter of oil droplet (m)

Using the data on the distribution of oil droplets, the corresponding geometrical mean value x_g and geometrical standard deviation σ_g can be obtained, and by the following equation, the corresponding Saouter diameter D_{32} is obtained (Allen 1981):

$$ln D_{32} = ln x_g - 0.5(ln\sigma_g) \tag{5}$$

TABLE 1. The structural parameters of experimental devices.

Serial No.	Inner Diameter (mm)	Length of Corrugated Plate Packing L (mm)	Corrugation Height h (mm)	Inclined Angle of Corrugated Plate
1	95	450	5	45°
2	95	300	5	45°
3	95	150	5	45°
4	400	3,000	12	45°
5[a]	400	3,000	12	45°

(a) Treating oily wastewater from production at Da Gang Oilfield.

Correlation of Rectifying Factor

The correlation between the rectifying factor k and the Re is

$$k = A Re^b, \qquad Re = \frac{d_e u p}{\mu} \tag{6}$$

where A = constant
b = constant
d_e = equivalent diameter of packing (m)

Calculating on the basis of the nonlinear least-square estimation by Newton's iterative method, within the range of 2.96 to 81.68 of Re, A = 0.0453 and b = 0.701, their correlation coefficient will be R = 0.994.

Comparing the model predictions with the experimental data, the relative errors are converged within the range of 5%. It shows that the mathematical model and the corresponding equations are in good agreement with the actual situation.

REFERENCES

Bioremediation of Oil-Contaminated Shorelines: Effects of Different Nitrogen Sources

Svein Ramstad and Per Sveum

ABSTRACT

The present study was designed to examine the fate and effect of various nitrogen sources in oil-contaminated sediments in a continuous-flow seawater column system fed with nutrient-enriched seawater. Degradation of oil components is stimulated by a supply of an enhanced concentration of nitrogen. The most pronounced effect was found with nitrate, compared to ammonium and organic nitrogen. Ammonium was more readily sorbed by the sediment system, either by chemical adsorption or by microbial immobilization.

INTRODUCTION

The mitigation of petroleum spill through removal of hydrocarbons by naturally occurring microorganisms has been reviewed in several papers (e.g., Colwell and Walker 1977, Prince 1993). It has been shown that biological degradation of oil in the environment is limited by the availability of nutrients like nitrogen and phosphorus (Atlas and Bartha 1972), and that oil degradation can be stimulated by addition of limited nutrients (Atlas and Bartha 1973). Several fertilizers for use in marine bioremediation have been developed and tested (Prince 1993). The cleanup following the grounding of *Exxon Valdez* in Alaska in March 1989 increased scientific efforts to prove both the efficiency of nutrient-facilitated bioremediation of oil-contaminated beaches, and the use and acceptance of biological methods at an operational scale.

Bragg et al. (1994) demonstrated that changes in the oil composition relative to the very stable conservative internal marker hopane could be explained as a function of the nitrogen concentration in the interstitial water, the fraction of polars in the oil, and the total oil concentration. Thus, the difference in biodegradation rates resulted from different levels of nutrients in sediment pore water. However, no data are available on how different forms of nitrogen affect degradation rates; i.e., the preferred form of nitrogen for oil-degrading microorganisms. Billen (1984) concluded that bacteria primarily use amino acids as nitrogen source, whereas phytoplankton primarily use ammonium, nitrate and urea. Wheeler and Kirchman (1986) examined the use of various inorganic and organic nitrogen sources by marine heterotrophic bacteria with ^{15}N techniques. Their data suggest that a significant portion of ammonium uptake in the euphotic zone could be correlated to heterotrophic bacterial activity. The present study was designed to examine the fate and effect of various nitrogen sources in oil-contaminated sediments.

MATERIALS AND METHODS

The experiments were done in a continuous-flow seawater column system (Ramstad et al., 1995), in a constant temperature room (room temperature, 11°C; seawater temperature, approx. 10°C) with no exposure to light. Two experiments (sediment texture 0 to 40 mm and 2 to 10 mm, respectively), each with eight columns, were carried out. The column systems were operated with tidal variation and seawater supply and exchange for 7 days prior to oil application to establish marine conditions in the sediment. Topped Statfjord crude oil (150+, 8.2 mL) was used as the hydrocarbon source and applied at the water surface during high tide. In the experiments, the time distribution of the tidal variation was 4, 2, 4, and 2 h for low, rising, high, and falling tides, respectively. At high tide, the overflow rate was 12.9 $cm^3 \cdot cm^{-2} \cdot hr^{-1}$.

The columns were fed with nutrient-enriched seawater with an eight-channel peristaltic pump from 25-L reservoirs (Table 1). Fresh enriched-nutrient mixtures were made three times a week (inorganic nutrients) or daily (organic nitrogen). In the first experiment, the feeding of nutrients in the seawater started on the first high tide after the oil application. In the second experiment, the columns were running with natural seawater for 7 days after oil application before feeding nutrient-enriched seawater was begun.

During both column series, sediment samples were taken from the top of the sediment. At the termination of the second experiment, 1-cm strata were taken from the upper 10-cm section of the sediment. Water samples were taken 2 cm above the sediment surface, and occasionally from column sampling ports in the middle of the high tide period. The water samples were sterile filtered and stored at −18°C until analysis.

Microbial activity in the sediment samples was measured as esterase activity with a procedure modified from Schnürer and Rosswall (1982). Next, 1 g of sediment sample was incubated with TRIS buffer (60 mM in filtered seawater, pH 8.1, 10 mL) and fluorescein diacetate (FDA) solution (250 µL, 2 g/L in acetone) in sterile test tubes for 60 min at room temperature on a rotary mixer (15 rpm). The samples were filtered through a coarse filter (black band) and a sterile filter (0.2 mm) before measurement.

The numbers of heterotrophic and oil-degrading bacteria were determined by the Sheen Screen MPN-method (Brown and Braddock 1990). Marine Broth medium (Difco 2216) and a modified Bushnell-Haas medium with Statfjord crude

TABLE 1. Nutrient concentration in the seawater supplied in column experiments, and the oil degradation, measured as the nC_{17}/pristane ratio, in the surface sediment at the end of the experimental period.

No.	NH$_4$	NO$_3$	Organic-N	PO$_4$	Other	nC$_{17}$/pristane
	µmol-N/L			µmol/L		
1-1	375.1			1.56		0.77
1-2	107.1			1.56		0.81
1-3	28.6			1.56		0.80
1-4		107.1		1.56		0.55
1-5			107.1	1.56		0.83
1-6	28.6	18.6		1.56		0.62
1-7	143.3	14.3		1.56		0.72
1-8	107.1			1.56	HgCl$_2$	1.15
2-1					100 mM	1.10
2-2	21.4			0.83		0.76
2-3	7.14			0.83		0.88
2-4		21.4		0.83		0.48
2-5		7.14		0.83		0.99
2-6	10.7	10.7		0.83		0.86
2-7	3.57	3.57		0.83		0.85
2-8			21.4	0.83		0.97

oil (150+) were used for heterotrophic and oil-degrading bacteria, respectively. The sediment samples (2 g) were mixed in filtered seawater (10 mL) for 30 min on a rotary mixer in sterile test tubes. The plates were read off after 3 and 7 days, and 7 and 14 days for heterotrophic bacteria and oil-degrading bacteria, respectively.

The water samples were analyzed for ammonium and nitrate using an Aquatec system (Tecator AB), which is a fully automatic system for nutrient analysis based on colorimetric reactions. The concentrations of ammonium and nitrate were determined directly in the filtered samples.

Hydrocarbons in the sediment samples (3 to 15 g) were extracted in a soxhlet extraction system (Soxtec System, Tecator) with hexane (40 mL) at 140°C for 2 h. The samples were analyzed with gas chromatography/flame ionization detector (GC/FID) (Hewlett-Packard Series II Gas Chromatograph with splitless injector) after filtration (0.2 µm) and dilution to the appropriate concentration.

RESULTS AND DISCUSSION

Neither the total number of bacteria nor the number of oil-degrading bacteria (Figure 1) differed significantly between various columns when different sediment depths were compared. The concentration of oil-degrading bacteria showed a

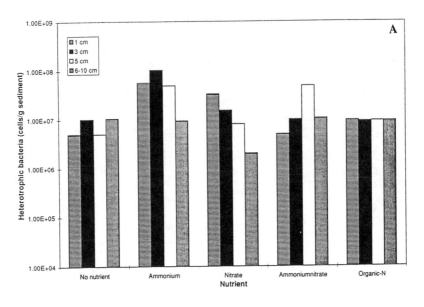

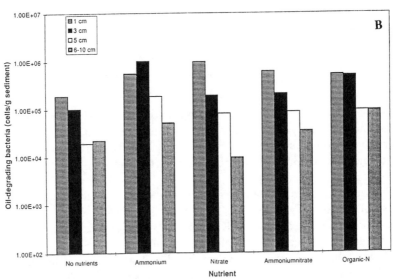

FIGURE 1.   Concentration of heterotrophic bacteria (A) and oil-degrading
      bacteria (B) at different sediment depths in columns at the end of the
      experimental period.

slight but not statistically significant decrease with increasing sediment depth
and with decreasing oil concentration. As the concentrations of nitrogen did
not decrease with increasing sediment depth when the upper 10-cm layer of the
sediment was considered, the number of oil-degrading bacteria in the sediments

seemed to be more dependent on the oil concentration in the sediment than on the concentration of nitrogen in the interstitial water.

The addition of nutrients resulted in increased microbial activity (measured as esterase activity) in all treated sediments when compared to the control (Figure 2). The highest microbial activity at the end of the experiment was recorded in the upper strata of the column-added nitrate. The activity decreased with increasing sediment depth when nitrate was added. In the other sediments the activity did not decrease with depth. The esterase activity, together with the concentration of oil-degrading bacteria, indicates that the specific activity of the oil-degrading bacteria was enhanced in the presence of nitrate as compared to other nitrogen sources, resulting in a more pronounced change in the chemical composition of the oil. Oxygen was not limiting in the sediments, and nitrate probably was not used as an electron acceptor.

In the first part of the experiment, neither nitrate nor ammonium was detected in the water samples in the column supplied with seawater containing equal concentrations of ammonium and nitrate (10.7 μmol-N/L). However, later in the experiment, the measured concentration increased (Figure 3). Toward the end of the experiment, the nitrate concentration decreased very little with sediment depth. The ammonium concentration was always lower than the nitrate concentration, indicating either a different rate of microbial utilization or different sorption rate of the column material for the two nitrogen forms. For the column to which only one form of nitrogen was added, the sediment seemed to be a

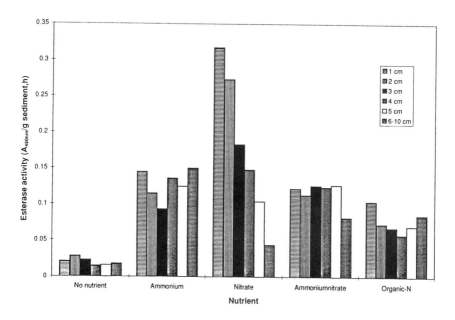

FIGURE 2. Microbial activity, measured as esterase activity, at different sediment depths at the end of the experimental period in the columns to which 21.4 μmol N·liter^{-1} was added continuously.

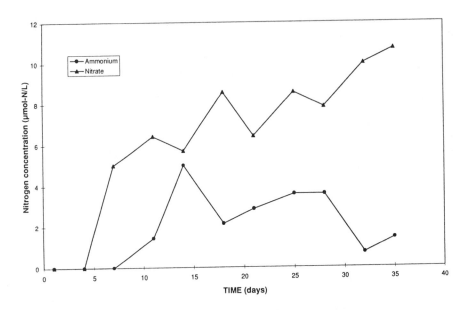

FIGURE 3. Concentration of ammonium and nitrate in the interstitial water in column experiments with nutrient-enriched seawater with an initial concentration of 10.7 μmol N·liter^{-1} of both nitrogen sources.

nutrient sink in the same way. The nitrogen concentrations in water samples from the upper parts of the sediment had the same low concentration, while samples from the two lower ports had concentrations similar to those in the enriched seawater reservoir. Thus, most of the nitrogen was lost or consumed in the upper part of the column where the highest microbial activity occurred. Theoretically, the amount of exchangeable ammonium in the sediments is a function of a number of factors, including the ammonium concentration in solution, the ammonium ion activity, and the concentration and activity of other exchangeable cations (Berner 1976). Exchangeable ammonium concentrations increase linearly with increasing dissolved ammonium concentrations in aquatic sediments (Keney et al. 1970, Rosenfeldt 1979). It is likely, therefore, that some of the added ammonium could be retained in the sediment in an exchangeable form, that the reduction in ammonium during the transport is caused by adsorption, and that the reduction in nitrate is caused mainly by microbial immobilization.

The oil degradation in each column was measured as changes in the nC_{17}/pristane ratio at the end of the experiment (Table 1). The addition of nutrients to the inflowing seawater gave a significant decrease in the nC_{17}/pristane ratio compared to the column supplied with natural seawater only, or the sterile column with HgCl (Tukey Kramer test: Abs(Dif)-LSD 0.16; cf. SAS 1989 for statistical details). The most pronounced changes were found in the columns with nitrate. The nC_{17}/pristane ratio of the oil at different sediment depths (Figure 4) differed significantly from all other combinations of nitrogen with the same

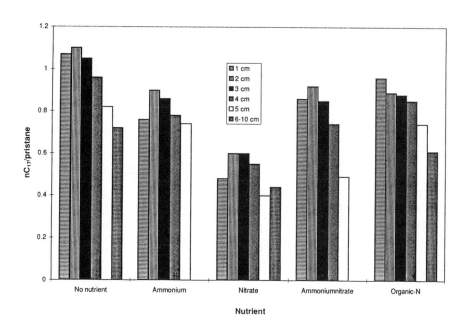

FIGURE 4. Oil degradation, measured as $n\mathrm{C}_{17}$/pristane, at different sediment depths at the end of the experimental period in the columns to which 21.4 μmol N·liter^{-1} was added continuously.

amount of nitrogen added (Tukey Kramer test: Abs[Dif]-LSD ranging from 0.006 to 0.04). The $n\mathrm{C}_{17}$/pristane ratio decreased with decreasing depth in all the sediments, due to decreasing oil concentration ($r^2 = 0.32$, $p > F = 0.0001$, $n = 44$). The oil concentration decreased by 90% across the top 10 cm of the sediments.

Based on the combination of factors studied in the present experiment, a multiple regression model, it was found that the variation in the $n\mathrm{C}_{17}$/pristane ratio could be explained successfully by the NO_3^- and oil concentrations. The multiple regression fit which does not take time into account may be written as:

$$C(n\mathrm{C}_{17}/\text{pristane}) = 0.85 + [\text{Oil}] \, [\mathrm{NO}_3^-] - 0.02 \, [\mathrm{NO}_3^-]$$
$$(n = 44, \ r^2 = 0.55, \ \text{Prob.} > F = 0.0001)$$

This is consistent with the findings of Bragg et al. (1994), who showed that the total interstitial soluble nitrogen concentration can be used to explain changes in oil composition. The present results demonstrate that, of the nitrogen compounds present, nitrate is the most important.

The results of this study show that degradation of oil components is stimulated by a supply of an enhanced concentration of nitrogen. The most pronounced effect was found with nitrate, as compared to ammonium and organic nitrogen. On the other hand, ammonium was more readily sorbed by the sediment system, either by chemical adsorption or by microbial immobilization. The present data do not give information to explain which process is the most important.

As shown above the concentration of both oil-degrading and heterotrophic bacteria was similar in both experiments, but a slightly higher microbial activity was found in the columns to which nitrate was added. Because oxygen was not limited, it is likely that nitrates stimulate the microbial activity directly, and do not serve as an alternative terminal electron acceptor in the studied sediment.

ACKNOWLEDGMENTS

This study is part of the Esso SINTEF Coastal Oil Spill Treatment Program (ESCOST), which is supported by Esso Norge A/S. Special thanks are due to Dr. Roger Prince, Exxon Research and Engineering, and Mr. Geir Indrebø, Esso Norge A/S, for their continuous advice and support throughout the ESCOST program.

REFERENCES

Atlas, R. M., and R. Bartha. 1972. "Degradation and mineralization of petroleum in seawater: Limitation by nitrogen and phosphorus." *Biotechnol. Bioeng.* 14: 309-317.

Atlas, R. M., and R. Bartha. 1973. "Stimulated biodegradation of oil slicks using oleophilic fertilizers." *Environ. Sci. Technol.* 7: 538-541.

Berner, R. A. 1976. "Inclusion of adsorption in the modeling of early diagenesis." *Earth and Planetary Science Letters* 19: 333-340.

Billen, G. 1984. "Heterotrophic utilization and regeneration of nitrogen." In J. E. Hobbie and P. J. leB. Williams (Eds.), *Heterotrophic Activity in the Sea*. pp. 313-355. Plenum, New York, NY.

Bragg, J. R., R. C. Prince, J. B. Wilkinson, and R. M. Atlas. 1992. *Bioremediation for Shoreline Cleanup Following the 1989 Alaskan Oil Spill: Exxon Company*, Houston, TX.

Bragg, J. R., R. C. Prince, E. J. Harner, and R. M. Atlas. 1994. "Effectiveness of bioremediation for the *Exxon Valdez* oil spill." *Nature 368*: 413-418.

Brown, J., and J. F. Braddock. 1990. "Sheen Screen, a miniaturized most-probable-number method for enumeration of oil-degrading microorganisms." *Appl. Environ. Microbiol.* 56: 3895-3896.

Colwell, R. R., and J. D. Walker. 1977. "Ecological aspects of microbial degradation of petroleum in the marine environment." *Crit. Rev. Microbiol.* 5: 423-445.

Keney, D. R., J. G. Konrad, and G. Chester. 1970. "Nitrogen distribution in some Wisconsin lake sediments." *Journal of the Water Pollution Control Federation.* 42: 341-392.

Prince, R. C. 1993. "Petroleum spill bioremediation in marine environments." *Critical Reviews Microbiology* 19: 217-242.

Ramstad, S., P. Sveum, C. Bech, and L.-G. Faksness. 1995. "Modeling shoreline bioremediation: Continuous flow and seawater exchange columns." In R. E. Hinchee, G. S. Douglas, and S. K. Ong (Eds.), *Monitoring and Verification of Bioremediation*, pp. 77-86. Battelle Press, Columbus, OH.

Rosenfeldt, J. K. 1979. "Ammonium adsorption in nearshore anoxic sediments." *Limnol. Oceanog.* 24: 356-364.

SAS. 1989. *JMP® User's Guide*. Version 2 of JMP.

Schnürer, J., and T. Rosswall. 1982. "Fluorescein diacetate hydrolysis as a measure of total microbial activity in soil and litter." *Appl. Environ. Microbiol.* 43: 1256-1261.

Wheeler, P. A., and D. L. Kirchman. 1986. "Utilization of inorganic and organic nitrogen by bacteria in marine systems." *Limnol. Oceanog.* 31: 998-1009.

Effect of Bioremediation Agents on Oil Biodegradation in Medium-Fine Sand

Barry C. Croft, Richard P. J. Swannell, Alyson L. Grant, and Kenneth Lee

ABSTRACT

A spill of weathered Arabian light crude oil (3.7 kg·m^{-2}) on an intertidal sand zone was simulated in the laboratory. Respirometry, chemical, and microbiological methods were employed to assess the effectiveness of two bioremediation agents: a slow-release inorganic (Max Bac) and an oleophilic organic fertilizer (Inipol EAP22). Inipol EAP22 stimulated additional CO_2 evolution, and significantly increased both the total chemoheterotrophic population and the number of hydrocarbon-degrading microorganisms. At the end of the experiment, the residual oil extracted from the Inipol-treated sand was significantly more biodegraded, based on the application of the conserved biomarkers (phytane and 17α, 21β hopane), than that removed from the other sand columns, albeit by a relatively small amount. The results suggested that Inipol EAP22 stimulated the chemoheterotrophic and hydrocarbon-degrading microbial population and, after a lag phase, encouraged oil biodegradation in fine sandy sediments subjected to a vertical tidal cycle.

INTRODUCTION

The bioremediation agents Inipol EAP22 and "Customblen" were shown to stimulate oil biodegradation on cobble beaches in Alaska after the *Exxon Valdez* incident (Pritchard & Costa 1991; Bragg et al. 1994). Improvements in bioremediation strategies now need to focus on operational aspects of the technology (Swannell & Head 1994). The aim of our research was to compare the use of a slow-release inorganic fertilizer (Max Bac — a product similar to the "Customblen" used in Alaska) (Grace-Sierra 1993) with an oleophilic organic fertilizer (Inipol EAP22, produced by Elf, France) (Sirvins & Angles 1986) to stimulate the biodegradation of Arabian light crude oil on columns of medium-fine sand.

Lee and Levy (1987) noted that a single application of Inipol EAP22 failed to stimulate oil biodegradation, due to the rapid removal of the oleophilic fertilizer by tidal action. The failure of Inipol EAP22 to stimulate oil biodegradation on fine sediments was also noted by Sveum and Ladousse (1989). Safferman (1991) recorded that Inipol EAP22 was rapidly removed from oiled cobble in the laboratory. To examine the discrepancy between the results noted in the field in Alaska, and these earlier field observations of the effects of fertilizers, cores of sand were subjected to a tidal cycle in the laboratory to assess the significance of vertical water movement on the efficacy of the selected bioremediation agents.

EXPERIMENTAL PROCEDURES AND MATERIALS

Column Operation and Oil Addition

Cores of quartz beach sand 30 cm in length were obtained from Long Cove, Nova Scotia, Canada (Lee & Levy 1987, 1992) and shipped to the United Kingdom at 4°C. On arrival the cores were sieved, washed with synthetic seawater (Instant Ocean, Aquarium Systems Inc.), and placed in 3 columns (glass, 0.32 m high, 0.1 m internal diameter, containing approximately 1.3 kg of sand). These were equilibrated in 14 tidal cycles before addition of oil and fertilizer. Peristaltic pumps were used to simulate a tidal cycle (maximum bulk flow velocity of 0.33 m·h^{-1} matching peak spring tides at the original sample site). The sediment at the surface of the core was covered with Arabian light crude oil at 3.7 kg·m^{-2} (weathered naturally to 25% weight loss, and emulsified with 25% seawater) just as the water level was falling after high tide. To provide 73 g·m^{-2} of nitrogen to each column (2% of the oil concentration) (Bartha & Atlas 1987), Inipol EAP22 was added to one core at 984 g·m^{-2}, and Max Bac was added to a second core at 266 g·m^{-2}, 6 h after oil addition. The third column remained as an oiled but unfertilized control. The experiment was carried out at $21 \pm 2°C$.

Sampling Strategy

Previous experience had shown that the oil penetrated unevenly into the surface of the sand. The most consistent distribution was noted in an annular region (0.02 m wide) positioned 0.01 m from the side of the column. Hence, the outer 0.01 m and the central area (0.04 m in diameter) of each core were not sampled. To avoid sampling bias, 18 potential sample points were mapped out in the annular region, and a random number generator was used to select 3 points from each column each sampling day. Samples were taken using a 5-mL (0.01-m-diameter) coring device. The first sample was taken 1 h after the addition of the oil and 6 h before nutrient addition.

Monitoring

CO_2 evolution was monitored daily to assess the respiration rate. Immediately prior to the analysis, the headspace above each column was flushed with soda-lime–filtered air for 5 min to equilibrate the levels of CO_2 in the headspace to ambient levels. Headspace air was then recycled through an Infra Red Gas Analyser (Servomex, UK), and readings of CO_2 concentration were taken regularly over a 5-min period. The CO_2 production rates were calculated by linear regression analysis. Readings were taken whenever possible 1 h after high tide, because respiration was observed to vary with the tidal cycle.

Most probable number (MPN) determinations were used in triplicate on six sampling occasions to estimate the total number of chemoheterotrophic microorganisms and the number of organisms capable of growth on the Arabian light crude oil (Meynell & Meynell 1970). The former was carried out by studying growth on marine broth (Difco), which supports growth of most marine chemoheterotrophs, and the latter was conducted using the "Sheen Screen" method described by Brown and Braddock (1990) and modified by Venosa et al. (1993), positively identifying hydrocarbon degraders by both crude oil emulsification and reduction of 2-(4-iodophenyl)-3-(4-nitrophenyl)-5-phenyltetrazolium chloride by microbial electron transport system activity. The results were expressed per gram dry sand.

Samples of the tidal seawater leaving the cores were taken regularly and stored at $-20°C$. At the end of the experiment, the organic and inorganic nitrogen in the seawater was oxidized to nitrate using a method modified from Shepherd and Davies (1981) and analyzed by liquid chromatography (Lee & Levy 1992).

Triplicate sediment samples removed on each sampling occasion from each column were pooled, the oil was extracted, and the extracts were analyzed using gas chromatography with flame ionization detection (GC/FID), according to the method given in Lee et al. (1993). At the end of the experiment, three further samples were taken from each core and analyzed separately. The oil was separated into aromatic and aliphatic fractions using column chromatography on silica gel with a bed of sodium sulphate as drying agent, and using successive elutions of light petroleum (boiling point 40 to 60°C) and light petroleum:DCM (1:1) respectively. The hydrocarbon fractions were analyzed by GC/FID (using a Hewlett Packard 5890 instrument) and gas chromatograph with mass spectrometry detection. Data acquisition and processing was carried out using a Vax-based Fisons Multichrom 2 data system. Quantitation was achieved by addition of internal standards to both fractions (heptadecylcyclohexane, naphthalene d8, phenanthrene d10, and dodecylperhydroanthracene).

Statistics

The numbers of microorganisms determined using the MPN technique were analyzed statistically according to the method described by Jones (1979). The oil chemistry results were analyzed using a one-way analysis of variance (ANOVA), which assumes the errors are normally and independently distributed, with a zero mean and constant variance. The model adequacy was checked by plotting the residuals and found to be satisfactory. Orthogonal contrasts were used to partition the treatment sum of squares into independent components, allowing the comparison of individual treatment effects.

RESULTS AND DISCUSSION

CO_2 Evolution

The evolution rates of CO_2 from the control core increased approximately 11-fold over the first 5 days following oil addition, thereafter achieving steady state (Figure 1), presumably as a result of oil biodegradation (Atlas & Bartha, 1972). The cores treated with Max Bac gave similar evolution rates until day 15, when a small increase in evolution rate over the control was detected (Figure 1). The pattern of CO_2 evolution with oleophilic fertilizer was markedly different. Three days after Inipol EAP22 addition, CO_2 evolution had increased dramatically above that noted in the other cores, peaked at day 5 and then declined, but maintained moderately high activity (approximately twice that in the control) until the end of the experiment (Figure 1). The elevated values recorded on days 15 and 41 were probably due to measurements being taken 3 h later than normal on those days; respiration rate varied during the tidal cycle, so absolute changes were less reliable than relative differences between treatments.

Estimates of Microbial Numbers

All columns showed a rapid increase in both total chemoheterotrophic (H) and oil-degrading (O) organisms following addition of oil at day 0 (Figure 2). By day 5, both the control and Max Bac columns had similar populations and were approaching a plateau at new levels, achieving a mean of 5×10^7 chemoheterotrophs, and 2.5×10^7 oil-degraders per g of sand. These numbers remained relatively constant for the remainder of the experiment, although the number of

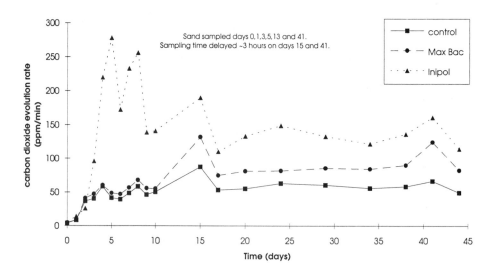

FIGURE 1. Absolute carbon dioxide evolution rates over the course of the experiment.

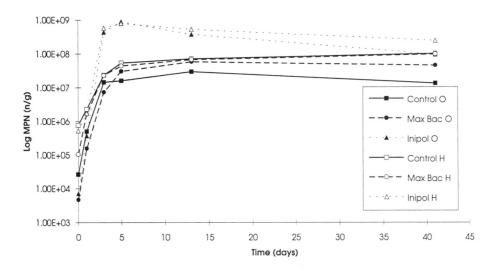

FIGURE 2. Heterotrophic (H) and oil-degrading (O) organisms measured using the MPN technique.

hydrocarbon-degraders in the Max Bac-treated sand remained consistently higher than that recorded in the control (Figure 2).

The Inipol-treated column showed a different pattern (Figure 2). By day 5 total chemoheterotrophs had achieved $8 \times 10^8 \cdot g^{-1}$, and approximately the same number were recorded as oil-degraders. This peak coincided with highest head-space CO_2 generation rate (Figure 1). Thereafter numbers declined slowly, and at the end of observations (day 41), a mean of $2.5 \times 10^8 \cdot g^{-1}$ chemoheterotrophs with $10^8 \cdot g^{-1}$ hydrocarbon-degraders were recorded.

Using the statistical methods described by Jones (1979), there was no signifi-cant difference between the numbers of microorganisms in the Max Bac column and that recorded in the control (Table 1). However, the chemoheterotrophic and hydrocarbon-degrading microbial populations were significantly different from the control in the Inipol-treated column (Table 1). The difference is greatest between 3 and 5 days after treatment, and was most marked for hydrocarbon degraders ($p < 0.01$). Thereafter, the magnitude of the differences declined and were statistically insignificant ($p > 0.1$) by day 41.

Nutrient Analysis

No detectable increase in nitrogen concentration was found in the effluent seawater from the core treated with Max Bac (Figure 3). This suggests that any nutrient released from this product was assimilated rapidly by the microbial com-munity, or that it may not have been released. In contrast, nitrogen was detected in effluent seawater from the Inipol-treated core directly after product addition (Figure 3). Maximum releases of nitrogen from the Inipol-treated column were

TABLE 1. Numbers of microorganisms measured in each sand column. Significant differences in the treated columns were recorded in comparison to the control.

Mean log (hydrocarbon degraders)/g sand			
Time (d)	Control	Max Bac	Inipol
0	4.4	3.6 (NS)	3.7 (NS)
1	5.5	5.1 (NS)	5.4 (NS)
3	7.2	6.9 (NS)	8.6 [a]
5	7.2	7.5 (NS)	8.9 [a]
13	7.4	7.7 (NS)	8.5 [b]
41	7.0	7.6 (NS)	6.7 (NS)
Mean log (total chemoheterotrophs)/g sand			
Time (d)	Control	Max Bac	Inipol
0	5.5	5.0 (NS)	5.6 (NS)
1	6.3	6.2 (NS)	6.2 (NS)
3	7.2	7.2 (NS)	8.7 [a]
5	7.7	7.6 (NS)	8.9 [b]
13	7.9	7.8 (NS)	8.7 [c]
41	7.9	8.0 (NS)	8.4 (NS)
(a) $p < 0.01$	(b) $p < 0.05$	(c) $p < 0.10$	

noted 5 days after addition of the nutrient, suggesting the product was retained to some extent in the oiled sand.

Chemical Analysis

Using the phytane:C_{18} ratios as an indicator of oil degradation, the highest rates of oil biodegradation occurred in the core treated with Inipol EAP22 (Figure 4). Because there appeared to be a 5- to 7-day lag before crude oil composition changed in this column, changes in respiration and microbial numbers during this period are probably related largely to preferential biodegradation of organic components within Inipol EAP22. Enhanced crude oil decomposition was noted from 13 days after Inipol treatment. There was no evidence that Max Bac stimulated natural oil biodegradation rates relative to those observed in the control.

At the end of the experiment, the control, Max Bac, and Inipol-treated columns were found to contain on average 23.6, 26.6, and 18.2 mg total petroleum hydrocarbons per g sand. Statistical analysis using a one-way ANOVA showed that the addition of fertilizer had a significant effect on the oil concentration

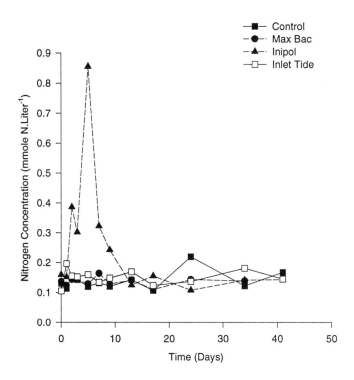

FIGURE 3. Nitrogen concentration in the effluent seawater from each column.

(p = 0.00018). Orthogonal contrasts showed there to be a significantly higher concentration of oil in the Max Bac column (p = 0.013), which could be due to unequal oil penetration. The difference between the mean results from the Max Bac and control columns, versus the Inipol-treated column was highly significant (p = 0.000081). Clearly Max Bac did not stimulate oil biodegradation in comparison to the control, whereas Inipol EAP22 may have stimulated oil removal. The mechanism for oil removal may be physical mobilization by the surfactants in Inipol EAP22, or enhanced rates of biodegradation.

Ratios of selected hydrocarbon fractions to the conserved biomarkers 17α, 21β hopane (Bragg et al. 1994) and phytane were used to establish whether enhanced biodegradation had occurred (Table 2). In each case, the ratio suggested that most biodegradation had occurred in the column treated with Inipol EAP22, although the differences were small. Statistical analysis (Table 3) showed that fertilizer treatment stimulated the biodegradation of saturated hydrocarbons, phenanthrene, and the substituted phenanthrenes (p < 0.1). The difference for the total resolvable aromatic hydrocarbons (p = 0.11) was just outside the range generally accepted as statistically significant. Contrasts showed that there was no significant difference between the control columns and that treated with Max Bac, except for the total GC resolvable saturated:hopane ratio (p = 0.083). The mean ratios found in the Max Bac-treated and control columns, were significantly different from

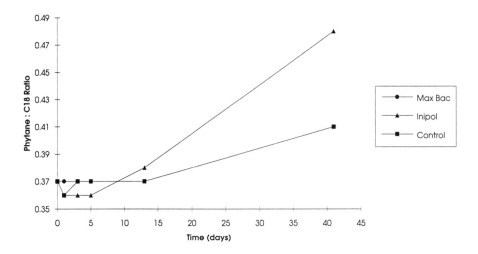

FIGURE 4. The change in phytane:C_{18} ratio of Arabian light crude oil during the experiment.

that found in the Inipol-treated sand (Table 3). The lower significant difference noted for the total GC resolvable saturated hydrocarbon:hopane ratio was probably due to the differences between the control and the Max Bac column.

SUMMARY AND CONCLUSIONS

Inipol EAP22 appeared to be the most effective bioremediation agent on the basis of microbiological and chemical data. The total CO_2 evolution rate in the Inipol-treated column increased to approximately five times the control at day 5, then fell gradually to plateau at approximately twice the rate recorded from the control column from day 15 to day 44. Total chemoheterotrophs increased from 10^5 to $10^8 \cdot g^{-1}$ sand by day 5, with the number of hydrocarbon-degraders increasing to a similar level. By day 41, with a reduction in available hydrocarbon, the average number of chemoheterotrophs had fallen to $10^7 \cdot g^{-1}$ and the hydrocarbon-degraders had reduced to $5 \times 10^6 \cdot g^{-1}$. The residual oil showed depletion of C_{18} (relative to phytane) at more than twice the rate of the control (approximately 25% change compared to 10% change over 41 days), although no evidence of enhanced oil biodegradation was noted until 13 days after treatment. At the end of the experiment, significantly more oil was biodegraded in the Inipol-treated column than in the control, as determined by the ratios of C_{18}:phytane, total GC resolvable aromatic hydrocarbons:hopane, and the sum of phenanthrene, methyl phenanthrenes, and dimethyl phenanthrenes:hopane. However, the differences were not dramatic (Tables 2 and 3).

The evidence therefore suggests that organic components of Inipol EAP22 (e.g., oleic acid) may be preferentially decomposed by microorganisms with a

TABLE 2. Chemical analyses of oil remaining in the columns at the end of the experiment.

Ratio to Conserved Biomarkers	Mean Value		
	Control	Max Bac	Inipol
C_{18}:phytane	3.12	3.03	2.78
Total GC resolvable saturated hydrocarbons:17α, 21β hopane	551	663	518
Total GC resolvable aromatic hydrocarbons:17α, 21β hopane	180	193	136
Sum of phenanthrene, 1, 2 & 3 methyl phenanthrenes and 1, 2 & 3 dimethyl phenanthrenes: 17α, 21β hopane	4.48	4.73	1.85

concomitant release of CO_2. This may have caused the significant increase in the total number of chemoheterotrophs and the proportion of competent hydrocarbon-degrading microorganisms noted in the Inipol-treated column. Lee and Levy (1989) also proposed that the microbiota of Long Cove preferentially metabolized the organic component of Inipol EAP22. Rivet et al. (1993) demonstrated that the oleic acid portion of Inipol EAP22 was mineralized by a hydrocarbon-degrading microorganism before the onset of alkane degradation. Our results and those of others concur with the hypothesis proposed by Basseres and Ladousse (1992), that Inipol EAP22 initially stimulates the hydrocarbon-degrading microbial population by supplying readily degradable organic carbon and subsequently encourages hydrocarbon decomposition.

All chemical and biological parameters measured in the sand column treated with Max Bac were barely distinguishable from the control over the course of the experiment. Only a very gradual rise in total respiration rate, to 1.5 times control at day 44, was noted (Figure 1). The results of the chemical analysis showed no evidence of enhanced biodegradation (Figure 3, Table 2). Both the control and the Max Bac-treated cores showed total chemoheterotrophs increasing from 10^5 to $10^7 \cdot g^{-1}$ with oil addition, and both showed a rapid increase in hydro-carbon degraders by day 5, with a slow decline in total numbers and the number of hydrocarbon degraders thereafter. Visual observations of the Max Bac-treated column confirmed that the slow-release pellets were dissolving very slowly, many persisting to termination of the experiment.

Under the simulated conditions of the experiment, with vertical flow but no horizontal flow or wash-off, Inipol EAP22 was the most effective bioremediation agent. However, the effect on oil biodegradation was small. This result apparently contrasts with the field observations of Lee and Levy (1987) where Inipol EAP22 had no detectable stimulatory effect on oil biodegradation. These authors

TABLE 3. Statistical analyses of the ratios of selected hydrocarbons to phytane and hopane on Day 41.

Ratio of Selected Hydrocarbon Components to Nonbiodegradable Biomarkers	One-Way Analysis of Variance (p)		
	Overall Treatment Effect	Control vs. Max Bac	Inipol EAP22 vs. (Max Bac & Control)
C_{18}:phytane	0.000045	0.38	0.000015
Total GC resolvable saturated hydrocarbons: 17α, 21β hopane	0.079	0.083	0.10
Total GC resolvable aromatic hydrocarbons: 17α, 21β hopane	0.11	0.61	0.046
Sum of phenanthrene, 1, 2 & 3 methyl phenanthrenes and 1, 2 & 3 dimethyl phenanthrenes: 17α, 21β hopane	0.00017	0.73	0.000056

noted a rapid decline in nitrogen concentrations in the sand treated with Inipol EAP22, supporting their hypothesis that the fertilizer was being washed from the sand, a finding also supported by the observations of Safferman (1991). Bragg et al. (1994) demonstrated that the success of bioremediation was critically dependent on increasing the nitrogen concentration in the interstitial water of the contaminated shoreline. Clearly in this experiment, the Inipol EAP22 persisted for a longer period in the sand, and a significant increase in biodegradation of the oil was observed in 41 days. We propose that the horizontal component of the sea motion (wave energy), surface and subsurface runoff, and rainfall may be significant factors, influencing the persistence, and therefore efficacy of Inipol EAP22 in sand. The absence of horizontal (especially wave) energy may also possibly explain the ineffectiveness of Max Bac in the laboratory columns, as additional in situ energy sources may stimulate pellet disruption and hence nutrient release.

Our research points to the importance of the interactions between the physical and chemical form of bioremediation agents and of the chemical and physical processes occurring in the environment. Although microcosm-scale studies are a valuable method of studying the action of bioremediation agents, research must be validated by experimental plot studies in the field.

ACKNOWLEDGMENTS

Additional Chemical analysis was conducted by Dr. D. M. Jones at the Department of Fossil Fuels and Petroleum Geochemistry, University of Newcastle upon Tyne, UK. This work was funded by the Marine Pollution Control Unit (Coastguard Agency) of the UK Department of Transport, and the Department of Fisheries and Oceans, Canada, and the University of Sunderland, UK.

REFERENCES

Atlas, R. M., and R. Bartha. 1972. "Degradation and Mineralization of Petroleum in Seawater: Limitation by Nitrogen and Phosphorous." *Biotechnology and Bioengineering 52:* 149-156.

Bartha, R., and R. M. Atlas. 1987. "Transport and Transformation of Petroleum: Biological Processes." In D. F. Boesch and N. N. Rabalais (Eds.), *Long Term Environmental Effects of Offshore Oil and Gas Development*, pp. 287-341. Elsevier Applied Science Publishers Ltd., London, UK.

Basseres, A., and A. Ladousse. 1992. "Experience in Enhanced Bioremediation Processes on Shorelines." In *CONCAWE/DGMK Symposium Remediation of Oil Spills*. Hamburg, 18-21 May 1992. CONCAWE, Brussels, Belgium.

Bragg, J. R., R. C. Prince, E. J. Harner, and R. M. Atlas. 1994. "Effectiveness of Bioremediation for the *Exxon Valdez* Oil Spill." *Nature 368*(6470): 413-418.

Brown, E. J., and J. F. Braddock. 1990. "Sheen Screen: A Miniaturized Most-Probable-Number Method for the Enumeration of Oil-Degrading Microorganisms." *Applied and Environmental Microbiology 56:* 3895-3896.

Grace-Sierra International B.V. 1993. *Max Bac Controlled Release Nutrient Package.* Rijnzathe 6, 3454 PV De Meern, Netherlands.

Jones, J. G. 1979. *A Guide to Methods for Estimating Microbial Numbers and Biomass in Freshwater.* Freshwater Biological Association, Ferry House, Ambleside, Cumbria, UK.

Ladousse, A., and B. Tramier. 1991. "Results of 12 Years of Research in Spilled Oil Bioremediation: INIPOL EAP22." *Proceedings of 1991 International Oil Spill Conference.* pp. 577-581. American Petroleum Institute Pub. No. 4529, Washington, DC.

Lee, K., and E. M. Levy. 1987. "Enhanced Biodegradation of a Light Crude Oil in Sandy Beaches." *Proceedings of 1987 International Oil Spill Conference.* pp. 411-416. American Petroleum Institute Pub. No. 4452., Washington, DC.

Lee, K., and E. M. Levy. 1989. "Enhancement of the Natural Biodegradation of Condensate and Crude Oil on Beaches of Atlantic Canada." *Proceedings of 1989 International Oil Spill Conference.* pp. 479-486. American Petroleum Institute Pub. No. 4479, Washington, DC.

Lee, K., and E. M. Levy. 1992. "Microbial Degradation of Petroleum in an Intertidal Beach Environment - In Situ Sediment Enclosures Study." In *Marine Ecosystem Enclosed Experiments*, pp. 140-155. International Development Centre, Ottawa, Canada.

Lee, K., G. H. Tremblay, and E. M. Levy. 1993. "Bioremediation: Application of Slow Release Fertilizers on Low-Energy Shorelines." *Proceedings of 1993 International Oil Spill Conference (Prevention, Preparedness, Response)*, pp. 449-454. American Petroleum Institute Publication No. 4580, Washington, DC.

Meynell, G. G., and E. Meynell. 1970. *Theory and Practice in Experimental Bacteriology.* 2nd ed., Cambridge University Press, Cambridge, UK.

Pritchard, P. H., and C. F. Costa. 1991. "EPA's Alaska Oil Spill Bioremediation Project." *Environ. Sci. Technol. 25:* 372-379.

Rivet, L., G. Mille, A. Basseres, A. Ladousse, C. Gerin, M. Acquavia, and J-C Bertrand. 1993. "n-Alkane Biodegradation by a Marine Bacterium in the Presence of an Oleophilic Nutriment." *Biotechnol. Lett. 15*(6): 637-640.

Safferman, S. I. 1991. "Selection of Nutrients to Enhance Biodegradation for the Remediation of Oil Spilled on Beaches." *Proceedings of the 1991 Oil Spill Conference*, pp. 571-576. American Petroleum Institute Publication No. 4529, Washington, DC.

Shepherd, R. J., and Davies, I. M. 1981. "A Semi-Automatic Alkaline Peroxodisulfate Method for Routine Determination of Total Dissolved Nitrogen in Seawater." *Analytica Chimica Acta 130:* 55-63.

Sirvins, A., and M. Angles. 1986. "Development and Effects on the Marine Environment of a Nutrient Formula to Control Pollution by Petroleum Hydrocarbons." In C. S. Giam and H.J.M. Dou (Eds.), *Strategies and Advanced Techniques for Marine Pollution Studies: Mediterranean Sea*, pp. 357-404. Springer-Verlag, Berlin, Germany, NATO ASI Series, Vol. G9.

Sveum, P., and A. Ladousse. 1989. "Biodegradation of the Oil in the Arctic: Enhancement by Oil-Soluble Fertilizer Application." *Proceedings of 1989 International Oil Spill Conference*, pp. 436-446. American Petroleum Institute Pub. No. 4529., Washington, DC.

Swannell, R.P.J., and I. M. Head. 1994. "Bioremediation Comes of Age." *Nature 368*(6470): 396-397.

Venosa, A. D., M. Kadkhodayan, D. W. King, B. A. Wrenn, J. R. Haines, T. Herrington, K. Strohmeier, and M. T. Suidan. 1993. "Testing the Efficacy of Oil Spill Bioremediation Products." In *Proceedings of 1993 International Oil Spill Conference (Prevention, Preparedness, Response)*, pp. 487-493. American Petroleum Institute Pub. No. 4580, Washington, DC.

Surfactant-Aided Recovery/ In Situ Bioremediation for Oil-Contaminated Sites

Jean Ducreux, Marc Bavière, Paulo Seabra,
Olivier Razakarisoa, Gerhard Shäfer, and Clothilde Arnaud

ABSTRACT

Bioremediation has been the most commonly used method way for in situ cleaning of soils contaminated with low-volatility petroleum products such as diesel oil. However, whatever the process (bioventing, bioleaching, etc.), it is a time-consuming technique that may be efficiency limited by both accessibility and too high concentrations of contaminants. A currently developed process aims at quickly recovering part of the residual oil in the vadose and capillary zones by surfactant flushing, then activating in situ biodegradation of the remaining oil in the presence of the same or other surfactants. The process has been tested in laboratory columns and in an experimental pool (25 m × 12 m × 3 m), located at the Institut Franco-Allemand de Recherche sur l'Environnement (IFARE) in Strasbourg, France. Laboratory column studies were carried out to fit physico-chemical and hydraulic parameters of the process to the field conditions. The possibility of recovering more than 80% of the oil in the flushing step was shown. For the biodegradation step, forced aeration as a mode of oxygen supply, coupled with nutrient injection aided by surfactants, was tested. The results of optimized surfactant treatment show reduced final oil content and composition. The experimental pool was packed with homogeneous fine sand, which was infiltrated by 476 L of diesel oil. After removal of remaining free product by hydraulic techniques, a large amount of the entrapped residual oil was displaced by surfactant flushing in both horizontal and vertical migration zones. In situ bioremediation is still in progress.

INTRODUCTION

An increasing number of experimental studies have shown the potential usefulness of surfactants to enhance soil contaminant biodegradation by increasing residual contaminant bioavailability (Ducreux et al. 1994). For in situ remediation, nutrients can be added, if necessary, at an optimized rate to the injected water, together with surfactants to increase biodegradation kinetics relative to simple processes (such as bioventing) that consist only of forced aeration of the soil. It was also shown that surfactants can mobilize a fraction of a low-viscosity oil phase trapped as residual saturation in both the vadose zone and capillary fringe as a nonmobile discontinuous phase (Abdul et al. 1990; Ang & Abdul 1991; Oma et al. 1992; Kimball 1992; Peters et al. 1992; Bavière et al. 1993). The physical removal of a large fraction of the residual oil phase can reduce bioremediation times.

The reported work is a part of a program that aims at developing a process combining surfactant-aided extraction and biodegradation of residual oil on a modular alternative basis. It involved laboratory optimization of different parameters and a large-basin experiment still in progress. A field demonstration test is planned.

LABORATORY INVESTIGATIONS

Two aerobic biodegradation experiments were carried out on three unsaturated sand columns contaminated by diesel oil. Two columns were flushed by applying surfactant solution drainage before the biodegradation process. The third column was not flushed with the surfactant solution. The sand columns (6.0-cm i.d. × 80.0-cm long) were packed with 3 kg quartz sand with a hydraulic conductivity of 8×10^{-4} m/s. An unsaturated zone was created. A mixture of oil-degrading bacteria (Ducreux et al. 1994) was then injected into the columns from both the top and the bottom. The columns were then contaminated from the top with oil (injection flowrate: 60 mL/h) and allowed to drain to residual saturation. The oil residual saturation was in the range of 11 to 16% of the porous volume (Vp).

Surfactant-Aided Drainage

In the first experiments, activated surfactant drainage was carried out to mobilize, in a short period of time, a large part of oil irreducibly trapped in the sand. Eight pore volumes (Vp) of a RESOL 30 solution (containing nonionic and anionic biodegradable surfactants at a concentration of 10 g/L and 1.5 g/L sodium chloride) was passed down through columns 1 and 2, under a constant hydraulic head of 10 cm, followed by 2 Vp of washing water. The mobilized diesel oil was quantified both by oil decantation and by analyzing the emulsified oil in water (after dilution in isopropanol [1:1,V/V]) by gas chromatography (GC) on a nonpolar capillary column. The concentration of residual oil in sand was determined to calculate the surfactant drainage efficiency.

Figure 1 presents the recovery of residual oil from the sand columns by surfactant-aided drainage (Phase 1). More than 90% of the residual oil in column 1 was removed by the surfactant flushing. About 90% of the displaced oil was recovered after 2 Vp surfactant solution was passed through the column. After surfactant flushing a residual oil concentration of 1.9 g/kg, was found.

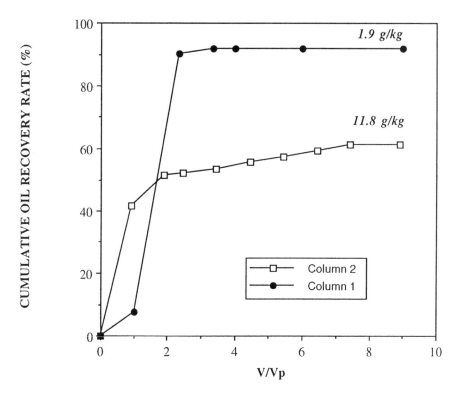

FIGURE 1. Activated oil recovery by using surfactant-aided drainage (Phase 1).

With column 2, it appears that at the end of the first Vp of injected surfactant solution, more than 40% of residual oil entrapped in the sand was mobilized. The total oil recovery rate was 61.4%. In column 2, the residual oil concentration in sand decreased from 31.1 g/kg to 11.8 g/kg. If this result is compared to those obtained with column 1, it could be suggested that this limitation in drainage efficiency is due to an uncontrolled effect of bacteria strains present in the porous medium. In a previous paper (Ducreux et al. 1994), it was shown that oil retention in a porous medium is increased by the presence of microorganisms but with great variability. If the shapes of the curves are compared, it can be noted that the greater part of mobilized oil is recovered after injection of the first two Vp of surfactant solution. Moreover, more than 90% of this oil was easily separated as an oil phase by decantation or centrifugation.

Surfactant-Aided Biodegradation

This step was carried out either after the surfactant treatment or because an aqueous solution containing mineral nutrients (nitrates and phosphates) as the main components and a RESOL 30 solution at a concentration of 0.05 wt % were passed through the sand over 45 days at a flowrate of 1 Vp/24 h (about

0.750 L/h). To be in nonlimiting conditions in oxygen, an air stream was pumped through the porous medium at a flowrate of 1 Vp/h. At the end of the tests, both the concentration and composition of oil in sand and effluents were determined as previously described (Ducreux et al. 1994).

Following the surfactant drainage, the surfactant-aided biodegradation process was applied over a period of 45 days on both columns. Because of the low oil residual concentration obtained after the surfactant drainage step on column 1 (<2.0 g/kg), only the results of the experiment with the higher oil residual concentration (column 2) will be discussed. During the biodegradation phase, a surfactant solution was delivered at a low concentration (0.5 g/L) to columns 1 and 3. Sand column 3, that was not drained by a RESOL 30 solution had a residual oil concentration of 23.3 g/kg.

Tables 1 and 2 show the microbiological enumeration on sand, the chemical characterization of residual oil at the end of the experiment, and the effect of activated surfactant drainage on hydrocarbon biodegradation rate. In Table 1, the nature of residual oil, at different levels in the column, is described. The oil concentration at top, middle, and bottom of column 3 varied greatly, and may be related to the surfactant flushing. In column 2, which was flushed with surfactant, the residual oil concentration after biodegradation was lower (<1 g/kg) than in column 3, which was not flushed with the surfactant, mainly in the bottom of the column (> 13 g/kg). That corresponds to removal of 97.6% and 66.2% of the oil in columns 2 and 3 respectively. In column 3, in spite of pumping air through the sand, the less biodegraded oil corresponds to the oil accumulated on the bottom of the column. This was probably due to stronger oxygen-limiting conditions created by higher oil contents in this part of the porous medium. In both columns, the polar compound percentages decreased from the top to the bottom of the column, and the values were higher in the drained column. In both columns, the bacterial population concentrations were relatively high (>10^8 bacteria/g sand), and the enumeration values were higher in the upper part of the column where the airstream was introduced and the water residual saturation the lowest. The mean values of the residual surfactant concentrations were relatively low (less than 70 mg/kg).

Not all hydrocarbons removed from sand during the experiments were removed by biodegradation. In fact, some of them were washed out in liquid effluents (1.4 g in column 2 and 7.8 g in column 3). Hydrocarbon biodegradation rates (Table 2) were calculated without taking into account these hydrocarbons. The surfactant-aided biodegradation seems to be effective in both columns, even in the column where no surfactant-aided drainage step was carried out. Because of the higher residual oil in the nonflushed column, the total hydrocarbon biodegradation rate appeared lower (54.8%) compared to the rate obtained in the surfactant-flushed column (89.5%). Biodegradation effectiveness was calculated from Figure 2, where the surfactant drainage effect of Phase 1 and the biodegradation process (Phase 2) are compared. The values (0.27 g HC/kg/day for the nonflushed column and 0.23 g HC/kg/day for the flushed column), were relatively similar. Compared to the experiment where no surfactant flushing was used, residual oil left in sand after surfactant flushing was probably trapped in

TABLE 1. Chemical composition of residual oil and microbiological enumeration in sand at end of experiment.

Level in Column		Original Diesel Oil	With Surfactant Drainage				Without Surfactant Drainage			
			Top	Middle	Bottom	Average	Top	Middle	Bottom	Average
Enumeration bacteria/gram sand		—	6.0 E+08	4.0 E+08	2.0 E+08	4.0 E+08	1.2 E+09	6.4 E+08	2.1 E+08	6.8 E+08
Residual oil concentration (mg/kg)		—	978.0	770.0	652.0	800.0	3,366.0	5,357.0	13,543.0	7,422.0
Residual surfactants concentration (mg/kg)		—	52.0	108.0	n.d.	53.3	129.0	52.0	22.1	67.7
Aliphatics (%)	Total	65.3	58.5	58.0	60.0	58.8	54.4	59.3	65.0	62.0
	n-alkanes	16.6	0.7	0.5	0.6	0.6	0.7	0.9	3.9	2.7
Aromatics (%)	Total	33.6	33.0	36.8	35.2	34.8	41.6	38.2	33.0	35.6
Polars (%)	Total	1.1	8.5	5.2	4.8	6.5	4.0	2.5	2.00	2.4

TABLE 2. Percentage of biodegraded hydrocarbons.

	Total (%)	Aliphatics n-alkanes (%)	Iso + cycloalkanes (%)	Aromatics Total (%)	Hydrocarbons Total (%)
With surfactant drainage	90.1	97.0	88.0	88.5	89.5
Without surfactant drainage	57.8	84.7	48.9	48.9	54.8

the smallest pores. Even in that case where the entrapped oil was probably the most unavailable and where its residual concentration was the lowest, the biodegradation process was not limited.

LARGE-SCALE BASIN TEST

The large-scale basin (SCERES: Site Contrôlé Expérimental de Réhabilitation des Eaux et des Sols) is located at the CNRS Campus of Strasbourg-Cronenbourg

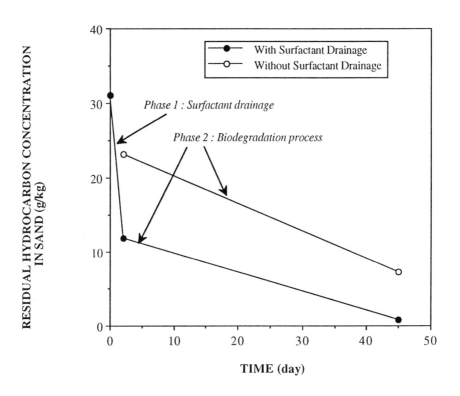

FIGURE 2. Effect of surfactant-aided drainage on residual hydrocarbon concentration in sand.

(France). This project involves an association of scientific and industrial partners (Arnaud et al. 1993). It is a large, impervious concrete basin (25-m-long × 12-m-wide × 3-m-deep) (Figure 3), packed with quartz sand. A sand dome of 1 m thickness was created to get a more accurate depth of the unsaturated zone. After achieving equilibrium state in the aquifer system, 476 L of diesel oil was spilled on the top of the sand dome onto a limited area of 1.5 m diameter, at 2.90 m above the water-table level. A 0.50-m water-table fluctuation was achieved. The shape and the extent of oil contamination are shown in Figure 3. The diameter of the oil impregnation body in the unsaturated zone varied between 1.5 and 1.85 m. The diameter of horizontal extent of the oil phase, in the capillary fringe, was in the range of 5.60 m to 5.90 m. The specific operations and equipment to control oil contamination in the basin were previously described (Razakarisoa et al. 1994). Before applying the combined surfactant-aided recovery/in situ bioremediation process, 122 L of oil was hydraulically recovered by pumping in the central well (recovery rate: 25.6%).

To improve the combined surfactant-aided recovery/in situ bioremediation process, an experiment was performed in a controlled large-scale basin. At first, 19.2 m³ of RESOL 30 solution were injected above the oil-contaminated zone onto the limited area (1.5 m diameter) with a constant hydraulic head. That volume was determined on the basis of a calculated porous volume of about 4 m³.

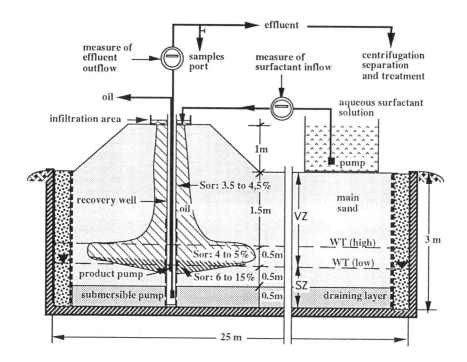

FIGURE 3. Scheme of the large-scale basin test. (Sor = residual oil saturation; VZ = vadose zone; SZ = saturated zone; WT = water table.)

It was shown, in laboratory tests, that no more oil was mobilized after 4 or 5 Vp injected surfactant (Figure 1). The initial injection flowrate was fixed at 4.7 m³/h by scaling up from the values measured in laboratory columns. At the same time, the groundwater level was lowered (10 to 12 cm) by pumping to form a catchment, just under the treated zone, which traps the removed oil and emulsion. A part of the oil in effluents was separated by continuous centrifugation.

The kinetics of oil recovery during the surfactant-activated drainage process is shown in Figure 4. The total oil recovery volume, corresponding to 19.2 m³ of injected surfactant solution, can be extrapolated to 60 L. Knowing that the oil residual saturation volume in the oil vertical migration zone (surfactant-flushed zone) has been estimated at 128 L by controlling the fluxes carried out during the experiment, the oil recovery rate could be considered about 50%. This result will have to be confirmed by soil core sampling results. The 42.4% of removed oil was very quickly decantable. The surfactant-aided/in situ bio-degradation process is still in progress.

CONCLUSION

By combining a preliminary surfactant-aided recovery technique to a surfactant-aided in situ bioremediation process, the residual oil concentration

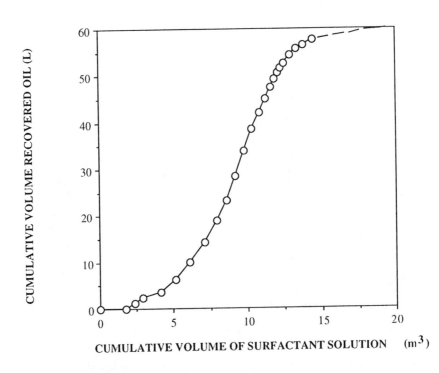

FIGURE 4. Oil recovery in the large-scale basin test.

in soils contaminated by nonvolatile or semivolatile hydrocarbons greatly decreases. To obtain the same level of remediation using only the biodegradation process, the duration of the experiment will have to be greatly extended.

The first results obtained on a large-scale basin test seem to corroborate the efficiency of surfactant-activated drainage proved in laboratory column tests. The bioremediation experiment, still in progress at this controlled site, will improve our understanding of the use of that new technology.

ACKNOWLEDGMENTS

This work has been carried out as part of the Franco-Italian EUREKA project "RESCOPP," funded in France by the Ministère de la Recherche. Partners for the development of the studied process are Compagnie Générale des Eaux, Elf, and IFP. The authors are grateful for the support of P. Muntzer (IFARE), D. Ballerini and C. Bocard (IFP), G. Pottecher (CGE), and A. Perez (Elf).

REFERENCES

Abdul, A. S., T. L. Gibson, and D. N. Rai. 1990. "Selection of Surfactants for the Removal of Petroleum Products from Shallow Sandy Aquifers." *Ground Water, 28*(6): 920-926.

Ang, C. C., and A. S. Abdul. 1991. "Aqueous Surfactant Washing of Residual Oil Contamination from Sandy Soil." *Ground Water Monitoring Review*, Spring: 121-127.

Arnaud, C., J. Ducreux, P. Muntzer, G. Pottecher, G. Schäfer. 1993. "An Experimental Site to Improve Soil and Groundwater Decontamination." In F. Arendt, G. J. Annokée, R. Bosman and W. J. van den Brink (Eds.), *Contaminated Soil '93*, pp. 789-797. Kluwer Academic Publishers, The Netherlands.

Bavière, M., J. Ducreux, and N. Monin. 1993. "Remediation of Soils Contaminated by Petroleum Products with Surfactants." Paper No. 430333, Presented at *First World Congress on Emulsion*. Paris, France, October 19-22.

Ducreux, J., D. Ballerini, and C. Bocard. 1994. "The Role of Surfactants in Enhanced In Situ Bioremediation." In R. E. Hinchee, B. C. Alleman, R. E. Hoeppel, and R. N. Miller (Eds.), *Hydrocarbon Bioremediation*, pp. 237-242. Lewis Publishers, Boca Raton, FL.

Kimball, S. L. 1992. "Surfactant-Enhanced Soil Flushing: An Overview of an In Situ Remedial Technology for Soils Contaminated with Hydrophobic Hydrocarbons." In *Hydrocarbon Contaminated Soil*, pp. 629-640. Lewis Publishers, Boca Raton, FL.

Oma, K., D. J. Wilson, and R. D. Mutch, Jr. 1992. "Surfactant Flushing/Washing: Economics of an Innovative Remedial Process Including Recovery and Recycle." In *Proc. Fourth Ann. Hazardous Materials Manag. Conf./Central*, HazMat '91 Central, Rosemont, IL, p. 68.

Peters, R. W., C. D. Montemagno, L. Shem, and B. A. Lewis. 1992. "Surfactant Screening of Diesel-Contaminated Soil." *Hazardous Waste & Hazardous Materials, 9*(2): 113-136. Mary Ann Liebert, Inc., Publishers.

Razakarisoa, O., P. Muntzer, C. Ott, G. Schäfer, L. Zilliox, and J. Ducreux. 1994. "Evaluation of the Degree and Extent of Aquifer Contamination by Diesel Oil in an Experimental Controlled Site." In Proc. of the *International Conference on Restoration and Protection of the Environment II*. Patras, Greece, August 24-26.

Biodegradation of Oil Refinery Wastes

Julian M. Myers, Ben S. Banipal, and Charles W. Fisher

ABSTRACT ━━━━━━━━━━━━━━━━━━━━━━━━

Land treatment of oil refinery wastes has been used as a disposal method for decades. More recently, numerous laboratory studies have been performed attempting to quantify degradation rates of more toxic polycyclic aromatic hydrocarbon compounds (PAHs). This paper examines the results of treatability testing in the evaluation of biodegradation as a treatment method to achieve site-specific cleanup criteria. Full-scale biodegradation operations are described as applied at an abandoned oil-refining facility. Also presented are degradation rates for organic compounds for which cleanup criteria have been established. Results of analysis of degradation indicate that degradation rates that were observed in the laboratory can be met and exceeded in the field under rigorous engineering controls and that the site-specific cleanup criteria can be attained.

INTRODUCTION

The 100-acre Macmillan Ring-Free Oil Company site is located in rural Norphlet Township, Arkansas. It is bordered by a residential subdivision and the Norphlet Public School on the west, Hayes Creek on the north and east, and Massey Creek and lowlands associated with the creek on the south. Crude oil processing at the site began in 1929. Unlined surface impoundments used to store crude oil wastes periodically overflowed and contaminated two adjacent creeks. Waste generated by oil refining and water treatment operations at the facility consists of volatile and semivolatile organic compounds. The primary contaminants of concern are PAHs.

Two 0.8-hectare land treatment units (LTUs) were constructed to biodegrade approximately 33,000 m^3 of oil refinery wastes that threaten nearby water bodies. PAH-degradation rate constants and half-life values were determined in the laboratory using a mixture of refinery wastes (API 1987). Full-scale treatment of PAHs in LTUs is beginning to be documented in the literature (Sims et al. 1994). In addition, this project is contributing to the U.S. Environmental Protection Agency's (U.S. EPA) call for full-scale biodegradation data for inclusion in several EPA treatment results databases (EPA 1994).

EXPERIMENTAL PROCEDURES AND MATERIALS

A laboratory biodegradation treatability study was performed to determine if biodegradation was feasible given the contaminant type(s), concentrations, and soil matrix. The study also determined the presence of indigenous bacteria and the population levels, whether they were hydrocarbon-utilizing bacteria, and which genera of bacteria were present. An on-site pilot biodegradation assessment of these wastes focused on optimizing the biodegradation processes and provided evidence of attainment of site-specific cleanup criteria. The pilot assessment provided evidence of reduction in contaminant concentrations to below site-specific cleanup criteria.

Full-scale biodegradation LTU construction began in the summer of 1994 and was completed in the fall of that year. The following discussion describes the methodology utilized for full-scale biotreatment operations to establish site-specific field degradation rates of PAH compounds.

Figure 1 depicts the schematic design for biodegradation operations. Components of the operation include an LTU designed for optimum precipitation control, a bacteria-culturing bioreactor, and an irrigation/bacterial application system supplied by the fire-water pond. A dissolved-air flotation water treatment system is currently being utilized as a leachate treatment system. An initial batch of approximately 2,300 m^3 of contaminated soil was placed into each LTU for biodegradation. A comprehensive air monitoring and sampling program was conducted prior to and concurrently with lagoon excavation and biodegradation operations. Because of the large size of the LTUs and the study of volatilization during treatment in the laboratory (API 1987), no attempt was made to measure the degree of volatilization of contaminants from the LTUs.

Biodegradation Operations

Table 1 lists the operating parameters for the LTUs. Environmental variables which were beyond engineering control (temperature and indigenous phosphorus concentrations) are listed as they were recorded. All other variables, at least partially controllable, are listed as preferable ranges and were generally observed in the field. Table 2 contains test methods that assisted in monitoring and maintenance of the desired parameter range. Approximately 1 kg of prilled ammonium nitrate was applied per m^3 of the LTU soils every 2 to 3 weeks (as nutrient testing indicated and moisture content allowed). Although an optimum N:P ratio was not maintained, it was deemed unreasonable to apply the amount of nitrogen necessary to achieve this ratio given the indigenous phosphorus concentration. Indigenous soil bacteria (including *Pseudomonas stutzeri*) were cultured in a 3,785-L bioreactor. The bacteria were applied to the soils using a wheel-line irrigation system as illustrated in Figure 1. In addition, freeze-dried bacteria purchased from Environmental Remediation, Inc. were cultured for their ability to degrade the more recalcitrant petroleum hydrocarbon constituents. Tilling of the contaminated soils was performed weekly for homogenization, reduction of

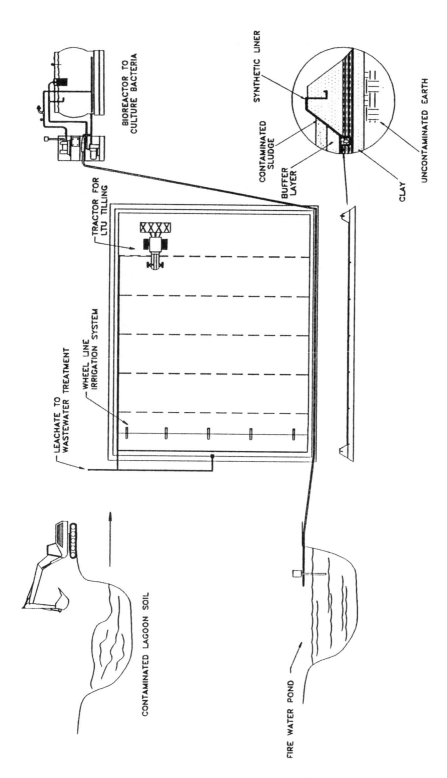

FIGURE 1. Schematic of biodegradation operations.

TABLE 1. Land treatment unit operating parameters.

Soil Temperature (°C)	Moisture Content (%)	Tilling Frequency	Nitrate Nitrogen (ppm)	Phosphorus (ppm)	pH (S.U.)	Bacterial Population (colonies/gram)
10-20	65-75	weekly	50-150	25-250	7.1-7.7	10^6-10^{14}

soil aggregate size, oxygenation of the soils, and distribution of nutrient and bacterial amendments.

Biological Monitoring

An on-site laboratory was established to perform the first four tests listed in Table 2: soil moisture content, particle size analysis, soil nutrient analyses (including nitrate, nitrite, ammonia nitrogen, phosphorus, potassium, and pH), and microbiological analyses including total heterotrophic bacteria plate counts. Microbiological and nutrient testing were conducted to aid in maintenance of

TABLE 2. Summary of biodegradation test methods.

Parameter	Test Method
Moisture content	LINCOLN soil moisture meter and gravimetric
Particle-size analysis of soils	ASTM: D 422-63 Standard Test Method for Particle-Size Analysis of Soils
Nitrate nitrogen, nitrite nitrogen, ammonia nitrogen, phosphorus, potassium, pH	Lamotte, Inc. Combination soil test kit: SOILTEST, Inc.
Heterotrophic bacterial population colony-forming units (CFUs)	STANDARD METHODS for the Examination of Water and Wastewater. APHA:AWWA:WPCF Method 907 (modified for soil)(15th Edition, 1980)
Hydrocarbon-utilizing bacterial population (HCCFUs)	Bushnell & Haas media plus hydrocarbon substrate. Method 907 as referenced above
Bacterial identification (typing)	BIOLOG, Inc. Bacterial identification system
Volatile aromatic compounds (BTEX)	EPA SW-846 Method 8020 Gas chromatography/photoionization detection
Base neutral/acid extractable compounds (BNAs)	EPA SW-846 method 8270 Gas chromatography/mass spectroscopy

the LTU operational parameters. The goal of the monitoring was to ascertain that environmental factors and concentrations of nutrients were optimized to expedite degradation of contaminants. Enumeration of both the heterotrophic and the hydrocarbon-utilizing bacterial populations was performed to ascertain that populations were sufficient for degradation and to correlate population densities with contaminant degradation results. Bacterial strains were identified to ensure the species present were consistent with those identified in treatability testing as known hydrocarbon degraders.

Soil Sampling and Analysis

There were two principal objectives for the sampling and analysis of the soil being treated in the LTUs: monitoring the biological parameters to optimize biological degradation of the targeted compounds, and monitoring the degradation of these compounds.

Health-risk-based concentrations associated with 1E-06 cancer risk were furnished by the U.S. EPA Regional Toxic Integration Coordinator (EPA 1991a,b,c). Based on these health-risk concentrations, site-specific cleanup levels were established. Table 3 lists the cleanup criteria. Soil sampling was conducted on 8-m grid nodes superimposed over the LTUs at a proportion of one composite or grab sample per 230 m^3 of soil. The samples were analyzed for the compounds for which cleanup criteria had been established.

RESULTS

Laboratory treatability results indicated that the contaminant types and concentrations presented in Table 3 were generally amenable to biotreatment. Total heterotrophic microorganisms were present in the soil at levels of 2×10^7 colony-forming units (CFU)/g and there was a population of 4×10^6 CFU/g hydrocarbon-utilizing bacteria present as well. The soil matrix was heterogeneous and varied from medium to fine sand, silt, and clay. Quantitative chemical analysis of a control and a nutrient/bacteria-supplemented bioreactor showed a statistically significant difference in contaminant concentrations (24% at a 99% confidence level) between the bioreactors.

Monitoring of the first full-scale batch of soil treated in an LTU indicated that the bacterial population fluctuated dramatically as environmental and biological factors changed. Upon excavation and deposition of the contaminated soil into the LTU, there was an increase in bacterial activity (10^6 to 10^7) due to aeration and nutrient application. High moisture content and low nutrient concentrations explained the resultant decrease in bacteria to pretreatment levels. Subsequent nutrient application and tilling for aeration increased bacterial growth up to seven orders of magnitude (10^7 to 10^{14}). This increased bacterial presence dropped over a period of 4 weeks because of wet weather conditions and the inability to aerate the soils. Monitoring of contaminant degradation indicated that the most significant degradation occurred within the first 4 weeks of treatment (Table 3).

TABLE 3. Cleanup criteria, analytical results, degradation rates, and percent reduction.[a]

Compound	Treatment Standard	T_0 (Day 0) 8-29-94	T_1 (Day 34) 10-2-94	T_2 (Day 58) 10-26-94	T_3 (Day 99) 12-6-94	Degradation Rate (mg/kg/day)	Percent Reduction
Benzene	14	0.51	0.04	0.02 J	0.01	—	-98
Benzo(a)pyrene*	12	0 J	<2.17	0.06 J	0.03 J	—	—
Bis(2-ethylhexyl)phthalate	7.3	7.39 J	1.12 J	4.11 J	0.31 J	0.07	-96
Chrysene*	9	5.13	1.15 J	1.90 J	0.77 J	0.05	-85
Di-n-butyl phthalate	3.6	8.88 J	5.29	7.81	1.50 J	—	-83
Ethylbenzene	14	6.71	0.46	0.37 J	0.41	—	-94
Fluorene	NA	15.74 J	<2.17	0.59 J	0.20 J	0.16	-99
Naphthalene*	42	23.57 J	<2.17	0.64 J	0.17 J	0.24	-99
Phenanthrene*	34	36.25 J	<2.17	0.39 J	0.65 J	0.36	-98
Phenol	3.6	0 J	0 J	0.06 J	0.05 J	—	—
Pyrene*	36	14.03 J	<2.17	1.28 J	0.81 J	0.13	-94
Toluene	14	0.34	0.12	0.01 J	0.01	—	-97
Total xylenes	22	13.59	0.40	0.61 J	0.35	0.13	-97
Total Target PAHs	—	94.72	12.00	4.86	2.63	0.93	-97

(a) Values for T_0, T_1, and T_2 are the mean of three samples (grab samples for volatiles and three grid node composites for semivolatile). Values for T_3 are the mean of nine samples (grab samples for volatiles and five point composites for semivolatiles).

* = Target PAHs; NA = not available; J = estimated value.

— = Percent reduction could not be calculated because zero values were furnished for T_0.

Site-specific treatment standards and values which exceed treatment standards are highlighted.

Analytical results show reductions in volatile compounds ranging from 94% (ethylbenzene) to 98% (benzene). Ambient air sampling data generated during pilot and full-scale biodegradation activities indicated minimal (<3 ppm) volatile contaminant emission during the loading and homogenization operations of the lagoon soil. Semivolatile compound concentration reductions ranged from 85% (chrysene) to 99% (naphthalene). Real-time air monitoring data, using an organic vapor meter (OVM-580S), indicated that volatile contaminant concentrations were below health-risk concentrations.

DISCUSSION

Treatability testing indicated that using biodegradation to reduce contaminant concentrations of these wastes is feasible and meets the U.S. EPA's criteria for inclusion in the potential remedies for the Macmillan Ring-Free Oil Company site. During the biodegradation project, site-specific cleanup criteria were attained under field conditions.

REFERENCES

American Petroleum Institute. 1987. *Land Treatability of Appendix VIII Constituents Present in Petroleum Refinery Wastes: Laboratory and Modeling Studies.* No. 4455.

Sims, R. C., J. L. Sims, D. L. Sorenson, D. K. Stevens, S. G. Huling, B. E. Bledsoe, J. E. Matthews, and D. Pope. 1994. "Performance Evaluation of Full-Scale In Situ and Ex Situ Bioremediation of Creosote Wastes in Ground Water and Soils." *U.S. EPA Symposium on Bioremediation of Hazardous Wastes: Research, Development, and Field Evaluations (Abstracts),* pp. 35-39. EPA/600/R-94/075. San Francisco, CA.

U.S. Environmental Protection Agency. 1991a. *Risk Assessment Guidance for Superfund: Volume 1 — Human Health Evaluation Manual, Part B. Development of Risk Based Preliminary Remediation Goals.* OSWER Policy Directive No. 9285.7-01B, December, 1991.

U.S. Environmental Protection Agency. 1991b. *Health Effect Assessment Survey Tables* (HEAST).

U.S. Environmental Protection Agency. 1991c. *Integrated Risk Information System* (IRIS).

U.S. Environmental Protection Agency. 1994. *Bioremediation in the Field.* Office of Research and Development. EPA/540/N-94/500. No. 10, March 1994.

In Situ Aquifer Bioremediation
at the French Limited Superfund Site

James A. M. Thomson, Michael J. Day,
Richard L. Sloan, and Mark L. Collins

ABSTRACT

In situ aquifer bioremediation of a wide range of volatile organic compounds (VOCs) at the French Limited Superfund site is being performed using nitrate and oxygen as sequential electron acceptors. High dissolved oxygen (DO) concentrations (> 40 mg/L) are achieved using excess input of cryogenic oxygen and automatic venting of surplus gas; oxygen transfer efficiency using this method is 25%. Significant nitrate consumption (from 50 mg/L-N to not detected) coincides with first-order VOC attenuations ($t_{1/2}$ = 61 to 139 days) attributable to denitrifying metabolism. These attenuations were conservatively quantified by normalizing against benzene. The additional attenuation under denitrifying conditions is highest (13 to 38% of total attenuation) in the first few months of active remediation; as total organic carbon (TOC) and VOC concentrations decline, the additional attenuation due to in situ bioremediation (ISB) is reduced to 1 to 5%. Breakthrough of aerobic conditions is marked by sustained increases in DO to > 5 mg/L and generally follows dissolved TOC reduction to below 20 mg/L. Temporary reversals in DO breakthrough are attributed to increased biological oxygen demand (BOD) caused by spent biomass. Rapid VOC attenuation ($t_{1/2}$ = 12 to 40 days) follows aerobic breakthrough.

BACKGROUND

The French Limited Superfund site is a former sand pit (now referred to as the French Limited Lagoon) in the floodplain of the San Jacinto River near Crosby, Texas, approximately 30 km northeast of Houston. The site was used for liquid chemical waste disposal between 1966 and 1971. The wastes, containing elevated concentrations of organic compounds, affected lagoon water and formed a sludge layer at the bottom of the lagoon. Hydraulic communication between the lagoon and the shallow alluvial aquifer resulted in impacted groundwater containing elevated VOCs extending approximately 180 m downgradient (generally south) of the lagoon.

SITE HYDROGEOLOGY

The shallow alluvial aquifer is subdivided into four hydrostratigraphic units: an unconsolidated (UNC) clay, silt, and sand unit, from 0 to 3 m; a fine- to coarse-grained sand (S1) unit with occasional gravel layers, from 3 to 9 m; a clay (C1) unit, from 0 to 3 m thick; and an interbedded (INT) silty sand and silt unit with variable clay, from 9 to 12 to 17 m (approximate depths below ground surface). The S1 and INT units are largely separated by the C1 clay, although interconnections occur where the C1 clay is thin or absent; active remediation treats the S1 and INT units separately. Permeabilities are higher in the S1 unit ($k = 10^{-3}$ cm/sec) than the INT unit ($k = 10^{-4}$ cm/sec). The shallow alluvial aquifer is underlain by a 70-ft-thick Beaumont Clay aquitard ($k = 10^{-7}$ cm/sec). This unit acts as an effective barrier to vertical migration of impacted groundwater and dense, nonaqueous-phase liquid (DNAPL). The initial affected groundwater volume in each unit (i.e., affected pore volume) was approximately 60 million L.

CONTAMINANT DISTRIBUTION AND DNAPL OCCURRENCE

The principal constituents of the groundwater plume are relatively mobile VOCs, including aromatics such as benzene, and generally lower-chlorinated compounds such as 1,2-dichloroethane (1,2-DCA), and vinyl chloride, which are probable by-products of anaerobic degradation of higher-chlorinated aliphatics. Localized DNAPL zones have been defined in both units close to the lagoon; DNAPL samples collected from these areas contain up to 44% VOCs by weight, mainly higher-chlorinated VOCs such as chloroform, carbon tetrachloride, perchloroethene, and trichloroethene. DNAPL areas are contained inside steel sheetpile barriers. Downgradient of DNAPL areas, limited groundwater plumes characterized by higher-chlorinated VOCs have been identified.

IN SITU BIOREMEDIATION DESIGN AND OPERATIONS

Design Basis

The Record of Decision (ROD; U.S. EPA 1988) for the site specified "pump-and-treat" technology for aquifer remediation. However, because of the success of in situ bioremediation (ISB) pilot tests for lagoon sludges (leading to the inclusion of ISB for lagoon sludges in the ROD), the use of ISB for groundwater was reappraised, initially for recalcitrant areas of the aquifer, and ultimately for the entire plume area in each unit. Pilot aquifer ISB tests were performed for each unit after pump-and-treat remediation startup in January 1992. Injection wells, sited to enhance flushing, now deliver fresh water amended with nutrients, oxygen, and nitrate. Fresh injection water is obtained from the underlying Chicot aquifer via three 75-m-deep supply wells; extracted water is treated to meet surface water discharge standards and is not used for reinjection. Locations of extraction and injection wells are shown in Figure 1.

Flushing Rates and Capture

From startup to December 1994, the S1 unit has had 4.1 pore volumes injected and 9.7 extracted; the INT unit has had 3.5 pore volumes injected and 4.8 extracted; 180 tonnes of dissolved total organic carbon have been removed. The overall extraction rate (average 570 L/min since startup) is approximately twice the injection rate (295 L/min); monthly groundwater-level monitoring confirms capture of all affected and injected water. Capture of injected water is required to prevent potential nitrate buildup in the shallow aquifer and prevent migration of displaced groundwater.

Selection of Electron Acceptors

Of the electron acceptors available to stimulate ISB, oxygen and nitrate were selected for the French Limited site. Oxygen is considered essential for biodegradation of benzene; nitrate is associated with denitrifying biodegradation of chlorinated VOCs (Bouwer 1994). For a mixed suite of chemicals including benzene, an appropriate sequence includes stimulation of denitrifying conditions to attenuate chlorinated VOCs, followed by stimulation of aerobic conditions to attenuate benzene. In practice, this sequence occurs by default; chemical oxygen demand and preferential consumption of oxygen effectively "retards" migration of the dissolved oxygen (DO) front, whereas nitrate's higher solubility allows input at higher concentrations, resulting in more rapid migration of the nitrate front.

Electron Acceptor and Nutrient Delivery

Target injection water concentrations are: DO, 40 mg/L; nitrate, 50 mg/L-N. DO concentrations in excess of theoretical equilibrium levels with ambient air (approximately 8.5 mg/L at site temperatures) are achieved by adding excess gaseous oxygen to production headers and venting surplus gas from injection wellheads using automatic vent valves. Oxygen delivery efficiency using this method is approximately 25%. Nitrate initially was added as ammonium nitrate and subsequently as potassium nitrate; no problems were experienced with either method or with the changeover. Injection water contains adequate (> 1 mg/L-P) phosphate concentrations.

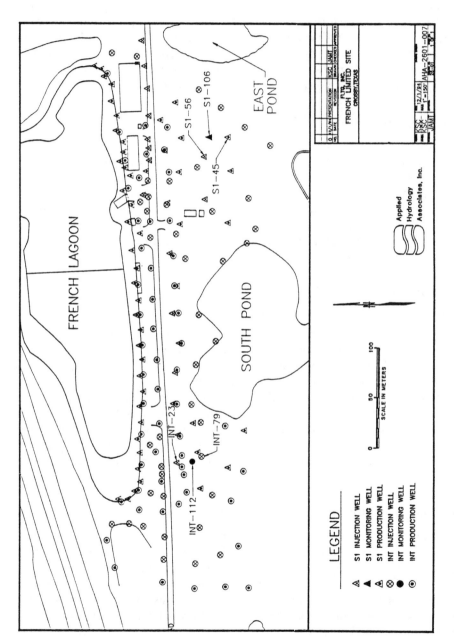

FIGURE 1. French Limited aquifer remediation system.

IN SITU BIOREMEDIATION PROGRESS

ISB Attenuation Rates Under Denitrifying Conditions

The relative removal rates of flushing and ISB are evaluated by examining chemical removal rates over time at all monitoring wells. For this technical note, results from two representative monitoring wells (shown graphically in Figures 2 and 3) are discussed. Well S1-106 is located in the flow path between injection well S1-56 and extraction well S1-45; it is approximately 20 m from both wells (see Figure 1). To date, aerobic breakthrough has not occurred; DO has stayed at or below background concentrations since startup. This well provides a good example of the effects of fresh water flushing and denitrifying conditions, and is typical of areas of the site where these conditions exist.

Nitrate consumption is indicated by depletion, relative to associated ammonium or potassium, ranging from 73% to 100%. Relative VOC-removal rates since startup are shown on Figure 2. All VOCs plotted show approximate first-order decay, with half-lives ($t_{1/2}$) of 139 days for benzene, 87 days for toluene, and 61 days for vinyl chloride. Initial removal rates are slower because addition of nutrients and electron acceptors for ISB did not start until Day 158.

The slower decay of benzene relative to toluene and chlorinated VOCs is attributed to anaerobic conditions. Using the conservative assumption that benzene attenuation was due only to flushing with injected water, concentrations for the other VOCs under a flushing-only scenario were predicted. Predicted concentrations were compared with actual concentrations; the degree to which the actual concentration falls below the predicted concentration indicates the amount of additional attenuation due to ISB.

Note that relative retardation rates of VOCs are not quantified in the above calculations. However, the VOCs considered cover a range of soil/water partition

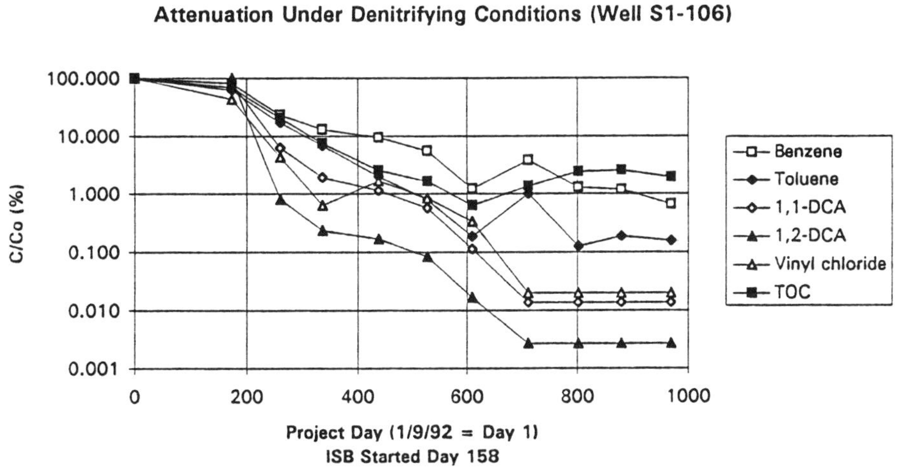

Attenuation Under Denitrifying Conditions (Well S1-106)

FIGURE 2. Attenuation under denitrifying conditions (Well S1-106).

coefficients (K_{oc}s) both significantly above and somewhat below that of benzene. If retardation due to adsorption onto soil organic carbon slows removal, then the ISB rates for those VOCs with K_{oc}s above benzene are underestimates.

ISB attenuation calculated in this way was highest in the first 3 months following the start of active ISB, ranging from 13% for ethylbenzene to 38% for vinyl chloride. Rates dropped to between 1 and 5% over the next 15 months. The reduction in microbiological activity is attributed to the overall reduction in the organic carbon supply. TOC attenuation at this well showed a steady first-order decay for 18 months after ISB startup, from 1,400 to 9 mg/L ($t_{1/2}$ = 90 days). After 18 months, TOC showed a short-term increase to 40 mg/L; similar increases have been observed at several monitoring wells and are attributed to decaying spent biomass. After 18 months of active ISB, all VOCs were below detection limits, except for benzene, ethylbenzene, and toluene; only benzene remained above its cleanup criterion.

ISB Attenuation Rates Under Aerobic Conditions

Well INT-112 is located in the flow path between injection well INT-79 and extraction well INT-23; it is approximately 12 m from both wells (see Figure 1). Injection at INT-79 started on Day 599. Before then, well INT-112 was influenced only by flushing with ambient groundwater due to extraction from well INT-23. Aerobic breakthrough was first observed on Day 665. This well provides a good example of the transition from ambient flushing to aerobic conditions, and is typical of areas of the site where these conditions exist.

Nitrate consumption rates are harder to quantify in the INT unit because cation exchange (due to the higher clay content) causes ammonium and potassium retardation. However, nitrate breakthrough on Day 615 indicates that nitrate is not a limiting factor. DO breakthrough occurred relatively quickly after nitrate breakthrough; hence the period of only denitrifying conditions is too short to evaluate.

Relative removal rates since startup are shown in Figure 3. Under ambient flushing before the start of ISB, VOCs showed notable increases, reflecting the typical heterogeneity of the VOC plume. After the start of ISB, marked by nitrate and DO breakthrough, concentrations of all VOCs declined rapidly. Decay half-lives range from 39.6 days for 1,1-DCA to 12.5 days for benzene. Removal rates are significantly greater than under denitrifying conditions only, and cleanup conditions were achieved at this well by Day 719; i.e., after approximately 100 days ISB.

Under aerobic conditions, VOC degradation occurs too fast for relative rates to be determined from quarterly monitoring. TOC showed informative trends. A slow TOC decay during ambient flushing was notably accelerated after the start of ISB, dropping to 4 mg/L. As at S1-106, a subsequent short-term increase to 21 mg/L coincides with the effective completion of remediation, and probably indicates decaying spent biomass.

Site cleanup criteria (drinking water standards) for the S1 unit were largely met by the target date of December 1994; the target date for achieving site cleanup criteria for the INT unit is June 1996.

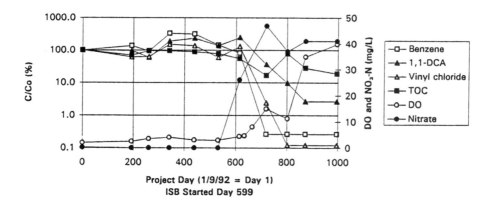

FIGURE 3. Attenuation under aerobic conditions (Well INT-112).

FUTURE CLEANUP STRATEGY

It is clear from this limited review of progress monitoring data that, at this site, in situ bioremediation using both nitrate and oxygen electron acceptors is effective in accelerating cleanup. Therefore, the key technical issues in remediation management are monitoring and hydrogeology, and identifying recalcitrant areas and maximizing the delivery of nutrients and electron acceptors.

REFERENCES

Bouwer, E. J. 1994. "Bioremediation of Chlorinated Solvents Using Alternate Electron Acceptors." In R. D. Norris et al. (Eds.), *Handbook of Remediation.* Lewis Publishers. pp. 149-175.

U.S. EPA. 1988. *Superfund Record of Decision, French Limited, TX.* EPA/ROD/R06-88/030. U.S. Environmental Protection Agency. March 24.

Mass Transport in Physical and Biological BTEX Removal in a Sandy Aquifer

Paul J. Sturman, Alfred B. Cunningham,
Steve L. Niehaus, and James H. Wolfram

ABSTRACT

Injection of oxygen and nutrient-amended water facilitated alkylbenzene biodegradation in a sandy aquifer. Pumping recovery wells and air-stripping groundwater further hastened contaminant removal downgradient from the source area. High monitoring well density allowed calculation of a contaminant mass balance using contour plots developed with Surfer® software. Physical removal (air-stripping) and in situ attenuation appear equally responsible for contaminant removal within this aquifer. Dissolved oxygen data implicate biodegradation as the responsible in situ mechanism, with a good stoichiometric fit to BTEX attenuation data. Selective plating confirmed the presence of hydrocarbon-degrading bacteria. Calculations indicate desorption is a major source for recontamination of site groundwater. Contaminant reduction is most pronounced immediately downgradient from reinjection wells. Advective transport and mixing of oxygen in the contaminated zone, rather than microbial kinetics, appears to limit in situ contaminant attenuation.

INTRODUCTION

A leaking natural gas dehydrator released dissolved benzene, toluene, ethylbenzene, and xylenes (BTEX) into a sandy phreatic aquifer with groundwater at a depth of approximately 65 feet. The resulting groundwater plume extended 800 feet downgradient, with BTEX concentrations of up to 10,000 µg/L. Remedial actions included groundwater recovery, air-stripping of BTEX, nutrient amendment (beginning in April 1993), and reinjection of treated water near the source of contamination. Dissolved BTEX and O_2 were measured monthly at 39 monitoring wells, 4 recovery wells, and 4 reinjection wells. Determination of kinetic parameters for the microbial consortium present indicated that rapid biodegradation should be occurring in the absence of mixing limitations such as transport and sorption (Sturman et al. 1994). Contaminant persistence at this site suggested such limitations may control biodegradation rates in situ. This study sought to quantify the rate of in situ biodegradation and to determine the mechanisms controlling this rate.

METHODS

A mass balance approach was used to quantify BTEX attenuation in the field and estimate the fraction attributable to biodegradation. High monitoring well density and timely recording of BTEX and dissolved oxygen (DO) levels in monitoring wells, extraction wells, and reinjection wells allowed calculation of a BTEX mass balance and correlation of in situ BTEX removal with DO availability. Total mass of dissolved BTEX and oxygen were calculated using Surfer® software. Contaminant/oxygen isohyets were generated from monitoring well data, and total mass was calculated through integration of the isohyetal map. A BTEX mass balance was calculated for the time period December 1992 (1) to December 1993 (2) over the control volume of the aquifer as:

$$\Delta BTEX_{aqueous(1-2)} =$$

$$BTEX_{stripped(1-2)} + BTEX_{biodegraded(1-2)} - BTEX_{desorbed(1-2)}$$

(1)

A highly homogeneous sand aquifer with consistent organic matter (0.1%) and consistent relative quantities of BTEX compounds allowed the estimation of the sorbed contaminant mass as a linear function of aqueous phase concentrations. The mass stripped was calculated from stripper influent- and effluent-BTEX concentrations and system throughput. Equation (1) was solved for $Mass_{biodegraded(1-2)}$.

Oxygen mass injected into the aquifer was measured at the reinjection points. This mass was then compared with the BTEX removed in the aquifer for a stoichiometric fit. Dissolved oxygen concentration changes over time were determined by comparing isohyetal maps for December 1992 (12/92) and December 1993 (12/93). Hydrocarbon-degrading bacterial numbers were quantified at both time periods by plating on selective agars using BTEX compounds as the sole carbon source.

RESULTS

Total BTEX concentration contours in the aquifer in 12/92 and 12/93 are shown in Figure 1(a) and (b). Points of groundwater removal and reinjection are indicated. The mass of dissolved BTEX measured in the aquifer decreased from 32 kg (12/92) to 18 kg (12/93) (Figure 2). Sorption isotherm experimentation (data not shown) indicated linearity in the concentration range studied (10 to 10,000 µg/L). Aquifer homogeneity over the control volume with respect to soil porosity, texture, and organic matter content allowed the estimation of the total sorbed BTEX mass as a linear function of aqueous mass (Figure 2). Sorbed

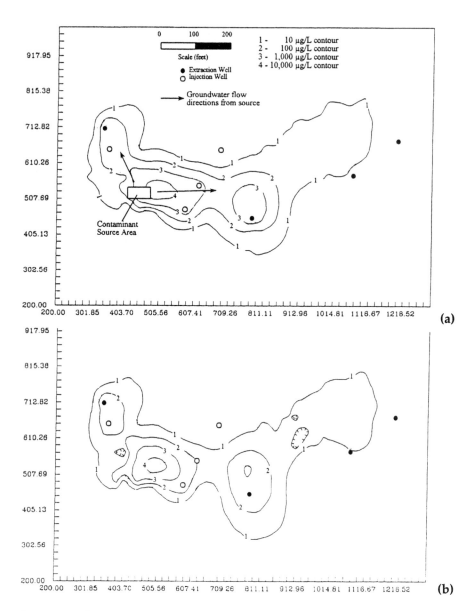

FIGURE 1. (a) Aqueous BTEX contours in mg/L (December 1992). Contaminant source is located above a local high in potentiometric surface, causing the plume to spread in two directions. (b) Aqueous BTEX contours in mg/L (December 1993).

contaminant mass was calculated by dividing the control volume into sections of representative aqueous phase concentrations, then using weighted average values of K_d (soil/water partitioning coefficient) for the mixture of BTEX

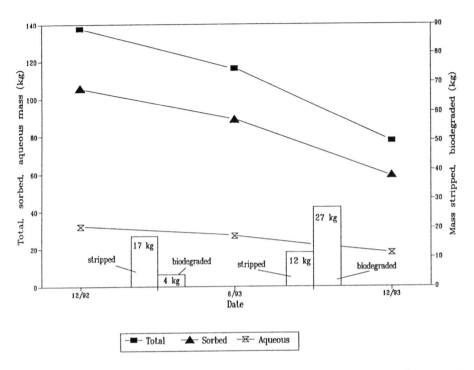

FIGURE 2. Aqueous, sorbed, and total BTEX mass; biodegraded and stripped mass, December 1992–December 1993.

compounds present. Summing aqueous and sorbed BTEX masses yields the total BTEX line in Figure 2. BTEX mass removed via the air-stripper was 17.4 kg for the period 12/92 to 6/93 and 11.7 kg for 6/93 to 12/93. BTEX mass biodegraded was calculated using equation (1) as 4 kg and 27 kg for the two periods (Figure 2, inset).

Planktonic BTEX-degrading bacteria were enumerated at 17 monitoring wells within the plume during both time periods. BTEX-degrading populations maintained concentrations of 10^4 to 10^6 colony-forming units (cfu) per mL. Consistent increases in concentrations of planktonic BTEX-degrading bacteria were not observed.

DISCUSSION

The BTEX contour plots shown in Figure 1(a) and (b) indicate that the dissolved contaminant plume attenuated most rapidly immediately downgradient from the reinjection wells. This observation is corroborated by calculation of rates of BTEX removal from the aqueous phase. Aqueous-phase BTEX attenuation rates (measured in $\mu g\ L^{-1}\ d^{-1}$) in monitoring wells close to reinjection points were generally higher than those in monitoring wells adjacent to groundwater

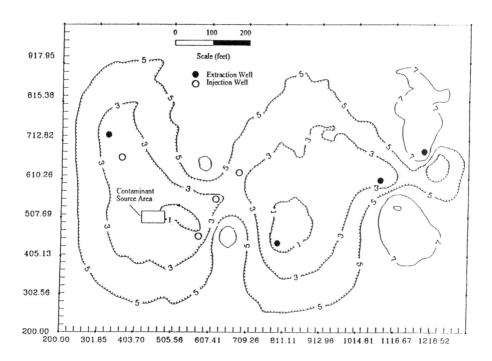

FIGURE 3. Dissolved oxygen contours in mg/L (December 1992).

pumping wells (data not shown). Dissolved oxygen levels downgradient from reinjection points (Figure 3) were elevated compared with the surrounding aquifer. Biodegradation was calculated at 4 kg BTEX from 12/92 to 6/93, and 27 kg from 6/93 to 12/93. This increase can be attributed to the commencement of nutrient (principally nitrogen) amendment of reinjected water in late April 1993. Previous studies indicated this aquifer was stoichiometrically deficient in nitrogen. In situ BTEX removal through biodegradation was evidently promoted by the zone of mixing created downgradient from the reinjection wells. This mixing enhanced oxygen, nutrient, and contaminant availability to aerobic microorganisms.

Because of the difficulty in estimating DO recharge to the contaminated zone through advective and dispersive oxygen transport within the aquifer, it was not possible to develop an oxygen mass balance. Dissolved oxygen concentration contours indicated the presence of a DO-depleted area in the contaminated zone in 12/92 (Figure 3). This contour plot did not change significantly between 12/92 and 12/93 (12/93 data not shown). Over the 12-month study period, approximately 145 kg oxygen was introduced into the contaminated zone via the reinjection wells. The maintenance of a DO-deficient condition in the contaminated zone despite the addition of oxygen-saturated reinjection water indicates an oxygen demand in this area. If all 145 kg of reinjected oxygen had been utilized by microorganisms to degrade the 31 kg BTEX, a stoichiometric oxygen demand of 4.6 kg O_2/kg BTEX biodegraded would be indicated. Considering the maximum demand attainable under complete mineralization conditions is 3.5 kg O_2/kg BTEX, some oxygen is unaccounted for either in abiotic demand, noncontaminant mineralization, or calculation error.

Previous work (Sturman et al. 1994) determined that the maximum specific growth rate for the site BTEX degraders was 0.23 hr^{-1}. Using the calculated biomass yield of 0.67 g biomass/g BTEX and the observed maximum colonization of 10^6 cfu/ml, the maximum rate of contaminant removal is in the range of 8 to 16×10^3 µg $(L^*day)^{-1}$. By contrast, the actual in situ degradation rate is calculated at 6.14 µg $(L^*day)^{-1}$.

CONCLUSIONS

The biodegradation of BTEX compounds in situ is implicated by the development of a contaminant mass balance. These data are corroborated by the maintenance of a DO deficit in the contaminated zone, despite injection of oxygen-saturated water, and by the maintenance of a population of hydrocarbon-degrading bacteria. Contaminant contour plots indicate that the most active zone of contaminant attenuation is directly downgradient from reinjection wells. Although biodegradation in situ proceeds at levels two orders of magnitude lower than laboratory-determined maximum rates, it is facilitated by the enhanced advective transport in the mixing zone.

REFERENCE

Sturman P. J., R. R. Sharp, J. B. DeBar, P. S. Stewart, A. B. Cunningham, and J. H. Wolfram. 1994. "Scale-up Implications of Respirometrically Determined Microbial Kinetic Parameters." In R. E. Hinchee, D. B. Anderson, F. B. Meeting Jr., and G. D. Sayles (Eds.), *Applied Biotechnology for Site Remediation*, pp. 300-304. Lewis Publishers, Boca Raton, FL.

Enhancing In Situ Bioremediation With Pneumatic Fracturing

Daniel B. Anderson, Brent M. Peyton, John J. Liskowitz,
Conan Fitzgerald, and John R. Schuring

ABSTRACT

A major technical obstacle affecting the application of in situ bioremediation is the effective distribution of nutrients to the subsurface media. Pneumatic fracturing can increase the permeability of subsurface formations through the injection of high pressure air to create horizontal fracture planes, thus enhancing macroscale mass-transfer processes. Pneumatic fracturing technology was demonstrated at two field sites at Tinker Air Force Base, Oklahoma City, Oklahoma. Tests were performed to increase the permeability for more effective bioventing, and evaluated the potential to increase permeability and recovery of free product in low-permeability soils consisting of fine-grain silts, clays, and sedimentary rock. Pneumatic fracturing significantly improved formation permeability by enhancing secondary permeability and by promoting removal of excess soil moisture from the unsaturated zone. Postfracture airflows were 500% to 1,700% higher than prefracture airflows for specific fractured intervals in the formation. This corresponds to an average prefracturing permeability of 0.017 darcy, increasing to an average of 0.32 darcy after fracturing. Pneumatic fracturing also increased free-product recovery rates of number 2 fuel from an average of 587 L (155 gal) per month before fracturing to 1,647 L (435 gal) per month after fracturing.

INTRODUCTION

In situ bioremediation has great potential to clean large volumes of soil and groundwater; however, the process is plagued by the lack of ability to effectively distribute nutrients throughout the contaminated area. This limitation often controls both the rate and extent of the cleanup effort by significantly reducing the amount of nutrients or microbes that can be delivered to the subsurface environment. Integrating in situ bioremediation with "enabling technologies" can increase the number of sites where bioremediation can be applied.

One such enabling technology is pneumatic fracturing (PF). The PF process may be generally described as injecting air into a contaminated geologic formation at a pressure that exceeds the natural strength of the formation. The resulting failure of the medium creates a fracture network radiating from the injection point, which increases the formation's macroscale permeability. Once established, the fractures increase the rate at which vapors or liquids can travel through the formation and thereby make the contaminants more accessible to remediation. This results in a greater distribution and radius of influence for each nutrient-injection or contaminant-extraction well. For formations containing significant amounts of silt and clay, the process creates new convective pathways in the formation, which increase permeability and shorten the distance nutrients must travel to reach contaminated soils. In sedimentary rock formations, such as sandstone and shale, the process dilates and extends existing discontinuities and thereby increases permeability and improves interconnectivity. The technology has been applied in both the unsaturated and saturated zones of contaminated formations (Liskowitz et al. 1993). A recent modification of the pneumatic fracturing system permits delivery of biological supplements (e.g., nutrients, buffers, and microorganisms) directly into the fractured formation to enhance in situ bioremediation (Fitzgerald 1993). When injection of microbes is necessary, for example when specialized contaminant-degrading organisms are used, PF can overcome some of the associated problems. The conventional method for injection of bacteria into the subsurface can lead to filtration and the formation of a "biofilm" at the point of injection. This biofilm can foul the injection well to the point that no further injection is possible without costly well-cleaning procedures. Delivery of bacteria during pneumatic fracturing will significantly improve injection and distribution of microorganisms in the subsurface.

A field demonstration of PF was conducted at Tinker Air Force Base between May 15 and August 15, 1993. The objective was to apply PF at two separate locations and evaluate its ability to enhance remediation activities in the low-permeability formations at the base. Data are presented on the ability of PF to increase soil permeability in the field. The project was sponsored by the United States Department of Energy (U.S. DOE) and the United States Air Force (USAF).

FIELD TESTS AND OBSERVATIONS

Southwest Tanks Site

At the Southwest Tanks Site (STS), the superficial soils in the test zone consisted principally of clayey silt (approximately 3 m [10 ft]), grading to silt and silty sand with increasing depth. A perched water table was located approximately 5.5 m (18 ft) below the ground surface. Previous laboratory analyses show that soil permeabilities ranged from 10^{-7} cm/s in the clay layer to 10^{-5} cm/s in the silty sand layers. Past operations of an underground storage tank (UST) complex for fuels and waste oil at this site resulted in free-floating product and extensive soil contamination with total petroleum hydrocarbons (TPHs) and benzene, toluene, ethylbenzene, and xylenes (BTEX).

Free-product removal and bioventing were the preferred technologies for the STS remediation. Fracturing tests were done to determine the effect of PF on the formation permeability and to determine if extraction of volatile organic compounds (VOCs) would improve significantly after fracturing. Injection pressures ranged from 1.52×10^7 to 5.07×10^7 Pa (150 to 500 psi). The injections lasted from 10 to 30 s, resulting in a total injected air volume of 10.6 to 22.7 m^3 at standard temperature and pressure (STP) (375 to 800 scf). The effects of fracturing were measured as surface heave (the vertical rise at the ground surface) and an increase in the vacuum radius of influence. Fracture injections were made in two different zones: six shallow injections in the depth range from 1.8 to 3.7 m (6 to 12 ft); and one injection 5.5 to 6.1 m (18 to 20 ft) deep. Surface-heave measurements, which reflect the extent of fracture propagation, generally agreed with the radii observed in vacuum tests. Figure 1 shows surface-heave contours during the fracturing process; maximum heave was just over 1.3 cm (0.5 in.), and measurable radius of influence exceeded 6.1 m (20 ft).

For bioventing applications, the vacuum radius of influence is often used as an important determinant of well spacing. Prefracturing and postfracturing vacuum radii of influence are shown in Figure 2. Fracturing significantly increased the volume of soil that can be reached with a given bioventing well.

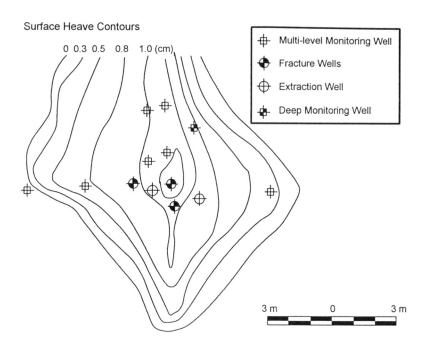

FIGURE 1. Typical surface-heave contours measured during the fracturing process.

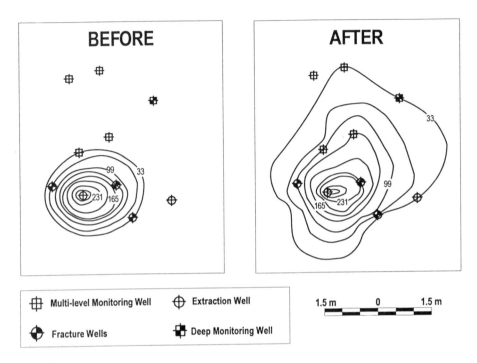

FIGURE 2. Typical increase in vacuum radius of influence as a result of pneumatic fracturing. Contours are in cm of water.

Helium tracer tests were performed at the STS, but tracer arrival times did not differ substantially between the prefracture and postfracture conditions. Helium was also detected in all soil gas samples taken from piezometers in 1-ft-depth intervals (data not shown). The data suggest that evenly distributed natural fractures were already present at the site. Modeling was used to show that oxygen diffusion from the fractures would be sufficient for application of bioventing techniques for remediation. A possible explanation for the discrepancy between the helium test results and the vacuum permeability results may lie in the differing test modes. The helium tracer was injected under a positive pressure, and the air extraction tests were conducted under vacuum conditions. The vacuum tests may draw excess moisture from the unsaturated formation into the fractures, effectively sealing them off to gas flow.

Vapor extraction tests were conducted over 21 days in the shallow fracture zone. Postfracture airflows were 500% to 1,700% higher than prefracture airflows for specific fractured intervals in the formation. This corresponds to an average prefracturing permeability of 0.017 darcy, increasing to an average of 0.32 darcy after fracturing. In combined vapor injection and extraction tests conducted in the deep fracture zone over a period of 17 days, with sealed monitoring wells, postfracture airflows increased 150%. When the test was continued with unsealed monitoring wells, airflow enhancement ranged between 500% and 1,000%, suggesting substantial connection with outlying wells. The corresponding average permeability increased from 0.026 darcy prefracture to 0.142 darcy after fracturing.

It should be noted that permeability increases can lead to a significant improvement in the mass flowrate of air that can be delivered through a given well. However, the number and distribution of fractures will determine the oxygen delivery rate to specific regions of the vadose zone. An overall increase in the air flowrate cannot guarantee that oxygen has reached all locations of the contaminated region.

North Tank Area

At the North Tank Area (NTA), an operational unit associated with a 1990 Record of Decision (COE 1990) for building 3001, UST 3404, which was used to store #2 fuel oil, had released petroleum hydrocarbons into the subsurface. Interim remedial actions included installing a floating-product removal system, removing and disposing of the other tanks at the site, and conducting in situ treatability studies to evaluate the potential of bioventing to treat residual contaminated soils. Additional site investigations conducted in 1992 resulted in the development of a conceptual site model suggesting stratification of the perched water system as shown in Figure 3. These studies also suggested that a significant portion of the product was trapped beneath an upper confining shale unit 5.2 to 7.6 m (17 to 23 ft) beneath the surface. The base of the tank appears to rest near the base of the upper shale unit, and excavation during installation of the tank most likely disrupted this shale layer. Because of this and the positive

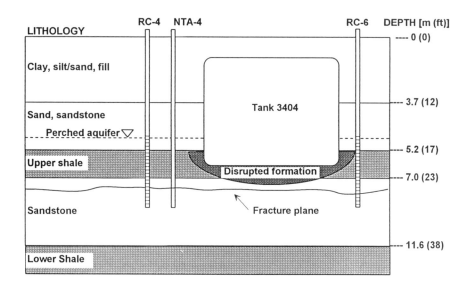

FIGURE 3. Schematic diagram of the stratified geology and perched aquifer system at the North Tank Area.

differential pressure that would exist between Tank 3404 and the groundwater when the tank was filled, fuel oil was most likely chronically pushed into these permeable units, predominately the lower sandstone. To remove the free product beneath the tank, four recovery wells were installed along the perimeter of the tank. Although significant amounts of free product were present in the wells initially, the recharge rates and product recovery over nearly 2 years were limited.

Pneumatic fracturing was tested to help improve the rate of free-product recovery by producing fractures to connect an existing recovery well (RC-4) with the free product trapped below the upper shale unit. Enhanced free-product recovery would be the essential first step in an integrated remediation scheme with bioventing processes to biodegrade the residual soil contamination in a timely fashion. A deep pneumatic fracturing injection was conducted in the saturated zone in a newly installed fracturing well, NTA-4, between the tank and RC-4. Injection pressures ranged from 1.52×10^7 to 5.07×10^7 Pa (150 to 500 psi). The injections lasted from 10 to 30 s, resulting in a total injected air volume of 10.6 to 22.7 m^3 at STP (375 to 800 scf). The fracture interval, 7.9 to 8.5 m (26 and 28 ft) below ground surface, was immediately below the upper confining shale unit. The pneumatic injection at NTA-4 connected with at least seven wells besides RC-4. Pneumatic connection became apparent when the outlying wells became pressurized after completion of the deep injection. The farthest connection was RC-2, approximately 18.3 m (60 ft) from the injection point.

A baildown test was performed in RC-4 to quantify the increase in product recovery. During the prefracture component of the test, the static product thickness was 0.5 m (1.5 ft), with about a 200-h recovery period. After fracturing, the static product thickness increased to 6.2 m (20.2 ft). Postfracture equilibrium was obtained 75 h after baildown, and 76 L (20 gal) of free product recharged into the well during the 22 h after evacuation. After the pneumatic fracturing demonstration, the Air Force resumed product recovery at the NTA. Figure 4 summarizes the recovery data for August 1993 through June 1994, which includes total product removed. Product recovery increased from an average of 587 L (155 gal) per month for all the wells in the North Tank Area before fracturing to 1,647 L (435 gal) per month after fracturing for only two wells. The gradual decline in postfracture recovery rates is at least partly attributable to depletion of product near the well, to a gradual deterioration of the fracture network, or both. Another factor that may explain the decline in recovery rate is related to site operations; the recovery wells were shut down for extended periods after fracturing for site characterization and system maintenance.

SUMMARY

Pneumatic fracturing significantly improved formation permeability by enhancing secondary permeability and by promoting removal of excess soil moisture from the unsaturated zone. Results of these field tests show that PF may provide enhancements to in situ bioremediation processes, including (1) increased

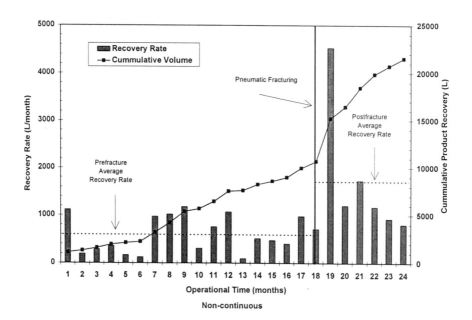

FIGURE 4. Product recovery data for the North Tank Area before and after pneumatic fracturing.

permeability for faster delivery of air in bioventing applications, and (2) improved free-product recovery. Pneumatic fracturing could also be used to deliver biological supplements (e.g., nutrients, buffers, and microorganisms) directly into the fractured formation to enhance in situ bioremediation.

ACKNOWLEDGMENT

Pacific Northwest Laboratory is operated for the U.S. Department of Energy by Battelle Memorial Institute under contract DE-AC06-76RLO 1830.

REFERENCES

COE. 1990. *Building 3001 (NPL Site) Record of Decision.* U.S. Army Corps of Engineers (COE), Tulsa District, Tinker AFB, Oklahoma City, OK.

Fitzgerald, C. D. 1993. "Integration of Pneumatic Fracturing to Enhance In Situ Bioremediation." Master's thesis, New Jersey Institute of Technology, Newark, NJ.

Liskowitz, J. J., J. R. Schuring, and J. Mack. 1993. "Application of Pneumatic Fracturing Extraction for the Effective Removal of Volatile Organic Compounds in Low Permeability Formations." Presented at the *Focus Conference on Eastern Groundwater Issues*, National Groundwater Association, Sept. 1993, Burlington, VT.

Electrokinetic Control of Moisture and Nutrients in Unsaturated Soils

Eric R. Lindgren and Patrick V. Brady

ABSTRACT

Unsaturated soils are contaminated with metals and organic solvents at many U.S. Department of Energy (DOE) facilities. Because of the large volumes, in situ remediation is often the most economically attractive remediation technique. The success of many in situ treatment technologies depends critically on the degree to which the movement of water and desired ions can be engineered in the vadose zone. Bioremediation efforts are limited by the ability to provide moisture and nutrients to contaminant-metabolizing microorganisms. An in situ electrokinetic remediation process has been developed at Sandia National Laboratories (SNL) for use in unsaturated soils and is presently undergoing field demonstration. The electrokinetic process is not limited by low soil permeabilities and, therefore, provides a level of control not achievable by hydraulic means. Moisture is added to the subsurface in a controlled fashion so that field capacity is never exceeded, preventing unwanted mobilization of dissolved contaminants by saturated wetting fronts. The electrokinetic process can potentially transport both water and nutrients for bioremediation efforts and is compatible with vapor-phase in situ techniques such as bioventing.

ELECTROKINETICS BACKGROUND

The application of direct current in a soil-water system leads to at least two effects: ionic species dissolved in the soil-water solution migrate to the oppositely charged electrode (electromigration) at a rate that depends on the local potential gradient and the charge and mobility of the ion and, accompanying this migration, a bulk flow of soil-water is induced toward the cathode (electroosmosis) at a rate which depends on the local potential gradient and the soil zeta potential (Hunter 1981). The combination of these two phenomena leads to a net movement of ions toward one or the other electrode. The direction and rate of ion transport are not highly dependent on the hydraulic nature of the soil; thus, ions may be introduced to or removed from soils of low hydraulic conductivity, which is difficult (or impossible) to effect by hydraulic means. Desired ions can be introduced at the electrodes and contaminant ions arriving at the electrodes can be removed by mechanical extraction techniques.

When electrical current is passed through an aqueous solution, electron transfer reactions must occur at the electrode surface to transfer the current from the metallic medium. Free electrons then carry the current to the aqueous medium, where ions carry the current. Under most conditions, the electrolysis of water at each electrode is the predominant electron transfer reaction:

$$H_2O \leftrightarrow \tfrac{1}{2}O_2(g) + 2H^+ + 2e^- \qquad (1)$$

forming acidic conditions at the anode, which propagate toward the cathode and

$$2H_2O + 2e^- \leftrightarrow H_2(g) + 2OH^- \qquad (2)$$

forming basic conditions at the cathode, which propagate toward the anode.

Electrokinetic remediation shows great promise for moisture conditions near saturation in both laboratory cell experiments (Alshawabkeh and Acar 1992; Probstein and Hicks 1993) and in field trials (Lageman 1993). However, it may be desirable to avoid saturating a contaminant plume that resides in the vadose zone. Electrokinetic remediation should be applicable to unsaturated soil systems as long as there is an electrical connection through the pore water between the electrodes. Recent experiments at SNL (Lindgren et al. 1991, 1992, 1994) indicate that electromigration rates of anions are appreciable in unsaturated sandy soils at moisture contents as low as 7 wt% (approximately 25% saturation). Furthermore, electromigration rates are maximal at moisture contents less than saturation. These experimental results are encouraging because many heavy-metal plumes have a significant portion of the contamination residing in the unsaturated zone.

This electrokinetic electrode system consists of an upper plastic well casing with a lower porous ceramic section that contains the active portion of the electrode system. A constant electrolyte solution level is maintained above the ceramic/plastic interface, and the solution is held under tension by applying a vacuum to the casing headspace. It is the applied vacuum that limits the degree of saturation that soils adjacent to the electrode casings will attain and assures that the field capacity of the soils is never exceeded. A drive electrode is deployed within the electrolyte solution to complete the electrical connection with the soil. When a DC current is passed between electrodes, electrolysis reactions form hydrogen ions at the anode and hydroxyl ions at the cathode. A pumping system circulates the electrolyte solution past a pH probe and controls the addition of neutralizing agents to maintain the pH at a desired level. Contamination is removed from the system in a small effluent stream from each electrode system and is treated for disposal.

The present design of the electrode system allows the in situ removal of anionic contaminants from unsaturated soils. Anionic forms of heavy metal contaminants (e.g., CrO_4^{2-}, MoO_4^{2-}, SeO_3^{2-}, $HAsO_4^{2-}$, TcO_4^-, $UO_2(CO_3)_2^{2-}$, etc.) typically are highly water soluble, adsorb weakly to most soil surfaces, and are therefore amenable to the electrokinetic extraction process. It has been shown theoretically

(Mattson and Lindgren 1995), and demonstrated experimentally (Lindgren et al. 1991, 1992, 1994), that anionic contaminants migrate toward the anode at a rate 5 to 10 times faster than the opposing electroosmotic flowrate.

ELECTROKINETIC IONIC NUTRIENT FLUX

In the electrokinetic process, the electrode reactions are buffered to maintain neutral pH conditions. The neutralization reaction essentially exchanges the hydroxyl ion with a nitrate ion or a chelating ion, such as citrate for a carbon source, and the hydrogen ion with a sodium or other bionutrient ion depending on the neutralizing agent. For efficient electrokinetic introduction, the biostimulant must have acid or basic forms that can be used to neutralize the electrode reactions. For example, nitrate is best introduced electrokinetically into the soil by using nitric acid to neutralize the hydroxyl ions formed by reaction 2. Citrate is best introduced using citric acid. Because this method eliminates soil pH shifts, it is an optimal approach for electromigrating ions into soils. Other methods, such as introducing a salt, are ineffective because the mobility of the hydroxyl and hydrogen ions is much greater than for any other ions. The unwanted result is that H^+ and OH^- ultimately transport most of the current, rather than the contaminants (or nutrients). By neutralizing acid and base production stoichiometrically, the concentrations of H^+ and OH^- ions are minimized, and the addition rate of desired ions to the soil is maximized and is proportional to the imposed current.

Recent theoretical calculations (Lindgren et al. 1995) show that the pore water conductivity (which relates closely to ionic strength) remains relatively constant during the electrokinetic process. The net result of operating the process is that the ions initially in the pore water are replaced by the ions (or mix of ions) introduced at the electrodes at a concentration comparable to the initial ionic strength. Dissolution or precipitation reactions cannot be completely avoided, of course, but are minimized by eliminating pH changes. The ions initially in the pore water are replaced by ions (or mix of ions) introduced at the electrodes at a rate that maintains constant pore water ionic strength. For constant pH conditions, the pore water conductivity relates closely to ionic strength. Thus, the maximum concentration at which a bionutrient can be distributed through the pore water is roughly equal to the ionic strength of the pore water. Pore water ionic strengths for saturated soils typically range from 1 to 10 mM, and for unsaturated soils from 10 to 100 mM (Rice et al. 1989). Concentrations less than the initial ionic strength can be achieved by using a mix of neutralizing agents at the electrode. For example, the final concentration of nitrate can be reduced by a factor of 10 by using a 10:1 mix of hydrochloric and nitric acids to neutralize the electrolysis reactions at the cathode.

The maximum flux rate of nitrate achievable per meter of length of a typical electrokinetic electrode and required in a typical in situ bioremediation injection well (Hooker et al. 1994) can be compared to provide a general idea of the adequacy of the electrokinetic process for providing the nutrient flux required.

The present design of the unsaturated soil electrokinetic electrode systems can handle about 12 amps per meter of electrode, which is a limitation of the power supplies being used. In principle, higher currents could be imposed, but electrode and soil heating problems would require careful consideration. At this current, at most, 0.45 g NO_3 will be injected to the soil pore water each minute. For the in situ bioremediation process, an average of 2.3 g NO_3 is required each minute for each meter of injection well screen, or five times higher than that achievable in the electrokinetic process. However, to optimize the in situ bioremediation process and prevent biofouling, the nutrients must be delivered in pulses at higher rates of 26.5 g NO_3/min, which is clearly greater than can be achieved electrokinetically. Obviously, because of low flux rates, it is unlikely that electrokinetic delivery of nutrients alone could overcome the problems of biofouling near the electrodes. However, regions of low soil permeability missed by hydraulic injection methods can be treated by the electrokinetic injection methods. This suggests that electrokinetic injection methods could be used in conjunction with hydraulic injection methods to increase the uniformity of treatment in heterogeneous soils.

ELECTROKINETIC MOISTURE CONTROL

Microorganisms in deep vadose zones are typically nutrient-limited because of the lack of moisture. Although vadose sediments may contain nutrients, added moisture is required to make the nutrients more bioavailable (Fredrickson et al. 1993). However, required nutrients may still be lacking; most notably, insufficient oxygen may be available for stimulation of aerobic organisms (Brockman et al. 1994). To achieve reasonable rates of bioremediation of hydrocarbons, the subsurface must be aerated to some extent. Performance is improved if moisture is added along with the air. The zone of aeration influence may be increased by forcing a larger volume of air into the subsurface without increasing air emissions, which would require additional off-gas treatment (Baker et al. 1994). Thus, in many cases it appears that the primary limitations to stimulating bioremediation in arid vadose soils are the supply of moisture and oxygen.

The electrokinetic electrode system may be used to increase the moisture content of vadose soils. By properly controlling the vacuum and voltage, the rate and amount of water that enters the soil can be controlled and moisture levels maintained below the field capacity of the soil. When operated in arid soils (moisture contents <10 wt%), an unsaturated wetting front is propagated from the anode to the cathode by electroosmosis at a rate of about 1 cm/day. When using the electrokinetic extraction process to remediate anionic contamination from unsaturated soils with low moisture content (~5 wt%), an unsaturated moisture front (10 to 15 wt%) is electroosmotically driven from the anodes to the cathodes. This has been demonstrated in bench-scale experiments (see Figure 1). Water added between the electrodes is also moved by electroosmosis. In practice, this water could be added through open-ended tubing installed in

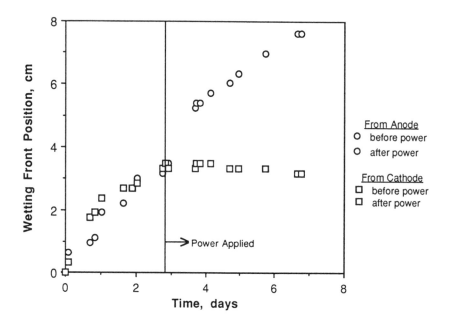

FIGURE 1. Bench-scale measurement of wetting front movement as a function of time.

1-in-diameter hydropunched holes. Desirable reagents (such as methanol) could be added as well. These new methods provide the means to increase the moisture content in a well-defined treatment zone. The dry soil outside the treatment zone acts as an insulating boundary and focuses the applied current into the desired treatment zone, increasing the efficiency of the electrokinetic process.

In addition, the process is compatible with other in situ vapor-phase remediation processes, such as soil vapor extraction or soil venting. Because unsaturated conditions are always maintained (typically <50% saturation), there is always residual void space. This compatibility adds to the robustness of the electrokinetic remediation process because numerous combinations can be envisioned. Numerous nutrients (e.g., methane, nitrous oxide, triethyl phosphate) can be added in a gaseous phase as was demonstrated at Savannah River (Hazen et al. 1994). The electrokinetic process can also introduce desirable ions (such as nutrients or chelating agents) into the soil pore water in preparation for biostimulation with air or other gaseous nutrients. In an optimal scenario, anionic heavy-metal contamination is collocated with organic contamination in unsaturated soil. The anionic heavy-metal contamination could be removed electrokinetically, in the process raising the soil moisture content to about 15 wt%. During the electrokinetic processing, some pore water nutrients could also be added. After the moisture content of the treatment zone had been adjusted, air or gaseous nutrients could be injected into the treatment zone to stimulate bioremediation of the organic contamination.

CONCLUSIONS

Electrokinetic remediation appears to be a robust in situ remediation process for unsaturated soils, which is compatible with other in situ vapor-phase remediation techniques such as bioventing. While the nutrient flux rates achievable electrokinetically appear to be too small to support in situ bioremediation, electrokinetics may provide a useful tool for stimulating bioremediation in unsaturated soils where degradation is usually limited by soil moisture content. Electrokinetics in unsaturated soils provides a means for increasing the moisture content in a controlled fashion so that the field capacity of the soil is not exceeded. Because unsaturated soil conditions are maintained, there is always vapor space for efficient implementation of gaseous nutrient injection. Needed nutrients can be introduced to the pore water electrokinetically and biostimulation is initiated by the introduction of the final missing nutrient in the gas phase. This synergistic relationship between in situ electrokinetics and bioremediation may allow the use of chelating agents in the subsurface to effect the electrokinetic removal of strongly adsorbed cationic heavy-metal contamination. The regulatory concern of using chelating agents in situ would be addressed by choosing a chelating agent that is amenable to bioremediation after the metal removal has been accomplished.

ACKNOWLEDGMENT

This work was supported by the United States Department of Energy under contract DE-AC04-94AL85000.

REFERENCES

Alshawabkeh, A. N., and Y. B. Acar. 1992. "Removal of Contaminants from Soils by Electrokinetics: A Theoretical Treatise." *J. Environ. Sci. Health A27*(7): 1835-1861.

Baker, R. S., J. Ghaemghami, S. Simkins, and L. M. Mallory. 1994. "Demonstrating the Efficacy of Bioventing Using Radiotracers." In G. W. Gee and N. R. Wing (Eds.), *Thirty-Third Hanford Symposium on Health and the Environment — In-Situ Remediation: Scientific Basis for Current and Future Technologies*, Pasco, WA. November 7-11, p. 259.

Brockman, F. J., J. K. Fredrickson, S. W. Li, W. Sun, and T. L. Kieft. 1994. "Microbial Response to Remediation and Other Perturbations of Subsurface Environments." In G. W. Gee and N. R. Wing (Eds.), *Thirty-Third Hanford Symposium on Health and the Environment — In-Situ Remediation: Scientific Basis for Current and Future Technologies*, Pasco, WA, November 7-11, p. 151.

Francis, A. J., C. J. Dodge, and J. B. Gillow. 1992. "Biodegradation of metal citrate complexes and implications for toxic-metal mobility." *Nature 356*: 140-143.

Fredrickson, J. K., F. J. Brockman, B. N. Bjornstan, P. E. Long, S. W. Li, J. P. McKinley, J. V. Wright, J. L. Conca, T. L. Lieft, and D. L. Balkwill. 1993. "Microbiological Characteristics of Pristine and Contaminated Deep Vadose Sediments from an Arid Region." *Geomicrobiology J.*, 11: 95-107.

Hazen, T. C., K. H. Lombard, B. B. Looney, M. V. Enzien, J. M. Doughtery, C. B. Fliermans, J. Wear, and C. A. Eddy-Dilek. 1994. "Summary of In-Situ Bioremediation Demonstration (Methane Biostimulation) via Horizontal Wells at the Savannah River Site Integrated Demonstration Project." In G. W. Gee and N. R. Wing (Eds.), *Thirty-Third Hanford Symposium on Health and the Environment — In-Situ Remediation: Scientific Basis for Current and Future Technologies*, Pasco, WA, November 7-11, p. 137.

Heath, W. O., and M. J. Truex. 1994. "Enhanced In-Situ Bioremediation Using Six-Phase Electrical Heating." In G. W. Gee and N. R. Wing (Eds.), *Thirty-Third Hanford Symposium on Health and the Environment — In-Situ Remediation: Scientific Basis for Current and Future Technologies*, Pasco, WA, November 7-11, p. 781.

Hooker, B. S., R. S. Skeen, M. J. Truex, and B. M. Peyton. 1994. "A Demonstration of In-Situ Bioremediation of CCl4 at the Hanford Site." In G. W. Gee and N. R. Wing (Eds.), *Thirty-Third Hanford Symposium on Health and the Environment — In-Situ Remediation: Scientific Basis for Current and Future Technologies*, Pasco, WA, November 7-11, p. 281.

Hunter, R. L. 1981. *Zeta Potential In Colloid Science*, Academic Press, New York, NY.

Lageman, R. 1993. *Environ. Sci. Technol.* 27: 2648.

Lindgren, E. R., M. W. Kozak, and E. D. Mattson. 1991. "Electrokinetic Remediation of Contaminated Soils." *Proceedings of the ER'91 Conference at Pasco, WA*, Sept., p. 151.

Lindgren, E. R., M. W. Kozak, and E. D. Mattson. 1992. "Electrokinetic Remediation of Contaminated Soils: An Update." *Proceedings of the Waste Management 92 Conference at Tucson, AZ*, March, p. 1309.

Lindgren, E. R., M. W. Kozak, and E. D. Mattson. 1994. "Electrokinetic Remediation of Anionic Contaminants from Unsaturated Soils." In D. W. Tedder and F. G. Pohland (Eds.), *Emerging Technologies in Hazardous Waste Management IV*, ACS Symposium Series 554; ACS: Washington, DC. pp. 33-50.

Lindgren, E. R., R. R. Rao, and B. A. Finlayson. 1995. "Numerical Simulation of Electrokinetic Phenomena." Accepted for publication in D. W. Tedder and F. G. Pohland (Eds.), *Emerging Technologies in Hazardous Waste Management V*, ACS Symposium Series, Washington, DC.

Mattson, E. D., and E. R. Lindgren. 1995. "Electrokinetic Extraction of Chromate from Unsaturated Soils." Accepted for publication in D. W. Tedder and F. G. Pohland (Eds.), *Emerging Technologies in Hazardous Waste Management V*, ACS Symposium Series, Washington, DC.

Oak Ridge National Laboratory. 1993. *Removal of Uranium from Uranium Contaminated Soils, Phase 1: Bench Scale Testing*. ORNL-6762. Oak Ridge, TN.

Probstein, R. F., and R. E. Hicks. 1993. *Science* 260: 498-503.

Rice, R. C., R. S. Bowman, and H. Bouwer. 1989. "Ionic Composition of Vadose Zone Water in an Arid Region." *Groundwater*, 27(6): 813.

Runnells, D. D., and J. L. Larson. 1986. *Ground Water Monitoring Review* 6: 85-88.

Selection of Electron Acceptors and Strategies for In Situ Bioremediation

Robert D. Norris

ABSTRACT

The most critical aspect of designing in situ bioremediation systems is, typically, the selection and method of delivery of the electron acceptor. Nitrate, sulfate, and several forms of oxygen can be introduced, depending on the contaminants and the site conditions. Oxygen can be added as air, pure oxygen, hydrogen peroxide, or an oxygen release compound. Simplistic cost calculations can illustrate the advantages of some methods over others, providing technical requirements can be met.

INTRODUCTION

Bioremediation continues to incorporate new and more cost efficient methods of providing oxygen and, increasingly, methods of utilizing alternative electron acceptors such as nitrate and sulfate. This activity is a result of the observation that the rate of in situ bioremediation of contaminated aquifers is frequently determined by the rate at which the electron acceptor(s) is delivered throughout the impacted area. Following the pioneering work of Richard L. Raymond, in which aerated water was injected into the aquifer, the addition of hydrogen peroxide (H_2O_2) to reinjected groundwater was developed as a method to increase the rate of introducing oxygen to the contaminated zone (Brown et al. 1984). More recently, Brown et al. (1991), Marley et al. (1990), and others have promoted the use of air sparging wells to introduce oxygen by direct injection to the aquifer.

The addition of nitrate- and sulfate-amended water; the increased awareness of the contribution of nitrate, iron, and sulfate during intrinsic bioremediation; and the use of biological migration barriers as an alternative to groundwater recovery and treatment all represent areas of active development contributing to our understanding of the role and methods of introducing electron acceptors for bioremediation. In designing a bioremediation system, the selection of one or more electron acceptors and/or methods of addition needs to take into account whether the contaminant(s) are biodegradable in the presence of the electron acceptor, the ease and cost of delivering the electron acceptor throughout the contaminated zone under the site conditions (hydrogeology, depth to water, and infrastructure), the impact on remediation times, and the regulatory considerations.

INTRINSIC REMEDIATION

Intrinsic bioremediation may be both the most cost-effective and environmentally sound approach to providing electron acceptors at many sites. It has long been known that naturally occurring bioremediation can limit the extent of migration of biodegradable compounds. Typically, this phenomenon was spoken of in terms of oxygen availability. Studies by Wilson et al. (1993) and by Piontek et al. (1994), for example, have demonstrated that biodegradation of many compounds of environmental interest occurs through utilization of many alternative electron acceptors. In these studies, metabolism based on electron acceptors other than oxygen (e.g., nitrate, sulfate, iron, carbon dioxide) accounted for the major portion of the biodegradation of dissolved-phase organics.

Intrinsic bioremediation is, appropriately, gaining wider acceptance within the regulatory agency and has been the subject of dedicated symposia. However, costs associated with monitoring, site management, and documentation of intrinsic bioremediation can be substantial over the project life cycle. Cost of monitoring, reporting, and management at a service station with a small amount of residual dissolved-phase gasoline, for instance, typically ranges from $12,000 to $25,000 per year not including costs to document that biodegradation is occurring. Costs over 5 to 10 years can thus be substantial. In some cases, it may be less costly to introduce small amounts of an electron acceptor.

MINIMAL BIOREMEDIATION SYSTEMS

To be competitive with intrinsic bioremediation, the method of introduction of the electron acceptors must require minimal capital costs and very little maintenance (Norris et al. 1994). Approaches include the use of a small number of air sparging wells, batch additions of water amended with nitrate or H_2O_2, and wells containing an oxygen release compound (ORC). Air sparging systems offer the advantage of delivering oxygen over a radius of influence greater than can be accomplished by the other methods. For a small area, a three-well air sparging system might be installed for between $10,000 and $20,000. Provided observation and maintenance can be easily provided, the additional costs for this form of active remediation could be recouped by shortening the period of monitoring and management of the site by 1 year.

Batch addition of nitrate- or H_2O_2-amended water, particularly if existing wells are used, requires little capital or other direct expenditures. The cost for tanks and pumps should be less than $2,000 and nitrate or H_2O_2 costs should be less than $500 per year. However, labor costs will be substantial because of the need for relatively frequent addition of low concentrations of electron acceptor unless the site owner can provide most of the labor.

Placement of ORC in wells located within the impacted area offers the advantages of relatively low capital investment, particularly if existing wells can be used, and requires very little labor. For five 9.75-cm (4-in.) wells with 3 m (10 ft) of saturated screen, the ORC cost would be approximately $1,250. The major cost would be the installation of additional wells, if needed, which would cost approximately \$2,000 each. ORC would be replaced approximately twice per year depending on the oxygen release profile of the specific material used.

ALTERNATIVE ELECTRON ACCEPTORS

Among the several approaches to the use of alternative electron acceptors are the following:

1. Nitrilotriacetic acid can be introduced to bind and thus increase the bioavailability of the otherwise insoluble iron (III) present in the sediments, as reported by Lovley et al. (1994).
2. Sulfate can be added in conjunction with sodium benzoate and oxygen, as developed by Beeman et al. (1993).
3. Nitrate can be added to accelerate the degradation of monoaromatic hydrocarbons (except benzene [Reinhard 1994]), as described by Hutchins and Wilson (1991).

Nitrate is highly soluble in water, does not adsorb readily to soils, and, consequently, is more readily distributed within the aquifer than is oxygen. Further, nitrate is less expensive per pound of carbon degraded and does not undergo as many side reactions as does hydrogen peroxide. As a result, nitrate addition is an attractive alternative to oxygen or hydrogen peroxide in many cases. However, some agencies may restrict the use of nitrate to concentrations below the drinking water standard.

At the French Limited site in Crosby, Texas, injected water was amended with ammonium nitrate, oxygen, and initially, with potassium tripolyphosphate. In the areas where nitrate concentrations increased but dissolved oxygen (DO) did not, the disappearance of toluene at a much faster rate than benzene suggested denitrifying bacteria may have been responsible for the degradation of toluene. The apparent biodegradation of chlorinated ethenes was also observed (Day 1994, personal communication) and may have been related to the presence of nitrate.

Potential chemical cost savings over the use of H_2O_2 based on stoichiometry and purchase prices can be derived from the cost of electron acceptor per kilogram of hydrocarbon converted to carbon dioxide; these costs are approximately \$5 for sodium nitrate and \$12 for H_2O_2, assuming 100% utilization for the intended purpose. The cost differential is likely to be greater because of inefficiencies in the utilization of H_2O_2 at most sites. The use of nitrate alone or in conjunction with oxygen sources offers potentially greater cost savings by shortening the time of active operations, particularly at sites where either low hydraulic conductivity and/or a large contaminant mass would result in a relatively long treatment time. For example, at a site with operating costs of \$10,000 per month, a reduction in total operating costs of \$120,000 would result from reducing the remediation time from 4 years to 3 years.

MIGRATION BARRIERS

Historically, migration of dissolved species has been controlled using groundwater capture and treatment systems, which, while effective, typically are expensive to construct and operate. Creation of an electron acceptor-rich groundwater zone that intercepts the migration pathway can prevent migration of biodegradable compounds. There are several approaches to creating these zones, including a row of air sparging wells, aerated interceptor trenches, and rows of wells or a trench containing ORC or a source of alternative electron acceptors.

REGENESIS Bioremediation Products has developed an ORC consisting of magnesium peroxide formulated to release oxygen at a predetermined release profile. The ORC contained in an appropriate matrix is placed in sleeves and lowered down the wells. Oxygen is released to the aquifer to increase the rate of biodegradation in the impacted area. Because the oxygen is released slowly to the groundwater, stripping of volatiles from the groundwater is negligible. The system is maintenance free except for periodic replacement of the ORC and monitoring. There are no requirements for electricity or other utilities.

Four field studies have demonstrated a reduction in concentrations of dissolved benzene, toluene, ethylbenzene, and xylenes (BTEX). Kao and Borden (1994) reported increased DO levels in wells located 10 feet downgradient of the ORC wells and a decrease in BTEX from 7 mg/L to 1 mg/L after 23 days and to 0.2 mg/L after 38 days. They also reported decreased conductivity after several months. Workers at the University of Waterloo (Bianchi-Mosquera et al. 1994) conducted studies at the Borden Landfill in Ontario, Canada, which resulted in increased DO levels from less than 0.5 mg/L to between 8 and 11 mg/L and decreases in benzene levels from 1,800 mg/L to less than 50 mg/L. A field test recently conducted at a former service station site in New Mexico resulted in sufficient increased DO and decreased BTEX concentrations to obtain agency approval to install a complete barrier. The fourth field test, conducted in Alaska, demonstrated the potential for ORC to intercept a hydrocarbon plume. ORC did not cause fouling of the aquifer as did an air sparging system that was tested on the same site.

CONCLUSION

Bioremediation projects will incorporate an increasing variety of electron acceptors and methods to introduce them. In most instances, the selection will involve a number of trade-offs which will be unique for each site. For example, the use of air sparging versus ORC compounds for migration barriers involves trade-offs between capital and maintenance costs as well as technical issues. To create a barrier across a 50-ft interval might require three air sparging wells, an air compressor, electrical source, and trenches for the air lines at an installation cost of $12,000 to $20,000. A series of 10 wells containing ORC might cost $15,000 to $25,000 to install. Inspection and maintenance of the air sparging system might cost $10,000 to $20,000 per year versus $4,000 to $8,000 to replace the ORC compound. As with any comparison between alternatives to providing electron acceptors, the size of the area to be treated, the demand for electron acceptor, monitoring requirements, incremental personnel costs, and remoteness of the site to the operating personnel, are among the several variables that must be considered.

REFERENCES

Beeman, R. E., J. E. Howell, S. H. Shoemaker, E. A. Salazar, and J. R. Buttram. 1993. "A Field Evaluation of In-Situ Microbial Reductive Dehalogenation by the Biotransformation of Chlorinated Ethenes." In R. E. Hinchee, A. Leeson, L. Semprini, and S. K. Ong. (Eds.), *Bioremediation of Chlorinated and Polycyclic Aromatic Compounds*. Lewis Publishers, Ann Arbor, MI.

Bianchi-Mosquera, G., R. M. Allen-King, and D. M. Mackay. 1994. "Enhanced Degradation of Dissolved Benzene and Toluene Using a Solid Oxygen Releasing Compound." *Groundwater Monitoring Review*, (Winter): 120-128.

Brown, R. A., C. Herman, and E. Henry. 1991. "The Use of Aeration in Environmental Cleanups." *Proceedings, Haztech International Pittsburgh Waste Conference*. Pittsburgh, PA.

Brown, R. A., Norris, R. D., and Raymond, R. L. 1984. "Oxygen Transport in Contaminated Aquifers." *Proceedings of the Petroleum Hydrocarbon and Organic Chemicals in Groundwater: Prevention, Detection, and Restoration*. National Water Well Association, Houston, TX.

Hutchins, S. R., and J. T. Wilson. 1991. "Laboratory and Field Studies on BTEX Biodegradation in a Fuel-Contaminated Aquifer Under Denitrifying Conditions." In R. E. Hinchee and R. F. Olfenbuttel (Eds.), *In Situ Bioreclamation, Applications and Investigations for Hydrocarbon and Contaminated Site Remediation*. Butterworth-Heinemann, Boston, MA. pp. 157-172.

Kao, C. M. and R. C. Borden. 1994. "Enhanced Aerobic Bioremediation of a Gasoline-Contaminated Aquifer for Oxygen-Releasing Barriers." In R. E. Hinchee et al. (Eds.), *Hydrocarbon Bioremediation*. Lewis Publishers, Boca Raton, FL. pp. 262-266.

Lovley, D. R., J. C. Woodward, and F. H. Chapelle. 1994. "Stimulated Anoxic Biodegradation of Aromatic Hydrocarbons Using Fe(III) Liquids." *Nature*, 370: 128-136.

Marley, M. C., M. T. Walsh, and P. E. Nangeroni. 1990. "Case Study on the Application of Air Sparging as a Complementary Technology to Vapor Extraction at a Gasoline Spill Site in Rhode Island." *Proceedings, HMC Great Lakes 90*. Hazardous Materials Control Research Institute, Silver Spring, MD.

Norris, R. D., J. C. Dey, and D. P. Shine. 1994. "The Potential Use of Low Level Activities to Assist Intrinsic Bioremediation." Presented at the USEPA Symposium On Intrinsic Bioremediation of Ground Water, Denver, CO.

Piontek, K., T. Sall, S. de Albuquerque, and J. Cruze. 1994. "Demonstrating Intrinsic Bioremediation of BTEX at National Gas Plant." Presented at the Symposium on Intrinsic Bioremediation of Groundwater, Denver, CO.

Reinhard, M. 1994. "In-Situ Bioremediation Technologies for Petroleum-Derived Hydrocarbons Based on Alternate Electron Acceptors (other than Molecular Oxygen)." In R. D. Norris et al. (Eds.), *Handbook of Bioremediation*. Lewis Publishers, Boca Raton, FL. p. 134.

Vogel, T. M. 1993. "National Bioremediation of Chlorinated Solvents." In R. D. Norris et al. (Eds.), *The Handbook of Bioremediation*. Lewis Publishers, Boca Raton, FL.

Wilson, J. T., D. H. Kampbell, and J. Armstrong. 1993. "Natural Bioreclamation of Alkyl-benzenes (BTEX) from a Gasoline Spill in Methanogenic Groundwater." In R. E. Hinchee, B. C. Alleman, R. E. Hoeppel, and R. N. Miller (Eds.), *Hydrocarbon Bioremediation*. Lewis Publishers, Ann Arbor, MI.

Landfarming of Municipal Sewage Sludge at Oak Ridge, Tennessee

Monica Lee Tischler, Charles Pergler, Marialice Wilson, David Mabry, and Michael Stephenson

ABSTRACT

The City of Oak Ridge, Tennessee, has been applying municipal sanitary sludge to 9 sites comprising 90 ha on the U.S. Department of Energy (DOE) Oak Ridge Reservation (ORR) since 1983. Approximately 13,000,000 L are applied annually by spraying sludge (2 to 3% solids) under pressure from a tanker. Under an ongoing monitoring program, both the sludge and the soil in the application areas are analyzed for organic, inorganic, and radioactive parameters on a regular basis. Organic pollutants are analyzed in sludge on a semiannual basis and in the soil application areas on an annual basis. Inorganic parameters are analyzed daily (e.g., pH, total solids) or monthly (e.g., nitrogen, manganese) in sludge and annually in soil in application areas. Radionuclides (Co-60, Cs-137, I-131, Be-7, K-40, Ra-228, U-235, U-238) are scanned daily during application by the sewage treatment plant and analyzed weekly in composite sludge samples and annually in soil. Additionally, data on radioactive body burden for maximally exposed workers who apply the sludge show no detectable exposures. This monitoring program is comprehensive and is one of the few in the United States that analyzes radionuclides. Results from the monitoring program show heavy metals and radionuclides are not accumulating to harmful levels in the soil application areas.

INTRODUCTION

The City of Oak Ridge, Tennessee, has been applying municipal sanitary sludge to land on the DOE ORR since 1983 under an agreement with DOE and the Tennessee Department of Environment and Conservation (TDEC). Previous work on the benefits of this sludge application to sycamore (*Plantanus occidentalis*) and loblolly pine (*Pinus taeda*) on the ORR showed that even a single dose application of sludge resulted in a long-term (> 10-year) positive growth and biomass (Van Miegroet et al. 1991). The majority of the nutrients from the application

490

were retained in the upper soil, with a significant increase in the total and available nitrogen. This benefit lasted several years after the sludge application, in contrast to another experimental plot where inorganic nitrogen was leached away within a few months of application (Van Miegroet et al. 1991).

Other researchers have shown the benefits of land application of municipal sludge. For example, McNab and Berry (1985) found that three species of pine seedlings planted in soil amended with dried sludge produced approximately three times more tree biomass and 8% more wood as a percentage of total tree weight when compared to trees grown in soil amended with inorganic fertilizer. Peterson and coworkers (1984) grew poplars in a greenhouse environment and compared poplars grown in sludge-amended soil with those grown in ammonium nitrate-fertilized soil. The poplars grown in the sludge-amended soil grew faster than those grown in soil amended with inorganic nitrogen. Peterson et al. (1984) also showed that the trees grown in sludge-amended soil did not accumulate more of any nutrient or heavy metal than those grown with inorganic nitrogen.

The City of Oak Ridge sewage treatment plant receives wastewater from both domestic and industrial sources. The land application consists of spraying sludge (2 to 3% solids) under pressure from a tanker at a rate of approximately 10 metric tons/ha. Nine sites comprising 90 ha have been used by the city: four sites comprising 28 ha have been closed following land application, and five sites comprising 63 ha are still active application sites. Currently, 2 to 6 loads per day (40 to 120 loads/month) of sewage sludge are trucked in a 20,000-L tanker truck to the application sites and transferred to a 5,300-L field vehicle for surface spray application. Approximately 13,000,000 L/year are applied, resulting in a thin layer of sludge on surface vegetation.

Sewage sludge typically contains both natural and human-made radio-nuclides. Because there are currently no applicable federal sludge radioactivity standards, conservative radionuclide limits for ORR sludge application have been established (DOE 1994). These limits require that the resulting average concentration of uranium and other radionuclides with longer decay periods in the receiving soil will not generally exceed 2× background. In addition, to ensure long-term acceptability of the Oak Ridge sludge application program, a risk-based model for determining acceptable radionuclide concentrations in sludge has been established.

Industrial customers of the City of Oak Ridge sewage treatment plant include a DOE facility and several private companies that use radioactive materials. These customers must meet U.S. Nuclear Regulatory Commission (NRC) regulations governing sewage discharges to municipal treatment plants from NRC licensees; however, radioactive materials coming from medical facilities, such as the local hospital, currently do not have to meet the same program limits as other standard industrial customers. Because radionuclides may become concentrated in the sludge during the treatment process, the municipal sludge has been monitored for radionuclides in addition to other federal- and state-mandated components.

Although there are no federal requirements to test sludge for radionuclides, both the sludge and the landfarm areas on the ORR are part of an ongoing monitoring program. The radiological content of municipal sludges is of concern to the NRC and the U.S. Environmental Protection Agency (EPA); however, DOE's local monitoring program is one of the few programs in the United States that analyzes radiological content in sludge (GAO 1994). The data compiled from this comprehensive program provide the opportunity to monitor any potentially harmful buildup of metals and radionuclides over a long period of time.

METHODS

The City of Oak Ridge, in cooperation with DOE, analyzes organic, inorganic, and heavy metal parameters in digested sewage sludge and sludge application site soils in compliance with EPA 40 CFR 503.10-503.18, the State of Tennessee Land Application Approval (LAA), and the City of Oak Ridge National Pollutant Discharge Elimination System (NPDES) Permit #TN0024155. LAA inorganic parameters in sludge (such as pH, total solids percent, and percentage of volatile solids) are monitored daily (City of Oak Ridge 1994). Other LAA inorganic parameters in sludge include ammonia, nitrate, nitrite, inorganic nitrogen, total Kjeldahl nitrogen, organic nitrogen, manganese, potassium, and phosphorus, which are analyzed monthly (City of Oak Ridge 1994). Heavy metals in sludge are analyzed monthly, and toxic organic compounds are analyzed twice a year by both EPA methods 8270 and 8080 (City of Oak Ridge 1994). Radionuclides (Co-60, Cs-137, I-131, Be-7, K-40, Ra-228, U-235, U-238) are analyzed weekly in composite sludge samples, and sludges to be hauled and applied on the ORR are scanned daily. Soils from sludge application sites are analyzed annually for organic, inorganic, heavy metal, and radioactive chemicals.

Three City of Oak Ridge employees at the sewage treatment plant have the potential for occupational exposure to the sludge, either at the treatment plant or during spraying operations. All have been employed at the plant since the land application of the sludge has been in operation. They have been monitored for exposure to radionuclides through whole body counts and urinalysis (DOE 1994).

RESULTS

Table 1 shows the highest levels of heavy metals detected in the sludge in 1993 and compares them with the federal limits under 40 CFR 503.13. In all instances, the heavy metal concentrations in the sludge were well below the federal ceiling limits for these compounds. Chlordane (0.55 µg/kg) was the only organic contaminant reported above the detection limit in the sludge in 1993 (City of Oak Ridge 1994).

Table 2 shows the radionuclide levels in the municipal sludge from 1988 to 1993. The concentrations of naturally occurring radionuclides such as ^{7}Be, ^{40}K, and ^{226}Ra have remained relatively constant throughout the reporting period.

TABLE 1. City of Oak Ridge highest heavy metal levels for 1993 vs. 40 CFR
503.13 ceiling concentration limits.

Heavy Metal	Highest Detected Sludge Level in 1993[a]	40 CFR 503.13 Ceiling Concentration Limits[a]
Arsenic	25.1	75
Cadmium	15.1	85
Chromium	185	3,000
Copper	544	4,300
Lead	95	840
Mercury	16.2	57
Molybdenum	33.8	75
Nickel	51	420
Selenium	20.9	100
Zinc	2,070	7,500

(a) All levels are in mg/kg dry weight.

Concentrations of radionuclides that are a result of nuclear testing fallout (^{60}Co
and ^{137}Cs) dropped between 1988 and 1993. Uranium entering the sewage treatment plant has dropped dramatically since 1988 and is thought to be the result
of improved practices on the part of local industrial customers. The increased
use of medical isotopes by Oak Ridge Methodist Medical Center is seen in the
6-fold increase in ^{131}I from 1988 to 1993.

Table 3 shows the cumulative radionuclide loading at five application sites
that are currently active. Although it appears that radionuclides are accumulating
to some extent at some sites (e.g., ^{137}Cs is twice as high at the Scarboro Road
application site than in the adjacent reference site), there is little or no difference
between radionuclide concentrations at the application sites and adjacent reference
sites for most radionuclides reported. Radionuclides do not appear to concentrate
and accumulate at the application sites.

Whole body counts and urinalysis of the three municipal workers showed no
detectable radioactivity from occupational exposure to sludge. Quantitative risk
assessment using standard methods in compliance with DOE Order 5400.5 and
standard EPA methodologies (EPA 1989, 1991) has shown no appreciable risks
to these workers who would be maximally exposed to the sludge (DOE 1994).

DISCUSSION

Land application of municipal sludge is a viable option for beneficial reuse
of the organic nutrients and nitrogen contained in the sludge. Studies have shown

TABLE 2. Historical radiological characterization of Oak Ridge sanitary sewage sludge (selected radionuclides).

Radionuclide	Half-Life	Source[a]	Average Concentration, pCi/g dry weight					
			1988	1989	1990	1991	1992	1993
^{7}Be	53.6 d	1	1.2	1.5	1.7	1.6	1.3	1.7
^{40}K	1.28×10^9 y	1	7.0	6.8	7.2	5.9	5.1	5.8
^{60}Co	5.27 y	2,4	5.3	2.5	3.3	0.9	0.8	0.6
^{131}I	8.04 d	5	6.8	8.5	5.9	9.7	17	42
^{137}Cs	30.2 y	2,4	2.0	1.3	2.7	1.4	0.5	0.6
^{226}Ra	5.8 y	1	0.6	0.9	1.2	0.7	0.7	0.9
U - total	4.5×10^9 y	1,2,3	140	50	30	25	23	13[b]
U-235 assay			0.32%	0.51%	0.71%	0.80%	0.90%	0.8%[b]

(a) (1) Natural radionuclide, (2) nuclear reactor, (3) uranium industry, (4) nuclear testing fallout, and (5) medical radionuclide.
(b) Based on gamma spectroscopy; prior year total uranium by neuron activation, U-235 assay by mass spectroscopy.

TABLE 3. Cumulative radionuclide loading on active sludge land application sites.

Selected Radionuclide	Cumulative Radionuclide Loading on Indicated Site, pCi/g									
	Hayfield #1		Hayfield #2		High Pasture		Watson Road		Scarboro Road	
	Ref[a]	Total[b]	Ref	Total	Ref	Total	Ref	Total	Ref	Total
Potassium-40	3.0	2.7	3.0	4.8	3.1	4.1	11.2	7.4	4.0	3.8
Cobalt-60	0.01	0.05	0.01	0.01	bld	0.06	bld	0.01	bld	0.03
Strontium-90	0.07	0.12	0.07	0.19	0.12	0.14	0.15	0.17	0.18	0.17
Technetium-99	0.01	0.01	0.01	0.05	0.04	0.08	0.06	0.09	bld	0.04
Cesium-137	0.54	0.57	0.54	0.77	0.47	0.45	0.54	0.59	0.48	0.81
Uranium-total	2.8	3.6	2.8	3.2	2.3	3.4	3.0	2.9	2.4	3.2

(a) Assumed background radiation for given site based on radioanalysis of soil taken from adjacent site not used for sludge; bld signifies radionuclide measurement below level of detection.

(b) Radionuclides found in top 15 cm of application site soil by lab radioanalysis of samples taken in 1992 and 1993; values include background.

that sludge application increases timber yields (Sopper & Kerr 1980, Van Miegroet et al. 1991, Chapman-King et al. 1990, McNab & Berry 1985, and Peterson et al. 1984), and land application can be a cost-efficient alternative for final disposal (DOE 1994).

There are both practical limits and regulatory limits to the amount of sludge that can be applied to a land area. Practically, excess nitrogen is harmful. There are legal constraints on both the daily and cumulative application of both nutrients and heavy metals. DOE has established conservative loading limits that are below those established by federal law (DOE 1994). Because there are no standard loading limits for radionuclides, buildup of these compounds is of concern to the public. Extensive monitoring of the land application areas on the ORR has shown that buildup of radionuclides from municipal sludge is not occurring.

REFERENCES

Chapman-King, R., T. H. Hinckley, and C. C. Grier. 1990. "Growth response of forest trees to wastewater and sludge application." *Can. J. For. Res. 14*: 900-904.

City of Oak Ridge. 1994. *1993 State of Tennessee Biosolids Management Report.* CORSTARE.DOC-REV.0. April 15.

DOE. 1994. *Environmental Assessment for the Proposed Expansion of the Land Application of Sanitary Sludge on the Oak Ridge Reservation.* U.S. Department of Energy, Oak Ridge Operations, Oak Ridge, TN.

EPA. 1989. *Risk Assessment Guidance for Superfund, Volume I: Human Health Evaluation Manual (Part A).* EPA/540/1-89/002. U.S. Environmental Protection Agency.

EPA. 1991. *Human Health Evaluation Manual, Supplemental Guidance: Standard Default Exposure Factors.* U.S. Environmental Protection Agency, Office of Solid Waste and Emergency Response. OSWER Directive 9285.6-03. Washington, DC. March 25.

GAO. 1994. *Report to Congressional Requestors. Nuclear Regulation: Action Needed to Control Radioactive Contamination at Sewage Treatment Plants.* GAO/RCED-94-133. General Accounting Office. May.

McNab, W. H., and C. R. Berry. 1985. "Distribution of aboveground biomass in three pine species planted on a devastated site amended with sewage sludge or inorganic fertilizer." *Forest Science 31*: 373-382.

Peterson, J. M., S. R. Riha, G. P. Senesac, and L. Naylor. 1984. *Nitrogen Fertilizer and Sewage Sludge Effects on Hybrid Poplars.* NYSERDA Report 85-1. New York State Energy Research and Development Authority.

Sopper, W. E., and S. N. Kerr. 1980. "Potential use of forest land for recycling municipal wastewater and sludge." *Proceedings, National Urban Forestry Conference.* pp. 392-409.

Van Miegroet, H., H. L. Boston, and D. W. Johnson. 1991. "The role of land application of municipal sludge in short rotation woody biomass production." *1991 Southern Biomass Conference*, Louisiana Department of Agriculture and Forestry, Baton Rouge, LA.

In Situ Bioremediation of Food-Service Waste Grease

Bobby F. Dowden

ABSTRACT ━━━━━━━━━━━━━━━━━━━━━━━━━━━━━━━━━━

Waste grease from food service establishments causes ongoing and very costly problems in publicly owned treatment works (POTW) and their sewage collection systems. The processes and systems used in food service establishment grease traps are not usually applied and operated so that treatment is successful, the first time, every time. Properly handled, waste grease can be amenable to bacterial treatment. In situ bioremediation of grease wastes at the food service establishment is predictable when the chemicals and soaps, the cleaning practices and applications, the entire drainline system, and a properly sized grease interceptor are considered parts of and treated as an ecosystem. A process that ensures successful bioremediation of grease trap wastes is described. This once-through treatment process is compared to some of those practiced in POTW employing secondary (biological) sewage treatment.

INTRODUCTION

A costly problem for POTW is waste grease contributed to the sewer system by butter, lard, margarine, vegetable fats and oils, and tallow from prepared meat. Worse yet, some of the waste grease drops to floors and becomes contaminated with dirt, cleaning compounds, and pesticides (Metcalf & Eddy 1991).

Grease interceptors, or grease traps, are designed to remove food-waste grease from wastewater prior to its entry into the city sewer lines (Babbitt & Baumann 1958, Fowler 1946, Imhoff & Fair 1956). Soaps and detergents suspend waste oil and grease but, diluted by other wastewater, deposit the waste grease on the walls of sewer pipes (Babbitt & Baumann 1958). Grease deposits on the walls of the pipes and other structures may become very hard when neglected (Hardenbergh & Rodie 1960).

Fats are among the more stable organic compounds (Metcalf & Eddy 1991). Waste grease is rich in calories. Capitalizing on this condition, many schemes have been devised to apply bacteria or bacterial byproducts to grease traps to remove or destroy the grease. In almost all instances, these efforts failed (Babbitt & Baumann 1958, Baïg & Grenning 1976).

Most attempts to deal with waste grease approach the problem as if it were merely a recalcitrant waste isolated in some kind of undersized cess pool. Many people agree that "bioremediation using 'biocatalytic' converters, preserved bacteria formulations, enzymatic preparations, extracts from plants and animal by-products, and *all sorts of 'fu-fu' dust* are useless" (emphasis added) (Lancaster unpublished).

A patented process described herein utilizes a multistep approach to resolving this problem, and experience has proved its efficacy.

DISCUSSION

It is useful to view grease traps as miniature wastewater treatment plants. Similar design and operations principles are utilized in grease traps and in POTW. Three basic factors make wastewater-treatment plants work:

Factor 1 — Proper Design and Engineering, Including Volume of Tanks or Vessels

One of the most important attributes of a treatment plant is the volume of the tanks in which treatment takes place. When the volume of the treatment structures is calculated, the expected flow of liquid waste is defined. The size of a sewage treatment plant is determined in large part by the number of gallons per day released by the people in the community served.

A grease trap should be designed in a similar way. Proper sizing allows adequate removal of waste grease in the trap. Many plumbing codes call for the volume of a grease trap to be sized according to the number of seats in the food service establishment, the number of serving periods, and dishwashing water usage (whether or not a commercial dishwasher is present). The volume of a properly designed grease trap approximates its calculated 24-hour flow volume. Most interceptors have detention time of 10 to 30 minutes (Metcalf & Eddy 1991). Precipitated food and waste solids and deposited waste grease usually cause such short detention times by supplanting and filling functional treatment volume (size). Detention time is maximized in regularly, properly maintained grease traps.

Many, if not most, grease traps are woefully undersized. The volume (and retention time) available for treatment of waste grease is increased by treating the drain lines, making them a part of the treatment system. Many undersized grease traps can operate within sewage system pretreatment permit limits by emphasizing a treatment process that attains adequate grease remediation. Even so, there is a lower limit in volume beyond which microbes do not have sufficient detention time to complete treatment functions.

Factor 2 — Proper Construction

Construction of an activated sludge sewage treatment plant incorporates established engineering and construction criteria. If the criteria are not followed, the plant probably will not meet the parameter limits imposed by an appropriate permit issued by an environmental regulatory agency.

The structural components of a properly designed grease trap embody, first, a tank of adequate volume. An inlet "downcomer" pipe releases the wastewater holding grease, dirt, trash, and other solids into the middle level (water elevation) of the grease trap. Many times, the tank contains baffles. The baffles are under-flow weirs, protruding above the water surface. Openings at the bottom of the baffles allow water flow beneath and grease separation between them. An outlet pipe is placed opposite the inlet so that its outlet height from the bottom defines the "wet depth," or operating water level, of the grease trap. The outlet "riser" pipe allows water to flow up from the lower levels of the grease trap (away from floating grease) to the sewer. A well-constructed trap will have three ports: one inspection port each on the inlet pipe and the outlet pipe plus a sampling port on the outlet pipe.

Waste grease interceptors may be considered projects too small to involve a responsible design engineer. Unless a properly designed prefabricated inter-ceptor is installed, a grease trap will probably be constructed as a simple box by a plumbing contractor who may not complete it properly. The simple box structure may reflect the perceptions, prejudices, and pressures of the moment under which the contractor operates.

Factor #3 — Proper Operation

An activated sludge wastewater treatment plant will have an operations manual written by the design engineering firm or other professionals. Standards of operator education have been compiled and are enforced. Operators are continually trained and tested for competence. Ordinances will safeguard the treatment process of the plant. Usually, pretreatment regulations to protect the POTW are required by multiple levels of environmental regulatory agencies.

Usually, an interceptor is not properly operated. The management and employees ignore it until something bad happens. "Something bad" usually consists of sewage backing up into the food preparation areas or odors emanating from drain lines. By the time these occur, grease and food solids have usually filled the grease trap, passed through the trap, and deposited grease — with solids — in the sewer lines. In most instances, the grease must be dug out and removed from the sewers (Imhoff & Fair 1956).

Waste grease, as it floats in a grease trap, is usually a lard- or tallow-like material. Almost always, the grease in a neglected trap contains trash such as napkins, silverware, plastic straws, dirt, plastic ware, floor sweepings, food solids (scraps), etc. Pesticide content usually precludes recycling.

Pappas and Pappas (1993) describe a process in which proper operation of the drain line and grease trap system is more important than the application of bacteria, nutrients, buffers, and other microbe-enhancing materials. Education of food service personnel in the process takes precedence over continual cleaning out the drain lines and grease trap. Unlike programs that have failed, this process treats the entire grease trap and drain line system as an ecosystem. The drain lines are included because the success of a bioremediation program is greatly improved after a restaurant's drain lines are well "cleaned" physically, waste and scraps are pumped out of the grease trap, and the side walls of the grease trap are washed down with water under high pressure.

Grease is difficult for bacterial decomposition (Metcalf & Eddy 1991). The resistance of the hardened grease to bioremediation seems to be related to the surface area available to the bacteria. When large clusters of grease deposits are reduced in size by physical methods, decomposition of incoming grease by bacteria is enhanced and more rapid. Bacteria readily decompose smaller particles of grease suspended in water and entering a physically "clean" grease trap.

Treating the drain lines is essential for other reasons. Low pH levels cause corrosion. POTW pretreatment permit limits for pH are stringently enforced. Control of pH occurs best in the drain lines — access is easiest at their openings.

Personnel may carelessly wash food solids into the drain lines. The food scraps decay, releasing organic acids (Babbitt & Baumann 1958). Other materials, such as soap, detergents, or other cleaning materials, released into the lines draining food preparation areas alter the pH of the wastewater, and raise the biochemical oxygen demand (BOD5) loading of the system. The pH of the water readily changes the composition of the bacterial biomass that can grow in the grease trap. Usually, the pH of the water in a neglected grease trap is about 4 standard units. Anoxic or septic conditions accompany the growth of acidogenic bacteria as they metabolize the organic materials in the waste. Very offensive odors accompany septic conditions. Many food-service establishments add household bleach and other disinfectants almost indiscriminately into the drain lines, decimating beneficial microbial populations. No biological system can function under such dystrophic conditions. Successful treating of drain lines includes terminating reckless use of bleach or disinfectants.

Adequate servicing of grease traps using the described process entails removing grease before it becomes encrusted. Encrusted grease becomes very hard. It can then be removed only with great effort. Many times, not even physical cleaning ("rodding out") and hydroflushing with "water knives" at 3,500 pounds per square inch (244 kg/cm^2) pressure will remove the harder portions of deposited grease. The hardened grease resists microbial activity. This difficulty seems related to the surface area of grease available to the bacteria. Physically breaking up larger clusters of grease enhances bacterial decomposition. Some of the hard crust can be removed only after bacterial activity has slowly softened it. Follow-up service should take into account the effects of loosened grease clumps possibly clogging the drain lines after bioremediation service commences. Concentrations of certain pretreatment permit parameters — BOD5, total suspended solids — sometimes increase after initiating bioremediation service. As the microbes metabolize or loosen excess grease from the drain lines and grease trap, the usual permit parameter limits are exceeded less often.

This treatment process aims to bioremediate grease waste in the grease trap system before the grease waste can enter the POTW sewer lines. The treatment process attains adequate wastewater treatment by:

1. Stopping Water Leaks. Replacement of faucet washers and completion of other repairs stop water leaks, especially hot water that may mobilize grease and carry it into sewer lines. There, other sewage lowers the temperature, reduces the carrying capacity of the water, and grease precipitates inside the sewer line. Excess water usage caused by leaks overloads a grease trap by adding too much water to the drain lines and grease trap, reducing detention time. An added benefit from reducing water usage is lowering of utility charges. A further benefit is a decrease of fines and surcharges based on the amount of water bought by the food service establishment.

2. Keeping Food Wastes Out of the Drain Lines. Food wastes from unscreened lines overload and clog grease traps, reducing their retention time. Food wastes, coated with grease, are carried into the grease trap where they "stick" to other materials in the grease trap. Crowding by food waste (or excess water) denies beneficial bacteria the time needed to break down waste or complete their life cycles. To keep out the food wastes, screens and strainers are installed in the openings to all drain lines. Food waste strained onto the screens is removed and placed into a garbage receptacle.

It is not uncommon for food service personnel to resist resolutely the use of screens placed over drain line openings. Education of personnel implementing this process includes the relationship between food wastes in the drain lines and grease trap with bothersome plumbing problems.

3. Stop Killing Beneficial Bacteria. This is also achieved by education of personnel. Very few, if any, POTW could successfully treat wastewater if a couple of kiloliters of creosote or disinfectant were released into the collection system two or three times a day. Neither can a grease trap treatment community survive if it is continually dosed with 25 to 30 mL of disinfectant or bleach throughout the working day. Many food service operators assert strongly that the state or local department of health requires sterilization in food preparation areas, and they use bleach to accomplish it. This assertion is almost true. Most health departments require sterilization of utensils touching food to be served. In other activities of the kitchen, the health department requires only that the area or utensils be clean. This requirement is in force whether or not the food service operator uses bleach for sterilization of items other than food preparation or serving utensils. Too often is found sterile grit arising from use of disinfectants in poorly cleaned utensils. It provides good cover for the growth of harmful bacteria.

A technique has been devised to meet the seeming dilemma arising from the health department requirement for sterility of utensils contacting food to be served. Kitchen personnel are educated to use disinfectant to sterilize silverware as the health department requires. Then, just prior to releasing the spent dishwater, the employees add a buffer that mitigates the effect of bleach in the grease trap. In addition to neutralizing the disinfectant, the buffer aids the fourth task of successful grease trap bioremediation.

4. *Adjusting the Environment in the Grease Trap.* Periodic applications of a buffer maintain the drain line and grease trap ecosystem at about pH 7. Nutrients, activators, and enhancers may be added as needed.

5. *Considerations During Ongoing Treatment.* Early in the treatment period, educate the food preparation personnel in the bioremediation process and how it works. Meanwhile, monitor the drain lines and the grease trap closely. About 2 to 4 days after initial inoculation with bacteria, there may be a backup of water from the drain lines. This seeming contradiction is actually the greatest indication that the bioremediation process is working in the system as prepared. The bacteria inoculated into the system break down hardened residual grease, softening it. As it softens, it may slough off the walls and gather at the nearest "choke point." It is then necessary to "rod out" and hydroflush the lines a second (rarely a third) time, and reinoculate the drain lines. After all the hardened grease is consumed by the "bugs" or is sloughed off the pipe walls to be drained away, there is rarely a plumbing problem in the food service establishment drain line system.

In a grease trap, there is no return sludge to inoculate incoming waste as there is in a POTW. The drain lines and grease trap make up a flow-through system. The system must be reinoculated periodically, at least once a month to ensure its proper function. More heavily used or undersized systems must be reinoculated more often.

Commonly, bacteria that remediate a grease trap, especially an old, neglected one, are present in situ. They may have been limited by a lack of nutrients, trace metals, or activators so the community has not grown to a "critical mass" that will complete the remediation. Sometimes, the only materials or actions required to achieve successful bioremediation are the addition of buffers, nutrients, or activators or the physical breaking up of large clumps of the grease.

SUMMARY

A U.S. patented process has been developed for in situ bioremediation of food service waste grease traps. The process:

1. **Stops the water leaks.** When water flow decreases the detention time of the system, water has become a pollutant.
2. **Stops the solids.** This gets out the stuff that obstructs the functions of the microbes and lowers the pH of the grease trap environment when the solids decay.
3. **Stops the killing of a living part of the ecosystem.** The organisms that complete bioremediation cannot survive much disinfectant or bleach. When the use of disinfectants is mandated by health regulatory agencies, the toxic chemicals are neutralized prior to their release into the grease trap.
4. **Balances the environment.** The trap must have sufficient volume and pH must be maintained within a range that supports microbial life successfully.

5. **Emphasizes follow up**. Activities include education of personnel, additional "cleaning" of the system as needed, and maintaining a balanced ecosystem in the drain lines and grease trap.

The process works the first time, every time — in grease traps, in sewer lines, and in wastewater treatment plants.

REFERENCES

Babbitt, H. E., and E. R. Baumann. 1958. *Sewerage and Sewage Treatment*, 8th ed. John Wiley & Sons, New York, NY. pp. 135, 341, 305, 429.

Baïg, N., and E. M. Grenning. 1976. "The Use of Bacteria to Reduce Clogging of Sewer Lines by Grease in Municipal Sewage." In J. Tourbier et al. (Eds.), *Biological Control of Water Pollution*, pp. 245-252. U.S. Environmental Protection Agency. University of Pennsylvania Press, Philadelphia, PA.

Fowler, J. D. 1946. "Screens, Grit-Chambers, Detritors, Grinders, and Grease Traps." *Manual for Sewage Plant Operators*, p. 96. Texas State Department of Health, Austin, TX.

Imhoff, K., and G. M. Fair. 1956. *Sewage Treatment*, p. 41. John Wiley & Sons, New York, NY.

Hardenbergh, W. A., and E. B. Rodie. 1960. *Water Supply and Waste Disposal*, p. 334. International Textbook Co., Scranton, PA.

Lancaster, R. W. Unpublished. "Oil & Grease — It Won't Just Go Away." Presented at the 1994 Solid and Hazardous Waste Conference, University of Southwestern Louisiana, Lafayette, LA.

Metcalf and Eddy, Inc. 1991. *Wastewater Engineering*, 3rd ed., p. 66. McGraw-Hill Book Co., New York, NY.

Pappas, T. C., and J. S. Pappas. 1993. "Method for Bioremediation of Grease Traps." U.S. Patent Number 5,225,083.

In Situ Bioreclamation of Accumulated Poultry-Processing Solids

Ralph M. Guttman

ABSTRACT

A chicken processing facility had to reduce the sludge in its lagoon system to retrieve wastewater storage capacity and to comply with local discharge limits. The process wastewater contained blood, fats, oils, and other solids. The daily production of wastewater exceeded the maximum volume allowed for discharge to the local sewerage treatment authority. This excess wastewater was held in on-site lagoons. Over the weekend, when production was shut down, it was released to the city sewer system. However, during storage, most of the oil and grease separated out and remained in the lagoon system. Accumulated solids formed a surface crust and settled solid waste layers on the bottom of the lagoons. The loss of storage volume became a critical hindrance to production. The program objectives of the lagoon treatment system included the following: (1) in situ bioreclamation to remove the accumulation of congealed oil, grease, and solids from the lagoon surface; (2) reduction of accumulated bottom sludge deposits; (3) prevention of future waste solids buildup in the lagoons, and maintenance of maximum lagoon capacity; and (4) development of a biological augmentation strategy to reduce effluent levels below anticipated tighter regulatory parameters. Biological activity was improved by adding aerators and bioaugmentation products, which included a blend of surfactants and highly effective fat-digesting bacteria.

INTRODUCTION

A chicken processing facility wanted to bioremediate processing solids that had accumulated in its equalization lagoons over a period of years. About 1,000,000 gal (3,785,400 L) of wastewater was generated while processing approximately 140,000 birds daily. It had high biochemical oxygen demand (BOD), total suspended solids (TSS), oil and greases (O&G), and total Kjeldahl nitrogen (TKN).

The daily production of wastewater that could be processed through the dissolved-air flotation unit (DAF) and discharged to the local sewerage treatment authority exceeded the facility's maximum volume limit. This excess volume necessitated retention of approximately 200,000 gal (757,080 L) of raw water per workday in on-site lagoons. Over the weekend, when production was shut down, this excess water was pumped out of the lagoons, through the DAF, to the city sewer system. However, during temporary storage, most of the oil, grease, and other solids separated out and remained in the lagoons.

Several years of solids accumulation formed a surface crust with an underlying fatty slurry and a layer of sludge on the bottom of the lagoons. These top and bottom layers, each 10 to 20 in. (25.4 to 51 cm) thick, significantly reduced the available storage volume of the lagoons to the point where they were inadequate for the facility's needs. In addition, the facility was facing more stringent effluent quality requirements, which would not be met with the existing system.

Estimates for the mechanical removal of these solids from the pond and landfill disposal were as high as $500,000.00. Bioreclamation offered an alternative solution at a total cost of approximately $62,000.00. Conversion of the pond from a holding facility to a treatment lagoon system had ongoing benefits. Rerouting of the wastewater flow would reduce the accumulation of solids in the lagoons. Biotreatment of the BOD to biosolids would reduce loading to the DAF unit and economize on the amount of coagulant used. The DAF would be able to remove most of the resulting biosolids rather than just the undigested oil, grease, and solids in the raw process water.

LAGOON AND TREATMENT SYSTEM DESIGN

The initial treatment system consisted of two lagoons for equalization and a DAF system for solids removal. The front lagoon was 7 ft (2.1 m) deep and had an estimated capacity of 256,000 gal (969,062 L). The back lagoon had a capacity of 2,600,000 gal (9,842,040 L). The two were separated by a spillway. Pumping to the DAF was halted when the daily effluent-volume limit was reached and the excess raw wastewater overflowed into the larger rear holding lagoon. Initially, a 6-in. (15-cm)-diameter pipe was routed from the front lagoon to the far end of the large lagoon. This pipe redirected approximately 20% of the untreated wastewater to the rear of the large lagoon and facilitated a minimal amount of recirculation. This configuration was later upgraded so that 100% of the plant effluent was pumped directly to the rear of the large lagoon and had to traverse both lagoons before being discharged through the DAF. The slurry of concentrated solids separated by the DAF, a combination of biofloc and undigested solid wastes, was removed by a commercial waste hauler.

The lagoons contained a rigid top layer of oil and grease estimated to be 8 to 12 in. (20 to 30 cm) thick. A slurry of oil and grease was below the top layer. The bottom sludge was estimated to range between 10 and 15 in. (25 and 38 cm).

Anticipated regulatory parameters for water released to the sewer were BOD, 300 mg/L; TSS, 350 mg/L; O&G, 100 mg/L; and TKN, 68 mg/L.

BIORECLAMATION PROCEDURE AND MATERIALS

Treatment of the lagoons and effluent wastestream was accomplished using two products from Polybac Corporation: POLYBAC®, a blend of selected and adapted aerobic and facultative anaerobic microorganisms specifically formulated for food-processing wastewater-treatment systems; and POLYBAC-E®, a proprietary blend of nonionic surfactants with demonstrated biodegradability. The dosing schedule used for biological remediation began at 400 lb (181 kg) of the first product and 18 gal (68 L) of the second product per week. These doses were reduced over a period of 7 weeks to 10 lb (4.5 kg) and 0.5 gal (1.9 L), respectively. Aeration equipment was also installed in the lagoon system to provide adequate dissolved oxygen levels. Laboratory analysis of the water was done to determine BOD, TSS, O&G, and TKN (American Public Health Association, 1989).

VISUAL OBSERVATIONS AND RESULTS

Visual observation of the lagoons during the bioreclamation project showed a dramatic change in appearance. The floating oil and grease layer disappeared over a 6- to 10-week period. During the 11th to 14th week, the dark bottom sludge of the back lagoon continued to rise to the surface and was dissipated. By week 15, most of the accumulated solids, both floating and settled, were removed, and the clay liner was observable during periods of low water level. The total storage volume recovered by the end of the cleanup was 200,000 to 300,000 gal (757,080 to 1,135,620 L).

Biological solids that were generated by the remediation process remained suspended in the water by the combined action of the aerators and flow through the lagoons. As the wastewater traversed the ponds and was processed by the DAF unit, these solids were removed. This slurry of concentrated biosolids was hauled away for disposal. The conversion of the soluble and insoluble BOD resulted in production of biomass solids and in a significant reduction of material for disposal.

Freeboard Trend Analysis

The freeboard and cumulative wastewater data are shown in Figure 1; the sawtooth pattern is due to gradual accumulation of retained wastewater during the workweek and "catch-up" pumping over the weekend. Before biological treatment was begun (May 1 to June 25), the demand for wastewater storage was

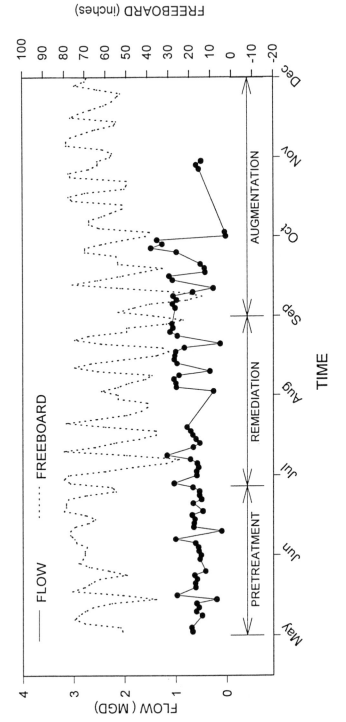

FIGURE 1. Freeboard and flow to storage lagoons.

increasing gradually, with the result that the amount of surplus storage capacity (freeboard) was becoming more limited. During the first weeks of July, water usage increased steadily. This added demand exacerbated the limited freeboard problem. Had this trend continued, the plant would have had to curtail further growth in water use, and thus their business. However, by the end of July, the treatment program began to have a significant effect and actually reversed this trend of diminishing storage capacity. During August, despite the sharp growth in wastewater production, the amount of storage reservoir actually increased. This improvement was due to the biological breakup and degradation of the accumulated floating and settled solids. This cleanup process appeared to be substantially complete by September, when the facility's peak season dropped off.

Laboratory Testing

BOD analyses on the DAF effluent is depicted in Figure 2. The values vary significantly from May until January. This variation is not unusual considering the complex combination of events that occurred during the cleanup. During the initial phase of treatment the top layer was broken apart, resulting in higher loading. In addition, a faulty DAF was not discovered until near the end of the cleanup when effluent levels failed to stabilize as expected. The proportion of wastewater that was fed to the rear aeration basin varied depending on processing schedules and production demands. This variation in flow from the processing facility caused residence time in the biologically active lagoons to change with production levels.

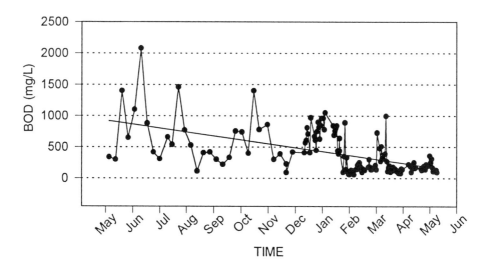

FIGURE 2. BOD of final DAF effluent.

ONGOING BIOAUGMENTATION

After the bioreclamation phase, the changes to the system were left in place to act as on ongoing biotreatment system. Augmentation of the system included the use of biodegradable nonionic surfactants into the influent line at 10 ppm to facilitate emulsification of oil and grease in the wastewater, especially in cold weather. After the occasional system upset, commercial dried bacterial cultures were used to reseed the system and minimize the recovery time of the biomass. During cold weather, additional bacteria were used to improve the overall BOD-removal performance. The system is now operating below permit limits, while achieving a small cost savings in polymer and ferric chloride usage.

CONCLUSION

All four objectives of the treatment program have been met.

1. Several years of accumulation of oil and grease from the top layer on the front and back lagoons was removed.
2. The solids accumulation on the bottom of the lagoons was dissipated.
3. Future buildup of greases, oils, and fats in the lagoons is being prevented through the use of the two products at maintenance dosages.
4. The system is consistently maintaining effluent wastewater levels within permit levels.

This study shows that biological treatment methods can be used to reclaim the use of outdoor wastewater holding ponds that have been choked with accumulated biodegradable solid wastes. This approach is not only more economical than other methods, it may become essential as the availability of other solid-waste disposal options become more limited. Bioconversion of the BOD typically reduces the mass of solids by 40 to 60%. It should be possible to design systems with near-zero solids discharge. This approach, of course, works only if the material is biodegradable. In this example the poultry waste is easily degradable. Augmentation of this project with commercial dried bacteria and surfactants was chosen to speed the process and ensure completion within the limited time available. In other situations, the addition of bacteria and other adjuvants could be used to overcome toxic situations or recalcitrant substances.

REFERENCE

American Public Health Association. 1989. *Standard Methods for the Examination of Water and Wastewater*, 17th ed. Washington, DC.

AUTHOR LIST

Abbott, James E.
Battelle Columbus
505 King Avenue
Columbus, OH 43201-2693 USA

Abou-Rizk, Jacqueline A.M.
Union Carbide Corporation
3200-3300 Kanawha Turnpike
S. Charleston, WV 25303 USA

Albergo, Nicholas
HSA Environmental, Inc.
4019 E. Fowler Avenue
Tampa, FL 33617 USA

Anderson, Daniel B.
Battelle Pacific Northwest
P.O. Box 999 Mail Stop P7-41
Richland, WA 99352 USA

Arnaud, Clothilde
GRS
13 Villa Groix Nivert
75015 Paris
FRANCE

Baker, Ralph S.
ENSR Consulting & Engineering
35 Nagog Park
Acton, MA 01720 USA

Banipal, Ben S.
Ecology and Environment, Inc.
1999 Bryan St., Suite 2000
Dallas, TX 75201 USA

Bantle, Jack A.
Oklahoma State University
201 Life Sciences East
Stillwater, OK 74078-0266 USA

Barnes, David L.
Colorado State University
Engineering Research Center
Foothills Campus
Ft. Collins, CO 80523 USA

Battermann, Gerhard
TGU-GmbH
Kurfürstenstrasse 80
Postfach 225
56068 Koblenz
GERMANY

Bavière, Marc
Institut Français du Pétrole
1 et 4 Ave de Bois-Préau BP 311
92506 Rueil Malmaison Cedex
FRANCE

Beck, Frank P.
U.S. Environ. Protection Agency
R.S. Kerr Environ. Research Lab
P.O. Box 1198
Ada, OK 74820 USA

Bedient, Philip B.
Rice University
National Center for Groundwater
   Research
6100 S. Main Street
Houston, TX 77005 USA

Beeman, Ralph E.
DuPont Co.
Environmental Remediation Srvcs.
Glasgow Site, Building 300
P.O. Box 6101
Newark, DE 19714 USA

Biehle, Alfred A.
DuPont Co.
Environmental Remediation Srvcs.
140 Cypress Station Dr., Suite 140
Houston, TX 77090 USA

Bleckmann, Charles A.
U.S. Air Force
Inst. of Technology Environmental
    Mgmt. AFIT/ENV
2950 P Street, Building 640
Wright-Patterson AFB, OH
45433-7765 USA

Bolliger, Reinhard
EcoTerra
Environ. Consulting and Engrg.
Himmelrychweg 12
CH-5734 Reinach, AG
SWITZERLAND

Botto, Robert E.
Argonne National Laboratory
Chemistry Division
9700 S. Cass Avenue
Argonne, IL 60439 USA

Bouillard, Jacques X.
Argonne National Laboratory
9700 S. Cass Ave./Building 200
Argonne, IL 60439-4831 USA

Boulanger, Charles
Ecosite, Inc.
872, Newton, Suite 270
Québec, Québec G1P 4M4
CANADA

Brady, Patrick V.
Sandia National Laboratories
Dept. 6622 MS 0750
P.O Box 5800
Albuquerque, NM 87185-0750 USA

Cacciatore, David
Groundwater Technology, Inc.
4080 Pike Lane
Concord, CA 94520 USA

Carlson, Keith A.
Integrated Science & Tech., Inc.
1349 Old Highway 41, Suite 225
Marietta, GA 30060-1000 USA

Caso, Osvaldo
Centro de Ecofisiologia Vegetal
    (CONICET)
Serrano 669
1414 Buenos Aires
ARGENTINA

Chapuis, Renaud
Antipollution Techniques Entreprise
Public Relations
17 rue de Perigord
69330 Meyzieu
FRANCE

Cody, George
Argonne National Laboratory
Chemistry Division
9700 S. Cass Avenue
Argonne, IL 60439 USA

Collins, Mark L.
French Limited Project
1024 Gulf Pump Road
Crosby, TX 77532 USA

Connolly, Mark D.
Connolly Systems Pty. Ltd.
99 Willow Bend
Bulleen, Victoria 3105
AUSTRALIA

Croft, Barry C.
AEA Technology
Biotechnology Services
353 Harwell
Didcot, Oxfordshire OX11 ORA
UNITED KINGDOM

Cunningham, Alfred B.
Montana State University
Center for Biofilm Engineering
413 Cobleigh Hall
Bozeman, MT 59717 USA

Dablow, Jay
Groundwater Technology, Inc.
20000 Mariner Ave., Suite 200
Torrance, CA 90503 USA

Davis, Kimberly L.
University of Tennessee
Waste Management Research and
    Education Inst.
327 South Stadium Hall
Knoxville, TN 37996-0710 USA

Day, Michael J.
Applied Hydrology Assoc., Inc.
1325 S. Colorado Blvd., Suite 770
Denver, CO 80222 USA

Devine, Kate
DEVO Enterprises, Inc.
1003 K St. NW, Suite 501
Washington, DC 20001-4425 USA

Dott, Wolfgang
Institute of Hygiene and
    Environmental Medicine
Rwth Aachen Pauwelsstrasse 30
D-52057 Aachen
GERMANY

Dowden, Bobby F.
The Natural Solution, Inc.
1034 Boulevard Street
Shreveport, LA 71104 USA

du Plessis, Chris A.
University of Natal
Department of Agronomy
Private Bag X01
Scottsville 3209
REP. OF SOUTH AFRICA

Ducreux, Jean
Institut Français du Pétrole
1 et 4 Ave de Bois-Préau Bp 311
92506 Rueil Malmaison Cedex
FRANCE

Eiermann, Daniel R.
Ebiox AG
Wassermatte 1
CH-6210 Sursee
SWITZERLAND

Ellis, David E.
DuPont Co.
Engineering Dept.
300 Bellevue Pkwy., Suite 390
Wilmington, DE 19809-3722 USA

Enzien, Michael V.
Argonne National Lab
9700 S. Cass Ave., Bldg. ES/362
Argonne, IL 60439-4815 USA

Fetter, Daniel J.
Barr Engineering Company
8300 Norman Center Drive
Minneapolis, MN 55437-1026 USA

Fisher, Charles W.
U.S. Environ. Protection Agency
1445 Ross Avenue, 9th Floor
Dallas, TX 75202 USA

Fitzgerald, Conan D.
Accutech Remedial Systems
Cass Street @ Hwy 35
Keyport, NJ 07735 USA

Frank, James R.
Argonne National Laboratory
9700 S. Cass Ave. ES/362
Argonne, IL 60439 USA

Fulton, David A.
Montgomery Watson
4525 S. Wasatch Blvd., Suite 200
Salt Lake City, UT 84124 USA

Gaglione, Robert J.
McInnis, Fitzgerald, Rees & Sharkey
1230 Columbia Street, Suite 800
San Diego, CA 92101 USA

Gemperline, Andrew F.
U.S. Air Force
Environmental Mgmt. Division,
    00-ALC/EMR
7274 Wardleigh Road
Hill AFB, UT 84056-5137 USA

Gibbs, Bruce M.
Caltex Oil (Australia) Pty. Limited
167-187 Kent Street
Sydney, NSW 2000
AUSTRALIA

Glascott, Robert A.
Montgomery Watson
4525 S. Wasatch Blvd., Suite 200
Salt Lake City, UT 84124 USA

Glass, David J.
D. Glass Associates, Inc.
124 Bird Street
Needham, MA 02192-4358 USA

Goetz, Frederick E.
U.S. Navy
NFESC Code 411
560 Center Drive
Port Hueneme, CA 93043 USA

Graham, Lori L.
Biorenewal Technologies, Inc.
The Faraday Center
2800 S. Fish Hatchery Rd.
Madison, WI 53711 USA

Grant, Alyson L.
University of Sunderland
School of Computing and
    Information Systems
Priestman Building
Sunderland SRI 3SD
UNITED KINGDOM

Graves, Duane A.
IT Corporation
312 Directors Drive
Knoxville, TN 37923-4799 USA

Guttman, Ralph M.
Polybac Corporation
3894 Courtney Place
Bethlehem, PA 18017-8999 USA

Haas, Patrick E.
U.S. Air Force
HQ AFCEE/ERT
8001 Arnold Drive
Brooks AFB, TX 78235-5357 USA

Hammerbeck, LeeAnn M.
Braun Intertec Corp.
1345 Northland Drive
Mendota Heights, MN 55120-1141
USA

Harrison, Barry
Barr Engineering Company
8300 Norman Center Drive
Minneapolis, MN 55437-1026 USA

Hayes, Kelly W.
Conoco, Inc.
Environmental Services Division
P.O. Box 1267
Ponca City, OK 74602-1267 USA

Hercyk, Neta L.
Conoco, Inc.
P.O. Box 1267
Ponca City, OK 74602 USA

Hicks, Ronald J.
Groundwater Technology, Inc.
4080 Pike Lane
Concord, CA 94520 USA

Hinchee, Robert E.
Battelle Columbus
505 King Avenue
Columbus, OH 43201-2693 USA

Hoeppel, Ronald E.
U.S. Navy
Naval Facilities Engrg. Svcs. Center
ERD Code ESC4
560 Center Drive
Port Hueneme, CA 93043-4328 USA

Hopkins, Gary D.
Stanford University
Western Region Hazardous
Substance Research Center
(MC-4020)
Stanford, CA 94305-4020 USA

Hubbard, Jr., Perry
Integrated Science & Tech., Inc.
1349 Old Hwy 41, Suite 225
Marietta, GA 30060-1000 USA

Huddleston, Robert L.
Delta Environmental Co.
6 Fawn Lane
Ponca City, OK 74604 USA

Hutchins, Stephen R.
U.S. Environ. Protection Agency
R.S. Kerr Environ. Research Lab
P.O. Box 1198
Ada, OK 74820 USA

Johnston, Robert S.
Dames & Moore
9665 Chesapeake Dr., Suite 201
San Diego, CA 92123 USA

Kampbell, Don H.
U.S. Environ. Protection Agency
R.S. Kerr Environ. Research Lab
919 Research Drive
P.O. Box 1198
Ada, OK 74820 USA

Keet, Ben
Geo & Hydro Milieu
Stationsplein 18
6953 AC Dieren
THE NETHERLANDS

Kittel, Jeffrey A.
Battelle Columbus
505 King Avenue
Columbus, OH 43201-2693 USA

Kovacs, A. Laszlo
Apex Environmental, Inc.
15850 Crabbs Branch Way, Ste. 300
Rockville, MD 20855 USA

Lageman, Reinout
Geokinetics
Dannenberg 16
7461 TK Rijssen
THE NETHERLANDS

Landsman, Michael C.
Apex Environmental, Inc.
15850 Crabbs Branch Way, Ste. 300
Rockville, MD 20855 USA

Leavitt, Maureen E.
Scientific Applications Intl. Corp.
(SAIC)
800 Oakridge Turnpike
Oak Ridge, TN 37831 USA

Lebron, Carmen A.
Naval Facilities Engrg. Svcs. Center
Restoration Development Branch
NFESC EXC 411
560 Center Drive
Port Hueneme, CA 93043 USA

Lee, Michael D.
DuPont Co.
Environ. Remediation Srvcs.
Glasgow Site, Building 300
P.O. Box 6101
Newark, DE 19714-6101 USA

Lee, Kenneth
Dept. of Fisheries & Oceans Canada
Maurice Lamontagne Institute
P.O. Box 1000
Mont-Joli, Québec G5H 3Z4
CANADA

Leeson, Andrea
Battelle Columbus
505 King Avenue
Columbus, OH 43201-2693 USA

Leethem, John T.
DuPont Environ. Remediation Srvs.
140 Cypress Station Dr., Suite 140
Houston, TX 77090 USA

Lindgren, Eric R.
Sandia National Labs
P.O. Box 5800, MS 0727
Albuquerque, NM 87185-0727 USA

Liskowitz, John J.
Accutech Remedial Systems
Cass Street @ Hwy 35
Keyport, NJ 07735 USA

Mabry, David
Oak Ridge National Laboratory
P.O. Box 2008
Oak Ridge, TN 37831 USA

McWhorter, David B.
Colorado State University
Engineering Research Center
Foothills Campus
Ft. Collins, CO 80523 USA

Meier-Löhr, Matthias
TGU-GmbH
Kurfürstenstrasse 80
56068 Koblenz
GERMANY

Mendoza, Rodolfo E.
Centro de Ecofisiologia Vegetal
   (CONICET)
Serrano 669
1414 Buenos Aires
ARGENTINA

Meyers, Jeffrey D.
Conoco, Inc.
P.O. Box 2197
Houston, TX 77252-2197 USA

Miksch, Korneliusz
Silesian Technical University
Dept. of Environmental Engineering
ul. Konarskiego 18
44 100 Gliwice
POLAND

Miller, Dennis E.
U.S. Environ. Protection Agency
R.S. Kerr Environ. Research Lab
P.O. Box 1198
Ada, OK 74820 USA

Miller, Ross N.
U.S. Air Force
8001 Arnold Drive, Building 642
Brooks AFB, TX 78235-5357 USA

Montney, Paul A.
Georgia-Pacific Corporation
290 Ferry Street
Newark, NJ 01705 USA

Moon, Ralph E.
HSA Environmental, Inc.
4019 E. Fowler Avenue
Tampa, FL 33617 USA

Mountain, Stewart A.
Integrated Science & Tech., Inc.
1349 Old Highway 41, Suite 225
Marietta, GA 30060-1000 USA

Myers, Julian M.
Ecology and Environment, Inc.
1999 Bryan Street, Suite 2000
Dallas, TX 75201 USA

Nelson, G. L. (Sam)
Midwest Gas
401 Douglas Street, P.O. Box 778
Sioux City, IA 51102 USA

Niehaus, Steve
Gosling Czubak Assoc.
Environmental Remediation
525 W. 14th Street
Traverse City, MI 49684 USA

Norris, Robert D.
Eckenfelder, Inc.
227 French Landing Drive
Nashville, TN 37228 USA

Orwin, Eva
Stanford University
Western Region Hazardous
    Substance Research Center
    (MC-4020)
Stanford, CA 94305-4020 USA

Pergler, Charles
Science Applications Intl. Corp.
    (SAIC)
P.O. Box 2502
Oak Ridge, TN 37831 USA

Peters, Robert W.
Argonne National Laboratory
9700 S. Cass Ave. ES/362
Argonne, IL 60439 USA

Peyton, Brent M.
Battelle Pacific Northwest
P.O. Box 999, MS P7-41
Richland, WA 99352 USA

Phaal, Clinton B.
University of Natal
Intl. Centre for Waste Technology
Private Bag X01
Scottsville 3209
REP. OF SOUTH AFRICA

Poetzsch, Emmo
Umweltschutz Nord GmbH & Co.
Industriepark 6
D-27777 Ganderkesee
GERMANY

Pool, Wieberen
Geokinetics
Dannenberg 16
7461 TK Rijssen
THE NETHERLANDS

Portal, René
Total Austral S.A.
San Martin 323
1004 Buenos Aires
ARGENTINA

Prince, Roger
Exxon
Research & Engineering
Clinton Township
Route 22 East
Annandale, NJ 08801 USA

Ramstad, Svein
SINTEF
Applied Chemistry
Environmental Technology Group
N-7034 Trondheim
NORWAY

Raphael, Thomas
Umweltberatung/U.T.R.
TechnoPark
Lohbachstrasse 12
D-58239 Schwerte
GERMANY

Razakarisoa, Olivier
IFARE
Campus CNRS
23 Rue du Loess
67037 Strasbourg-Cronenbourg
FRANCE

Reed, Gregory D.
University of Tennessee
Civil and Environmental Engrg.
Perkins Hall
Knoxville, TN 37996-0710 USA

Reinhard, Martin
Stanford University
Western Region Hazardous
    Substance Research Center
    (MC-4020)
Stanford, CA 94305-4020 USA

Reisinger, H. James
Integrated Science & Tech., Inc.
1349 Old Highway 41, Suite 225
Marietta, GA 30060-1000 USA

Rho, Denis
National Research Council-Canada
Biotechnology Research Institute
6100 Royalmount Avenue
Montréal, Québec H4P 2R2
CANADA

Richard, Don E.
Barr Engineering Company
8300 Norman Center Drive
Minneapolis, MN 55437-1026 USA

Rodriguez, Daniel
Centro de Ecofisiologia Vegetal
    (CONICET)
Serrano 669
1414 Buenos Aires
ARGENTINA

Ross, Arnold
Serrener Consultation, Inc.
855 rue Pépin
Sherbrooke, Québec J1L 2P8
CANADA

Roudier, Pascal
Antipollution Techniques Entreprise
Public Relations
17 rue de Périgord
69330 Meyzieu
FRANCE

Samson, Réjean
École Polytechnique de Montréal
Chemical Engineering Dept.
P.O. Box 6079 Station Centre-Ville
Montréal, Québec H3C 3A7
CANADA

Schulz-Berendt, Volker
Umweltschutz Nord GmbH & Co.
Industriepark 6
D-27777 Ganderkesee
GERMANY

Schuring, John R.
New Jersey Institute of Technology
Dept. of Chemical Engineering,
    Chemistry, & Environ. Science
Newark, NJ 07102 USA

Seabra, Paulo
Institut Français du Pétrole
1 et 4 Ave de Bois-Préau Bp 311
92506 Rueil Malmaison Cedex
FRANCE

Senior, Eric
University of Natal
Intl. Center for Waste Technology
Dept. of Microbiology and Plant
    Pathology
Private Bag X01
Scottsville 3209, Kwazulu-Natal
REP. OF SOUTH AFRICA

Shäfer, Gerhard
IFARE
Campus CNRS
23 rue du Loess
F-67037 Strasbourg-Cronenbourg
FRANCE

Shang, Shubo
Stanford University
Western Region Hazardous
    Substance Research Center
    (MC-4020)
Stanford, CA 94305-4020 USA

Shoemaker, Steve H.
Du Pont Co.
140 Cypress Station Dr., Suite 135
Houston, TX 77090 USA

Sloan, Richard L.
ARCO Chemical Co.
15010 FM 2100, Suite 200
Crosby, TX 77532 USA

Spychała, Andrzej
Military University of Technology
Faculty of Civil Engineering and
    Geodesy
ul. Kaliskiego 2
Warsaw 49 01 489
POLAND

Steiof, Martin
Technical University of Berlin
Dept. of Hygiene
Amrumer Str. 32
13353 Berlin
GERMANY

Stephenson, Michael
Oak Ridge National Laboratory
P.O. Box 2008
Oak Ridge, TN 37831 USA

Sturman, Paul J.
Montana State University
Center for Biofilm Engrg
409 Cobleigh Hall
Bozeman, MT 59717 USA

Surmacz-Górska, Joanna
Silesian Technical University
Dept. of Environ. Biotechnology
ul. Konarskiego 18
44 101 Gliwice
POLAND

Sveum, Per
SINTEF Applied Chemistry
Environmental Technology
Brattora Research Centre
N-7034 Trondheim
NORWAY

Swannell, Richard P.J.
AEA Technology
Biotechnology Services
353 Harwell
Didcot, Oxfordshire OX11 ORA
UNITED KINGDOM

Taboada, Miguel A.
Centro de Ecofisiologia Vegetal
    (CONICET)
Serrano 669
1414 Buenos Aires
ARGENTINA

Tahraoui, Karim
National Research Council—Canada
Biotechnology Research Institute
6100 Royalmount Avenue
Montréal, Québec H4P 2R2
CANADA

Thomas, Alison
U.S. Air Force
Armstrong Laboratory AL/EQW
139 Barnes Drive, Suite 2
Tyndall AFB, FL 32403-5323 USA

Thomson, James A. M.
Applied Hydrology Associates, Inc.
1720 S. Bellaire Street, Suite 600
Denver, CO 80222 USA

Tischler, Monica Lee
Science Applications Intl. Corp.
    (SAIC)
P.O. Box 2502
Oak Ridge, TN 37831 USA

Tremblay, Charles
Ecosite, Inc.
47 rue Duke
Montréal, Québec H3C 2L8
CANADA

Valo, Risto
Soil and Water, Ltd.
Italahdenkatu 2
Helsinki 00210
FINLAND

van Vulpen, Marcel
Geokinetics
Dannenberg 16
7461 TK Rijssen
THE NETHERLANDS

Van Eyk, Jack
Delft Geotechnics
P.O. Box 29
2600 AB Delft
THE NETHERLANDS

Walter, Lee
University of Tennessee
Waste Management Research &
    Education Institute
327 South Stadium Hall
Knoxville, TN 37996-0710 USA

Ward, C. Herb
Rice University
Energy & Environ. Systems Inst.
P.O. Box 1892 MS-316
Houston, TX 77251-1892 USA

Wen, Lian-Kui
University of Petroleum China
P.O. Box 902
Beijing 100083
CHINA

Weymann, David F.
Environ. Science and Engrg., Inc.
3208 Spring Forest Road
Raleigh, NC 27604 USA

Wiesner, Mark
Rice University
National Center for Groundwater
    Research
6100 S. Main Street
Houston, TX 77005 USA

Williams, Stephen E.
Environmental Restoration Program
646 CES/CEVR
501 Deleon Street, Suite 100
Eglin AFB, FL 32542-5101 USA

Willis, Guy D.
EA Engrg., Science & Technology
119A N. Eglin Parkway, Suite 308
Shalimar, FL 32579 USA

Wilson, Ernest J.
Conoco, Inc.
P.O. Box 1267
Ponca City, OK 74602 USA

Wilson, Marialice
Science Applications Intl. Corp.
    (SAIC)
P.O. Box 2502
Oak Ridge, TN 37831 USA

Wilson, John T.
U.S. Environ. Protection Agency
R.S. Kerr Laboratory
919 Research Drive
P.O. Box 1198
Ada, OK 74820 USA

Wolfram, James H.
LITCO/Idaho National Engineering
    Laboratory
Bioprocess Technology
P.O. Box 1625
Idaho Falls, ID 83415-2203 USA

Zheng, Yuan-Yang
University of Petroleum China
P.O. Box 902
Beijing 100083
CHINA

INDEX